ERNEST G. F. WONG

黄

子

勳

Mathematical
Methods *in*
Chemical
Engineering

Mathematical Methods *in* Chemical Engineering

V. G. JENSON
Lecturer
Department of Chemical Engineering
The University, Birmingham, England

and

G. V. JEFFREYS
Senior Lecturer
Department of Chemical Engineering
Faculty of Technology
The University, Manchester, England

1963

ACADEMIC PRESS

LONDON and NEW YORK

ACADEMIC PRESS INC. (LONDON) LTD
24-28, OVAL ROAD
LONDON, N.W.1

U.S. *Edition published by*
ACADEMIC PRESS INC.
111 FIFTH AVENUE
NEW YORK, NEW YORK 10003

Library of Congress Catalog Number: 63–22092
SBN 12 384450 9

Printed in Great Britain by Galliard (Printers) Ltd Great Yarmouth

PREFACE

THE development of new processes in the chemical industry is becoming more complex and increasingly expensive. If the research and development of the process can be carried out with confidence, the ultimate design will be more exact, and therefore the plant will operate more economically. In all facets of such a project, mathematics, which is the language of the quantitative, plays a vital role. Therefore training in mathematical methods is of the utmost importance to chemical engineers. The present text has been written with these ideas in mind, and we would emphasize that our aim is to present mathematics in a form suitable for the engineer rather than to teach engineering to mathematicians. To the pure mathematician an elegant proof is an end in itself, but to the chemical engineer it is merely a means to an end. Consequently this book only sketches demonstrations of the validity of theorems, to encourage the reader to have more confidence in the use of the technique for the solution of engineering problems. In addition, an attempt has been made to sort out the useful from the trivial and flamboyant of the wide variety of mathematical techniques available.

The material presented in this book is based on various undergraduate and post graduate courses given in the Chemical Engineering Department of the University of Birmingham. Many of the worked examples have been selected from research work carried out in the department, and these are supplemented with problems taken from the chemical engineering literature. Some chapters of the book (notably Chapters 4 and 5) are almost entirely mathematical, but wherever possible the text has been illustrated with chemical engineering applications.

The book was written when both authors were lecturers in the Chemical Engineering Department of the University of Birmingham. It is hoped that the text will encourage chemical engineers to make greater use of mathematics in the solution of their problems.

We wish to express our thanks to Professor J. T. Davies for initiating the venture, and to Professor F. H. Garner, and Professor S. R. M. Ellis for their interest and advice in the preparation of the text.

Birmingham
July, 1963   V.G.J. and G.V.J.

CONTENTS

Chapter 7

VECTOR ANALYSIS

Chapter 8

PARTIAL DIFFERENTIATION AND PARTIAL DIFFERENTIAL EQUATIONS

Chapter 9

FINITE DIFFERENCES

THE MATHEMATICAL STATEMENT OF THE PROBLEM

1.1. INTRODUCTION

NEARLY all applied science consists of performing experiments and interpreting the results. This may be done quantitatively by taking accurate measurements of the system variables which are subsequently analysed and correlated, or qualitatively by investigating the general behaviour of the system in terms of one variable influencing another. The first method is always desirable, and if a quantitative investigation is to be attempted it is better to introduce the mathematical principles at the earliest possible stage, since they may influence the course of the investigation. This is done by looking for an idealized mathematical model of the system.

The second step is the collection of all relevant physical information in the form of conservation laws and rate equations. The conservation laws of chemical engineering are material balances, heat balances, and other energy balances; whilst the rate equations express the relationship between flow rate and driving force in the fields of fluid flow, heat transfer, and diffusion of matter. These are then applied to the model, and the result should be a mathematical equation which describes the system.

The type of equation (algebraic, differential, finite difference, etc.) will depend upon both the system under investigation, and the detail of its model. For a particular system, if the model is simple the equation may be elementary, whereas if the model is more refined the equation will be a more difficult type. The appropriate mathematical techniques are then applied to this equation and a result is obtained. This mathematical result must then be interpreted through the original model in order to give it a physical significance.

In this chapter, only the simplest problems will be considered and the ideas of simple models will be introduced. The more complicated models will be introduced throughout the book in the chapters dealing with the particular mathematical techniques which are needed for the completion of the solutions.

1.2. REPRESENTATION OF THE PROBLEM

A simple example of the application of these ideas will be given first. The apparatus shown diagrammatically in Fig. 1.1 is to be used for the continuous extraction of benzoic acid from toluene, using water as the extracting solvent. The two streams are fed into a tank A where they are stirred vigorously, and the mixture is then pumped into tank B where it is allowed to settle into two layers. The upper toluene layer and the lower water layer are removed separately, and the problem is to find what proportion of the benzoic acid has passed into the solvent phase.

FIG. 1.1.   Single-stage mixer settler

The problem is idealized in Fig. 1.2 where the two tanks have been combined into a single stage. The various streams have been labelled and two material balances have already been used, (a) conservation of toluene, and (b) conservation of water. These flow rates have been expressed on a solute

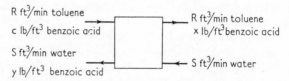

FIG. 1.2.   Idealized single-stage solvent extraction

free basis to simplify the analysis. The concentration of benzoic acid in each stream has also been stated and this completes the mathematical model.

So far, it has been assumed that all flow rates are steady, and that toluene and water are immiscible. Further assumptions are now made that the feed concentration c remains constant, and that the mixer is so efficient that the two streams leaving the stage are always in equilibrium with one another. This last fact can be expressed mathematically by

$$y = mx \qquad (1.1)$$

where m is the distribution coefficient.

The equation is now derived from the model by writing down a mass balance for benzoic acid.

Input of benzoic acid $= Rc$ lb/min
Output of benzoic acid $= Rx + Sy$ lb/min

Since benzoic acid must leave at the same rate as it enters,

$$Rc = Rx + Sy \qquad (1.2)$$

The pair of equations (1.1) and (1.2) contain four known quantities

(R, S, c, m) and two unknown quantities (x, y), and they can be solved for the unknowns as follows.

$$Rc = Rx + mSx$$

$$\therefore \quad x = \frac{Rc}{R+mS}, \qquad y = \frac{mRc}{R+mS} \tag{1.3}$$

Therefore, the proportion of benzoic acid extracted is

$$\frac{Sy}{Rc} = \frac{mS}{R+mS} \tag{1.4}$$

As a numerical example, if $S = 12R$, $m = 1/8$, and $c = 0.1$; then $x = 0.04$, $y = 0.005$, and the proportion of acid extracted is 60%.

At this stage, it can be seen that even in this simple problem, two dimensionless groups which are characteristic of the problem, have arisen quite naturally as a result of the investigation. Putting

$$\alpha = R/mS \tag{1.5}$$

and $E = Sy/Rc$, equation (1.4) becomes

$$E = 1/(\alpha+1) \tag{1.6}$$

That is, the proportion extracted is governed solely by the value of the dimensionless group α.

1.3. Solvent Extraction in Two Stages

The above example will now be reconsidered, but two stages will be used for the extraction of benzoic acid instead of one stage. Each stage still consists of two tanks, a mixer and a settler, with counter-current flow through the stages. The idealized flow system is shown in Fig. 1.3 where the symbols

Fig. 1.3.   Idealized two-stage extraction

have the same meaning as in the previous example, and the different concentrations in a particular phase are distinguished by suffixes. In accordance with chemical engineering practice, the suffix denotes the number of the stage from which the stream is leaving. The assumptions which were made above are made again, and equation (1.1) is still valid for each stage separately, giving

$$y_1 = mx_1 \qquad y_2 = mx_2 \tag{1.7}$$

A benzoic acid mass balance is now taken for each stage.

	Stage 1	Stage 2
Input of acid (lb/min)	$Rc + Sy_2$	Rx_1
Output of acid (lb/min)	$Rx_1 + Sy_1$	$Rx_2 + Sy_2$

The fact that benzoic acid must enter and leave a stage at the same rate, gives the two equations

$$Rc + Sy_2 = Rx_1 + Sy_1$$
$$Rx_1 = Rx_2 + Sy_2$$

Using equations (1.7) to eliminate x_1 and y_2, the inter-stage concentrations,

$$Rc + mSx_2 = (Ry_1/m) + Sy_1 \tag{1.8}$$

and
$$Ry_1/m = Rx_2 + mSx_2 \tag{1.9}$$

Eliminating y_1 between equations (1.8) and (1.9),

$$R(Rc + mSx_2) = (R + mS)(Rx_2 + mSx_2)$$
$$\therefore \quad R^2c = x_2(R^2 + mRS + m^2S^2)$$

$$\therefore \quad x_2 = \frac{R^2c}{R^2 + mRS + m^2S^2} \tag{1.10}$$

$$\therefore \quad y_1 = \frac{mRc(R + mS)}{R^2 + mRS + m^2S^2} \tag{1.11}$$

Again, the proportion of benzoic acid extracted is

$$\frac{Sy_1}{Rc} = \frac{mS(R + mS)}{R^2 + mRS + m^2S^2} \tag{1.12}$$

Introducing the dimensionless groups E and α again from equation (1.5), equation (1.12) becomes

$$E = \frac{\alpha + 1}{\alpha^2 + \alpha + 1} = \frac{\alpha^2 - 1}{\alpha^3 - 1} \tag{1.13}$$

Using the same numerical example as before, i.e. $S = 12R$, $m = 1/8$, and $c = 0.1$; then $x_2 = 0.021$, $y_1 = 0.0066$, and the proportion extracted is 79%.

A greater degree of extraction has thus been obtained with two stages than with one stage, everything else being the same.

1.4. Solvent Extraction in N Stages

This improved extraction leads to the consideration of more than two stages in the extraction system. The algebraic treatment was quite simple for one stage, only requiring the solution of two equations in two unknowns. The application to two stages involved the solution of four equations in four unknowns, and following the same procedure for N stages, it would be necessary to solve $2N$ equations in $2N$ unknowns. This is too laborious and would require an individual solution for every integer value of N, and more advanced mathematical techniques are obviously needed to reduce the work. One method using matrix algebra will be illustrated in Chapter 12, but a second method, using finite differences and anticipating the contents of Chapter 9 will be used here.

The general arrangement is as shown in Fig. 1.4 where the flow rates of the two streams are still denoted by R and S, and the benzoic acid concentrations by x and y. The suffix notation is again used to distinguish between

FIG. 1.4.   Idealized N-stage extraction

the different states of each stream, the suffix denoting the stage which the stream has just left. This time, a benzoic acid material balance is applied to the general stage n of the system.

$$\text{Input of acid (lb/min)} \quad = Rx_{n-1} + Sy_{n+1}$$
$$\text{Output of acid (lb/min)} = Rx_n + Sy_n$$

Since entry rate and exit rate must be equal,

$$Rx_{n-1} + Sy_{n+1} = Rx_n + Sy_n \qquad (1.14)$$

The distribution coefficient equation (1.1) is still valid for any value of n

$$\therefore \quad y_n = mx_n$$

and equation (1.14) becomes

$$Rx_{n-1} + mSx_{n+1} = (R + mS)x_n$$

Introducing α again from equation (1.5),

$$x_{n-1} + x_{n+1} = (\alpha + 1)x_n$$

or in standard form,

$$x_{n+1} - (\alpha + 1)x_n + x_{n-1} = 0 \qquad (1.15)$$

This is a second order linear finite difference equation and the method of solution will be discussed in Chapter 9. The solution is quoted here for completeness, viz.

$$y_n = mx_n = mc(\alpha^{N+1} - \alpha^n)/(\alpha^{N+1} - 1) \qquad (1.16)$$

and this may be verified by substitution into equation (1.15). The proportion extracted, E, is given by

$$E = \frac{Sy_1}{Rc} = \frac{\alpha^N - 1}{\alpha^{N+1} - 1} \qquad (1.17)$$

which gives equation (1.13) for the special case $N = 2$.

TABLE 1.1. *Proportion Extracted in* N *Stages*
($S = 12R$, $m = 1/8$)

N	1	2	3	5	10
$E(\%)$	60·0	78·9	87·7	95·2	99·4

Table 1.1 gives a few values of E for different values of N for the particular system considered. This shows how the proportion extracted increases with the number of stages, and indicates that more than ten stages are likely to be wasteful whereas one stage gives a poor degree of extraction. This type of problem will be continued in Chapter 13, where the most economical number of stages will be determined by financial considerations.

1.5. SIMPLE WATER STILL WITH PREHEATED FEED

Figure 1.5 illustrates a distillation apparatus consisting of a boiler B with a constant level device C, fed with the condenser cooling water. The steam is condensed in A and collected in the receiver D. Some of the latent heat of

FIG. 1.5.   Water still with heat exchanger

evaporation is returned to the boiler by preheating the feed. Denoting the condenser feed rate by F lb/h and the temperature by T_0° F, the exit water temperature by $T\,^\circ$F, the excess water over-flow rate by W lb/h and the distillation rate by G lb/h, the performance of the apparatus can be investigated.

$$\text{Input of water to the still (lb/h)} \quad = F$$
$$\text{Output of water from the still (lb/h)} = W$$
$$\text{Output of steam from the still (lb/h)} = G$$
$$\therefore \quad F = W + G \tag{1.18}$$

If heat is supplied to the boiler at a rate H Btu/h, the latent heat of evaporation of water is L Btu/lb, and 0°F is taken as the datum temperature, a heat balance can be taken over the boiler.

$$\text{Heat input (Btu/h)} \quad = H + (F - W)T$$
$$\text{Heat output (Btu/h)} = 212G + LG$$
$$\therefore \quad H + GT = (212 + L)G \tag{1.19}$$

where equation (1.18) has been used to eliminate W. Equation (1.19) contains two unknown quantities, G and T, and another equation is needed to complete the description. This is obtained from a heat balance over the condenser.

$$\text{Heat gained by cooling water (Btu/h)} \quad = F(T - T_0)$$
$$\text{Heat lost by condensing steam (Btu/h)} = G(L + 212 - T)$$
$$\therefore \quad F(T - T_0) = G(L + 212 - T) \tag{1.20}$$

In deriving equation (1.20) it has been assumed that the distillate is cooled to the exit water temperature.

Eliminating G between (1.19) and (1.20),

$$F(T - T_0) = H$$
$$\therefore \quad T = T_0 + H/F \tag{1.21}$$

From (1.19) and (1.21),

$$H = G(212 + L - T_0 - H/F)$$
$$\therefore \quad G = \frac{FH}{F(212 + L - T_0) - H} \tag{1.22}$$

This equation gives the rate of distillation in terms of the heat input, and the temperature and flow rate of the cooling water.

If an attempt is made to interpret equation (1.22) for a constant heat supply rate and constant feed temperature, it is seen that as F is decreased, G increases. In fact when $F = H/(212 + L - T_0)$ it appears that G is infinite, which is a physical impossibility. Reference to equation (1.21) resolves the difficulty as follows. As F decreases, T increases; but T cannot exceed 212° F as it leaves the condenser, and this gives the restriction

$$T_0 + H/F = T \leqslant 212$$
$$\therefore \quad F \geqslant H/(212 - T_0) \tag{1.23}$$

If F does not satisfy this inequality, T will remain constant at 212 and equation (1.19) becomes

$$H = LG$$
$$\therefore \quad G = H/L$$

The temperature restriction has a further influence in that the amount of steam produced by the boiler exceeds the capacity of the condenser. Denoting the rate of collection of distillate by D, equation (1.20) becomes

$$F(212 - T_0) = DL$$

$$\therefore \quad D = (212 - T_0)F/L \tag{1.24}$$

The complete solution is thus given by equations (1.22), (1.23), and (1.24); i.e.

$$D = (212 - T_0)F/L \quad \text{for } F \leqslant H/(212 - T_0)$$

and

$$D = \frac{FH}{F(212 + L - T_0) - H} \quad \text{for } F \geqslant H/(212 - T_0)$$

and this solution is illustrated by the continuous line in Fig. 1.6. This shows that when $F = H/(212 - T_0)$, the rate of collection of distillate is a maximum at a value H/L.

The above analysis has been made without reference to heat losses, and an attempt to allow for these would lead to a much more complicated model. A qualitative investigation would suggest that heat losses in the feed line to the boiler would be detrimental, and more serious at low values of F; but heat losses in the vapour line can have two effects. If F is greater than the optimum value, losses from the vapour line will be detrimental, but if F is smaller than the optimum value, heat losses from the vapour line will actually increase the yield. On the basis of these considerations, the second, dotted line has been drawn in Fig. 1.6.

Fig. 1.6. Variation of distillation rate with feed rate

1.6. UNSTEADY STATE OPERATION

In the examples considered so far, the system has been in a steady state, allowing the material entering the system to be equated to the material leaving the system and this has always given algebraic equations. In unsteady state problems, however, time enters as a variable and some properties of the system become functions of time. In the application of conservation laws it is no longer true that the rate of entry of material will equal the rate of exit, since an allowance must be made for material accumulating within the system. The general conservation law now becomes

$$\text{INPUT} - \text{OUTPUT} = \text{ACCUMULATION} \qquad (1.25)$$

The example of Section 1.2 will now be reconsidered as it starts from the following situation. Assume that the single stage contains V_1 ft^3 of toluene, V_2 ft^3 of water, and no benzoic acid. Assume, as before, that the mixer is so efficient that the compositions of the two liquid streams are in equilibrium at all times, and, in addition, that a stream leaving the stage is of the same composition as that phase in the stage   This is all illustrated in Fig. 1.7,

FIG. 1.7.   Time dependent single-stage extraction

which shows the state of the system at a general time θ, where x and y are now functions of time.

Since the flow rates of water and toluene are constant, V_1 and V_2 will remain constant. The conditions are always changing, and so the material balance must be applied during a small time increment $\delta\theta$. Any function of θ can be expanded by Taylor's theorem,† and this allows the state of the system at a time $\theta + \delta\theta$ to be expressed in terms of its state at time θ. In this case, it is helpful to draw up the following table.

TABLE 1.2. *The Condition of the System Before and After a Time Increment*

Property of the System	θ	$\theta + \delta\theta$
Flow rate of toluene phase	R	R
Flow rate of water phase	S	S
Volume of toluene phase in stage	V_1	V_1
Volume of water phase in stage	V_2	V_2
Conc. of acid in entrance toluene	c	c
Conc. of acid in exit toluene	x	$x + \dfrac{dx}{d\theta}\,\delta\theta$
Conc. of acid in exit water	y	$y + \dfrac{dy}{d\theta}\,\delta\theta$
Amount of acid in toluene layer	$V_1 x$	$V_1 x + V_1\dfrac{dx}{d\theta}\,\delta\theta$
Amount of acid in water layer	$V_2 y$	$V_2 y + V_2\dfrac{dy}{d\theta}\,\delta\theta$

† Mathematical functions exist which cannot be expanded by Taylor's theorem as shown in Section 3.3.7, but these do not normally occur in chemical engineering applications, and the statement in the text should not cause any difficulty.

During a time interval $\delta\theta$,

Input of acid $\quad= Rc\,\delta\theta$

Output of acid $\quad= R\left(x + \dfrac{1}{2}\dfrac{dx}{d\theta}\delta\theta\right)\delta\theta + S\left(y + \dfrac{1}{2}\dfrac{dy}{d\theta}\delta\theta\right)\delta\theta$

Accumulation $\quad= V_1\dfrac{dx}{d\theta}\delta\theta + V_2\dfrac{dy}{d\theta}\delta\theta$

Since input $-$ output $=$ accumulation,

$$Rc\delta\theta - R\left(x + \frac{1}{2}\frac{dx}{d\theta}\delta\theta\right)\delta\theta - S\left(y + \frac{1}{2}\frac{dy}{d\theta}\delta\theta\right)\delta\theta = V_1\frac{dx}{d\theta}\delta\theta + V_2\frac{dy}{d\theta}\delta\theta$$

$$\therefore\quad Rc - R\left(x + \frac{1}{2}\frac{dx}{d\theta}\delta\theta\right) - S\left(y + \frac{1}{2}\frac{dy}{d\theta}\delta\theta\right) = V_1\frac{dx}{d\theta} + V_2\frac{dy}{d\theta}$$

Taking the limit as $\delta\theta \to 0$,

$$Rc - Rx - Sy = V_1\frac{dx}{d\theta} + V_2\frac{dy}{d\theta} \tag{1.26}$$

In stating the output, the arithmetic mean of the concentrations was taken, but the later calculations show that this was not necessary; the same equation (1.26) would have been obtained by using the concentrations at time θ instead.

Only the first two terms were taken in the Taylor series for x and y, and these are all that are necessary since the further terms which contain a factor $(\delta\theta)^2$ will disappear when the limit $\delta\theta\to0$ is taken.

Equation (1.26) must now be solved in conjunction with the equilibrium relationship (1.1). Eliminating y,

$$Rc - Rx - mSx = V_1\frac{dx}{d\theta} + mV_2\frac{dx}{d\theta}$$

Rearranging,

$$\frac{dx}{Rc - (R + mS)x} = \frac{d\theta}{V_1 + mV_2}$$

and integrating,

$$\frac{-\ln\{Rc - (R+mS)x\}}{R+mS} = \frac{\theta}{V_1 + mV_2} + A \tag{1.27}$$

The constant of integration A can be evaluated by using the given initial state of the system that the stage contains no benzoic acid at zero time; i.e. when

$$\theta = 0, \quad x = 0 \tag{1.28}$$

$$\therefore\quad \frac{-\ln Rc}{R+mS} = A$$

$$\therefore\quad \ln Rc - \ln\{Rc - (R+mS)x\} = (R+mS)\theta/(V_1 + mV_2)$$

or in exponential form:

$$x = \frac{Rc}{R+mS}\left\{1 - \exp\left(-\frac{R+mS}{V_1 + mV_2}\right)\right\} \tag{1.29}$$

This equation satisfies the condition $x = 0$, at $\theta = 0$, satisfies the differential equation (1.26) for any positive value of θ, and when $\theta \to \infty$, $x \to Rc/(R+mS)$. This is the steady state solution which has already been obtained in equation (1.3).

1.7. SALT ACCUMULATION IN A STIRRED TANK

Two further points are illustrated by the following example. A tank contains 20 ft^3 of water. A stream of brine containing 2 lb/ft^3 of salt is fed into the tank at a rate of 3 ft^3/min. Liquid flows from the tank at a rate of 2 ft^3/min. If the tank is well agitated, what is the salt concentration in the tank when the tank contains 30 ft^3 of brine?

1.7.1. *Simple Treatment*

Firstly, the following simple model of this system can be set up. Liquid enters at a faster rate than it leaves, so that liquid accumulates in the tank at a rate of 1 ft^3/min. The increase in tank contents is $30-20 = 10$ ft^3, and hence the operation will last for 10 min.

During this 10 min, 30 ft^3 of brine enter carrying 60 lb of salt, and 20 ft^3 of brine leave. Assuming that the final concentration in the tank is X, and that the concentration of the outlet stream increases linearly with time, the following material balance can be established.

Input of salt during 10 min (lb) $= 60$
Output of salt during 10 min (lb) $= 20\,(X/2)$
Accumulation of salt in the tank (lb) $= 30X$

Using equation (1.25),

$$60 - 10X = 30X$$
$$\therefore \quad X = 1 \cdot 50\,\text{lb/ft}^3 \tag{1.30}$$

This is a very simple model of the system which yields an answer by elementary algebra. It does, however, contain a further assumption beyond those given in the question; the assumption concerns the time variation of the outlet concentration. This additional assumption need not be made if a more detailed model is taken in a similar manner to that in the previous section.

1.7.2. *More Detailed Treatment*

The state of the system at a general time θ is shown in Fig. 1.8, where both V and x are functions of θ. Again, a table can be constructed showing the state of the system at time θ and at time $\theta + \delta\theta$.

FIG. 1.8.   Accumulation of salt in surge tank

TABLE 1.3. *The Condition of the System Before and After a Time Increment*

Property of the System	θ	$\theta + \delta\theta$
Brine input rate (ft³/min)	3	3
Input salt concentration (lb/ft³)	2	2
Brine output rate (ft³/min)	2	2
Output salt concentration (lb/ft³)	x	$x + \dfrac{dx}{d\theta}\delta\theta$
Volume of liquid in tank (ft³)	V	$V + \dfrac{dV}{d\theta}\delta\theta$
Salt content of tank (lb)	Vx	$\left(V + \dfrac{dV}{d\theta}\delta\theta\right)\left(x + \dfrac{dx}{d\theta}\delta\theta\right)$

During a time interval $\delta\theta$,

Input of brine $= 3\delta\theta$
Output of brine $= 2\delta\theta$
Accumulation of brine $= \left(V + \dfrac{dV}{d\theta}\delta\theta\right) - V$

$$\therefore \quad 3\delta\theta - 2\delta\theta = \frac{dV}{d\theta}\delta\theta$$

$$\therefore \quad 1 = \frac{dV}{d\theta} \tag{1.31}$$

A material balance must also be satisfied by the salt, viz.

Input of salt $= 3.2\delta\theta$
Output of salt $= 2x\delta\theta$

Accumulation of salt $= \left(V + \dfrac{dV}{d\theta}\delta\theta\right)\left(x + \dfrac{dx}{d\theta}\delta\theta\right) - Vx$

Since input $-$ output $=$ accumulation,

$$6\delta\theta - 2x\delta\theta = Vx + x\frac{dV}{d\theta}\delta\theta + V\frac{dx}{d\theta}\delta\theta + \frac{dV}{d\theta}\frac{dx}{d\theta}(\delta\theta)^2 - Vx$$

$$\therefore \quad 6 - 2x = x\frac{dV}{d\theta} + V\frac{dx}{d\theta} + \frac{dV}{d\theta}\frac{dx}{d\theta}\delta\theta \tag{1.32}$$

Taking the limit $\delta\theta \to 0$, the last term in equation (1.32) vanishes. In deriving this equation, the salt concentration in the outlet stream at time θ has been used in the output term; since, as in Section 1.6, any correction to this contains a factor $\delta\theta$ which will lead to its elimination when the limit $\delta\theta \to 0$ is taken. The first important point is now evident; the accumulation consists of two terms. The one term is due to a volume change, the other is due to a concentration change, and both are essential in the solution.

Equations (1.31) and (1.32) must now be solved for x and V as functions of θ. Equation (1.31) can be solved immediately;

$$V = A + \theta$$

But when $\theta = 0$, $V = 20$

$$\therefore \quad V = 20 + \theta \tag{1.33}$$

Substituting equations (1.31) and (1.33) into (1.32),

$$6 - 2x = x + (20 + \theta)\frac{dx}{d\theta}$$

Rearranging,

$$\frac{dx}{6 - 3x} = \frac{d\theta}{20 + \theta}$$

and integrating,

$$-\tfrac{1}{3}\ln(6 - 3x) = \ln(20 + \theta) + B$$

where B is the constant of integration. But when

$$\theta = 0, \qquad x = 0 \tag{1.34}$$

$$\therefore \quad -\tfrac{1}{3}\ln 6 = \ln 20 + B$$

Eliminating B, and combining the logarithms,

$$-\tfrac{1}{3}\ln(1 - 0{\cdot}5x) = \ln(1 + 0{\cdot}05\theta)$$

$$\therefore \quad 1 - 0{\cdot}5x = (1 + 0{\cdot}05\theta)^{-3}$$

$$\therefore \quad x = 2 - 2(1 + 0{\cdot}05\theta)^{-3} \tag{1.35}$$

Equation (1.35) gives the salt concentration in the tank at any time, and equation (1.33) gives the volume of brine in the tank. From (1.33) it is seen that $V = 30$ when $\theta = 10$, as in Section 1.7.1, and therefore from (1.35)

$$X = 2 - 2(2/3)^3$$

$$\therefore \quad X = 1{\cdot}407\,\text{lb/ft}^3 \tag{1.36}$$

Comparison of this result with the previous result (1.30), shows that the first simple model has a significant error of $6{\cdot}6\%$ due to the additional assumption of a linear variation of x with θ; an assumption which is shown to be incorrect by equation (1.35).

The two treatments of this example illustrate the important point that the solution of a problem depends upon the choice of model. A simple model needs many assumptions and yields an approximate answer quickly, whereas a more complicated model needs fewer assumptions and yields a more accurate answer by more advanced mathematical techniques. It is evident that the most accurate result will be obtained by making the minimum number of assumptions consistent with obtaining a tractable mathematical problem. In this way the mathematical techniques which are available to an investigator control the applicability of any theoretical prediction made by him. It is therefore desirable that the widest selection of mathematical techniques should be at his disposal.

1.8. RADIAL HEAT TRANSFER THROUGH A CYLINDRICAL CONDUCTOR

In the last two problems the properties of the system were functions of time. There are many problems of a similar nature, where the properties of the system are functions of position instead of time, and the following example illustrates the application of the method to this type of problem.

Two concentric cylindrical metallic shells are separated by a solid material. If the two metal surfaces are maintained at different constant temperatures, what is the steady state temperature distribution within the separating material?

This is a steady state problem, but some of the properties of the system depend upon the position at which they are measured. In this case, the temperature (T) and the heat flow rate per unit area (Q) are both functions of the radius (r), and the heat balance must be related to a space interval between r and $r+\delta r$ as shown in Fig. 1.9. Following the same procedure as before, but considering variations of r instead of θ, Table 1.4 can be compiled

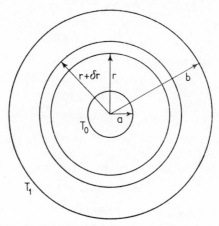

FIG. 1.9. Radial heat flow through cylindrical conductor

TABLE 1.4. *The Condition of the System on Either Side of a Space Increment*

Property of the System	r	$r + \delta r$
Temperature	T	$T + \dfrac{dT}{dr}\delta r$
Heat transfer area/unit length	$2\pi r$	$2\pi(r + \delta r)$
Radial heat flux density	Q	$Q + \dfrac{dQ}{dr}\delta r$
Total radial heat flow	$2\pi r Q$	$2\pi(r + \delta r)\left(Q + \dfrac{dQ}{dr}\delta r\right)$

Considering the element of thickness δr,

Heat input to inner surface $\quad = 2\pi r Q$

Heat output from outer surface $= 2\pi(r+\delta r)\left(Q + \dfrac{dQ}{dr}\,\delta r\right)$

Accumulation of heat $\quad\quad = 0$

Since input $-$ output $=$ accumulation,

$$2\pi r Q - 2\pi(r+\delta r)\left(Q + \frac{dQ}{dr}\,\delta r\right) = 0$$

$$\therefore \quad rQ - rQ - r\frac{dQ}{dr}\,\delta r - Q\delta r - \frac{dQ}{dr}(\delta r)^2 = 0$$

Cancelling out rQ, dividing by δr, and taking the limit $\delta r \to 0$,

$$r\frac{dQ}{dr} + Q = 0 \tag{1.37}$$

But Q is related to T by

$$Q = -k\frac{dT}{dr} \tag{1.38}$$

where k is the thermal conductivity. Equation (1.37) becomes,

$$-kr\frac{d^2T}{dr^2} - k\frac{dT}{dr} = 0$$

or

$$r\frac{d^2T}{dr^2} + \frac{dT}{dr} = 0 \tag{1.39}$$

since k is constant. Referring to Table 1.4, the change in heat flow rate across the element gives rise to two terms in this example, one due to a change in temperature gradient, and the other due to a change in the area of conduction.

This problem can be solved by treating (1.39) as a homogeneous second order differential equation (see Section 2.4.3), or by solving equations (1.37) and (1.38) in succession. Equation (1.37) gives,

$$\frac{dQ}{Q} = -\frac{dr}{r}$$

$$\therefore \quad \ln Q = -\ln r + \ln A$$

or

$$Q = A/r$$

where $\ln A$ is chosen for the constant of integration. Putting this value of Q into equation (1.38),

$$\frac{A}{r} = -k\frac{dT}{dr}$$

$$\therefore \quad \frac{dr}{r} = -\frac{kdT}{A}$$

$$\therefore \quad \ln r = -(kT/A) + B \tag{1.40}$$

Equation (1.40) involves two constants of integration, A and B, and these can be evaluated from the fixed boundary temperatures.

At

$$r = a, \qquad T = T_0$$

and at

$$r = b, \qquad T = T_1$$

$$\qquad\qquad (1.41)$$

$$\therefore \quad \ln a = -(kT_0/A) + B$$

and

$$\ln b = -(kT_1/A) + B$$

$$\ln a - \ln b = k(T_1 - T_0)/A$$

$$\therefore \quad A = k(T_1 - T_0)/(\ln a - \ln b)$$

$$\therefore \quad B = (T_1 \ln a - T_0 \ln b)/(T_1 - T_0)$$

Putting these values of A and B into equation (1.40),

$$(T_1 - T_0) \ln r = (\ln b - \ln a)T + T_1 \ln a - T_0 \ln b$$

$$= (T - T_0)(\ln b - \ln a) + (T_1 - T_0) \ln a$$

$$\therefore \quad \frac{T - T_0}{T_1 - T_0} = \frac{\ln r - \ln a}{\ln b - \ln a} \qquad\qquad (1.42)$$

1.9. Heating a Closed Kettle

The problems considered so far, have only used material or heat balances in the derivation of the equations. In the following example, the equation is derived from a rate equation.

A closed kettle of total surface area A ft^2 is heated through this surface by condensing steam at temperature T_s °F. The kettle is charged with M lb of liquid of specific heat C Btu/lb, at a temperature of T_0°F. If the process is controlled by a heat transfer coefficient h Btu/h ft^2 °F, how does the temperature of the liquid vary with time?

Consider a time interval $\delta\theta$.

$$\text{Heat input (Btu)} \quad = hA(T_s - T)\delta\theta$$
$$\text{Heat output (Btu)} \quad = 0$$
$$\text{Accumulation (Btu)} = MC\frac{dT}{d\theta}\delta\theta$$

Since input − output = accumulation,

$$hA(T_s - T)\delta\theta = MC\frac{dT}{d\theta}\delta\theta \qquad\qquad (1.43)$$

Rearranging,

$$\frac{dT}{T_s - T} = \frac{hAd\theta}{MC}$$

and integrating,

$$-\ln(T_s - T) = (hA/MC)\theta + B \qquad\qquad (1.44)$$

B can be evaluated by using the known fact that when $\theta = 0$, $T = T_0$

$$\therefore \quad -\ln(T_s - T_0) = B$$

$$\therefore \quad \ln\frac{T_s - T}{T_s - T_0} = -\frac{Ah}{MC}\theta \tag{1.46}$$

In this problem, equation (1.43) could have been written down immediately from the definition of the heat transfer coefficient, thus avoiding the necessity of taking a heat balance.

1.10. DEPENDENT AND INDEPENDENT VARIABLES, PARAMETERS

Any solution of a differential equation is an algebraic equation involving symbols. These symbols fall into three classes, (a) independent variables, (b) dependent variables, and (c) parameters.

1.10.1. *Independent Variables*

These are quantities describing the system which can be varied by choice during a particular experiment independently of one another. Examples are time and coordinate variables.

1.10.2. *Dependent Variables*

These are properties of the system which change when the independent variables are altered in value. There is no direct control over a dependent variable during an experiment. The relationship between independent and dependent variables is one of cause and effect; the independent variable measures the cause and the dependent variable measures the effect of a particular action. Examples of dependent variables are temperature, concentration, and efficiency.

1.10.3. *Parameters*

This is by far the largest group, consisting mainly of the characteristic properties of the apparatus and the physical properties of the materials. The group contains all properties which remain constant during an individual experiment, but since different constant values can be taken by a property during different experiments, the correct term for them is " parameters ". Examples are overall dimensions of the apparatus, flow rates, heat transfer coefficients, thermal conductivity, specific heat, density, and initial or boundary values of the dependent variables.

Referring to Section 1.6, the solution to the problem of starting a single stage liquid–liquid extraction system is given by equations (1.1) and (1.29).

$$y = mx \tag{1.1}$$

$$x = \frac{Rc}{R + mS}\left\{1 - \exp\left(-\frac{R + mS}{V_1 + mV_2}\theta\right)\right\} \tag{1.29}$$

and by eliminating x,

$$y = \frac{mRc}{R + mS}\left\{1 - \exp\left(-\frac{R + mS}{V_1 + mV_2}\theta\right)\right\} \tag{1.47}$$

The symbols can be classified as follows:

$$\text{Independent variable} \quad \theta$$
$$\text{Dependent variables} \quad x, y$$
$$\text{Parameters} \quad m, R, S, c, V_1, V_2$$

The parameters are all fixed in value during an experiment, but can be varied between experiments for comparison purposes. θ is the only variable whose value can be altered during an experiment. x and y vary during an experiment and between experiments; their values depend upon the choice of values for both the parameters and the independent variable.

The main use of this classification is in the interpretation of the differentiation process. We usually differentiate a dependent variable with respect to an independent variable, and occasionally with respect to a parameter. By differentiating either (1.29) or (1.47) with respect to θ, an expression giving the rate of change of concentration with time can be obtained, but differentiating (1.1) with respect to the dependent variable x, gives $dy/dx = m$, an almost useless piece of information which does not throw any light on the behaviour of the apparatus.

So far, the problems considered in Sections 1.2, 1.3, 1.4, and 1.5 have been equations between parameters since no independent variables were involved, and hence no dependent variables could be present. Each experiment found a set of related constant values, the only variation could be between experiments when some of the parameters may be altered in value.

The problems of Sections 1.6, 1.7, and 1.9 involved time as an independent variable, and in Section 1.8, a radial coordinate was the single independent variable. These problems all gave rise to ordinary differential equations. When more than one independent variable is needed to describe a system, the usual result is a partial differential equation, and this type of problem will be dealt with in Chapter 8.

1.11. BOUNDARY CONDITIONS

An ordinary differential equation usually arises in any problem which involves a single independent variable. The general solution of this differential equation will contain arbitrary constants of integration, the number of constants being equal to the order of the differential equation (see Chapter 2). To complete the solution of a particular problem, these arbitrary constants have to be evaluated.

In formulating the equation, the conservation law (1.25) is applied to an infinitesimal increment of the independent variable, and this yields a differential equation. There is usually a restriction on the range of values which the independent variable can take and this range describes the scope of the problem. Special conditions are placed on the dependent variable at these end points of the range of the independent variable. These are naturally called " boundary conditions ", and are used to evaluate the arbitrary constants in the solution of the differential equation.

These conditions have already been used in the examples considered earlier in this chapter. In Section 1.8, a second order differential equation (1.39) was derived, and its solution (1.40) contains two arbitrary constants A and B. The independent variable in this problem is r, and the boundaries are given by $r = a$, and $r = b$. The boundary conditions are given by equations (1.41) in the form of restrictions on the dependent variable (T) at the boundaries defined by values of the independent variable (r).

In the other examples in Sections 1.6, 1.7, and 1.9, θ was the independent variable, all of the equations were of first order, and each solution only contained one arbitrary constant. When time is the independent variable, the boundary condition is frequently called the " initial condition ". This is because it specifies the starting state of the apparatus.

The three most frequently used boundary conditions in heat transfer are:

(1) Boundary at a fixed temperature, $T = T_0$.

(2) Constant heat flow rate through the boundary, $dT/dx = A$.

(2a) Boundary thermally insulated, $dT/dx = 0$.

(3) Boundary cools to the surroundings through a film resistance described by a heat transfer coefficient, $kdT/dx = h(T-T_0)$. k is the thermal conductivity, h is the heat transfer coefficient, and T_0 is the temperature of the surroundings.

Boundary conditions in problems involving partial differential equations will be described when they arise in Chapter 8.

1.12. SIGN CONVENTIONS

Most sign difficulties are a result of trying to think too deeply about them, thus causing a state of complete confusion. The temptation to anticipate the solution of the problem is very strong but it must be resisted. The formulation of equations can be reduced to a set of rules which can be systematically applied and although it is difficult to frame such a set of rules to cover the wide variety of problems which can arise, an attempt has been made in the next section. The slavish observance of rules is not to be generally recommended, but it is best in the first instance to do just this because it completely eliminates any possibility of anticipating properties of the solution, and ensures that the signs are correct. The resulting equation can frequently be subjected to a physical sign check after it has been established.

All terms must be treated as positive during the formulation, and negative signs will only occur due to two causes.

(a) The first cause is the negative sign in the general conservation law (1.25), viz.

$$\text{Input} - \text{Output} = \text{Accumulation}$$

(b) The second cause is by the definition of the rate equations governing heat transfer, mass transfer, and fluid flow. This will be illustrated below for the case of heat transfer.

When an independent variable is defined for a system, an origin and positive direction have to be included in the definition. This has not been a serious problem so far, since when time is the independent variable, its direction is the natural one of successive events and its origin is always taken as the instant when the initial conditions are established. The radial coordinate (r) the other independent variable which has occurred is measured outwards from the axis of the body of revolution, the axis being the origin. In other cases it is always necessary to specify the origin of the independent variable and also its positive direction.

Turning to heat flow, the quantity of heat (Q) conducted past a point through unit cross-sectional area in unit time is counted as positive if it flows in the same direction as the positive direction of the independent variable (coordinate), and negative if it flows in the negative direction of the coordinate. According to Fourier's Law, the rate of conduction of heat is proportional to the temperature gradient, and the direction of the flow is down the temperature gradient as shown in Fig. 1.10 where the two possible

Fig. 1.10.   Sign convention in heat transfer

cases are shown. On the left hand side of the diagram, the temperature gradient is positive and as a result, the heat flows from right to left and is negative. The reverse is true in the right hand side of the diagram where the temperature gradient is negative and the heat flow positive. In both cases, the equation can be written in the consistent form

$$Q = -k\frac{dT}{dx} \tag{1.48}$$

where k is the conductivity. This equation has already been used (1.38), but in that application the negative sign was of no importance.

For mass transfer, material diffuses down a concentration gradient, and for fluids, the flow is down a pressure gradient. By analogy with the Fourier Law, these rate equations also contain a negative sign in the definition.

In conclusion, if the rules which have been illustrated in this chapter are followed, and the solution is not anticipated, the signs will take care of themselves. This can be illustrated by repeating the example of Section 1.7 with a different boundary condition. Instead of the tank containing 20 ft³ of water initially, let it contain 20 ft³ of brine of concentration 5 lb/ft³. The only physical difference that this makes, is that the brine concentration will now decrease with time instead of increase. Mathematically, only equation (1.34) need be altered. The list of properties in Table 1.3 will be unaltered, and the change in salt concentration with time is still adequately described by $dx/d\theta$ without artificially changing its sign. In this new problem, $dx/d\theta$ is now a negative quantity since x decreases with time and it would be a mistake to say that the output salt concentration at $\theta + \delta\theta$ is $x - (dx/d\theta)\delta\theta$. A further reason why this is a mistake can be seen from Taylor's theorem which is the origin of this term; the sign is governed by the sign of $\delta\theta$ which is positive. Table 1.3 is therefore still true for this modified problem, and the solution is identical until equation (1.34) is reached, and this now becomes:

when $$\theta = 0, \quad x = 5 \tag{1.49}$$

$$\therefore \quad -\tfrac{1}{3}\ln(-9) = \ln 20 + B$$

Here, the logarithm of a negative number is involved due to integrating $(6-3x)^{-1}$ in an unconventional manner. This need not give rise to any difficulty if $\ln(-1)$ is treated as an imaginary quantity by analogy with $\sqrt{(-1)}$, and B is eliminated as before by subtraction.

$$-\tfrac{1}{3}\ln\left(\frac{6-3x}{-9}\right) = \ln\left(\frac{20+\theta}{20}\right)$$

$$\therefore \quad \ln\left(\frac{x-2}{3}\right) = -3\ln(1+0\cdot05\theta)$$

$$\therefore \quad x = 2 + 3/(1+0\cdot05\theta)^3$$

This is the correct solution to this modified problem, and it illustrates how signs can be allowed to take care of themselves, and how the different boundary conditions select appropriate particular solutions from the general solution of the differential equation.

1.13. SUMMARY OF THE METHOD OF FORMULATION

(1) Pick a mathematical model of the process by making assumptions about its ideal behaviour.

(2) Define dependent variables to measure the properties being investigated.

(3) Define one or more independent variables in terms of which the dependent variables can be expressed.

(4) Define the parameters of the system which particularize the general relationship between the dependent and independent variables.

(5) Establish the state of the system at a typical point defined in terms of the independent variables.

(6) Take an infinitesimal increment in each of the independent variables, and establish the state of the system at neighbouring points in terms of the state at the typical point by using Taylor's theorem.

(7) Apply the relevant conservation laws and rate equations to the element of the system defined by (6).

B

(8) Cancel out terms where possible, including the incremental intervals.

(9) Take the limit as the size of the increments tends to zero.

These rules include the possibility that there may be more than one independent variable, resulting in the formulation of a partial differential equation. The treatment of such problems will be given in Chapter 8.

Although only the first two terms of Taylor's theorem are usually needed in practice, the infinite series of terms is effectively included, since the later terms involve incremental quantities raised to high powers and these disappear when the incremental quantities tend to zero.

The solution given by the analysis is related to the model of the system being investigated, and not to the system itself. The assumptions made in order to derive an equation for the model may or may not be valid, and if the result does not agree with the experiment, then the model is probably wrong and not the mathematics. As shown in Section 1.7, a more complicated model gives a more accurate result, but frequently, if the model is too detailed, the equation derived defies rigorous mathematical analysis. This difficulty can be overcome by using a numerical method to find an approximate solution to the difficult equation as shown in Chapter 11, or by simplifying the model with a further assumption. It must be realized, however, that as the number of assumptions increases, the likelihood of the result agreeing with practice decreases.

Tables 1.2, 1.3, and 1.4 have been compiled in this chapter to facilitate the description of the method of formulating equations. These tables should be compiled mentally and throughout the rest of the book they will be omitted. If any reader finds difficulty in formulating the equations in the rest of the book, it is suggested that similar tables should be constructed.

Chapter 2

ORDINARY DIFFERENTIAL EQUATIONS

2.1. INTRODUCTION

AN equation relating a dependent variable to one or more independent variables by means of its differential coefficients with respect to the independent variables is called a differential equation. If there is only one independent variable the equation is said to be an "ordinary differential equation". If there are two or more independent variables and the equation contains differential coefficients with respect to each of these, the equation is said to be a "partial differential equation". Thus

$$\frac{d^3y}{dx^3} - \frac{d^2y}{dx^2} + 5\left(\frac{dy}{dx}\right)^2 + 2x^3\frac{dy}{dx} + 4y = 4e^x\cos x \tag{2.1}$$

is an ordinary differential equation; whereas

$$\rho C_p \frac{\partial T}{\partial \theta} = k\left[\frac{\partial^2 T}{\partial x^2} + \frac{\partial^2 T}{\partial y^2} + \frac{\partial^2 T}{\partial z^2}\right] \tag{2.2}$$

is a partial differential equation. Equation (2.2) contains the partial differential coefficients of T with respect to each of the independent variables θ, x, y, and z.

Partial differential equations will be dealt with in Chapter 8, whilst in this chapter attention will be confined to ordinary differential equations.

2.2. ORDER AND DEGREE

The order of a differential equation is equal to the order of the highest differential coefficient that it contains. Thus in equation (2.1) the order of the highest differential coefficient is three and therefore equation (2.1) is a third order differential equation. The degree of a differential equation is the highest power of the highest order differential coefficient that the equation contains after it has been rationalized. Equation (2.1) is of the first degree, even though it contains the first order differential coefficient raised to the second power and the cube of the independent variable. However, as the first order differential coefficient is squared, equation (2.1) is referred to as a third order first degree non-linear ordinary differential equation. It is non-linear because the equation contains the term $(dy/dx)^2$ and generally differential equations are said to be non-linear if any products exist between the dependent variable and its derivatives, or between the derivatives themselves. Thus the following equations are non-linear.

$$\frac{dy}{dx} + y^2 = \sin x \tag{2.3}$$

$$\left[\frac{d^2y}{dx^2}\right]^2 + \frac{dy}{dx} + y = 0 \tag{2.4}$$

Equation (2.3) is non-linear because the dependent variable y appears as y^2, whereas equation (2.4) is non-linear because it is of the second degree.

The standard methods of solving the simplest types of ordinary differential equations that occur very frequently in chemical engineering will be considered in the present chapter, whereas more difficult types of ordinary differential equations will be considered later.

2.3. First Order Differential Equations

First order equations contain no derivatives higher than the first, but relate the first order differential coefficient to the two variables. Unfortunately there is no general method of solution of these equations because of their different degrees of complexity, but it is possible to classify the different types of first order equations so that each can be solved by a particular procedure. These are

(a) Exact equations.
(b) Equations in which the variables can be separated.
(c) Homogeneous equations.
(d) Equations solvable by an integrating factor.

Of these (d) is the most important and consequently (a), (b) and (c) will be treated briefly.

2.3.1. *Exact Equations*

Occasionally, a differential equation can be expressed in the form

$$df(x,y) = 0 \tag{2.5}$$

where $df(x,y)$ is an exact differential coefficient of some function. When this is so, the solution is obviously,

$$f(x,y) = C \tag{2.6}$$

where C is an arbitrary constant which must be evaluated from the boundary conditions of the problem. Frequently it is possible to show that $df(x,y)$ is an exact differential coefficient by inspection. Thus in the equation,

$$x\frac{dy}{dx} + y = 0 \tag{2.7}$$

the left-hand side is immediately seen to be the exact differential coefficient of xy with respect to x, and therefore the solution is

$$xy = C$$

However, consider the equation,

$$x^3 - y \sin x + (\cos x + 2y)\frac{dy}{dx} = 0 \qquad (2.8)$$

Only an experienced mathematician would recognize equation (2.8) to be an exact equation, but the reader familiar with the elementary concepts of partial differentiation could easily verify that equation (2.8) is an exact equation as follows. If $\phi = \phi(x,y)$, equation (8.16) shows that

$$d\phi = \frac{\partial \phi}{\partial x} dx + \frac{\partial \phi}{\partial y} dy \qquad (2.9)$$

Comparing this with equation (2.8),

$$\frac{\partial \phi}{\partial x} = x^3 - y \sin x$$

and

$$\frac{\partial \phi}{\partial y} = \cos x + 2y$$

The most general function which can be differentiated partially with respect to x to give the first of these expressions is

$$\phi = \tfrac{1}{4}x^4 + y \cos x + f(y) \qquad (2.10)$$

Differentiating equation (2.10) partially with respect to y gives

$$\frac{\partial \phi}{\partial y} = \cos x + f'(y) = \cos x + 2y$$

$$\therefore \quad f(y) = y^2 + \text{constant}$$

The solution of equation (2.8) is therefore

$$x^4 + 4y \cos x + 4y^2 = C \qquad (2.11)$$

2.3.2. *Equations in which the Variables can be Separated*

In the most simple first order differential equations, the independent variable and its differential can be separated from the dependent variable and its differential by the equality sign, using nothing more than the normal processes of elementary algebra. When this is possible, solution of the equation follows by straightforward integration of the rearranged equation. The example in Section 1.6 was of this type and as the procedure of solving is elementary, no further discussion of these equations will be made. It will suffice to state that they frequently appear in engineering problems.

2.3.3. *Homogeneous Equations*

A differential equation of the type,

$$\frac{dy}{dx} = f\left(\frac{y}{x}\right) \qquad (2.12)$$

is termed a homogeneous differential equation of the first order. Such an equation can be solved by making the substitution $y = vx$ and thereafter integrating the transformed equation. Thus let

$$y = vx \tag{2.13}$$

and therefore

$$\frac{dy}{dx} = v + x\frac{dv}{dx} \tag{2.14}$$

Substitution in equation (2.12), rearranging and integrating, gives

$$\ln x = \int \frac{dv}{f(v) - v} + C \tag{2.15}$$

Equation (2.15) is the solution of the general homogeneous equation (2.12). It should be pointed out, however, that the integral in equation (2.15) is not always expressible in terms of elementary functions. Thus the final solution after substituting for v may not be very useful in practice even though it is correct.

Homogeneous differential equations of first order arise in batch chemical reactor analyses when the materials undergo chemical reaction by two simultaneous second order reaction paths. A typical example is the halogenation of a hydrocarbon and the method of treating such a problem is illustrated in the example below.

Example 1.   Liquid benzene is to be chlorinated batchwise by sparging chlorine gas into a reaction kettle containing the benzene.   If the reactor contains such an efficient agitator that all the chlorine which enters the reactor undergoes chemical reaction, and only the hydrogen chloride gas liberated escapes from the vessel, estimate how much chlorine must be added to give the maximum yield of monochlorbenzene.   The reaction can be assumed to take place isothermally at 55°C when the ratios of the specific reaction rate constants are

$$\frac{k_1}{k_2} = 8 \cdot 0 \quad \text{and} \quad \frac{k_2}{k_3} = 30 \cdot 0$$

as published by Macmullen (*Chem. Eng. Prog.* **44**, 183, 1948). k_1 refers to reaction I, k_2 to reaction II, and k_3 to reaction III below.

$$C_6H_6 + Cl_2 \rightarrow C_6H_5Cl + HCl \qquad \qquad \text{I}$$
$$C_6H_5Cl + Cl_2 \rightarrow C_6H_4Cl_2 + HCl \qquad \qquad \text{II}$$
$$C_6H_4Cl_2 + Cl_2 \rightarrow C_6H_3Cl_3 + HCl \qquad \qquad \text{III}$$

Solution

Take a basis of $1 \cdot 0$ mole of benzene fed to the reactor and introduce the following variables to represent the state of the system at time θ,

p = mole fraction of chlorine present.
q = mole fraction of benzene present.
r = mole fraction of monochlorbenzene present.
s = mole fraction of dichlorbenzene present.
t = mole fraction of trichlorbenzene present.

Then, $$q+r+s+t=1 \qquad\qquad\text{IV}$$

and the total amount of chlorine consumed is given by
$$y = r+2s+3t \qquad\qquad\text{V}$$

Now assume that the reaction volume V is constant. Therefore, the rate of reaction of benzene is given by
$$V\frac{dq}{d\theta} = -k_1\,pq \qquad\qquad\text{VI}$$

and the rate of formation of each product is
$$V\frac{dr}{d\theta} = k_1\,pq - k_2\,pr \qquad\qquad\text{VII}$$

$$V\frac{ds}{d\theta} = k_2\,pr - k_3\,ps \qquad\qquad\text{VIII}$$

$$V\frac{dt}{d\theta} = k_3\,ps \qquad\qquad\text{IX}$$

The time θ can be eliminated as a variable by dividing equations VII to IX by equation VI. The first ratio gives
$$\frac{dr}{dq} = \frac{k_2 r}{k_1 q} - 1 = \frac{r-8q}{8q} \qquad\qquad\text{X}$$

This is now a first order homogeneous differential equation which can be solved by the substitution technique.

Let $$r = vq \qquad\qquad\text{XI}$$

and therefore $$\frac{dr}{dq} = v + q\,\frac{dv}{dq} \qquad\qquad\text{XII}$$

Substitution of XI and XII into X and integration of the result gives
$$\ln q = \ln K - 8/7\ln(7v+8) \qquad\qquad\text{XIII}$$

where K is the constant of integration.
Removing the logarithms,
$$q = K\left(\frac{7r}{q}+8\right)^{-8/7} \qquad\qquad\text{XIV}$$

But when $\theta = 0$, $q = 1$ and $r = 0$;
$$\therefore \quad K = 8^{8/7}$$

and after rearrangement,
$$r = 8(q^{1/8}-q)/7 \qquad\qquad\text{XV}$$

Similarly, from equations VI and VIII it can be shown that
$$\frac{ds}{dq} = \frac{s}{240q} - \frac{r}{8q} \qquad\qquad\text{XVI}$$

When r has been eliminated by using equation XV, equation XVI becomes a first order linear differential equation which can be solved by the integrating factor method given in Section 2.3.4. The result is

$$s = \frac{240}{7 \times 29 \times 239}(29q - 239q^{1/8} + 210q^{1/240}) \qquad \text{XVII}$$

For any value of q it is possible to determine the corresponding values of r and s from equations XV and XVII, and then the value of t from equation IV. Similarly by means of equation V the total quantity of chlorine gas consumed is determined. These last stages are arithmetical and are consequently not reported in detail; but the results of the calculations are summarized in graphical form in Fig. 2.1. in which the mole fraction of each

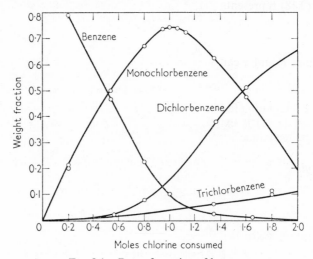

FIG. 2.1.   Rate of reaction of benzene

halogenated hydrocarbon is plotted against the total amount of chlorine consumed. The amount of chlorine required for the maximum production of monochlorbenzene is from Fig. 2.1. equal to $1 \cdot 0$ mole of chlorine per mole of benzene charged.

2.3.4. *Equations Solved by Integrating Factors*

There are many equations which can be solved by a variety of integrating factors, but the most useful integrating factor is the one used to integrate the first order linear differential equation,

$$\frac{dy}{dx} + Py = Q \qquad (2.16)$$

where P and Q are functions of x only.

The basis of the solution of equations of this type is that there exists a factor by which equation (2.16) can be multiplied so that the left-hand side becomes a complete differential coefficient. This factor is called "the integrating factor". Assume that the integrating factor R is a function of x only, and multiply equation (2.16) by R, thus

$$R\frac{dy}{dx} + RPy = RQ \tag{2.17}$$

when the left-hand side of equation (2.17) is the complete differential coefficient of some product, say Ry. Then

$$\frac{d}{dx}(Ry) = R\frac{dy}{dx} + y\frac{dR}{dx} \tag{2.18}$$

Equation (2.18) represents the left-hand side of equation (2.17) if

$$\frac{dR}{dx} = PR \tag{2.19}$$

The variables R and x can be separated in this equation, and the solution is

$$R = \exp\left(\int P dx\right) \tag{2.20}$$

That is, the integrating factor for the solution of the first order linear differential equation (2.16) is $\exp(\int P dx)$. The following examples are given to illustrate the technique.

Example 2. Solve $\qquad (1+x^2)\dfrac{dy}{dx} + xy = 1$

or $\qquad\qquad \dfrac{dy}{dx} + \dfrac{x}{1+x^2}y = \dfrac{1}{1+x^2}$ $\qquad$ I

The integrating factor is

$$\exp\left[\int\frac{x dx}{1+x^2}\right] = \exp\left[\tfrac{1}{2}\ln(1+x^2)\right]$$
$$= (1+x^2)^{\frac{1}{2}} \qquad \text{II}$$

Hence, multiplying throughout by $(1+x^2)^{\frac{1}{2}}$,

$$(1+x^2)^{\frac{1}{2}}\frac{dy}{dx} + \frac{x}{(1+x^2)^{\frac{1}{2}}}y = \frac{1}{(1+x^2)^{\frac{1}{2}}} \qquad \text{III}$$

Integrating,

$$(1+x^2)^{\frac{1}{2}}y = \int\frac{dx}{(1+x^2)^{\frac{1}{2}}} \qquad \text{IV}$$

This integral can be evaluated by using the substitution $x = \tan\theta$, or obtained from tables. The final solution is

$$y = \frac{\ln[x+\sqrt{(x^2+1)}]+C}{\sqrt{(1+x^2)}} \qquad \text{V}$$

Occasionally, a first order, first degree differential equation has to be solved in which P and Q are functions of both the dependent and the independent variable. When this arises it is often possible to linearize the equation by changing the dependent variable. Thus, consider the following example.

Example 3. Solve $\qquad xy - \dfrac{dy}{dx} = y^4 \exp\left(\dfrac{-3x^2}{2}\right)$

or $\qquad\qquad \dfrac{x}{y^3} - \dfrac{1}{y^4}\dfrac{dy}{dx} = \exp\left(\dfrac{-3x^2}{2}\right)$ $\qquad\qquad$ I

Let $z = 1/y^3$ thus changing the dependent variable. Then

$$\frac{dz}{dy} = -\frac{3}{y^4} \quad \text{and} \quad \frac{dz}{dx} = -\frac{3}{y^4}\frac{dy}{dx} \qquad\qquad \text{II}$$

Substitution of II into I gives

$$3xz + \frac{dz}{dx} = 3\exp\left(\frac{-3x^2}{2}\right) \qquad\qquad \text{III}$$

Equation III is a linear first order differential equation which has the solution,

$$z\exp\left(\frac{3x^2}{2}\right) = 3\int dx = 3x + C$$

$$\therefore \quad \frac{1}{y^3}\exp\left(\frac{3x^2}{2}\right) = 3x + C$$

$$\therefore \quad y^3(3x + C) = \exp\left(\frac{3x^2}{2}\right)$$

First order linear differential equations occasionally arise in chemical engineering problems in the fields of heat transfer, momentum transfer and mass transfer. Whichever aspect of chemical engineering is of interest the method of solution is the same. This is illustrated by the following example taken from the field of heat transfer.

Example 4. An elevated horizontal cylindrical tank 5 ft diameter and 12 ft long is insulated with asbestos lagging of thickness $l = 2''$, and is employed as a maturing vessel for a batch chemical process. Liquid at 200°F is charged into the tank and allowed to mature over 5 days. If the data below applies, calculate the final temperature of the liquid and give a plot of the liquid temperature as a function of time.

Liquid film coefficient of heat transfer (h_1) = 25·0 Btu/h ft² °F.
Thermal conductivity of asbestos (k) = 0·1 Btu/h ft² °F ft⁻¹.
Surface coefficient of heat transfer by convection
and radiation (h_2) = 1·8 Btu/h ft² °F.
Density of liquid (ρ) = 62·4 lb/ft³.
Specific heat of liquid (s) = 0·6.

Atmospheric temperature (t) which can be assumed to vary according to the relation $t = 55+15 \cos(\pi\theta/12)$, where θ is the time in hours.
Atmospheric temperature at time of charging $= 70°F$.
Heat loss through supports is negligible.

Solution

Area of tank $(A) = (\pi \times 5 \times 12) + 2\,(\tfrac{1}{4}\pi \times 5^2) = 72\cdot5\pi \text{ ft}^2.$
Rate of heat loss by liquid $= h_1 A\,(T-T_w).$

Rate of heat loss through lagging $= \dfrac{kA}{l}(T_w - T_s).$

where T represents the bulk liquid temperature,
$\quad T_w$ represents the inside wall temperature of the tank,
$\quad T_s$ represents the outside surface temperature of the lagging.
Rate of heat loss from the exposed surface of the lagging

$$= h_2 A(T_s - t)$$

Now,

$$\begin{bmatrix} \text{Rate of heat} \\ \text{loss from} \\ \text{liquid} \end{bmatrix} = \begin{bmatrix} \text{Rate of heat} \\ \text{transfer through} \\ \text{lagging} \end{bmatrix} = \begin{bmatrix} \text{Rate of heat} \\ \text{loss from} \\ \text{surface} \end{bmatrix} \qquad \text{I}$$

$$\therefore \quad h_1 A(T - T_w) = \frac{kA}{l}(T_w - T_s) = h_2 A(T_s - t) \qquad \text{II}$$

Rearranging the first part of this equation to give

$$T_w\left(h_1 + \frac{k}{l}\right) = h_1 T + \frac{k}{l}T_s \qquad \text{III}$$

and substituting into the last part of equation II gives

$$T_s = t + \left[\frac{kh_1}{h_1 h_2 l + h_1 k + h_2 k}\right](T - t) \qquad \text{IV}$$

or, $\qquad\qquad\qquad T_s = 0\cdot246T + 0\cdot754t \qquad\qquad\qquad \text{V}$

using the numerical values given earlier.
Considering the thermal equilibrium of the liquid,

$$\begin{aligned} \text{Input rate} \quad &= 0 \\ \text{Output rate} \quad &= h_2 A(T_s - t) \\ \text{Accumulation rate} &= V\rho s\frac{dT}{d\theta} \end{aligned}$$

$$\therefore \quad -h_2 A(T_s - t) = V\rho s\frac{dT}{d\theta} \qquad \text{VI}$$

Using the numerical values given above, and substituting for T_s from equation V,

$$\frac{dT}{d\theta} = -0\cdot0465\,(0\cdot246T + 0\cdot754t - t) \qquad \text{VII}$$

or in standard form,

$$\frac{dT}{d\theta} + 0{\cdot}0114T = 0{\cdot}0114t = 0{\cdot}628 + 0{\cdot}171\cos(\pi\theta/12)\qquad\text{VIII}$$

Equation VIII is a first order linear differential equation which can be solved by means of the integrating factor $e^{0{\cdot}0114\theta}$. The solution is

$$T\,e^{0{\cdot}0114\theta} = 0{\cdot}628\int e^{0{\cdot}0114\theta}\,d\theta + 0{\cdot}171\int e^{0{\cdot}0114\theta}\cos(\pi\theta/12)d\theta\qquad\text{IX}$$

The second term on the right-hand side can be integrated by parts to give

$$\frac{0{\cdot}171\,e^{0{\cdot}0114\theta}}{(0{\cdot}0114)^2+(0{\cdot}262)^2}\big[0{\cdot}0114\cos 0{\cdot}262\theta + 0{\cdot}262\sin 0{\cdot}262\theta\big]$$

Hence, the complete solution of equation VIII is

$$T = 55 + 0{\cdot}028\cos 0{\cdot}262\theta + 0{\cdot}653\sin 0{\cdot}262\theta + K\,e^{-0{\cdot}0114\theta}\qquad\text{X}$$

with the boundary condition that at $\theta = 0$, $T = 200$.

$$\therefore\quad 200 = 55 + 0{\cdot}028 + K$$

$$\therefore\quad K = 144{\cdot}97$$

Therefore, the final solution is

$$T = 55 + 0{\cdot}028\cos 0{\cdot}262\theta + 0{\cdot}653\sin 0{\cdot}262\theta + 144{\cdot}97\,e^{-0{\cdot}0114\theta}\qquad\text{XI}$$

Inspection of equation XI shows that the second term can only affect T by $\pm 0{\cdot}028°F$ at most. Similarly, the third term will only contribute

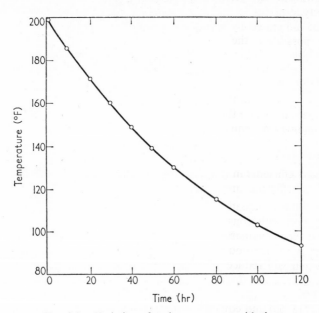

FIG. 2.2.   Variation of tank temperature with time

± 0·653°F at most. Both of these terms are negligible from a practical point of view, consequently it is justifiable to express equation XI as

$$T = 55 + 145\,e^{-0·0114\theta} \qquad \text{XII}$$

Figure 2.2. gives a plot of T vs θ in accordance with equation XII and after 120 h, T = 92°F.

2.4. SECOND ORDER DIFFERENTIAL EQUATIONS

As already stated, a second order differential equation is one in which the highest order differential coefficient appearing is the second. However, the equation may contain other terms involving first order differential coefficients in addition to functions of the independent and dependent variables. Furthermore the equation may be linear or non-linear. Thus,

$$\frac{d^2y}{dx^2} = f(x) \qquad (2.21)$$

is a simple second order differential equation easily solved by two successive integrations. On the other hand the equation,

$$y\frac{d^2y}{dx^2} + 1 = \left(\frac{dy}{dx}\right)^2 \qquad (2.22)$$

appears to be quite formidable on first inspection. These are both second order differential equations and the methods for solving them will be described in the following paragraphs. Essentially this will consist of proposals by which the above type of equation can be reduced to a first order equation which can then be integrated by one of the procedures already presented. Such a method is possible if the equation can be placed in one of the following classes.

A. Non-linear

(a) Equations where the dependent variable does not occur explicitly.
(b) Equations where the independent variable does not occur explicitly.
(c) Homogeneous equations.

B. Linear

(a) The coefficients in the equation are constant.
(b) The coefficients are functions of the independent variable.

The non-linear equations will be considered in this section, and the linear equation with constant coefficients will be discussed in Section 2.5, but the last type of equation is treated separately in Chapter 3.

In class A the method of solution depends upon the existence of a substituent which will reduce the second order differential equation to one of first order. In classes A(a) and A(b) it is customary to let p represent the first order differential coefficient. Substitutions of this kind were suggested by Clairaut (1713–65) and equations of the type,

$$y = x\frac{dy}{dx} + f\left(\frac{dy}{dx}\right) \tag{2.23}$$

are called Clairaut forms. They are solved by differentiation followed by the p substitution.

Returning to second order differential equations, the detailed substituting procedure depends on whether the equation falls into class A(a) or class A(b), and each of these will now be considered separately.

2.4.1. *Equations where the Dependent Variable does not occur Explicitly*

When the p substitution is made in this case, the second derivative of y is replaced by the first derivative of p thus eliminating y completely and producing a first order differential equation in p and x. The following example will clarify the technique.

Example 1. Solve $\qquad \dfrac{d^2y}{dx^2} + x\dfrac{dy}{dx} = ax \qquad\qquad$ I

Let $\qquad\qquad\qquad\qquad p = \dfrac{dy}{dx}$

and therefore $\qquad\qquad \dfrac{dp}{dx} = \dfrac{d^2y}{dx^2}$

Substitution into equation I gives

$$\frac{dp}{dx} + xp = ax \qquad\qquad \text{II}$$

Equation II is a first order linear differential equation which can be solved by using the integrating factor $\exp\left(\frac{1}{2}x^2\right)$.

$$\therefore \quad p\exp\left(\tfrac{1}{2}x^2\right) = a\int x\exp\left(\tfrac{1}{2}x^2\right)dx$$

$$= a\exp\left(\tfrac{1}{2}x^2\right) + C$$

$$\therefore \quad p = a + C\exp\left(-\tfrac{1}{2}x^2\right) = \frac{dy}{dx}$$

$$\therefore \quad y = ax + C\int \exp\left(-\tfrac{1}{2}x^2\right)dx \qquad\qquad \text{III}$$

$$\therefore \quad y = ax + A\,\mathrm{erf}\left(\frac{x}{\sqrt{2}}\right) + B \qquad\qquad \text{IV}$$

where A and B are the two constants of integration. The integration of the last term in equation III involving the "error function" will be treated in Chapter 5. Here, it is sufficient to quote the result.

2.4.2. *Equations where the Independent Variable does not occur Explicitly*

In this case, the same substitution of p for the first derivative is made, but the substitution for the second derivative of y is obtained as follows.

Let $$p = \frac{dy}{dx} \qquad (2.24)$$

$$\therefore \quad \frac{d^2y}{dx^2} = \frac{dp}{dx} = \frac{dp}{dy}\frac{dy}{dx} = p\frac{dp}{dy} \qquad (2.25)$$

Hence, when the independent variable does not appear explicitly, make the substitutions as given by equations (2.24) and (2.25). The following example will make the procedure quite clear.

Example 2. Solve $\quad y\dfrac{d^2y}{dx^2} + 1 = \left(\dfrac{dy}{dx}\right)^2$

Substitution of equations (2.24) and (2.25) gives

$$yp\frac{dp}{dy} + 1 = p^2 \qquad \text{I}$$

Separating the variables,

$$\frac{dy}{y} = \frac{p\,dp}{p^2 - 1}$$

Integrating,

$$\ln y + \ln a = \tfrac{1}{2}\ln(p^2 - 1) \qquad \text{II}$$

$$\therefore \quad a^2 y^2 = p^2 - 1$$

$$\therefore \quad p = \frac{dy}{dx} = \sqrt{(a^2 y^2 + 1)} \qquad \text{III}$$

$$\therefore \quad x = \int \frac{dy}{\sqrt{(a^2 y^2 + 1)}}$$

This is a standard integral, and therefore the solution of equation III is

$$x = (1/a)\sinh^{-1}(ay) + b$$

or $\qquad ay = \sinh(ax + c)$

where a and c are the two constants of integration.

2.4.3. *Homogeneous Equations.*

In Section 2.3.3, the first order homogeneous differential equation was expressed in the form,

$$\frac{dy}{dx} = f\left(\frac{y}{x}\right) \qquad (2.12)$$

Regarding x and y as of the same dimensions, equation (2.12) is an equation between dimensionless groups. The corresponding dimensionless group containing the second differential coefficient is $(x\,d^2y/dx^2)$. In general, the dimensionless group containing the nth differential coefficient is

$$x^{n-1}\frac{d^n y}{dx^n}$$

The second order homogeneous differential equation can be expressed in a form analogous to equation (2.12), viz.

$$x\frac{d^2y}{dx^2} = f_1\left(\frac{y}{x}, \frac{dy}{dx}\right) \tag{2.26}$$

The substitution for a first order homogeneous equation is

$$y = vx \tag{2.13}$$

If this substitution is made again,

$$\frac{dy}{dx} = v + x\frac{dv}{dx} \tag{2.14}$$

as before, and

$$\frac{d^2y}{dx^2} = 2\frac{dv}{dx} + x\frac{d^2v}{dx^2} \tag{2.27}$$

Substituting these expressions into equation (2.26) gives

$$2x\frac{dv}{dx} + x^2\frac{d^2v}{dx^2} = f_1\left(v, \ v + x\frac{dv}{dx}\right) \tag{2.28}$$

In equation (2.28), a factor x^2 is associated with the second differential coefficient of v, a factor x with the first differential coefficient of v on both sides of the equation, and v occurs alone. Equation (2.28) can therefore be written in the alternative equivalent form,

$$x^2\frac{d^2v}{dx^2} = f_2\left(v, \ x\frac{dv}{dx}\right) \tag{2.29}$$

It is to be noted that if equation (2.26) is multiplied throughout by x, the left-hand side assumes the same form as the left-hand side of equation (2.29). However, the right-hand sides only take the same form if the right-hand side of equation (2.26) is a linear homogeneous function of its two arguments. A short cut from equation (2.26) to (2.29) is therefore possible if the given differential equation is both homogeneous and linear.

Equation (2.29) is solved by using the second substitution

$$x = e^t \quad \text{or} \quad t = \ln x \tag{2.30}$$

$$\therefore \quad \frac{dv}{dx} = \frac{dv}{dt}\frac{dt}{dx} = \frac{1}{x}\frac{dv}{dt} \tag{2.31}$$

i.e.

$$x\frac{dv}{dx} = \frac{dv}{dt} \tag{2.32}$$

Differentiating equation (2.31) again with respect to x,

$$\frac{d^2v}{dx^2} = -\frac{1}{x^2}\frac{dv}{dt} + \frac{1}{x}\frac{d}{dx}\left(\frac{dv}{dt}\right)$$

$$= -\frac{1}{x^2}\frac{dv}{dt} + \frac{1}{x}\frac{dt}{dx}\frac{d}{dt}\left(\frac{dv}{dt}\right)$$

$$= -\frac{1}{x^2}\frac{dv}{dt} + \frac{1}{x^2}\frac{d^2v}{dt^2}$$

i.e.
$$x^2\frac{d^2v}{dx^2} = \frac{d^2v}{dt^2} - \frac{dv}{dt} \tag{2.33}$$

Putting equations (2.32) and (2.33) into equation (2.29) gives

$$\frac{d^2v}{dt^2} - \frac{dv}{dt} = f_2\left(v, \frac{dv}{dt}\right) \tag{2.34}$$

The original differential equation (2.26) has now been reduced to a form (2.34) where the independent variable (t) does not occur explicitly, and it can be solved by the method given in Section 2.4.2. The actual procedure is illustrated in the following example.

Example 3. Solve

$$2x^2y\frac{d^2y}{dx^2} + y^2 = x^2\left(\frac{dy}{dx}\right)^2 \qquad\qquad \text{I}$$

This equation is homogeneous since it can be expressed in the form (2.26) after division by $2xy$. Use the first substitution $y = vx$ and its differentiated forms (2.14) and (2.27).

$$\therefore \quad 2vx^3\left(2\frac{dv}{dx} + x\frac{d^2v}{dx^2}\right) + v^2x^2 = x^2\left(v + x\frac{dv}{dx}\right)^2 \qquad \text{II}$$

Simplifying into the form of equation (2.29),

$$2vx^2\frac{d^2v}{dx^2} + 2vx\frac{dv}{dx} = x^2\left(\frac{dv}{dx}\right)^2 \qquad\qquad \text{III}$$

Now making the second substitution $x = e^t$ and simplifying,

$$2v\frac{d^2v}{dt^2} = \left(\frac{dv}{dt}\right)^2 \qquad\qquad \text{IV}$$

Equation IV does not contain the independent variable explicitly, and it can be solved as suggested in Section 2.4.2. Put $p = dv/dt$, and obtain

$$2vp\frac{dp}{dv} = p^2 \qquad\qquad \text{V}$$

This has two solutions, viz.

$$2v\frac{dp}{dv} = p, \quad \text{or} \quad p = 0$$

The second solution, called a "singular solution", yields the result,

$$y = Ax \qquad\qquad \text{VI}$$

which undoubtedly satisfies the original equation I. The first solution can be integrated twice to give

$$y = x(B\ln x + C)^2 \qquad\qquad \text{VII}$$

By choosing the arbitrary constants in equation VII to be $B = 0$, $C = \sqrt{A}$, equation VI is seen to be included in equation VII as a special case. Equation VII is therefore the complete solution of equation I.

The value of the substitutions given in Sections 2.4. are rather limited, because in many engineering applications the transformed equation cannot be integrated. Such a difficulty was encountered by Marshall and Pigford† in their problem on the dynamics of a laminar jet. The authors of this text also met the same difficulty in attempting to predict the temperature profile along a graphite electrode by using the above substitution. The particular problem had to be solved by the method to be given in Chapter 11. However, the problem is presented here to illustrate the type of difficulty that can arise and to show that an approximate yet valuable solution can still be obtained by elementary procedures.

Example 4. A graphite electrode 6·0 in in diameter passes through a furnace wall into a water cooler which takes the form of a water sleeve. The length of the electrode between the outside of the furnace wall and its entry into the cooling jacket is 1·0 ft; and as a safety precaution the electrode is insulated thermally and electrically in this section, so that the outside surface temperature of the insulation does not exceed 120°F. If the lagging is of uniform thickness and the mean overall coefficient of heat transfer from the electrode to the surrounding atmosphere is taken to be 0·3 Btu/h °F ft² of surface of electrode; and the temperature of the electrode just outside the furnace is 2700°F, estimate the duty of the water cooler if the temperature of the electrode at the entrance to the cooler is to be 300°F. The following additional information is given.

Surrounding temperature $= 70°F$.
Thermal conductivity of graphite $= K_T = k_0 - \alpha T$
where $k_0 = 88\cdot9$, and $\alpha = 0\cdot0180$.‡

(These numerical values are calculated as an example in Chapter 10.) The temperature of the electrode may be assumed uniform at any cross section.

Solution

The sectional area of the electrode $(A) = 0\cdot196 \text{ ft}^2$.
Referring to Fig. 2.3 and using the symbols stated there; a heat balance

FIG. 2.3.   Heat transfer through electrode

† Marshall and Pigford, "Differential Equations in Chemical Engineering," p. 76. University of Delaware.
‡ I.C.T. **5**, 86, 1937. McGraw-Hill Book Co. Ltd. New York.

over the length of electrode δx at a distance x from the furnace is

$$\text{Input} = -k_T A \frac{dT}{dx} \qquad\qquad \text{I}$$

$$\text{Output} = -k_T A \frac{dT}{dx} + \frac{d}{dx}\left[-k_T A \frac{dT}{dx}\right]\delta x + \pi DU(T-T_0)\delta x \qquad \text{II}$$

Accumulation = 0

$$\therefore \quad \frac{d}{dx}\left[k_T \frac{dT}{dx}\right]\delta x = \frac{\pi DU}{A}(T-T_0)\delta x \qquad\qquad \text{III}$$

where U = overall heat transfer coefficient from the electrode to the surroundings

and D = electrode diameter.

Substituting for k_T and simplifying by dividing throughout by $A\delta x$ and
letting $\pi DU/A = \beta$, equation III becomes

$$(k_0-\alpha T)\frac{d^2T}{dx^2} - \alpha\left(\frac{dT}{dx}\right)^2 - \beta(T-T_0) = 0 \qquad \text{IV}$$

Equation IV is a second order non-linear differential equation which does
not contain the independent variable explicitly. Thus let

$$p = \frac{dT}{dx} \quad \text{and} \quad \frac{d^2T}{dx^2} = p\frac{dp}{dT}$$

Equation IV then becomes

$$(k_0-\alpha T)p\frac{dp}{dT} - \alpha p^2 - \beta(T-T_0) = 0 \qquad \text{V}$$

Inspection of equation V shows that the variables p and T cannot be separated, and one might be tempted to introduce simplifying assumptions at this
stage; or attempt to solve equation IV by some other method. However,
the way in which p occurs in equation V suggests the substitution $p^2 = z$.
Putting $y = (T-T_0)$ also, gives

$$[(k_0-\alpha T_0)-\alpha y]\frac{dz}{dy} - 2\alpha z - 2\beta y = 0 \qquad \text{VI}$$

which is a first order differential equation that can be solved by the integrating factor method. The integrating factor is

$$\exp\left[-\int\frac{2\alpha\,dy}{k_0-\alpha T_0-\alpha y}\right] = (k_0-\alpha T_0-\alpha y)^2$$

Substituting the integrating factor into equation VI and converting back to
the original variables gives

$$x = \int\frac{(k_0-\alpha T)\,dT}{\sqrt{[C+\beta(k_0-\alpha T)(T-T_0)^2-\tfrac{2}{3}\alpha\beta(T-T_0)^3]}} \qquad \text{VII}$$

Equation VII cannot be integrated analytically because of the cubic poly-nomial under the square root sign, or graphically because the arbitrary constant C is completely unknown.   Furthermore there is no way of evaluating C other than perhaps by trial and error which would not be very accurate.   Hence in order to obtain an estimate of the heat load on the cooler it will be assumed that the heat lost to the atmosphere per ft^2 of electrode surface (Q) is constant, and equal to 400 Btu/h ft^2.   Equation III then simplifies to

$$\frac{d}{dx}\left[(k_0-\alpha T)\frac{dT}{dx}\right]\delta x = \frac{\pi DQ}{A}\delta x \qquad \text{VIII}$$

or $$(k_0-\alpha T)\frac{d^2T}{dx^2} - \alpha\left(\frac{dT}{dx}\right)^2 = K \qquad \text{IX}$$

where $K = \pi DQ/A$.
The solution of equation IX is obtainable by the substitution

$$p = \frac{dT}{dx} \quad \text{and} \quad p\frac{dp}{dT} = \frac{d^2T}{dx^2}$$

which gives

$$p^2 = \frac{B}{\alpha(k_0-\alpha T)^2} - \frac{K}{\alpha} \qquad \text{X}$$

where B is the constant of integration.
Reducing the power of p to unity, and choosing the negative root because the temperature falls as distance x increases,

$$\frac{dT}{dx} = -\sqrt{\frac{B}{\alpha(k_0-\alpha T)^2} - \frac{K}{\alpha}} \qquad \text{XI}$$

Equation XI can be integrated with the aid of the substitution $z = (k_0-\alpha T)^2$. The result is

$$T = \frac{k_0}{\alpha} - \frac{1}{\alpha}\sqrt{\frac{B}{K} - \alpha K(x+C)^2} \qquad \text{XII}$$

where C is the second arbitrary constant.
The boundary conditions at the ends of the electrode give
at $x = 0$,

$$2700 = \frac{k_0}{\alpha} - \frac{1}{\alpha}\sqrt{\frac{B}{K} - K\alpha C^2} \qquad \text{XIII}$$

and at $x = 1$,

$$300 = \frac{k_0}{\alpha} - \frac{1}{\alpha}\sqrt{\frac{B}{K} - K\alpha(1+C)^2} \qquad \text{XIV}$$

It is more convenient to determine how B and C occur in the required solution, rather than solve these equations directly.   The duty of the water cooler is the rate at which heat arrives at $x = 1$, which is given by,

$$H = -(k_0 - 300\alpha)A\frac{dT}{dx}\bigg|_{x=1}$$

$$= \frac{-(k_0 - 300\alpha)AK(1+C)}{\sqrt{[(B/K) - K\alpha(1+C)^2]}}$$

by differentiating equation XII and putting $x = 1$.
Substituting from equation XIV for the denominator of this expression,

$$H = -AK(1+C) \qquad\qquad \text{XV}$$

Solving equations XIII and XIV for C gives

$$C = -\tfrac{1}{2} - 2400\,(k_0 - 1500\alpha)/K$$

Substituting into XV gives

$$H = AK[2400\,(k_0 - 1500\alpha)/K - \tfrac{1}{2}] \qquad\qquad \text{XVI}$$

$$= 28800 \text{ Btu/h}$$

and this is the duty of the water cooler.

2.5. Linear Differential Equations

This type of equation is frequently encountered in most chemical engineering fields of study, ranging from heat, mass and momentum transfer to applied chemical reaction kinetics. It is one of the most important types of equation to be found in applied science, and therefore considerable study has been devoted to finding solutions to the many different forms it may take.

The general linear differential equation of the nth order having constant coefficients may be written

$$P_0\frac{d^ny}{dx^n} + P_1\frac{d^{n-1}y}{dx^{n-1}} + \ldots + P_{n-1}\frac{dy}{dx} + P_ny = \phi(x) \qquad (2.35)$$

where $\phi(x)$ is any function of x.

The treatment to be described below for the second order equation applies equally well to linear equations of any other order. However, in the case of a higher order equation, the mathematical manipulations may be cumbersome as the reader will soon appreciate, but since no new principles are involved, further discussion will be restricted to the second order case.

2.5.1. *Second Order Linear Differential Equations*

The general equation can be expressed in the form,

$$P\frac{d^2y}{dx^2} + Q\frac{dy}{dx} + Ry = \phi(x) \qquad (2.36)$$

where P, Q, and R are the constant coefficients.

Let the dependent variable y be replaced by the sum of two new variables u and v, i.e.

$$y = u + v \qquad (2.37)$$

Substitution in (2.36) gives

$$\left[P\frac{d^2u}{dx^2} + Q\frac{du}{dx} + Ru\right] + \left[P\frac{d^2v}{dx^2} + Q\frac{dv}{dx} + Rv\right] = \phi(x) \qquad (2.38)$$

If v is a particular solution of the original differential equation, then

$$P\frac{d^2v}{dx^2} + Q\frac{dv}{dx} + Rv = \phi(x) \qquad (2.39)$$

and by comparison with equation (2.38) it can be seen that

$$P\frac{d^2u}{dx^2} + Q\frac{du}{dx} + Ru = 0 \qquad (2.40)$$

That is, u satisfies equation (2.40) which is the same as equation (2.36) with $\phi(x)$ replaced by zero. Therefore, since y is the general solution of equation (2.36) and is the sum of u and v, where v is a particular solution of the original differential equation; u must be the complement of the particular solution which must be added in order to get the general solution. That is, the general solution of the linear differential equation will be the sum of a "complementary function" and a "particular integral". The problem resolves itself into one of finding some specific solution that will satisfy the original equation—if necessary by trial and error, and finding the complete solution of the same equation assuming that the right-hand side is zero. The general solution will be the sum of these two solutions and will contain two arbitrary constants which can be evaluated from the boundary conditions of the specific problem being considered.

The above remarks on the general approach to the solution of the second order linear differential equation apply to any linear differential equation irrespective of its order. However, the number of arbitrary constants that will have to be evaluated will equal the order of the equation. That is, the general solution of an nth order differential equation will be the sum of a complementary function and a particular integral and will contain n arbitrary constants. The arbitrary constants will arise in the complementary function which will therefore have n terms. These points should be borne in mind when solving a linear differential equation.

2.5.2. *The Complementary Function*

Referring back to the second order differential equation (2.36), the problem is to find a solution of the equation when $\phi(x)$ is zero. That is a solution of the equation,

$$P\frac{d^2y}{dx^2} + Q\frac{dy}{dx} + Ry = 0 \qquad (2.41)$$

Initially let it be assumed that the solution is

$$y = A_m e^{mx} \qquad (2.42)$$

Then
$$\frac{dy}{dx} = A_m m e^{mx}$$

and
$$\frac{d^2 y}{dx^2} = A_m m^2 e^{mx}$$

Substitution of the above expressions for the first and second differential coefficients into equation (2.41) and simplifying gives

$$A_m e^{mx}(Pm^2 + Qm + R) = 0 \qquad (2.43)$$

Equation (2.43) will be satisfied if either A_m or the term within the brackets is zero. That is if

$$Pm^2 + Qm + R = 0 \qquad (2.44)$$

A_m cannot be zero by definition in equation (2.42) and therefore the values of m determined by equation (2.44) will satisfy the "reduced equation" (2.41). Equation (2.44) is termed the "auxiliary equation". It will have two roots which could be unequal or equal, real or complex (see Chapter 4), and these will be considered individually.

(a) *Unequal Roots to Auxiliary Equation.* Let the roots of equation (2.44) be distinct and of values m_1 and m_2. Therefore, the solution of equation (2.41) will be

$$y = A_1 e^{m_1 x} \quad \text{or} \quad y = A_2 e^{m_2 x}$$

and the most general solution of the reduced equation (2.41) will be

$$y = A_1 e^{m_1 x} + A_2 e^{m_2 x} \qquad (2.45)$$

Equation (2.45) is the "complementary function". It has two terms and two arbitrary constants as would be expected for a second order linear differential equation.

(b) *Equal Roots to Auxiliary Equation.* If the roots of the auxiliary equation are equal, that is if $m_1 = m_2 = m$, the auxiliary equation can be written

$$Pm^2 + Qm + R = 0 \qquad (2.46)$$

and the solution of the reduced equation is

$$y = A e^{mx} \qquad (2.47)$$

But as this only contains one term and one arbitrary constant it is not the complete complementary function of a second order equation. Therefore let

$$y = V e^{mx} \qquad (2.48)$$

be a second trial solution in which V is a function of x. Then

$$\frac{dy}{dx} = e^{mx}\frac{dV}{dx} + mVe^{mx}$$

and
$$\frac{d^2 y}{dx^2} = e^{mx}\frac{d^2 V}{dx^2} + 2me^{mx}\frac{dV}{dx} + m^2 Ve^{mx}$$

Substitution of these expressions for the first and second differential co-efficients into equation (2.41), using (2.46) and simplifying gives

$$\frac{d^2V}{dx^2} = 0$$

Double integration of this gives

$$V = Cx + D$$

and the complementary function becomes

$$y = (Cx + D)e^{mx} \qquad\qquad (2.49)$$

The above solution contains two terms and two arbitrary constants. Since the arbitrary constant D can be made equal to A in equation (2.47), it can be seen that the previous solution (2.47) is included in the later solution (2.49). Equation (2.49) is therefore acceptable as the complete complementary function when the auxiliary equation has equal roots.

Example 1. Solve $\dfrac{d^2y}{dx^2} - 5\dfrac{dy}{dx} + 6y = 0$ I

The auxiliary equation is

$$m^2 - 5m + 6 = 0 \qquad\qquad \text{II}$$

and the roots of this are

$$m_1 = 2, \quad m_2 = 3$$

The solution to equation I is therefore

$$y = Ae^{2x} + Be^{3x} \qquad\qquad \text{III}$$

where A and B are the two arbitrary constants.

Example 2. Solve $\dfrac{d^2y}{dx^2} + 6\dfrac{dy}{dx} + 9y = 0$ I

The auxiliary equation is

$$m^2 + 6m + 9 = 0 \qquad\qquad \text{II}$$

and the roots of this are

$$m_1 = m_2 = -3$$

The solution of equation I is therefore

$$y = (A + Bx)e^{-3x} \qquad\qquad \text{III}$$

where A and B are the two arbitrary constants.

(c) *Complex Roots to Auxiliary Equation.* Any reader who is unfamiliar with the elementary concepts of complex numbers is advised to read Sections 4.1 to 4.10 inclusive of Chapter 4 before proceeding with the following section.

For those who have become familiar with the elements of complex numbers it will be immediately appreciated that the roots of the auxiliary equation could be complex. This will become clear by considering the following example.

Example 3. Solve
$$\frac{d^2y}{dx^2} - 4\frac{dy}{dx} + 5y = 0 \qquad\qquad \text{I}$$

The auxiliary equation is

$$m^2 - 4m + 5 = 0 \qquad\qquad \text{II}$$

and the roots are

$$m = 2 \pm i$$

Therefore the complementary function is

$$y = A\exp[(2+i)x] + B\exp[(2-i)x] \qquad\qquad \text{III}$$

or the solution may be written as

$$y = e^{2x}(E\cos x + F\sin x) \qquad\qquad \text{IV}$$

using the relationships between exponential and trigonometric functions.

In conclusion it will be appreciated that irrespective of the nature of the roots, the complementary function takes the form:

Either
$$y = Ae^{m_1 x} + Be^{m_2 x} \qquad\qquad (2.50)$$

for distinct roots whether real or complex.

Or
$$y = (A + Bx)e^{mx} \qquad\qquad (2.51)$$

for equal roots, which must always be real. In all forms the expression will have arbitrary constants equal in number to the order of the differential equation.

2.5.3. *Particular Integrals*

To obtain the complete solution of the linear differential equation, it is necessary to find some particular solution of the equation,

$$P\frac{d^2y}{dx^2} + Q\frac{dy}{dx} + Ry = \phi(x) \qquad\qquad (2.36)$$

where $\phi(x)$ may be a constant, or a function of the independent variable x. If $\phi(x)$ is zero the complementary function is the complete solution and therefore nothing further is required. However, in most problems encountered, $\phi(x)$ is not zero and a particular integral will have to be found in order to complete the solution.

There are many general methods of determining the particular integral. Of these only three will be discussed here, as the three to be presented are capable of solving most problems arising in applied science. The three methods may be termed,

(a) The method of undetermined coefficients.
(b) The method of inverse operators.
(c) The method of variation of parameters.

Method (a) is confined to linear equations with constant coefficients, and particular forms of the function $\phi(x)$. Methods (b) and (c) are of more general applicability. Each of the methods will be discussed below.

2.5.4. *Particular Integrals by the Method of Undetermined Coefficients*

This is essentially a trial and error procedure, and whilst it is easy to apply, some experience is required before the form of the particular integral can be recognized. It is most unlikely that the chemical engineer will have had this experience and consequently the following rules which choose the form of the particular integral are submitted as a guide.

(i) $\phi(x)$ *is constant*, say C. Then obviously a particular integral of equation (2.36) is

$$y = C/R \qquad\qquad (2.52)$$

because all the differential coefficients will be zero. The complete solution will therefore be

$$y = Ae^{m_1 x} + Be^{m_2 x} + C/R \qquad\qquad (2.53)$$

This rule applies to any order linear differential equation with constant coefficients.

(ii) $\phi(x)$ *is a polynomial of the form* $a_0 + a_1 x + a_2 x^2 + \ldots a_n x^n$; *where all the coefficients* $a_0, a_1, \ldots a_n$ *are constants.*

The form of the particular integral will also be a rational integral function of the independent variable x because only functions of x whose differential coefficients are positive integral powers of the independent variable are themselves integral powers of x. Consequently the form of the particular integral will be,

$$y = \alpha_0 + \alpha_1 x + \alpha_2 x^2 + \ldots + \alpha_n x^n \qquad\qquad (2.54)$$

Furthermore the degree of the particular integral must equal the degree of x in $\phi(x)$, otherwise the degree of x on each side of the differential equation will be unequal and this is impossible in a linear differential equation with constant coefficients.

The solution procedure is therefore to assume a polynomial of the type shown in equation (2.54) and obtain the first, second, etc., differential coefficients of this expression. These differentiated expressions must then be substituted into the original differential equation and the coefficients α_0 to α_n evaluated by equating coefficients. The following example will make the procedure clear.

Example 4. Solve $\quad \dfrac{d^2 y}{dx^2} - 4\dfrac{dy}{dx} + 4y = 4x + 8x^3 \qquad\qquad$ I

Because the degree of $\phi(x)$ is 3, let

$$y = p + qx + rx^2 + sx^3 \qquad\qquad \text{II}$$

in order to evaluate the particular integral.

Then $\qquad\qquad\qquad \dfrac{dy}{dx} = q + 2rx + 3sx^2 \qquad\qquad \text{III}$

and $\qquad\qquad\qquad \dfrac{d^2 y}{dx^2} = 2r + 6sx \qquad\qquad\qquad \text{IV}$

Substitution of these expressions for the differential coefficients into I gives

$$(2r+6sx)-4(q+2rx+3sx^2)+4(p+qx+rx^2+sx^3) = 4x+8x^3 \qquad \text{V}$$

Equating coefficients of equal powers of x,

$$2r-4q+4p = 0$$
$$6s-8r+4q = 4$$
$$4r-12s = 0 \quad \text{or} \quad r = 3s$$
$$4s = 8 \quad \text{or} \quad s = 2$$
$$\therefore \quad r = 6, \quad q = 10, \quad \text{and} \quad p = 7$$
$$\therefore \quad y_p = 7+10x+6x^2+2x^3 \qquad \text{VI}$$

The complementary function for this case of equal roots is

$$y_c = (A+Bx)e^{2x} \qquad \text{VII}$$

and the complete solution is

$$y = y_c+y_p = (A+Bx)e^{2x}+7+10x+6x^2+2x^3 \qquad \text{VIII}$$

(iii) $\phi(x)$ *is the form* Te^{rx}; where T and r are constants. The form of the particular integral will also be of exponential form because all the differential coefficients of e^{rx} will be multiples of e^{rx}. Therefore, if the particular integral is assumed to be

$$y_p = \alpha e^{rx} \qquad (2.55)$$

The first differential coefficient will be $\alpha r e^{rx}$, and the second differential coefficient will be $\alpha r^2 e^{rx}$. Hence substitution into the original differential equation (2.36) gives

$$(Pr^2+Qr+R)\alpha e^{rx} = Te^{rx} \qquad (2.56)$$

or

$$\alpha = \frac{T}{Pr^2+Qr+R} \qquad (2.57)$$

Evaluation of α from the known constants enables the particular integral to be determined.

(iv) $\phi(x)$ *is of the form* $G \sin nx + H \cos nx$; where G and H are constants, either of which could be zero, whilst n is a non-zero constant. The form of the particular integral will also be a trigonometrical function of the same type because all the differential coefficients will be multiples of $\sin nx$ or $\cos nx$. Therefore assume the particular integral to be

$$y_p = L \sin nx + M \cos nx \qquad (2.58)$$

The first differential coefficient of equation (2.58) will be

$$\frac{dy}{dx} = nL \cos nx - nM \sin nx$$

and the second differential coefficient

$$\frac{d^2y}{dx^2} = -n^2(L \sin nx + M \cos nx)$$

Substitution in the original differential equation gives

$$L = \frac{(R - n^2 P)G + nQH}{(R - n^2 P)^2 + n^2 Q^2}$$ (2.59)

$$M = \frac{(R - n^2 P)H - nQG}{(R - n^2 P)^2 + n^2 Q^2}$$ (2.60)

Equations (2.59) and (2.60) enable the constants L and M to be evaluated and thus the particular integral can be determined.

The above four forms of the particular integral that would be obtained from each type of expression of $\phi(x)$ are summarized in Table 2.1.

TABLE 2.1. *Normal Forms of Particular Integrals*

Right-Hand Side of Differential Equation $\phi(x)$	Particular Integral	Coefficient Values
A constant C	A constant K	$K = \dfrac{C}{R}$
A polynomial $a_0 + a_1 x + \ldots + a_n x^n$	A polynomial $\alpha_0 + \alpha_1 x + \ldots + \alpha_n x^n$	To be determined by substituting in the differential equation and equating coefficients.
An exponential $T e^{rx}$	An exponential αe^{rx}	$\alpha = \dfrac{T}{Pr^2 + Qr + R}$
Trigonometrical $G \sin nx + H \cos nx$	Trigonometrical $L \sin nx + M \cos nx$	$L = \dfrac{(R - n^2 P)G + nQH}{(R - n^2 P)^2 + n^2 Q^2}$ $M = \dfrac{(R - n^2 P)H - nQG}{(R - n^2 P)^2 + n^2 Q^2}$

P, Q, and R refer to the coefficients in the differential equation (2.36).

(v) *Modified procedure when a term in the particular integral duplicates a term in the complementary function.* In each of the above forms of the particular integral, it is possible for one or more terms to be identical with one or more terms in the complementary function. When this occurs the general procedure is to multiply the assumed form of the particular integral by the independent variable, which will destroy the similarity of the terms. However, it is possible that this multiplication by the independent variable will make other terms in the particular integral and complementary function identical. If this should happen the assumed form of the particular integral should be multiplied by the square of the independent variable, and if similarities still exist the assumed form should be multiplied by the third power of independent variable and so on until no identical terms remain between the complementary function and the particular integral.

Identical terms in both parts of the solution of the differential equation can arise in many ways. For instance, when $\phi(x)$ is a constant, the first trial form for the particular integral will be a constant according to Table 2.1. If in addition, one of the roots of the auxiliary equation is zero one term in the complementary function will also be a constant. Hence the modified trial form of the particular integral should be a constant multiplied by the independent variable, in which case the similarity will have been removed. The following example will make the procedure clear.

Example 5. Solve
$$3\frac{d^2y}{dx^2} + 6\frac{dy}{dx} = 18 \qquad\qquad \text{I}$$

The auxiliary equation is
$$3m^2 - 6m = 0 \qquad\qquad \text{II}$$

and the roots are
$$m = 0 \quad \text{and} \quad m = 2$$

The complementary function is
$$y_c = Ae^{m_1x} + Be^{m_2x} = A + Be^{2x} \qquad\qquad \text{III}$$

Since one term in the complementary function is a constant, the particular integral cannot be a constant even though the right-hand side of equation I contains a constant.

Therefore let the form of the particular integral be
$$y = Cx \qquad\qquad \text{IV}$$

Then
$$\frac{dy}{dx} = C$$

and
$$\frac{d^2y}{dx^2} = 0$$

Substitution in equation I gives
$$(3 \times 0) + 6(C) = 18 \qquad\qquad \text{V}$$

or
$$C = 3$$

and the particular Integral is $3x$.

Therefore the complete solution is
$$y = 3x + A + Be^{2x} \qquad\qquad \text{VI}$$

The above complication can arise also when a root of the auxiliary equation is equal to the coefficient of the independent variable in the exponential term on the right-hand side of the equation. In this case too, an example will make the procedure clear. Therefore consider

Example 6. Solve
$$3\frac{d^2y}{dx^2} + 10\frac{dy}{dx} - 8y = 7e^{-4x} \qquad\qquad \text{I}$$

The auxiliary equation is

$$3m^2 + 10m - 8 = (3m-2)(m+4) = 0 \qquad \text{II}$$

$$\therefore \quad m = 2/3 \text{ or } -4$$

and the complementary function is

$$y_c = Ae^{2x/3} + Be^{-4x} \qquad \text{III}$$

The second term in equation III is of the same form as that given in Table 2.1 for the particular integral of equation I. Therefore, take the modified form

$$y = Cxe^{-4x} \qquad \text{IV}$$

for the particular integral.

$$\therefore \quad \frac{dy}{dx} = (1-4x)Ce^{-4x}$$

and

$$\frac{d^2y}{dx^2} = (16x-8)Ce^{-4x}$$

Substitution in equation I and solving for C gives $C = -\frac{1}{2}$, and the complete solution of equation I is

$$y = y_c + y_p = Ae^{2x/3} + Be^{-4x} - \tfrac{1}{2}xe^{-4x} \qquad \text{V}$$

Another way in which the above complication can appear, is when the roots of the auxiliary equation are both equal to the value m, the coefficient in the exponent in a term of the form Ce^{mx}. Thus for an auxiliary equation with equal roots the complementary function will be $(A+Bx)e^{mx}$ where the first term is similar to the expression Ce^{mx}. Hence the proposed form of the particular integral would be Ex^2e^{mx}, since multiplying by x alone would give a form similar to the second term of the complementary function. E would be evaluated in a manner similar to that illustrated in the above examples.

Finally, when the roots of the auxiliary equation are complex and the right-hand side of the differential equation contains the terms

$$(A\sin nx + B\cos nx)e^{px} \qquad (2.61)$$

the modified trial form of the particular integral will be

$$x(\alpha \sin nx + \beta \cos nx)e^{px} \qquad (2.62)$$

and the evaluation of α and β is as above.

2.5.5. *Particular Integrals by the Method of Inverse Operators*

The symbol (dy/dx) representing the differential coefficient signifies that the operation of differentiation of y has been carried out with respect to the independent variable x. In fact if there is no doubt whatever of the independent variable, it is acceptable to write simply "Dy" for the differential coefficient implying that the differentiation process has been carried out. Hence it is convenient to refer to the symbol "D" as the "differential operator", and prefixing it to a variable means that a differentiation has been carried out with respect to an obvious independent variable. The letter D alone has no significance and must be placed in front of the dependent variable to signify the differential coefficient.

I.e. $$Dy = dy/dx$$

Similarly $$D(Dy) = D^2y = d^2y/dx^2$$

and $$D(D^2y) = D^3y = d^3y/dx^3$$

so that $$D^ny = d^ny/dx^n$$

It should be noted that

$$(Dy)^2 = (dy/dx)^2$$

without ambiguity.

The above symbolic representation in terms of the differential operator can be extended to expressions involving different order differential coefficients. Thus the expression,

$$\frac{d^2y}{dx^2} + 3\frac{dy}{dx} + 2y \tag{2.63}$$

may be written

$$D^2y + 3Dy + 2y = (D^2 + 3D + 2)y \tag{2.64}$$

and the latter may also be factorized,

$$(D+1)(D+2)y \tag{2.65}$$

Hence it appears that the differential operator D can be treated as an ordinary algebraic quantity with certain limitations.

The three basic laws of algebra are the following.

(a) *The Distributive Law.* This states that,

$$A(B+C) = AB + AC \tag{2.66}$$

which also applies to the differential operator D, viz.

$$D(u+v+w) = Du + Dv + Dw \tag{2.67}$$

In fact the distributive law was applied to the operator in equation (2.64).

(b) *The Commutative Law.* This states that,

$$AB = BA \tag{2.68}$$

which does not in general apply to the differential operator D. It is conventional to consider that the differential operator differentiates every term which follows it, and not the terms preceding it. Transferring a term past the operator thus alters the value of the expression. For example

$$Dxy \neq xDy$$

but it is true that the expression (2.65) can be given the equivalent forms,

$$(D+1)(D+2)y = (D+2)(D+1)y$$

The operator will thus commute with itself but not with variables.

(c) *The Associative Law.* This states that,

$$(AB)C = A(BC) \tag{2.69}$$

which does not in general apply to the differential operator D. The following two equations illustrate how far the law is obeyed.

$$D(Dy) = (DD)y$$

but
$$D(xy) = (Dx)y + xDy \qquad (2.70)$$

In the first term on the right-hand side of equation (2.70) the closing of the bracket cuts y off from the operator thus destroying the simple equality.

The basic laws of algebra thus apply to the pure operators, but the relative order of operators and variables must be maintained. Also, the influence of the operator must not be hindered by brackets as in equation (2.70) unless this is specifically desired. Consequently these properties can be utilized particularly in the solution of linear differential equations thus simplifying the solving procedure. Some of these properties will be illustrated in order to familiarize the reader with the techniques.

Application of the Differential Operator to Exponentials. Let the differential coefficient of e^{px} be required. This expression could be written

$$De^{px} = pe^{px} \qquad (2.71)$$

Also for the second differential coefficient,

$$D^2 e^{px} = p^2 e^{px} \qquad (2.72)$$

and for the nth differential coefficient,

$$D^n e^{px} = p^n e^{px} \qquad (2.73)$$

In general, if $f(D)$ is some polynomial of the differential operator, it is possible to write

$$f(D)e^{px} = f(p)e^{px} \qquad (2.\,4)$$

I.e. the coefficient of x replaces D in the function. This is quite obvious, for if $f(D)$ is expanded and then each term in the expansion multiplied by e^{px}, each of these new terms will be similar to the left-hand side of equation (2.73) and the differentiated form similar to the right-hand side. Specifically, if in equation (2.64) $y = e^{px}$, then the expression can be written

$$(D^2 + 3D + 2)e^{px} = (p^2 + 3p + 2)e^{px} \qquad (2.75)$$

The above concept can be extended to more complex functions involving exponentials. For example, if the differential coefficient of ye^{px} is required, then

$$D(ye^{px}) = e^{px}Dy + yDe^{px} = e^{px}(D + p)y \qquad (2.76)$$

Similarly the second differential coefficient would be

$$D^2(ye^{px}) = D[e^{px}(D + p)y] = e^{px} . D(D + p)y + (D + p)y . D(e^{px})$$
$$= e^{px}(D + p)(D + p)y = e^{px}(D + p)^2 y \qquad (2.77)$$

Similarly it follows by comparison of equations (2.76) and (2.77) that

$$D^n(ye^{px}) = e^{px}(D + p)^n y \qquad (2.78)$$

or in even more general terms, if $f(D)$ is a polynomial in D,

$$f(D)(ye^{px}) = e^{px}f(D+p)y \qquad (2.79)$$

The above property of the differential operator involving exponentials is most important as will be seen later.

Finally, the operation performed on the exponential function in equations (2.71) to (2.79) can be extended to trigonometrical functions by using the complex relationships between exponential and trigonometrical functions to be given in Chapter 4. Let the nth differential coefficient of $\sin px$ be required.

Now
$$D^n(\sin px) = d^n \operatorname{Im} e^{ipx} \qquad (2.80)$$

$$= \operatorname{Im} D^n e^{ipx}$$

$$= \operatorname{Im}(ip)^n e^{ipx} \qquad (2.81)$$

where " Im " represents the imaginary part of the function which follows it.

The evaluation of equation (2.81) depends upon whether n is odd or even. Put $n = 2m$ to make n even.

$$\therefore \quad (ip)^n = (-p^2)^m$$

and because
$$e^{ipx} = \cos x + i \sin x$$

$$\therefore \quad D^{2m}(\sin px) = (-p^2)^m \sin px \qquad (2.82)$$

Similarly, for n odd,
$$D^{2m+1}(\sin px) = (-p^2)^m p \cos px \qquad (2.83)$$

The corresponding formulae for differentiating $\cos px$, which can be derived in the same way are

$$D^{2m}(\cos px) = (-p^2)^m \cos px \qquad (2.84)$$

$$D^{2m+1}(\cos px) = -(-p^2)^m p \sin px \qquad (2.85)$$

The principles involved in equations (2.80) to (2.85) can be extended to operations on more complicated trigonometrical functions by considering real or imaginary parts as shown. This is left to the initiative of the reader in attempting the examples at the end of the book.

The Inverse Operator. The operator D signifies differentiation,

i.e.
$$D\left[\int f(x)\,dx\right] = f(x) \qquad (2.86)$$

so that
$$\int f(x)\,dx = D^{-1}f(x) \qquad (2.87)$$

which suggests that the reciprocal of the operator D placed before a function implies integration of that function with respect to an obvious independent variable. Thus D^{-1} is the "inverse operator" and is an integrating operator. Because of its relationship to the differential operator D it would be expected that it can be treated as an algebraic quantity in exactly the same manner as D. This will now be considered.

Equations (2.74) and (2.79) can be extended to an infinite series of positive powers of D, so that if the function of D can be expanded in ascending powers of D, the equations still apply.

C

Example 7. Solve $\qquad \dfrac{dy}{dx} - 4y = e^{2x}$

$$\therefore \quad (D-4)y = e^{2x} \qquad\qquad \text{II}$$

Transferring the operator to the other side of the equation,

$$y = \frac{1}{D-4}e^{2x} \qquad\qquad \text{III}$$

$$= \frac{-1}{4(1-\tfrac{1}{4}D)}e^{2x}$$

$$\therefore \quad y = -\tfrac{1}{4}\left[1+(\tfrac{1}{4}D)+(\tfrac{1}{4}D)^2+(\tfrac{1}{4}D)^3+\ldots\right]e^{2x} \qquad \text{IV}$$

using the binomial expansion. Performing the operations on e^{2x} gives

$$y = -\tfrac{1}{4}e^{2x}\left[1+\tfrac{1}{2}+(\tfrac{1}{2})^2+(\tfrac{1}{2})^3+\ldots\right] \qquad\qquad \text{V}$$

The series in the brackets is a geometrical progression whose sum to infinity is 2.

$$\therefore \quad y = -\tfrac{1}{2}e^{2x} \qquad\qquad \text{VI}$$

is the particular integral of equation I.

Because the inverse operator in equation III can be expanded in a series of positive powers of D, it satisfies the condition stated above. Thus, the general property given in equation (2.74) could have been applied much earlier to equation III. Viz.

$$y = \frac{1}{D-4}e^{2x} = \frac{1}{2-4}e^{2x} = -\tfrac{1}{2}e^{2x}$$

as before.

In the above example, equation (2.74) has been used in the form,

$$\frac{1}{f(D)}e^{px} = \frac{1}{f(p)}e^{px} \qquad\qquad (2.88)$$

However, if $f(p) = 0$, $e^{px}/f(p)$ is infinite and reference has to be made to the more general equation (2.79) in order to resolve this difficulty. When $(p) = 0$, $(D-p)$ must be a factor of $f(D)$. Hence

$$f(D) = (D-p)^n \phi(D) \qquad\qquad (2.89)$$

where n is the lowest integer which makes $\phi(p)$ finite and not zero. Then

$$\frac{1}{f(D)}e^{px} = \frac{1}{(D-p)^n \phi(D)}e^{px}$$

$$= \frac{1}{(D-p)^n}\frac{e^{px}}{\phi(p)}$$

by applying equation (2.74). Application of equation (2.79) with $y = 1$ gives

$$\frac{1}{f(D)}e^{px} = \frac{e^{px}}{\phi(p)}\frac{1}{D^n}1 \qquad\qquad (2.90)$$

D is raised to a negative power in equation (2.90), and this implies integration.

$$\therefore \quad \frac{1}{f(D)}e^{px} = \frac{e^{px}x^n}{\phi(p)n!} \tag{2.91}$$

It is unnecessary to include the arbitrary constants arising in the integrations since these are included in the complementary function.

Example 8. Solve

$$\frac{d^2y}{dx^2} - 8\frac{dy}{dx} + 16y = 6xe^{4x} \qquad\qquad \text{I}$$

In terms of the differential operator, equation I becomes

$$(D^2 - 8D + 16)y = (D-4)^2 y = 6xe^{4x} \qquad\qquad \text{II}$$

and the particular integral is

$$y_p = \frac{6}{(D-4)^2}xe^{4x}$$
$$= 6e^{4x}D^{-2}x$$
$$= 3e^{4x}D^{-1}x^2$$
$$= x^3 e^{4x} \qquad\qquad \text{III}$$

The complementary function is

$$y_c = (A + Bx)e^{4x} \qquad\qquad \text{IV}$$

and the complete solution is

$$y = y_c + y_p = (A + Bx + x^3)e^{4x} \qquad\qquad \text{V}$$

Application of the Inverse Operator to Trigonometrical Functions. Trigonometrical functions can be written as the real or imaginary parts of e^{ipx} in which case they can be treated in that form by the inverse operator. The analytical procedure to follow would be very similar to that given above for real exponential functions combined with the principles presented in equations (2.80) to (2.85). Therefore no further discussion need be given to this particular topic.

Application of the Inverse Operator to Polynomial Functions. The inverse operator can be made to operate on the polynomial function $\phi(x)$ by expanding the function of the inverse operator in terms of D by the usual binomial series for negative exponents. The method is illustrated by the following example.

Example 9. Solve

$$\frac{d^2y}{dx^2} - \frac{dy}{dx} - 6y = 4x^3 + 3x^2 \qquad\qquad \text{I}$$

Introducing the differential operator, equation I becomes

$$(D^2 - D - 6)y = (D-3)(D+2)y = 4x^3 + 3x^2 \qquad\qquad \text{II}$$

and the particular integral is

$$y_p = \frac{1}{(D-3)(D+2)}(4x^3+3x^2) = -\frac{1}{5}\left[\frac{1}{(3-D)} + \frac{1}{(2+D)}\right](4x^3+3x^2) \qquad \text{III}$$

Expanding each term of the partial fractions by the binomial theorem gives

$$y_p = -\frac{1}{5}\left[\left(\frac{1}{3} + \frac{D}{9} + \frac{D^2}{27} + \frac{D^3}{81} + \frac{D^4}{243} + \ldots\right) + \right.$$
$$\left. + \left(\frac{1}{2} - \frac{D}{4} + \frac{D^2}{8} - \frac{D^3}{16} + \frac{D}{32} - \ldots\right)\right](4x^3+3x^2) \qquad \text{IV}$$

$$= -\frac{1}{5}\left[\frac{5}{6} - \frac{5}{36}D + \frac{35}{216}D^2 - \frac{65}{1296}D^3 + \frac{275}{7776}D^4 - \ldots\right](4x^3+3x^2) \qquad \text{V}$$

$$= -\frac{4x^3+3x^2}{6} + \frac{12x^2+6x}{36} - \frac{7(24x+6)}{216} + \frac{13\times24}{1296} - 0\ldots \qquad \text{VI}$$

$$= -\frac{144x^3+36x^2+132x-10}{216}$$

The complementary function is

$$y_c = Ae^{3x} + Be^{-2x} \qquad \text{VII}$$

and the complete solution is

$$y = y_c + y_p = Ae^{3x} + Be^{-2x} - (72x^3+18x^2+66x-5)/108 \qquad \text{VIII}$$

2.5.6. *Particular Integrals by the Method of Variation of Parameters*

This method of determining the particular integral of a differential equation is a very elegant procedure, but it depends on the complete complementary function being known and therefore its applicability is somewhat limited. Furthermore when applied to differential equations of order higher than three the solution of the simultaneous equations of the parameters is time-consuming, laborious and above all hazardous to the unfamiliar and inexperienced.

Consider once again the general differential equation of second order (2.36). Let P be unity and Q and R be functions of the independent variable. The equation can therefore be written

$$\frac{d^2y}{dx^2} + Q(x)\frac{dy}{dx} + R(x)y = \phi(x) \qquad (2.92)$$

and let the complementary function of this equation be

$$y_c = Au + Bv \qquad (2.93)$$

where A and B are the arbitrary constants and u and v are functions of the independent variable x.

Now assume that the particular integral can be expressed,

$$y_p = f_1(x)u + f_2(x)v \qquad (2.94)$$

where the functions of the independent variable $f_1(x)$ and $f_2(x)$ are called the parameters. There will be two parameters for a second order, three for a third order and so on. Then

$$\frac{dy_p}{dx} = f_1'(x)u + f_1(x)u' + f_2'(x)v + f_2(x)v' \qquad (2.95)$$

where f', u' and v' signify the first differential coefficient of f, u and v with respect to x. Since in equation (2.94), two variables have been introduced to represent one variable, it is legitimate to assume another arbitrary relationship between them. It is convenient at this point to assume that,

$$f_1'(x)u + f_2'(x)v = 0 \qquad (2.96)$$

in order to reduce the complexity of the second differential coefficient of equation (2.94). Hence,

$$\frac{d^2y_p}{dx^2} = u''f_1(x) + u'f_1'(x) + v''f_2(x) + v'f_2'(x) \qquad (2.97)$$

Substitution of equations (2.94), (2.95) and (2.97) into (2.92) and rearranging gives

$$f_1(x)\left[u'' + Q(x)u' + R(x)u\right] + f_2(x)\left[v'' + Q(x)v' + R(x)v\right] +$$
$$+ u'f_1'(x) + v'f_2'(x) = \phi(x) \qquad (2.98)$$

But $[u'' + Q(x)u' + R(x)u]$ and $[v'' + Q(x)v' + R(x)v]$ are both zero because u and v are solutions of the reduced equation when $\phi(x)$ is taken to be zero. Therefore,

$$u'f_1'(x) + v'f_2'(x) = \phi(x) \qquad (2.99)$$

and solving equations (2.96) and (2.99) simultaneously gives

$$\frac{df_1(x)}{dx} = \frac{v\phi(x)}{vu' - uv'} \qquad (2.100)$$

and

$$\frac{df_2(x)}{dx} = \frac{-u\phi(x)}{vu' - uv'} \qquad (2.101)$$

The parameters $f_1(x)$ and $f_2(x)$ can be obtained from these equations by integration. The final complete solution will be

$$y = uf_1(x) + vf_2(x) + Au + Bv \qquad (2.102)$$

which includes the complementary function, equation (2.93).

Example 10. Solve

$$2x^2\frac{d^2y}{dx^2} - x\frac{dy}{dx} + y = x^2e^{-x} \qquad \text{I}$$

Equation I is linear, and the solution therefore consists of a particular integral added to the complementary function. The left-hand side is homogeneous, and the complementary function can be found using the substitution $x = e^t$ given in Section 2.4.3.

The complementary function is the solution of

$$2\frac{d^2y}{dt^2} - 3\frac{dy}{dt} + y = 0 \qquad \text{II}$$

i.e.
$$y_c = Ae^t + Be^{\frac{1}{2}t}$$
$$\therefore \quad y_c = Ax + Bx^{\frac{1}{2}} \qquad \text{III}$$

Applying the method of variation of parameters, let

$$y_p = ux + vx^{\frac{1}{2}} \qquad \text{IV}$$

where u and v are functions of x.

$$\therefore \quad \frac{dy}{dx} = u + \tfrac{1}{2}vx^{-\frac{1}{2}} + x\frac{du}{dx} + x^{\frac{1}{2}}\frac{dv}{dx} \qquad \text{V}$$

Put
$$x\frac{du}{dx} + x^{\frac{1}{2}}\frac{dv}{dx} = 0 \qquad \text{VI}$$

$$\therefore \quad \frac{d^2y}{dx^2} = \frac{du}{dx} - \tfrac{1}{4}vx^{-3/2} + \tfrac{1}{2}x^{-\frac{1}{2}}\frac{dv}{dx} \qquad \text{VII}$$

Substituting V, VI and VII into equation I gives

$$2x^2\frac{du}{dx} - \tfrac{1}{2}vx^{\frac{1}{2}} + x^{3/2}\frac{dv}{dx} - xu - \tfrac{1}{2}vx^{\frac{1}{2}} + ux + vx^{\frac{1}{2}} = x^2e^{-x}$$

which can be simplified to,

$$2x\frac{du}{dx} + x^{\frac{1}{2}}\frac{dv}{dx} = xe^{-x} \qquad \text{VIII}$$

Subtracting equation VI from equation VIII gives

$$x\frac{du}{dx} = xe^{-x}$$
$$\therefore \quad u = -e^{-x} \qquad \text{IX}$$

Substituting this expression into equation VI,

$$xe^{-x} + x^{\frac{1}{2}}\frac{dv}{dx} = 0$$
$$\therefore \quad v = -\int x^{\frac{1}{2}}e^{-x}\,dx \qquad \text{X}$$

The integral in equation X can be expressed in terms of the "error function" by the methods to be given in Chapter 5. The solution is

$$v = x^{\frac{1}{2}}e^{-x} - \tfrac{1}{2}\sqrt{\pi}\,\text{erf}\sqrt{x} \qquad \text{XI}$$

Putting equations IX and XI into equation IV gives the particular integral,

$$y_p = -xe^{-x} + xe^{-x} - \tfrac{1}{2}\sqrt{\pi x}\,\text{erf}\sqrt{x}$$
$$= -\tfrac{1}{2}\sqrt{\pi x}\,\text{erf}\sqrt{x} \qquad \text{XII}$$

The complete solution is

$$y = Ax + Bx^{\frac{1}{2}} - \tfrac{1}{2}\sqrt{\pi x}\,\text{erf}\sqrt{x} \qquad \text{XIII}$$

In the above paragraphs, methods of finding the particular integral and the complementary function have been presented for a second order linear differential equation. These methods are quite general and are equally applicable to any order linear differential equation. The second order equation was chosen simply for convenience in order to bring out the salient principles in the solution of these equations. The same treatment would have to be given to a third, fourth or higher order equation.

2.5.7. *Illustrative Problems*

Linear differential equations arise very frequently in the solution of chemical engineering problems. Their appearance is not surprising when one considers that chemical engineers are chiefly concerned with the prediction of rates of transfer of heat, momentum and material. Consequently the method of solving such problems will now be illustrated by three examples taken from the various important fields of the subject.

Problem 1. Simultaneous Diffusion and Chemical Reaction in a Tubular Reactor

A tubular chemical reactor of length L and $1 \cdot 0$ ft^2 in cross section is employed to carry out a first order chemical reaction in which a material A is converted to a product B. The chemical reaction can be represented,

$$A \rightarrow B$$

and the specific reaction rate constant is k h^{-1}. If the feed rate is u ft^3/h, the feed concentration of A is c_0, and the diffusivity of A is assumed to be constant at D ft^2/h, determine the concentration of A as a function of length along the reactor. It may be assumed that there is no volume change during the reaction, and that steady state conditions are established.

Solution

Take a coordinate x to specify the distance of any point from the inlet of the reactor section, let c denote the variable concentration of A in the entry section ($x < 0$), and y denote the concentration of A in the reactor section ($x > 0$), as shown in Fig. 2.4. The concentration will vary in the

Fig. 2.4. Tubular reactor analysis

entry section due to diffusion, but will not vary in the section following the reactor.†

† Wehner, J. F. and Wilhelm, R. H. *Chem. Eng. Sci.* **6**, 89 (1956).

A material balance can be taken over the element of length δx at a distance x from the inlet.

	x	$x+\delta x$
Bulk flow of A	uy	$uy+u\dfrac{dy}{dx}\,\delta x$
Diffusion of A	$-D\dfrac{dy}{dx}$	$-D\dfrac{dy}{dx}+\dfrac{d}{dx}\left(-D\dfrac{dy}{dx}\right)\delta x$

The accumulation in this case is zero, but the input must exceed the output to supply the reaction taking place within the element.

Rate of removal of A by reaction $= ky\,\delta x$

since the reactor is of unit cross-sectional area. Alternatively, this term may be considered as either an output or an accumulation and the general conservation equation (1.25) applied directly.

Thus,

$$uy - D\frac{dy}{dx} - \left(uy + u\frac{dy}{dx}\delta x\right) - \left[-D\frac{dy}{dx} + \frac{d}{dx}\left(-D\frac{dy}{dx}\right)\delta x\right] = ky\,\delta x \qquad \text{I}$$

Simplifying, dividing by δx, and rearranging,

$$\therefore \quad D\frac{d^2y}{dx^2} - u\frac{dy}{dx} - ky = 0 \qquad\qquad \text{II}$$

Similarly, the material balance in the entry section gives

$$D\frac{d^2c}{dx^2} - u\frac{dc}{dx} = 0 \qquad\qquad\qquad \text{III}$$

which can also be obtained from II by removing the reaction term. Equations II and III are both second order linear differential equations with zero right-hand side, thus the complementary function is the complete solution in both cases.

The auxiliary equation of equation II is

$$Dm^2 - um - k = 0 \qquad\qquad\qquad \text{IV}$$

$$\therefore \quad m = u(1\pm a)/2D \qquad\qquad\qquad \text{V}$$

where $\qquad\qquad a = \sqrt{1+4kD/u^2} \qquad\qquad\qquad$ VI

Therefore, the solutions of equations II and III are

$$y = A\exp\left[\frac{ux}{2D}(1+a)\right] + B\exp\left[\frac{ux}{2D}(1-a)\right] \qquad \text{VII}$$

and $\qquad\qquad c = \alpha + \beta\exp(ux/D) \qquad\qquad\qquad$ VIII which contain four arbitrary constants, A, B, α and β. The four boundary conditions are

$$\text{at } x = -\infty, \quad c = c_0 \qquad\qquad \text{IX}$$
$$\text{at } x = 0, \quad c = y \qquad\qquad \text{X}$$
$$\text{at } x = 0, \quad \frac{dc}{dx} = \frac{dy}{dx} \qquad\qquad \text{XI}$$
$$\text{at } x = L, \quad \frac{dy}{dx} = 0 \qquad\qquad \text{XII}$$

The first condition specifies the state of the feed stream, and the second ensures continuity of composition. The third condition, taken with equation X, is necessary to conserve material at the boundary assuming that the diffusivities are equal in both sections. The final condition forbids diffusion out of the reactor and is necessary as a conservation law for the section following the reactor. A full argument supporting the last condition is given in the reference quoted at the start of the problem. Equations IX to XII give respectively,

$$\alpha = c_0 \qquad\qquad \text{XIII}$$
$$\alpha + \beta = A + B \qquad\qquad \text{XIV}$$
$$2\beta = A(1+a) + B(1-a) \qquad\qquad \text{XV}$$
$$A(1+a)\exp\left[\frac{uL}{2D}(1+a)\right] + B(1-a)\exp\left[\frac{uL}{2D}(1-a)\right] = 0 \qquad \text{XVI}$$

Eliminating α and β from XIII, XIV and XV gives

$$2c_0 = A(1-a) + B(1+a) \qquad\qquad \text{XVII}$$

Solving XVI and XVII for A and B gives

$$A = \frac{2c_0(a-1)}{K}\exp\left(-\frac{uLa}{2D}\right) \qquad\qquad \text{XVIII}$$

$$B = \frac{2c_0(a+1)}{K}\exp\left(\frac{uLa}{2D}\right) \qquad\qquad \text{XIX}$$

where $\qquad K = (a+1)^2 \exp(uLa/2D) - (a-1)^2 \exp(-uLa/2D) \qquad$ XX

Putting these values of A and B into equation VII gives the final result,

$$\frac{y}{c_0} = \frac{2}{K}\exp\left(\frac{ux}{2D}\right)\left[(a+1)\exp\left\{\frac{ua}{2D}(L-x)\right\} + (a-1)\exp\left\{-\frac{ua}{2D}(L-x)\right\}\right]$$
$$\text{XXI}$$

From equation XXI, if diffusion is neglected, the first order piston type flow equation results thus,

$$\frac{c_0 - y}{c_0} = 1 - \exp(-kL/u) \qquad\qquad \text{XXII}$$

after a rather involved application of L'Hôpital's rule as $D \to 0$ (see Section 3.3.8).

Problem 2. The Continuous Hydrolysis of Tallow in a Spray Column

8070 lb/h of a tallow fat mixed with 2270 lb/h of high pressure hot water is fed into the base of a spray column operated at a temperature of 450°F and a pressure of 600 lb/in^2. 4120 lb/h of water at the same temperature and pressure is sprayed into the top of the column and descends in the form of droplets through the rising fat phase. Glycerine is generated in the fat phase by the hydrolysis reaction and is extracted by the descending water so that 5560 lb/h of final extract containing 12·16% glycerine is withdrawn continuously from the column base. Simultaneously 8900 lb/h of fatty acid raffinate containing 0·24% glycerine leaves the top of the column. If the effective height of the column is 72 ft and the diameter 2 ft 2 in, the glycerine equivalent in the entering tallow 8·53% and the distribution ratio of glycerine between the water and the fat phase at the column temperature and pressure is 10·32, estimate the concentration of glycerine in each phase as a function of column height. Also find out what fraction of the tower height is required principally for the chemical reaction. The hydrolysis reaction is pseudo first order and the specific reaction rate constant is 0·17 sec^{-1}.

Solution

Consider Fig. 2.5. which illustrates the flows of extract and raffinate in the hydrolyser column. L represents lb/h of raffinate and G lb/h of extract

Fig. 2.5. Continuously operating fat-hydrolysing column under steady state conditions

whilst the appropriate suffix signifies the position in the hydrolyser column. In addition to the symbols given in Fig. 2.5, let

$x =$ Weight fraction of glycerine in raffinate.
$y =$ Weight fraction of glycerine in extract.
$y^* =$ Weight fraction of glycerine in extract in equilibrium with x.
$z =$ Weight fraction of hydrolysable fat in raffinate.
$S =$ Sectional area of tower.
$a =$ Interfacial area per unit volume of tower.
$K =$ Overall mass transfer coefficient expressed in terms of extract compositions.
$m =$ Distribution ratio.
$k =$ Specific reaction rate constant.
$\rho =$ Mass of fat per unit volume of column.
$h =$ Distance coordinate from base of column.
$w =$ lb fat per lb glycerine.
$H =$ Effective height of column.

Consider the changes occurring in the element of column of height δh. These are
(a) glycerine transferred from fat to water phase,

$$KaS(y^* - y)\delta h \qquad \text{I}$$

(b) rate of destruction of fat by hydrolysis,

$$k\rho Sz\,\delta h$$

and therefore the rate of production of glycerine is

$$k\rho Sz\,\delta h/w \qquad \text{II}$$

Then a glycerine balance over the element δh is by Fig. 2.5,

$$Lx + \frac{(k\rho Sz\,\delta h)}{w} - L\left(x + \frac{dx}{dh}\delta h\right) = Gy - G\left(y + \frac{dy}{dh}\delta h\right) = KaS(y^* - y)\delta h$$

$$\text{III}$$

A glycerine balance between the element and the base of the tower is

$$\frac{Lz_0}{w} + Gy = Lx + \frac{Lz}{w} + Gy_0 \qquad \text{IV}$$

Finally the glycerine equilibrium between the phases is

$$y^* = mx \qquad \text{V}$$

From the last two parts of equation III and equation V it can be shown that

$$KaSmx = KaSy - G\frac{dy}{dh} \qquad \text{VI}$$

and substitution of IV in the element glycerine balance III,

$$k\rho S\left[\frac{z_0}{w} + \frac{G}{L}(y - y_0) - x\right]\delta h - L\frac{dx}{dh}\delta h = -G\frac{dy}{dh}\delta h \qquad \text{VII}$$

Multiply equation VII by $(KaSm/LG)$ and substitute for x from VI,

$$\frac{k\rho S^2 Ka}{LG}\left[\frac{mz_0}{w} + \frac{mG}{L}(y-y_0)\right] - \frac{k\rho S}{L}\left[\frac{KaS}{G}y - \frac{dy}{dh}\right] -$$
$$- \left[\frac{KaS}{G}\cdot\frac{dy}{dh} - \frac{d^2y}{dh^2}\right] + \frac{KaSm}{L}\frac{dy}{dh} = 0 \qquad \text{VIII}$$

Equation VIII contains the following groups of constants which can be denoted by the following parameters,

$$r = \frac{mG}{L}; \qquad p = \frac{k\rho S}{L}; \qquad q = \frac{KaS}{G}(r-1) \qquad \text{IX}$$

Substitution of the above groups into VIII gives on rearranging,

$$\frac{d^2y}{dh^2} + (p+q)\frac{dy}{dh} + pqy = \frac{pq}{r-1}\left[ry_0 - \frac{mz_0}{w}\right] \qquad \text{X}$$

Equation X is a second order linear differential equation with constant coefficients.

The auxiliary equation is

$$m_1^2 + (p+q)m_1 + pq = 0 \qquad \text{XI}$$

The roots of XI are

$$m_1 = -p \text{ or } -q$$

and therefore the complementary function is

$$y_c = Ae^{-ph} + Be^{-qh} \qquad \text{XII}$$

The right-hand side of equation X is a constant and therefore the particular integral is a constant and equal to the right-hand side of equation X divided by the coefficient of y, as given in Section 2.5.4.

$$\therefore \quad y_p = \frac{ry_0 - mz_0/w}{r-1} = C \qquad \text{XIII}$$

and the complete solution is

$$y = Ae^{-ph} + Be^{-qh} + \frac{ry_0 - mz_0/w}{r-1} \qquad \text{XIV}$$

where A and B are arbitrary constants to be evaluated from the following boundary conditions.

At $\qquad\qquad h = 0, \qquad x = 0$

and at $\qquad\qquad h = H, \qquad y = 0$

From equation VI,

$$mx = y - \frac{r-1}{q}\frac{dy}{dh}$$

and from equation XIV,

$$\frac{dy}{dh} = -pAe^{-ph} - qBe^{-qh} \qquad \text{XV}$$

Therefore at
$$h = 0$$

$$A + B + \left(\frac{r-1}{q}\right)(pA + qB) + C = 0 \qquad \text{XVI}$$

and at
$$h = H$$

$$Ae^{-pH} + Be^{-qH} + C = 0 \qquad \text{XVII}$$

Equations XVI and XVII are two simultaneous equations in A and B. The arbitrary constants are best evaluated from these two equations by defining a further constant. Thus let

$$v = \frac{q + rp - p}{q} = 1 + \frac{k\rho G}{KaL} \qquad \text{XVIII}$$

Inserting this constant into equations XVI and XVII and solving gives
$$B(ve^{-qH} - re^{-pH}) = C(e^{-pH} - v) \qquad \text{XIX}$$

and
$$A(ve^{-qH} - re^{-pH}) = C(r - e^{-qH}) \qquad \text{XX}$$

Substituting these values of A and B into equation XII,

$$y(ve^{-qH} - re^{-pH}) = C[(r - e^{-qH})e^{-ph} + (e^{-pH} - v)e^{-qh} + ve^{-qH} - re^{-pH}] \qquad \text{XXI}$$

and expressing y_0 from C in terms of the other variables and using the fact that $y = y_0$ at $h = 0$,

$$y_0 = \frac{mz_0}{w(r - e^{-qH})}\left[1 - \left(\frac{r-1}{r-v}\right)e^{-pH} + \left(\frac{v-1}{r-v}\right)e^{-qH}\right] \qquad \text{XXII}$$

Substituting the above value of y_0 into equation XIII and then into equation XXI gives

$$y = \frac{mz_0}{w(r - v)}\left[e^{-ph} + \left(\frac{e^{-pH} - v}{r - e^{-qH}}\right)e^{-qh} + \left(\frac{ve^{-qH} - re^{-pH}}{r - e^{-qH}}\right)\right] \qquad \text{XXIII}$$

Equation XXIII gives the weight fraction of glycerine in the extract phase as a function of column height h.

Allowing for the solubility of water in tallow, taking mean flow rates, and using the data given in the problem, gives

$$L = 8540, \qquad G = 3760, \qquad y_0 = 0\cdot188$$

$$\therefore \quad r = 4\cdot544, \qquad p = 0\cdot198, \qquad q = 0\cdot00348\,Ka, \qquad v = 1 + \frac{201\cdot6}{Ka}$$

Solving equation XXIII for Ka with $H = 72\cdot0$ ft, gives the value of the mass transfer coefficient as

$$Ka = 14\cdot2\,\text{lb glycerine per hour per ft}^3 \qquad \text{XXIV}$$

With the value of $Ka = 14\cdot2$, values of y, y^* and z can be determined as functions of column height with the aid of equations XXIII, VI, V, IV. The results of the arithmetical calculations are shown in graphical form in Fig. 2.6. Figure 2.6. shows that the chemical reaction is virtually complete in the bottom 30 ft of the column, or 40% of the column.

Fig. 2.6. Concentration distributions in hydrolysing column

The above analysis of a continuous hydrolysing column was abstracted from "The Analysis of a Continuous Fat Hydrolysing Plant", by Jeffreys, Jenson and Miles.†

2.6. SIMULTANEOUS DIFFERENTIAL EQUATIONS

These are groups of differential equations containing more than one dependent variable but only one independent variable, and in these equations, all the derivatives of the different dependent variables are with respect to the one independent variable. This distinguishes an equation which is a member of a group of simultaneous differential equations, from a partial differential equation which will contain more than one independent variable and consequently will also contain partial derivatives. All the derivatives in the simultaneous differential equations will be total derivatives.

The basis of the solution of simultaneous differential equations is algebraic elimination of the variables until only one differential equation relating two of the variables remains. The final differential equation is solved in the ordinary way by one of the conventional methods. If the equation is linear with constant coefficients, one of the methods already presented in this chapter will be suitable, otherwise a method to be given later must be employed.

† Jeffreys, Jenson and Miles, *Trans. Inst. Chem. Eng.* **39,** 389 (1961).

The variables to be eliminated depend on the set of equations, and the ultimate information required from the mathematical analysis. The variable may be the independent variable or one of the dependent variables. These possibilities will now be considered.

2.6.1. *Elimination of the Independent Variable*

Consider the pair of simultaneous differential equations,

$$\frac{dx}{d\theta} = f_1(x, y) \tag{2.103}$$

and

$$\frac{dy}{d\theta} = f_2(x, y) \tag{2.104}$$

in which x and y are the dependent variables and θ is the independent variable. $f_1(x,y)$ and $f_2(x,y)$ are two functions of x and y. Equations of this kind can be solved by eliminating the independent variable by dividing one equation by the other, say equation (2.104) by equation (2.103) to give

$$\frac{dy}{dx} = \frac{f_2(x, y)}{f_1(x, y)} \tag{2.105}$$

which is an ordinary differential equation in x and y, and would be solved as such.

Example 1 solved in paragraph 2.3.3 was really one of the above type. Elimination of the time gave a homogeneous equation which was solved by standard solution methods for homogeneous equations.

The above method of eliminating the independent variable is restricted to first order first degree equations in which the independent variable appears only in the derivative. Consequently its scope is very limited.

2.6.2. *Elimination of One or More Dependent Variables*

This approach has considerably wider application, however it becomes very involved with equations of high order and therefore it would be better to make use of matrices if there are many equations. The matrix methods of solving large sets of simultaneous equations are presented in Chapter 12, whereas the following paragraphs will be restricted to the simpler situations. Thus the independent variable can be eliminated by,

(a) Taking advantage of the algebraic properties of the differential operator.

(b) Systematic elimination.

(a) *By Use of the Differential Operator.* It has been pointed out that the operator D obeys the fundamental laws of algebra and therefore can be used in the elimination process. The method is best illustrated by an example.

Example 1. Solve

$$(D^2 + D - 6)y + (D^2 + 6D + 9)z = 0 \qquad\qquad \text{I}$$

and

$$(D^2 + 3D - 10)y + (D^2 - 3D + 2)z = 0 \qquad\qquad \text{II}$$

Equations I and II can be written

$$(D+3)(D-2)y+(D+3)^2z = 0 \qquad\qquad \text{III}$$

and $\qquad\qquad (D-2)(D+5)y+(D-2)(D-1)z = 0 \qquad \text{IV}$

Multiply III by $(D+5)$ and IV by $(D+3)$ to give

$$(D+3)(D+5)(D-2)y+(D+5)(D+3)^2z = 0 \qquad \text{V}$$

and $\qquad (D+3)(D+5)(D-2)y+(D+3)(D-2)(D-1)z = 0 \qquad \text{VI}$

Elimination of y and simplifying the remainder gives

$$(11D+13)(D+3)z = 0 \qquad\qquad \text{VII}$$

whose solution is

$$z = Ae^{-13x/11} + Be^{-3x} \qquad\qquad \text{VIII}$$

where A and B are arbitrary constants.

Substitution of z from equation VIII into equation I gives

$$(D^2+D-6)y = Ee^{-13x/11} \qquad\qquad \text{IX}$$

where $\qquad\qquad E = \left[\left(\frac{13}{11}\right)^2 - \left(\frac{6\times13}{11}\right) + 9 \right] A$

The terms involving Be^{-3x} add up to zero.

The particular integral of y is

$$y_p = \frac{1}{D^2+D-6}Ee^{-13x/11} = \frac{E}{5}\left[\frac{1}{D-2}-\frac{1}{D+3}\right]e^{-13x/11} \qquad \text{X}$$

$$= Ge^{-13x/11} \qquad\qquad \text{XI}$$

where $\qquad\qquad G = -\tfrac{121}{700}E = \tfrac{4}{7}A$

The complementary function is

$$y_c = He^{2x}+Je^{-3x} \qquad\qquad \text{XII}$$

and the complete solution is

$$y = He^{2x}+Je^{-3x}+\tfrac{4}{7}Ae^{-13x/11}$$

(b) *Systematic Elimination.* This term is proposed for the elimination process which reduces the amount of algebra involved to a minimum. Essentially the method consists of setting up a table indicating the number of times and in what form each variable appears in the simultaneous equations. Then the variable that appears in the simplest manner is first eliminated by making the appropriate substitution. Following this the second least frequent variable is removed from the remaining equations by the appropriate substitution, and the substitution process is continued until only one equation remains. Generally terms which appear as derivatives are left to the final steps of the substitution process. The following example will demonstrate the technique.

Example 2.† 10000 lb/h of sulphuric acid (specific heat 0·36) is to be cooled in a two-stage countercurrent cooler of the following type. Hot acid

† Suggested by W. M. Crooks, Dept. of Chemical Engineering, University of Birmingham.

at 174°C is fed to a tank where it is well stirred in contact with cooling coils. The continuous discharge from this tank at 88°C flows to a second stirred tank and leaves at 45°C. Cooling water at 20°C flows into the coil of the second tank and thence to the coil of the first tank. The water is at 80°C as it leaves the coil of the hot acid tank. To what temperatures would the contents of each tank rise if due to trouble in the supply, the cooling water suddenly stopped for one hour?

On restoration of the water supply, water is put on the system at the rate of 10000 lb/h. Calculate the acid discharge temperature after one hour. The capacity of each tank is 10000 lb of acid and the overall coefficient of heat transfer in the hot tank is 200 C.H.U./h ft² °C and in the colder tank 130 C.H.U./h ft² °C. These coefficients may be assumed constant.

Solution

The steady state conditions of the cooling system are shown in Fig. 2.7, and the steady state data calculated from the illustrated conditions are:

Water rate before failure of supply = 7740 lb/h.
Intermediate water temperature between the two tanks = 40°C.
Heat transfer area of coil in hot tank = 69·3 ft².†
Heat transfer area of coil in cold tank = 95·8 ft².

FIG. 2.7. Sulphuric acid cooling system

Water Fails

Water flow is zero. For the purpose of the analysis let,

acid flow rate be M lb/h = 10000
acid specific heat be C = 0·36
feed acid temperature be T_0 °C = 174
acid temperature ex tank 1 be T_1 °C
acid discharge temperature be T_2 °C
capacity of each tank be V lb = 10000
time be θ hours.

† In practice, these figures would be rounded off to 70 and 96 but to reduce errors of calculation the extra figure has been retained (see Chapter 10).

Then the heat balances are as follows.

	Input	Output	Accumulation	
Tank 1	MCT_0	$- MCT_1$	$= VC\dfrac{dT_1}{d\theta}$	I
Tank 2	MCT_1	$- MCT_2$	$= VC\dfrac{dT_2}{d\theta}$	II

These are simultaneous first order differential equations, but they can be solved in succession. Because $M = V$ in the numerical example, equation I becomes

$$T_0 - T_1 = \frac{dT_1}{d\theta} \qquad\qquad \text{III}$$

which has the solution,

$$T_0 - T_1 = Ke^{-\theta} = 174 - T_1 \qquad\qquad \text{IV}$$

and when $\theta = 0$, $T_1 = 88°C$ the steady state temperature.

$$\therefore \quad K = 86$$

Therefore when $\theta = 1.0$,

$$T_1 = 174 - 86e^{-1.0} = 142.4°C \qquad\qquad \text{V}$$

Similarly for tank 2, from equation II,

$$174 - 86e^{-\theta} - T_2 = \frac{dT_2}{d\theta} \qquad\qquad \text{VI}$$

This is a first order linear equation which can be solved using the integrating factor e^{θ}.

Substitution of the integrating factor and solution of equation VI gives

$$T_2 = 174 - (86\theta + 129)e^{-\theta} \qquad\qquad \text{VII}$$

which gives for $\theta = 1.0$,

$$T_2 = 94.9°C \qquad\qquad \text{VIII}$$

Water Supply Restored

Water flow rate is now 10000 lb/h but for the purpose of the following derivation let the water rate be W lb/h and let water supply temperature be t_3 °C.

water temperature ex tank 2 be t_2°C.
water temperature ex tank 1 be t_1°C.

Then the heat balances are as follows.

	Input	Output	Accumulation	
Tank 1	$Wt_2 + MCT_0$	$- (Wt_1 + MCT_1)$	$= VC\dfrac{dT_1}{d\theta}$	IX
Tank 2	$Wt_3 + MCT_1$	$- (Wt_2 + MCT_2)$	$= VC\dfrac{dT_2}{d\theta}$	X

The heat transfer rate equations for the two tanks are

$$W(t_1 - t_2) = U_1 A_1 \left[\frac{(T_1 - t_1) - (T_1 - t_2)}{\ln(T_1 - t_1) - \ln(T_1 - t_2)} \right] \qquad \text{XI}$$

and

$$W(t_2 - t_3) = U_2 A_2 \left[\frac{(T_2 - t_2) - (T_2 - t_3)}{\ln(T_2 - t_2) - \ln(T_2 - t_3)} \right] \qquad \text{XII}$$

These equations simplify to,

$$\frac{T_1 - t_1}{T_1 - t_2} = \exp\left(-\frac{U_1 A_1}{W}\right) = \alpha \text{ (say)} \qquad \text{XIII}$$

and

$$\frac{T_2 - t_2}{T_2 - t_3} = \exp\left(-\frac{U_2 A_2}{W}\right) = \beta \text{ (say)} \qquad \text{XIV}$$

Equations XIII and XIV can be written more simply,

$$T_1(1 - \alpha) = t_1 - \alpha t_2 \qquad \text{XV}$$

$$T_2(1 - \beta) = t_2 - \beta t_3 \qquad \text{XVI}$$

Equations IX, X, XV and XVI are the four equations which have to be solved simultaneously. The difficulty is that of elimination. Hence the following table, Table 2.2, gives the frequency of the appearance of the four variables.

TABLE 2.2. *Frequency of Appearance of Variables*

T_1	T_2	t_1	t_2
1	1	1	1
+	+	1	1
1	1		1
1			1
3 plus +	2 plus +	2	4

In Table 2.2, "1" indicates the appearance of the variable and "+" its derivative. From Table 2.2, t_1 should be eliminated first, then t_2, because both T_1 and T_2 also appear in a differentiated form. Substitution of equation XV into equation IX, and using the numerical property that $M = W = V$, gives

$$t_2 + CT_0 - CT_1 - (1 - \alpha)T_1 - \alpha t_2 = C\frac{dT_1}{d\theta} \qquad \text{XVII}$$

Now eliminate t_2 from the system by substituting from equation XVI into equations XVII and X thus,

$$(1 - \alpha)(1 - \beta)T_2 + (1 - \alpha)\beta t_3 + CT_0 - CT_1 - (1 - \alpha)T_1 = C\frac{dT_1}{d\theta} \qquad \text{XVIII}$$

and

$$t_3 + CT_1 - CT_2 - (1 - \beta)T_2 - \beta t_3 = C\frac{dT_2}{d\theta} \qquad \text{XIX}$$

Rearranging equation XIX,

$$CT_1 = C\frac{dT_2}{d\theta} + (1-\beta+C)T_2 - (1-\beta)t_3 \qquad \text{XX}$$

and differentiating,

$$C\frac{dT_1}{d\theta} = C\frac{d^2T_2}{d\theta^2} + (1-\beta+C)\frac{dT_2}{d\theta} \qquad \text{XXI}$$

Using equations XX and XXI to eliminate T_1 and its differential coefficient from equation XVIII gives

$$C^2\frac{d^2T_2}{d\theta^2} + (2C+2-\alpha-\beta)C\frac{dT_2}{d\theta} + [C^2+C(1-\alpha\beta)+(1-\alpha)(1-\beta)]T_2$$
$$= [C(1-\alpha\beta)+(1-\alpha)(1-\beta)]t_3+C^2T_0 \qquad \text{XXII}$$

Equation XXII is a second order linear differential equation with constant coefficients. The operator does not have simple factors and it is advantageous to introduce the numerical values at this stage.

$$\frac{U_1A_1}{W} = \frac{200\times 69\cdot 3}{10000} = 1\cdot 386, \qquad \therefore \quad \alpha = 0\cdot 250$$

$$\frac{U_2A_2}{W} = \frac{130\times 95\cdot 8}{10000} = 1\cdot 245, \qquad \therefore \quad \beta = 0\cdot 288$$

$$\therefore \quad (1-\alpha)(1-\beta) = 0\cdot 534 \quad \text{and} \quad (1-\alpha\beta) = 0\cdot 928$$

Equation XXII thus becomes

$$\frac{d^2T_2}{d\theta^2} + 6\cdot 06\frac{dT_2}{d\theta} + 7\cdot 70T_2 = 308 \qquad \text{XXIII}$$

which has the solution,

$$T_2 = Ae^{-4\cdot 25\theta} + Be^{-1\cdot 81\theta} + 40\cdot 0 \qquad \text{XXIV}$$

The initial conditions for this solution are the final temperatures from the previous operation given by equations V and VIII. Before these can be used, T_1 has to be determined from equations XXIV and XX. The boundary conditions give

$$A+B = 54\cdot 9 \qquad \text{XXV}$$

and

$$-1\cdot 27A+1\cdot 17B = 62\cdot 8 \qquad \text{XXVI}$$

Solving for A and B, and substituting in equation XXIV gives

$$T_2 = 0\cdot 6e^{-4\cdot 25\theta} + 54\cdot 3e^{-1\cdot 81\theta} + 40\cdot 0 \qquad \text{XXVII}$$

so that the acid discharge temperature after 1 h is 48·9°C.

2.7. Conclusions

Methods have been presented in this chapter for solving the simpler types of differential equations which the chemical engineer is likely to encounter.

There is no general method of solution, but the methods included should solve most first order equations.

Non-linear second order equations are frequently insoluble analytically, but the procedures of Section 2.4 may be useful in providing at least an approximate yet valuable solution.

The most important type of equation dealt with is the linear differential equation with constant coefficients. The complementary function can always be found easily and the methods of undetermined coefficients and inverse operators are recommended for the determination of the particular integral. If both of these methods prove to be inadequate, the method of variation of parameters is always worth trying.

Chapter 3

SOLUTION BY SERIES

3.1. INTRODUCTION

METHODS of solution were presented in Chapter 2 for a limited number of types of ordinary differential equation. Most first order equations were solved in principle, and higher order equations were classified into linear and non-linear differential equations. It was shown that non-linear equations can be solved in the special cases where either x or y is absent, or the equation is homogeneous; and that the solution of any linear differential equation can be resolved into the sum of a complementary function and a particular integral. The complementary function was found in all cases where the coefficients of the derivatives are constant, or the reduced equation is homogeneous, but the general linear equation with variable coefficients was not solved. Particular integrals were found by a variety of methods, some of these involving knowledge of the corresponding complementary function. The purpose of the present chapter is to solve the general linear ordinary differential equation with variable coefficients. The conditions which these coefficients must satisfy are given in the chapter, but they are invariably satisfied in problems of chemical engineering importance. As is usual in treatments of this subject, only the complementary function will be found in most cases, the particular integral can then be found by using the methods of Chapter 2.

When the differential equation has constant coefficients, the solution involves the exponential function. This function, in common with many others, can be expanded into a series of ascending powers of x. The series itself can be considered to be a solution of the differential equation, a property which may be demonstrated by differentiation and substitution into the equation. Methods given in this chapter will show that solutions in the form of infinite series can be obtained for many linear differential equations with variable coefficients. Of the series that arise, only a few can be summed allowing the solution to be expressed in closed form, but the other series can be accepted as solutions provided that they are convergent. For practical purposes, the series will be useful only if they are rapidly convergent. It is therefore necessary to consider the convergence of series, before differential equations can be solved by their use.

3.2. INFINITE SERIES

A series of numbers

$$u_1 + u_2 + u_3 + \ldots + u_n = S_n \tag{3.1}$$

is classified by determining the behaviour of S_n as n increases to infinity.

(a) If $S_n \to S$ some finite number as $n \to \infty$, the series is termed "convergent".

(b) If $S_n \to \pm\infty$ as $n \to \infty$, the series is termed "divergent".

(c) In other cases, the series is termed "oscillatory".

When considering oscillatory series, the value of S_n may oscillate between either finite or infinite limits and a further classification can be based on this distinction.

In the application of series to differential equations, u_n will be a function of x, consequently S_n will also be a function of x. Because x may take positive or negative values, or even complex values it is desirable to allow u_n to be complex. The properties of complex numbers will be investigated in Chapter 4, but for those readers who are not familiar with the elementary properties of complex numbers, the term "absolute value" refers to the numerical magnitude of the number and is signified by vertical lines.

$$|u_n| \equiv \text{absolute value of } u_n.$$

The series (3.1) is said to be "absolutely convergent" if the series

$$|u_1| + |u_2| + |u_3| + \dots + |u_n|. \tag{3.2}$$

is convergent.

Example 1.
$$u_n = z^n$$
$$\therefore \quad S_n = z + z^2 + z^3 + \dots + z^n \qquad \text{I}$$

This series is a geometrical progression with common ratio z.

$$\therefore \quad S_n = \frac{z(1-z^n)}{1-z} \qquad \text{II}$$

$$= \frac{z}{1-z} - \frac{z^{n+1}}{1-z}$$

(a) If $|z| < 1$, $z^{n+1} \to 0$ as $n \to \infty$,
$$\therefore \quad S_n \to z/1-z$$

Hence the series is convergent.

(b) If $|z| > 1$, $|z^{n+1}| \to \infty$ as $n \to \infty$, therefore the series diverges if z is real and positive, or oscillates for all other values of z.

(c) If $z = 1$, $S_n = n$ which tends to infinity as n increases indefinitely. Hence the series is divergent.

(d) If $|z| = 1$ and $z \neq 1$, the series oscillates within finite limits.

This series thus illustrates all four types of behaviour.

3.2.1. *Properties of Infinite Series*

The following are three useful properties of infinite series.

(i) If a series contains only positive real numbers or zero, then it must be either convergent or divergent; it cannot oscillate.

(ii) If a series is convergent, then $u_n \to 0$ as $n \to \infty$. This is a property of a convergent series; it is not a proof of convergence. A divergent series for which $u_n \to 0$ is illustrated in example 2, part (b) below.

(iii) If a series is absolutely convergent, then it is also convergent.

Statement (iii) can be proved as follows by referring to (i). If u_n is real, put $u_n = a_n - b_n$ where $a_n = \frac{1}{2}(|u_n| + u_n)$ and $b_n = \frac{1}{2}(|u_n| - u_n)$. Thus a_n, the series of positive terms is separated from $-b_n$, the set of negative terms so that neither a_n nor b_n is negative.

$$a_n \leqslant |u_n|$$
$$\therefore \quad a_1 + a_2 + a_3 + \ldots + a_n \leqslant |u_1| + |u_2| + \ldots + |u_n| \leqslant S$$

Since the series a_n only contains positive or zero terms, and the sum cannot exceed S, then statement (i) above proves that $\sum a_n$ is convergent.

Similarly, $\sum b_n$ is convergent.

$$\therefore \quad \sum u_n = \sum a_n - \sum b_n$$

must tend to some finite limit between $+S$ and $-S$. If u_n is complex, a similar proof can be constructed by separating real and imaginary parts.

Thus, absolute convergence implies more than mere convergence.

3.2.2. *Comparison Test*

Only convergent series will be of importance in the solution of chemical engineering problems, but the following tests will be stated in full as they determine convergence or divergence. It is important to appreciate in these tests that if it is shown that a particular series is not convergent, this does not necessarily mean that it is divergent; it may oscillate.

The comparison test is the simplest of all and consists of two parts:

(i) If $|u_n| \leqslant v_n$ for all $n > N$ where N is some finite integer, and $\sum v_n$ is convergent, then $\sum u_n$ is absolutely convergent.

(ii) If $|u_n| \geqslant v_n$ for all $n > N$, and $\sum v_n$ is divergent to $+\infty$, then $\sum u_n$ is also divergent.

This test involves comparing the series under investigation with known convergent or divergent series, on a term by term basis, and it becomes more useful as the behaviour of more series becomes known. Comparison with the simple geometrical progression with a suitable common ratio as in example 1 is very useful for part (i) of the test, and the divergent series given in example 2 (b) below is useful in part (ii) of the test.

Example 2. $\qquad u_n = n^{-p}$ (p real)
$$S_n = 1 + 2^{-p} + 3^{-p} + \ldots + n^{-p} = \sum n^{-p}$$

The above series has different properties for different values of p.

(a) $p > 1$.

$$1 = 1$$
$$(\tfrac{1}{2})^p + (\tfrac{1}{3})^p < 2(\tfrac{1}{2})^p = (\tfrac{1}{2})^{p-1}$$
$$(\tfrac{1}{4})^p + (\tfrac{1}{5})^p + (\tfrac{1}{6})^p + (\tfrac{1}{7})^p < 4(\tfrac{1}{4})^p = (\tfrac{1}{4})^{p-1}$$
$$\ldots \ldots \text{etc.}$$

The rth line contains 2^{r-1} terms and begins with $(\tfrac{1}{2})^{rp}$.

$$\therefore \quad \sum n^{-p} < 1 + (\tfrac{1}{2})^{p-1} + (\tfrac{1}{4})^{p-1} + \dots$$

The right-hand side is a geometrical progression with a finite sum to infinity. Therefore the series is convergent by Section 3.2.1 (i).

(b) $p = 1$. In order to show that the series is divergent in this case, the following algebraic relationship is required.

$$\frac{1}{n-k} + \frac{1}{n+k} = \frac{2n}{n^2-k^2} > \frac{2}{n}$$

Grouping the terms of the series as shown below, and applying the above algebraic inequality, gives

$$\tfrac{1}{2} + \tfrac{1}{3} + \tfrac{1}{4} = (\tfrac{1}{2} + \tfrac{1}{4}) + \tfrac{1}{3} > \tfrac{2}{3} + \tfrac{1}{3} = 1$$

$$\tfrac{1}{5} + \tfrac{1}{6} + \tfrac{1}{7} + \tfrac{1}{8} + \tfrac{1}{9} + \tfrac{1}{10} + \tfrac{1}{11} + \tfrac{1}{12} + \tfrac{1}{13}$$

$$= (\tfrac{1}{5} + \tfrac{1}{13}) + (\tfrac{1}{6} + \tfrac{1}{12}) + (\tfrac{1}{7} + \tfrac{1}{11}) + (\tfrac{1}{8} + \tfrac{1}{10}) + \tfrac{1}{9}$$

$$> \tfrac{2}{9} + \tfrac{2}{9} + \tfrac{2}{9} + \tfrac{2}{9} + \tfrac{1}{9} = 1$$

$$\therefore \quad (1) + (\tfrac{1}{2} + \tfrac{1}{3} + \tfrac{1}{4}) + (\tfrac{1}{5} + \dots + \tfrac{1}{13}) + (\tfrac{1}{14} + \dots + \tfrac{1}{40}) + \dots > 1 + 1 + 1 + 1 + \dots$$

The rth bracket contains 3^{r-1} terms centred on 3^{1-r}. Therefore, the sum of the first $\tfrac{1}{2}(3^r - 1)$ terms is greater than r. By taking sufficient terms, the sum can be made to exceed any chosen finite value, and hence the series is divergent.

(c) $p < 1$.

$$\left(\frac{1}{n}\right)^p > \frac{1}{n} \quad \text{for } n > 1$$

The series is thus divergent by comparison with part (b) using the test of Section 3.2.2 (ii).

3.2.3. Ratio Test

This also consists of two parts:

(i) If

$$\left| \frac{u_n}{u_{n+1}} \right| \geqslant k > 1$$

for all $n > N$, then the series is absolutely convergent.

(ii) If

$$\left| \frac{u_n}{u_{n+1}} \right| < 1$$

for all $n > N$, then the series is not convergent.

Regarding the first part of the test it is necessary to find a fixed finite number k to satisfy the inequality for *all* $n > N$. In the second part, if the series only contains positive terms, the test proves that the series is divergent, but in general the series may oscillate.

When the second part is not satisfied and $k = 1$ in the first part, thus violating the inequality, the test is not conclusive. That is, the series may be convergent, divergent or oscillatory, the test will not determine which.

Example 3

$$S_n = 1 + \tfrac{1}{2} + \tfrac{1}{3} + \tfrac{1}{4} + \ldots + \tfrac{1}{n}$$

$$\left| \frac{u_n}{u_{n+1}} \right| = \frac{n+1}{n} = 1 + \frac{1}{n}$$

$\therefore |u_n/u_{n+1}| > 1$ for all $n > N$, but it is impossible to find a value of k such that part (i) of the ratio test is satisfied. The test is therefore inconclusive, but this series has already been proved divergent in Example 2 (b).

3.2.4. *Raabe's Test*

The ratio test is inconclusive when $k = 1$, but Raabe's test is designed to resolve this difficulty. The test is again in two parts:

(i) If
$$\left| \frac{u_n}{u_{n+1}} \right| \geq 1 + \frac{\alpha}{n}$$

where $\alpha > 1$, for all $n > N$, then the series is convergent.

(ii) If
$$\left| \frac{u_n}{u_{n+1}} \right| \leq 1 + \frac{1}{n},$$

then the series is divergent.
The second part of Raabe's Test proves that the series of Example 3 is divergent.

There is still a case unresolved when $\alpha = 1$ in part (i), a case which is covered by a further extension of the same technique.

3.2.5. *Gauss' Test*

There is only one part to this test.

If
$$\left| \frac{u_n}{u_{n+1}} \right| = 1 + \frac{1}{n} + \frac{f(n)}{n^2}$$

where $|f(n)| < C$ for $n > N$, then the series is divergent,

This test means that when $1 + 1/n$ has been subtracted from the ratio of successive terms, and the result has been multiplied by n^2; if the function $f(n)$ remains finite as $n \to \infty$, then the series is divergent.

These last three tests fall into a natural order of increasing resolving power, each one testing the behaviour of the ratio of successive terms in greater detail. As mentioned in Section 3.1, a series is of little practical value unless it is rapidly convergent; consequently, the more powerful tests are rarely necessary.

3.2.6. *The Integral Test*

If $f(x)$ is a positive integrable function of x which decreases for all $x > N$, where N is some positive integer, then the series $\sum f(n)$ converges if and only if $\int_N^\infty f(x)\, dx$ exists.

Each of the above tests is sufficient to prove convergence or divergence, but the large number of series for which they are inconclusive indicates that all of the tests need not necessarily be satisfied by any particular series. The following example illustrates an inconclusive case which is nevertheless convergent.

Example 4

$$1+\tfrac{3}{4}+\tfrac{1}{2}+(\tfrac{3}{4})^2+(\tfrac{1}{2})^2+(\tfrac{3}{4})^3+(\tfrac{1}{2})^3+... \qquad\qquad \text{I}$$

The successive values of u_n/u_{n+1} are

$$\tfrac{4}{3},\ \tfrac{3}{2},\ \tfrac{8}{9},\ \tfrac{9}{4},\ \tfrac{16}{27},\ \tfrac{27}{8},\ ...$$

where after the first term, alternate values are greater and less than unity. Therefore, the ratio test "proves" the series to be alternately convergent and divergent.

The series of odd terms is a geometric progression with sum to infinity 2; the sum of the even terms is 3. Therefore, the series I is convergent to the value 5.

3.2.7. *Alternating Series*

$$u_1-u_2+u_3-u_4+... \qquad\qquad (3.3)$$

is an alternating series if $u_n>0$ for all n. If, in addition, the magnitude of successive terms decreases for all values of n and $u_n\to 0$ as $n\to\infty$, then the series is convergent.

Proof

$$S_{2m} = (u_1-u_2)+(u_3-u_4)+...+(u_{2m-1}-u_{2m})$$

Since each term in the brackets is positive and the next term u_{2m+1} must be added, S_{2m} and S_{2m+1} must both be greater than zero.

$$S_{2m+1} = u_1-(u_2-u_3)-(u_4-u_5)-...-(u_{2m}-u_{2m+1})$$

Again, each term in the brackets is positive, and removing the last term to obtain S_{2m} reduces the value further. Therefore, S_{2m} and S_{2m+1} are both less than u_1.

$$\therefore\quad 0 \leqslant S_n \leqslant u_1 \quad \text{for all } n.$$

Both S_{2m} and S_{2m+1} increase as m increases but never exceed u_1, and hence they are separately convergent. Because $u_n\to 0$ as $n\to\infty$, S_{2m} and S_{2m+1} must both converge to the same limit S. Therefore the alternating series (3.3) is convergent.

3.3. POWER SERIES

Consider the power series

$$a_0+a_1 z+a_2 z^2 + ... = \sum_0^\infty a_n z^n \qquad\qquad (3.4)$$

If $|a_n/a_{n+1}|\to R$ as $n\to\infty$, then the ratio test can be applied as follows.

$$\left|\frac{u_n}{u_{n+1}}\right| = \left|\frac{a_n z^n}{a_{n+1} z^{n+1}}\right| = \left|\frac{a_n}{a_{n+1}}\right|\frac{1}{|z|} \to \frac{R}{|z|} \qquad\qquad (3.5)$$

as $n \to \infty$. Therefore, if $|z| < R$, $|u_n/u_{n+1}|$ will tend to some limit greater than unity and will be convergent by part (i) of the ratio test. In detail, if $|z| = R - \varepsilon$ where ε is some small positive number less than R,

$$\frac{R}{|z|} = \frac{R}{R-\varepsilon}$$

$$= 1 + \frac{\varepsilon}{R-\varepsilon}$$

$$> 1 + (\varepsilon/R)$$

Taking $k = 1+(\varepsilon/R)$ in Section 3.2.3, and substituting into equation (3.5) proves that the series (3.4) is convergent.

If $|z| > R$, a similar proof shows that the series (3.4) is divergent. Therefore, $\sum a_n z^n$ is convergent for $|z| < R$ and divergent for $|z| > R$. R is termed the "radius of convergence" of the power series and as shown above, R is the limit of the ratio of successive coefficients. If $|a_n/a_{n+1}| \to \infty$ as $n \to \infty$, then the power series will always converge. If $|a_n/a_{n+1}| \to 0$ as $n \to \infty$, then the power series will only converge if $z = 0$; i.e. if all terms are zero.

3.3.1. Binomial Series

The series obtained by expanding $(1+z)^p$ is

$$1 + pz + \frac{p(p-1)}{1.2}z^2 + \frac{p(p-1)(p-2)}{1.2.3}z^3 + \ldots = \sum_0^\infty \binom{p}{n}z^n$$

where $\binom{p}{n}$ signifies the binomial coefficient, z may be complex, but p is real. In this case

$$a_n = \frac{p(p-1)(p-2)(\ldots)(p-n+1)}{1.2.3.\ldots n}$$

$$\therefore \left| \frac{a_n}{a_{n+1}} \right| = \left| \frac{n+1}{p-n} \right| \to 1 \quad \text{as } n \to \infty$$

Therefore, the binomial series is convergent for $|z| < 1$.

3.3.2. Exponential Series

$$e^z = 1 + z + \frac{z^2}{2!} + \frac{z^3}{3!} + \ldots = \sum_0^\infty \frac{z^n}{n!} \tag{3.7}$$

Here, $a_n = 1/(n!)$

$$\therefore |a_n/a_{n+1}| = n+1 \to \infty \quad \text{as } n \to \infty.$$

Therefore, the exponential series is always convergent.

3.3.3. Logarithmic Series

$$\ln(1+z) = z - \tfrac{1}{2}z^2 + \tfrac{1}{3}z^3 - \tfrac{1}{4}z^4 + \ldots = \sum_1^\infty \frac{(-1)^{n-1}z^n}{n} \tag{3.8}$$

Here, $a_n = (-1)^{n-1}/n$

$$\therefore \quad \left| \frac{a_n}{a_{n+1}} \right| = \frac{n+1}{n} \to 1 \quad \text{as } n \to \infty.$$

Therefore, the series for $\ln(1+z)$ is convergent for $|z| < 1$. There are two further interesting cases of this series.

(a) $z = 1$. Equation (3.8) gives

$$\ln 2 = 1 - \tfrac{1}{2} + \tfrac{1}{3} - \tfrac{1}{4} + \dots \tag{3.9}$$

This is an alternating series with decreasing terms, and $u_n \to 0$ as $n \to \infty$. Therefore the series is convergent by Section 3.2.7.

(b) $z = -1$. Equation (3.8) gives

$$\ln 0 = -(1 + \tfrac{1}{2} + \tfrac{1}{3} + \tfrac{1}{4} + \dots)$$

which was shown to be divergent in Section 3.2.2 (b). The series (3.9) is thus "conditionally convergent" and not absolutely convergent.

3.3.4. *Trigonometric Series*

$$\sin z = z - \frac{z^3}{3!} + \frac{z^5}{5!} - \dots = \sum_0^\infty \frac{(-1)^n z^{2n+1}}{(2n+1)!} \tag{3.10}$$

$$\cos z = 1 - \frac{z^2}{2!} + \frac{z^4}{4!} - \dots = \sum_0^\infty \frac{(-1)^n z^{2n}}{(2n)!} \tag{3.11}$$

These two series are convergent for all values of z.

3.3.5. *Hyperbolic Series*

$$\sinh z = z + \frac{z^3}{3!} + \frac{z^5}{5!} + \dots = \sum_0^\infty \frac{z^{2n+1}}{(2n+1)!} \tag{3.12}$$

$$\cosh z = 1 + \frac{z^2}{2!} + \frac{z^4}{4!} + \dots = \sum_0^\infty \frac{z^{2n}}{(2n)!} \tag{3.13}$$

These two series are convergent for all values of z.

3.3.6. *Inverse Trigonometric and Hyperbolic Functions*

If $z = \tan y$, the inverse tangent function is defined by

$$y = \tan^{-1} z.$$

That is, y is the angle measured in radians, the tangent function of which has the value z. The other inverse trigonometric functions and inverse hyperbolic functions are defined similarly. The series expressions for two of these inverse functions are

$$\tan^{-1} z = z - \frac{z^3}{3} + \frac{z^5}{5} - \dots = \sum_0^\infty \frac{(-1)^n z^{2n+1}}{2n+1} \tag{3.14}$$

$$\tanh^{-1} z = z + \frac{z^3}{3} + \frac{z^5}{5} + \dots = \sum_0^\infty \frac{z^{2n+1}}{2n+1} \tag{3.15}$$

These two series are convergent for $|z| < 1$.

Series expansions can be developed for the functions $\tan z$, $\tanh z$, $\sin^{-1} z$, $\cos^{-1} z$, $\sinh^{-1} z$, $\cosh^{-1} z$ but their form is a little obscure and no purpose would be served by presenting them here. The above series and many others can be obtained by applying Taylor's theorem, which develops a power series in ascending powers of the variable.

3.3.7. Taylor's Theorem

If x is a real variable, and $f(x)$ can be differentiated n times at $x = a$, then

$$f(a+h) = f(a) + hf'(a) + \tfrac{1}{2}h^2 f''(a) + \ldots + \frac{h^{n-1}}{(n-1)!} f^{(n-1)}(a) + \frac{h^n}{n!}[f^{(n)}(a) + \delta]$$

(3.16)

where dashes denote differentiation with respect to x, and $\delta \to 0$ as $h \to 0$.

Most functions of a continuous independent variable which arise in chemical engineering can be differentiated indefinitely at all points of the problem, and the conditions for the application of Taylor's theorem are always satisfied.

3.3.8. L'Hôpital's Rule

It is sometimes necessary to resolve an indeterminate fraction of the form 0/0. This difficulty usually arises for some special value of a variable in a case such as

$$y = \frac{f(x)}{g(x)}$$

(3.17)

where $f(x)$ and $g(x)$ are differentiable n times, and $f(a) = g(a) = 0$. A value of y can be calculated for all values of x except $x = a$. Expanding $f(x)$ and $g(x)$ about the point $x = a$ by Taylor's theorem,

$$f(x) = f(a) + (x-a)f'(a) + \tfrac{1}{2}(x-a)^2 f''(a) + \ldots$$
$$g(x) = g(a) + (x-a)g'(a) + \tfrac{1}{2}(x-a)^2 g''(a) + \ldots$$
$$\therefore \quad y = \frac{f(a) + (x-a)f'(a) + \tfrac{1}{2}(x-a)^2 f''(a) + \ldots}{g(a) + (x-a)g'(a) + \tfrac{1}{2}(x-a)^2 g''(a) + \ldots}$$

(3.18)

If $f(a) = g(a) = 0$ and $g'(a) \neq 0$, then a factor $(x-a)$ can be taken out of both numerator and denominator of equation (3.18), giving

$$y = \frac{f'(a) + \tfrac{1}{2}(x-a)f''(a) + \ldots}{g'(a) + \tfrac{1}{2}(x-a)g''(a) + \ldots}$$

(3.19)

In the limit as $x \to a$,

$$y \to \frac{f'(a)}{g'(a)}$$

(3.20)

Example 1. Evaluate $y = (\sin x)/x$ when $x = 0$.

The value of y can be determined for any value of x no matter how small, but not for zero. The series expansion of $\sin x$, equation (3.10) can be used in this example, giving

$$y = \left(x - \frac{x^3}{3!} + \frac{x^5}{5!} - \ldots\right)\!\Big/x$$

$$= 1 - \frac{x^2}{3!} + \frac{x^4}{5!} - \ldots$$

which is valid for all x no matter how small. In the limit as $x \to 0$, it can be seen that $y \to 1$ and this is the obvious value to take for y when $x = 0$.

This process of resolving indeterminate fractions can be repeated k times provided that $k < n$.

$$f(a) = f'(a) = \ldots = f^{(k-1)}(a) = 0$$

and

$$g(a) = g'(a) = \ldots = g^{(k-1)}(a) = 0.$$

The first k terms in both numerator and denominator of equation (3.18) are zero, a factor $(x-a)^k$ can be taken out of the remaining terms and the limit as $x \to a$ will give

$$y = f^{(k)}(a)/g^{(k)}(a) \tag{3.21}$$

As soon as a non-zero derivative occurs in either series, both series must be terminated and the ratio evaluated as zero, infinity, or any finite value.

Example 2. Find the limit as $x \to 0$ of

$$y = \frac{x^2 \sin x}{1 - \cos x}$$

With the above notation, $f(x) = x^2 \sin x$, $g(x) = 1 - \cos x$.

$$\therefore \quad f(0) = g(0) = 0$$

$$\therefore \quad f'(x) = 2x \sin x + x^2 \cos x \qquad\qquad f'(0) = 0$$

and $\qquad g'(x) = \sin x \qquad\qquad\qquad\qquad\qquad g'(0) = 0$

$$\therefore \quad f''(x) = 2 \sin x + 4x \cos x - x^2 \sin x \qquad f''(0) = 0$$

and $\qquad g''(x) = \cos x \qquad\qquad\qquad\qquad\qquad g''(0) = 1$

$$\therefore \quad \text{as } x \to 0, \ y \to \frac{f(0)}{g(0)} \to \frac{f'(0)}{g'(0)} \to \frac{f''(0)}{g''(0)} \to 0$$

When the first non-vanishing derivative occurs in the denominator, as here, the limit is zero, and when the first non-vanishing derivative occurs in the numerator, the limit is infinite. If, as in the first example, both derivatives of the same order become non-zero simultaneously, then the limit is finite.

3.3.9. *Application of Series in Chemical Engineering*

Some of the problems encountered in chemical engineering prove very difficult by standard analytical methods, and some even defy analytical solution. Consequently, methods of successive approximation, and the numerical methods of Chapter 11 are used extensively. All of these methods can only be used when they are convergent, since in practice, a fundamentally infinite process is being terminated at some finite point. Later in this chapter, series solutions will be developed for some problems, and although a series solution may be convergent and therefore satisfactory from a mathematical point of view, it may converge too slowly to be of any practical value. Unless a series is rapidly convergent requiring only about five terms to express the solution adequately, the numerical work becomes prohibitive and the solution is of little practical value. No harm can come from this situation, since the eventual solution will be valid mathematically, and in Section 3.5.6, Example 6, illustrates this situation. The danger lies in the opposite situation, when the first few terms of a series decrease rapidly giving an apparently useful solution, while the series as a whole is divergent and therefore not valid mathematically. A divergent series is of no practical value, and therefore any series obtained must always be checked for convergence. In this respect the advanced tests given in Sections 3.2.4, 3.2.5, and 3.2.6 may be needed, but for most practical requirements the comparison and ratio tests will suffice.

The next example illustrates the danger of using a divergent series by mistake. Because the example shows that the method of solution does not work, there is little point in explaining the details, consequently only a rough outline of the method is presented.

Example 3.   In the mathematical description of a stagewise process involving simultaneous gas absorption and second order chemical reaction in the liquid phase, a finite difference equation of the following type was developed.

$$y_{n+1} - Ay_n + By_{n-1} + Cy_n y_{n-1} - Dy_{n-1}^2 - Ey_n^2 = 0 \qquad \text{I}$$

where
$$A = \alpha + \beta + 2 - E^0$$
$$B = \alpha + (1 - E^0)(1 + \beta)$$
$$C = \lambda[1 + 2(1 - E^0)/\alpha]$$
$$D = \lambda(1 - E^0)[1 + (1 - E^0)/\alpha]$$
$$E = \lambda/\alpha$$

$$\alpha = \frac{GmE^0}{L} \qquad \beta = \frac{kKH^2}{L^2 V} \qquad \lambda = \frac{kGH^2}{L^2 V}$$

L and G are the liquid and gas flow rates, m is the distribution ratio, E^0 is the Murphree plate efficiency, k is the reaction rate constant, K is the nett flow of the transferable component, V is the volumetric hold up per plate, and H is the corresponding molal hold up. Any consistent system of units which makes α, β, and λ dimensionless may be used.

The method of deriving equation I is given in Chapter 9. One method of solving finite difference equations is to expand y_{n+1} as a power series in y_n, and hence y_n as the same power series in y_{n-1}, viz.

$$y_{n+1} = a_1 y_n + a_2 y_n^2 + a_3 y_n^3 + \ldots \qquad \text{II}$$

Substitution of the series II into equation I and equating the coefficients of like powers of y_{n-1}, gives

$$a_1 = \tfrac{1}{2}(A - \sqrt{A^2 - 4B})$$

$$a_2 = \frac{Ca_1 - Ea_1^2 - D}{A - a_1 - a_1^2}$$

$$a_3 = \frac{Ca_2 + 2a_1 a_2(a_2 - E)}{A - a_1 - a_1^3}$$

$$a_4 = \frac{Ca_3 + (a_2 - E)(2a_1 a_3 + a_2^2) + 3a_1^2 a_2 a_3}{A - a_1 - a_1^4}$$

. . . .

$$(A - a_1 - a_1^{n+1})a_{n+1}$$
$$= Ca_n + (a_2 - E)\sum a_i a_j + a_3 \sum a_i a_j a_k + a_4 \sum a_i a_j a_k a_l + \ldots + a_n n a_1^{n-l} a_2$$

III

where $\sum a_i a_j$ signifies the coefficient of y_n^{n+1} in the expression of y_{n+1}^2 using equation II; $\sum a_i a_j a_k$ signifies the coefficient of y_n^{n+1} in y_{n+1}^3; etc.

In a numerical example which was attempted by the authors, the first few terms decreased quite rapidly and the method appeared to be successful. It was necessary to prove that the series was convergent by using the result of Section 3.3 that if $|a_n/a_{n+1}| \to R$ as $n \to \infty$, then the series would be convergent for $|y_{n-1}| < R$.

Due to the extreme complexity of the equation for the general term III it was difficult to subject it to the test, therefore two particular simplifications were investigated as below.

(a) *Fast Reaction*. k large, $\therefore \beta \to \infty$, $\lambda \to \infty$.

$$A^2 - 4B = (\alpha + \beta - E^0)^2 + 4\beta E^0$$

$$\therefore \quad A - \sqrt{A^2 - 4B} = 2 - \frac{2\beta E^0}{\alpha + \beta - E^0} + \frac{\beta^2 E^{02}}{2(\alpha + \beta - E^0)^3} + \ldots$$

$$\therefore \quad a_1 \simeq 1 - E^0 + E^0(4\alpha - 3E^0)/4\beta$$

$$\therefore \quad a_2 \simeq \lambda E^0(4\alpha - 3E^0)/4\beta^2$$

$$\therefore \quad a_3 \simeq \lambda^2 E^0(4\alpha - 3E^0)/4\beta^3$$

It appears that a_n/a_{n+1} may approximate to a constant (β/λ) in the early terms. The doubt concerns the rapid increase in the number of "correction" terms on the right hand side of equation III. An expression can be developed for these terms by using the approximate relationship that

$$a_n/a_{n+1} \simeq \beta/\lambda < 1 \qquad\qquad \text{IV}$$

$$a_1 a_n \simeq a_2 a_{n-1} \simeq a_3 a_{n-2} \ldots \text{etc.}$$

and each of the terms in $\sum a_i a_j$ will equal $a_1 a_n$. Similarly, all terms in $\sum a_i a_j a_k$ will equal $a_1^2 a_{n-1}$, and so on. With this approximation, equation III

D

becomes

$$(A - a_1 - a_1^{n+1})a_{n+1}$$

$$\simeq Ca_n + (a_2 - E)na_1 a_n + \tfrac{1}{2}a_3 n(n-1)a_1^2 a_{n-1} +$$

$$+ a_4 \frac{n(n-1)(n-2)}{1.2.3} a_1^3 a_{n-2} + \dots + a_n na_1^{n-1}a_2$$

V

Equation IV shows that a_n increases with n, and the number of terms on the right-hand side of equation V also increases as n increases. Each term tends to infinity, and the central term approaches infinity as $(n)^{\frac{1}{2}n}$, which is a very rapid rate of growth. In view of these considerations, it is most unlikely that the series will converge inside any circle of finite radius. It must be emphasized here that no proof has been provided, but the evidence indicates probable divergence.

(b) *Slow Reaction.* $k \to 0$, take $E^\circ = 1$, $\beta \to 0$, $\lambda \to 0$.

$$\therefore \quad A = \alpha + 1 - \beta$$

$$B = \alpha$$

$$A^2 - 4B = (\alpha - 1 - \beta)^2 - 4\beta$$

$$\therefore \quad A - \sqrt{A^2 - 4B} = 2 + \frac{2\beta}{\alpha - 1 - \beta} + \dots$$

$$\therefore \quad a_1 = 1 + \frac{\beta}{\alpha - 1 - \beta} + \dots$$

But since β is small, if $\alpha > 1$ then $a_1 > 1$. This result is physically wrong as may be seen by inspecting equation II. For small values of y_{n-1}, y_n will be greater than y_{n-1} and the column must therefore be generating the transferable gas rather than absorbing it.

Part (b) shows that the method is useless for one particular case $\alpha > 1$, $E^\circ = 1$, and k small, and part (a) throws serious doubt upon the convergence of the series, even though the first few terms decrease quite rapidly. The method should not therefore be used on an equation of the type I.

3.4. SIMPLE SERIES SOLUTIONS

In Section 2.5.1, the linear differential equation with constant coefficients was solved and shown to have solutions for the complementary function of the types

$$y = A_1 e^{m_1 x} + A_2 e^{m_2 x} \tag{2.45}$$

$$y = (A + Bx)e^{mx}$$

and

$$y = (A \cos \alpha x + B \sin \alpha x)e^{\beta x} \tag{2.49}$$

By referring to Sections 3.3.2 and 3.3.4, all of these solutions can be expanded in ascending power series of x. Thus for the first case,

$$y = A(1 + m_1 x + \tfrac{1}{2}m_1^2 x^2 + \dots) + B(1 + m_2 x + \tfrac{1}{2}m_2^2 x^2 + \dots) \tag{3.22}$$

This series form of y can be accepted as a solution of the equation provided that the differential equation is satisfied by it and the series is convergent. It can be shown that the first condition is satisfied by differentiating the series term by term and substituting the result into the differential equation when all terms will cancel out. The series can be checked for convergence by any of the tests given in Section 3.3.

Because the linear differential equation with constant coefficients always possesses a valid series solution, it is natural to expect at least some differential equations with variable coefficients to possess series solutions. Since the majority of series cannot be summed, it is to be expected that some solutions must be left in series form.

The general second order linear differential equation can be expressed in the form

$$\frac{d^2y}{dx^2} + P(x)\frac{dy}{dx} + Q(x)y = 0 \qquad (3.23)$$

If $P(x)$ and $Q(x)$ can be expanded in a convergent ascending power series in x, then the method of solution is as follows.

$$P(x) = P_0 + P_1 x + P_2 x^2 + \dots \qquad (3.24)$$
$$Q(x) = Q_0 + Q_1 x + Q_2 x^2 + \dots \qquad (3.25)$$

Put
$$y = a_0 + a_1 x + a_2 x^2 + \dots \qquad (3.26)$$

$$\therefore \quad \frac{dy}{dx} = a_1 + 2a_2 x + 3a_3 x^2 + \dots$$

$$\therefore \quad \frac{d^2y}{dx^2} = 2a_2 + 6a_3 x + 12a_4 x^2 + \dots$$

and substitute these series into equation (3.23).

$$(2a_2 + 6a_3 x + 12a_4 x^2 + \dots) + (P_0 + P_1 x + P_2 x^2 + \dots) \times$$
$$\times (a_1 + 2a_2 x + 3a_3 x^2 + \dots) + (Q_0 + Q_1 x + Q_2 x^2 + \dots) \times$$
$$\times (a_0 + a_1 x + a_2 x^2 + \dots) = 0 \qquad (3.27)$$

If equation (3.26) is to be the solution of equation (3.23), then all terms in equation (3.27) must cancel out. Thus, coefficients of like powers of x can be equated.

$$\therefore \quad 2a_2 + P_0 a_1 + Q_0 a_0 = 0 \qquad (3.28)$$
and
$$6a_3 + 2P_0 a_2 + P_1 a_1 + Q_0 a_1 + Q_1 a_0 = 0 \qquad (3.29)$$
and
$$12a_4 + 3P_0 a_3 + 2P_1 a_2 + P_2 a_1 + Q_0 a_2 + Q_1 a_1 + Q_2 a_0 = 0 \qquad (3.30)$$
etc.

Equation (3.28) can be rearranged to determine a_2 in terms of a_1 and a_0 thus,

$$a_2 = -\tfrac{1}{2}P_0 a_1 - \tfrac{1}{2}Q_0 a_0 \qquad (3.31)$$

Substituting equation (3.31) into equation (3.29) and solving for a_3 in terms of a_1 and a_0 gives

$$a_3 = \tfrac{1}{6}(P_0^2 - P_1 - Q_0)a_1 + \tfrac{1}{6}(P_0 Q_0 - Q_1)a_0 \qquad (3.32)$$

By substituting equations (3.31) and (3.32) into equation (3.30), a_4 can be determined in terms of a_1 and a_0. This process can be continued indefinitely, and thus each a_n can be determined in terms of a_1 and a_0 only. Treating a_1 and a_0 as the two arbitrary constants, equation (3.26) together with equations (3.31), (3.32), etc., can be accepted as the complete solution of equation (3.23).

This method is only valid when $P(x)$ and $Q(x)$ can be expanded in series of ascending powers of x which have a radius of convergence R. If $P(x)$ and $Q(x)$ can be so expanded then the simple series method will give a series solution which is convergent within a radius R. The next example illustrates what happens when these convergence conditions are not satisfied.

$$\textit{Example 1.} \qquad 4x\frac{d^2y}{dx^2} + 6\frac{dy}{dx} + y = 0 \qquad\qquad \text{I}$$

$P(x)$ and $Q(x)$ in equation I cannot be expanded in a series of ascending powers of x without negative powers of x occurring. Nevertheless, put $y = \sum_0^\infty a_n x^n$ from equation (3.26) into equation I.

$$4x(2a_2+6a_3x+12a_4x^2+...) + 6(a_1+2a_2x+3a_3x^2+...) +$$
$$+(a_0+a_1x+a_2x^2+...) = 0$$

Equating coefficients of like powers of x,

$$6a_1+a_0 = 0 \qquad \therefore \quad a_1 = -a_0/6 \qquad\qquad \text{II}$$
$$8a_2+12a_2+a_1 = 0 \qquad \therefore \quad a_2 = -a_1/20$$
$$24a_3+18a_3+a_2 = 0 \qquad \therefore \quad a_3 = -a_2/42$$

etc.

In this example, the general coefficient of x^n gives

$$4n(n+1)a_{n+1}+6(n+1)a_{n+1}+a_n = 0 \qquad\qquad \text{III}$$
$$\therefore \quad (2n+2)(2n+3)a_{n+1}+a_n = 0$$

$$\therefore \quad \frac{a_{n+1}}{a_n} = \frac{-1}{(2n+3)(2n+2)} \qquad\qquad \text{IV}$$

Equation IV must be true for all $n \geqslant 0$. The result of equating coefficients of x^{n-1} can be obtained by replacing n in equation IV by $(n-1)$. Thus,

$$\frac{a_n}{a_{n-1}} = \frac{-1}{(2n+1)2n}$$

This process can be repeated n times until a_0 is reached in the equation

$$\frac{a_1}{a_0} = \frac{-1}{3.2}$$

which checks with the previous result, equation II. Multiplying the last set of $(n+1)$ equations together, and simplifying,

$$\frac{a_{n+1}}{a_0} = \frac{(-1)^{n+1}}{(2n+3)!}$$

alternatively,
$$a_n = \frac{(-1)^n a_0}{(2n+1)!}$$
V

The solution therefore takes the form,

$$y = \sum_0^\infty \frac{(-1)^n a_0}{(2n+1)!} x^n$$

$$= a_0 \left(1 - \frac{x}{3!} + \frac{x^2}{5!} - \frac{x^3}{7!} + \ldots\right)$$
VI

The alternating signs and odd factorials indicate a strong similarity between this series and the series (3.10) for sin z. Equation VI can be written

$$y = a_0 x^{-\frac{1}{2}} \left(x^{\frac{1}{2}} - \frac{(x^{\frac{1}{2}})^3}{3!} + \frac{(x^{\frac{1}{2}})^5}{5!} - \ldots\right)$$

$$= a_0 (\sin \sqrt{x})/\sqrt{x}$$
VII

But the method has given a solution containing only one arbitrary constant. Comparing equation II with the general equation (3.28), it can be seen that the term containing a_2 is absent due to the second derivative in equation I being multiplied by x. Thus equation II determines a_1 in terms of a_0 leaving a_0 as the only arbitrary constant, whereas equation (3.28) leaves both a_0 and a_1 as arbitrary constants.

The second solution may be found by using the method given in Section 2.5.2 because one part of the complementary function is now known; equation VII.

Put
$$y = v(\sin \sqrt{x})/\sqrt{x}$$
VIII

Differentiating twice,

$$\frac{dy}{dx} = \frac{\sin \sqrt{x}}{\sqrt{x}} \frac{dv}{dx} + \frac{v \cos \sqrt{x}}{2x} - \frac{v \sin \sqrt{x}}{2x\sqrt{x}}$$
IX

$$\frac{d^2 y}{dx^2} = \frac{\sin \sqrt{x}}{\sqrt{x}} \frac{d^2 v}{dx^2} + \frac{\sqrt{x} \cos \sqrt{x} - \sin \sqrt{x}}{x\sqrt{x}} \frac{dv}{dx} + \frac{v \sin \sqrt{x}}{4x^2 \sqrt{x}}(3-x) - \frac{3v \cos \sqrt{x}}{4x^2}$$
X

Substituting equations VIII, IX, and X into equation I and simplifying gives

$$2x \sin \sqrt{x} \frac{d^2 v}{dx^2} + (2\sqrt{x} \cos \sqrt{x} + \sin \sqrt{x})\frac{dv}{dx} = 0$$

which is an equation where the dependent variable does not occur explicitly. Solving by the method given for this type of equation in Section 2.4.1, gives the complete solution.

$$y = (A \sin \sqrt{x} + B \cos \sqrt{x})/\sqrt{x}$$
XI

The second part of the solution can also be expressed in series form by using equation (3.11), thus

$$y = B(x^{-\frac{1}{2}} - \tfrac{1}{2}x^{\frac{1}{2}} + \tfrac{1}{12}x^{3/2} - \ldots)$$
XII

It is now clear why the series method used so far does not give the complete solution of example 1, even though a series solution does exist. The fundamental series substitution (3.26) only allows positive integer powers of x, and if this restriction could be relaxed, a more general type of equation could be solved. In the above example, equation XII shows that the successive powers of x still increase by integers even though they are all fractional, and that this series can be represented by the previous series if the latter is multiplied by $x^{-\frac{1}{2}}$. This means that instead of the first term being a constant a_0, it is $a_0 x^{-\frac{1}{2}}$. The series substitution is therefore modified to include this type of series.

3.5. METHOD OF FROBENIUS

If the general second order differential equation can be expressed in the form

$$x^2 \frac{d^2 y}{dx^2} + xF(x)\frac{dy}{dx} + G(x)y = 0 \tag{3.33}$$

where

$$F(x) = F_0 + F_1 x + F_2 x^2 + \dots \tag{3.34}$$

and

$$G(x) = G_0 + G_1 x + G_2 x^2 + \dots \tag{3.35}$$

with equations (3.34) and (3.35) having a radius of convergence R; then the equation can be solved completely by the method of Frobenius in the form of a power series which is also convergent for $|x| < R$.

By comparing equations (3.33) and (3.23) it can be shown that equation (3.33) includes equation (3.23) as the special case $F_0 = G_0 = G_1 = 0$. The method of Frobenius will therefore always apply when the simple series method applies, but it will also solve equations which the simple method leaves unsolved. Thus, the simple series method has been superseded by the more powerful method of Frobenius.

In order to solve equation (3.33), put

$$y = \sum_0^\infty a_n x^{n+c} \qquad (a_0 \neq 0) \tag{3.36}$$

$$\therefore \quad \frac{dy}{dx} = \sum_0^\infty a_n(n+c)x^{n+c-1} \tag{3.37}$$

$$\therefore \quad \frac{d^2 y}{dx^2} = \sum_0^\infty a_n(n+c)(n+c-1)x^{n+c-2} \tag{3.38}$$

Substituting these equations into equation (3.33) gives

$$\sum a_n(n+c)(n+c-1)x^{n+c} + (F_0 + F_1 x + F_2 x^2 + \dots)\sum a_n(n+c)x^{n+c} +$$
$$+ (G_0 + G_1 x + G_2 x^2 + \dots)\sum a_n x^{n+c} = 0 \tag{3.39}$$

where the extra powers of x in equation (3.33) have been absorbed in the series for y and its derivatives.

The lowest power of x which appears in equation (3.39) is x^c, and co-efficients of x^c can therefore be equated, giving

$$a_0 c(c-1) + F_0 a_0 c + G_0 a_0 = 0$$

$$\therefore \quad c^2 + (F_0 - 1)c + G_0 = 0 \tag{3.40}$$

This quadratic equation for the index of the first term (c) is called the "indicial equation".

Equating the coefficients of the next power x^{c+1},

$$a_1(1+c)c + F_0 a_1(1+c) + F_1 a_0 c + G_0 a_1 + G_1 a_0 = 0$$

$$\therefore \quad a_1[(c+1)^2 + (F_0 - 1)(c+1) + G_0] + a_0(F_1 c + G_1) = 0 \tag{3.41}$$

which determines a_1 in terms of a_0 and c.

The coefficient of a_1 in equation (3.41) can be obtained from the left-hand side of equation (3.40) by replacing c by $(c+1)$. In general, the co-efficient of a_j in the equation obtained by equating coefficients of x^{c+j} can be obtained from equation (3.40) by replacing c by $(c+j)$. If the two roots of equation (3.40) are denoted by c_1 and c_2 and they differ by a positive integer j so that $c_2 = c_1 + j$; when the root $c = c_1$ is used, the coefficient of a_j on the first occasion that it appears will be zero by the above explanation since $(c_1 + j)$ satisfies equation (3.40). But this equation should determine a_j, which is impossible when a_j is not present in the equation. The method thus encounters difficulties if the roots of equation (3.40) differ by an integer.

The general solution cannot be considered further, since the methods diverge into four channels depending upon the properties of the roots of the indicial equation (3.40). The treatment of each case will now be pursued separately.

3.5.1. *Case I. Roots of Indicial Equation Different, but not by an Integer*

In this case, equation (3.41) determines a_1 in terms of a_0 and c. By equating coefficients of increasing powers of x as they appear in equation (3.39), all coefficients a_n can be determined in terms of a_0 and c. The two different values of c which are solutions of equation (3.40) each give rise to an independent series having its first coefficient as an arbitrary constant. The sum of these two series is the complete solution of equation (3.33) for this case.

Example 1. The example from the last section will be solved again, using the method of Frobenius.

$$4x \frac{d^2 y}{dx^2} + 6 \frac{dy}{dx} + y = 0$$

The series substitution (3.36) and its differentiated forms are

$$y = a_0 x^c + a_1 x^{c+1} + \ldots = \sum_0^\infty a_n x^{n+c}$$

$$\frac{dy}{dx} = a_0 c x^{c-1} + a_1(c+1)x^c + \ldots = \sum_0^\infty a_n(n+c)x^{n+c-1}$$

$$\frac{d^2y}{dx^2} = a_0 c(c-1)x^{c-2} + a_1(c+1)cx^{c-1} + \ldots = \sum_0^\infty a_n(n+c)(n+c-1)x^{n+c-2}$$

and these may be substituted into equation I to give

$$4[a_0 c(c-1)x^{c-1} + a_1(c+1)cx^c + \ldots] + 6[a_0 cx^{c-1} + a_1(c+1)x^c + \ldots] +$$
$$+ [a_0 x^c + a_1 x^{c+1} + \ldots] = 0 \qquad \text{II}$$

Equating coefficients of like powers of x, starting with the smallest x^{c-1},

$$\therefore \quad 4a_0 c(c-1) + 6a_0 c = 0 \qquad \text{III}$$
$$\therefore \quad 4a_1(c+1)c + 6a_1(c+1) + a_0 = 0 \qquad \text{IV}$$
$$\therefore \quad 4a_2(c+2)(c+1) + 6a_2(c+2) + a_1 = 0 \qquad \text{V}$$

and for the coefficient of x^{c+r},

$$4a_{r+1}(c+r+1)(c+r) + 6a_{r+1}(c+r+1) + a_r = 0 \qquad \text{VI}$$

The indicial equation III has the two roots

$$c = 0, \quad \text{or } c = -\tfrac{1}{2} \qquad \text{VII}$$

When $c = 0$, the series reduces to the previous simple series solution with constant first term and the subsequent algebra is identical. The first solution corresponding to $c = 0$ is thus

$$y_1 = a_0(\sin \sqrt{x})/\sqrt{x} \qquad \text{VIII}$$

However, when $c = -\tfrac{1}{2}$, equations IV and VI become $-a_1 + 3a_1 + a_0 = 0$
and $\qquad a_{r+1}(2r+1)(2r-1) + 3a_{r+1}(2r+1) + a_r = 0$
Rearranging,

$$\frac{a_{r+1}}{a_r} = \frac{-1}{(2r+1)(2r+2)}$$

similarly,

$$\frac{a_r}{a_{r-1}} = \frac{-1}{(2r-1)2r}$$

etc.

until

$$\frac{a_1}{a_0} = \frac{-1}{1.2}$$

Multiplying these equations together gives

$$a_r = \frac{(-1)^r a_0}{(2r+2)!} \qquad \text{IX}$$

Substituting into the general series gives the solution

$$y_2 = a_0 x^{-\frac{1}{2}}\left[1 - \frac{x}{2!} + \frac{x^2}{4!} - \ldots\right] = \sum_0^\infty \frac{(-1)^n a_0 x^{n-\frac{1}{2}}}{(2n+2)!}$$

$$\therefore \quad y_2 = a_0(\cos \sqrt{x})/\sqrt{x} \qquad \text{X}$$

The general solution of equation I is thus

$$y = (A \sin \sqrt{x} + B \cos \sqrt{x})/\sqrt{x} \qquad \text{XI}$$

The coefficient a_0 which appears in both equations VIII and X should be different in the two solutions which are independent. It is good practice to change both of these coefficients to new arbitrary constants as in equation XI.

Equation VI, which was obtained by equating coefficients of a general power of x, is called the "recurrence relation" because it enables any coefficient a_r to be determined in terms of the earlier coefficients in the series. When only two coefficients are involved in the recurrence relation it is a simple matter to find the general term such as equation IX, whereas when more than two are involved it is virtually impossible to develop an analytical expression for the general coefficient.

3.5.2. Case II. Roots of Indicial Equation Equal

The first part of the complementary function can be found by using the method described above, but only one series containing one arbitrary constant can be determined because the indicial equation has equal roots. The second solution can be found by assuming that the two roots are different and taking the limit as the second root approaches the first through variable values of c. The complete solution for different roots can be written

$$y = Au(x, c_1) + Bu(x, c_2)$$
$$= (A - B)u(x, c_1) + B[u(x, c_2) - u(x, c_1)]$$
$$= (A - B)u(x, c_1) + B(c_2 - c_1)\left[\frac{u(x, c_2) - u(x, c_1)}{c_2 - c_1}\right]$$

Redefining the arbitrary constants A and B, in terms of α and β,

$$y = \alpha u(x, c_1) + \beta \left[\frac{u(x, c_2) - u(x, c_1)}{c_2 - c_1}\right] \tag{3.42}$$

If the limit as $c_2 \to c_1$ is taken of equation (3.42), the term in square brackets becomes the partial derivative of u with respect to c and evaluated at $c = c_1$. The complete solution for the case of equal roots of the indicial equation is thus

$$y = \alpha u(x, c_1) + \beta \left(\frac{\partial u}{\partial c}\right)_{c = c_1} \tag{3.43}$$

An alternative derivation of equation (3.43) can be seen more clearly by considering the following example.

Example 2.

$$x\frac{d^2y}{dx^2} + (1 - x)\frac{dy}{dx} - y = 0 \qquad \text{I}$$

Put
$$y = \sum_0^\infty a_n x^{n+c} \tag{3.36}$$

and its differentiated forms (3.37) and (3.38) into equation I

$$\therefore \quad \sum_0^\infty a_n(n+c)(n+c-1)x^{n+c-1} + \sum_0^\infty a_n(n+c)x^{n+c-1} -$$

$$- \sum_0^\infty a_n(n+c)x^{n+c} - \sum_0^\infty a_n x^{n+c} = 0$$

Equate coefficients of x^{c-1} to obtain the indicial equation.

$$a_0 c(c-1) + a_0 c = 0 \qquad\qquad \text{II}$$

This has a double root, $c = 0$
Equate coefficients of x^c,

$$a_1(1+c)c + a_1(1+c) - a_0 c - a_0 = 0$$

$$\therefore \quad a_1(1+c)^2 = a_0(1+c)$$

$$\therefore \quad a_1 = a_0/(1+c) \qquad\qquad \text{III}$$

Equate coefficients of x^{c+r},

$$a_{r+1}(r+c+1)(r+c) + a_{r+1}(r+c+1) - a_r(r+c) - a_r = 0$$

$$\therefore \quad a_{r+1}(r+c+1)^2 = a_r(r+c+1)$$

Since r is a positive integer, and c is zero, $(r+c+1)$ cannot be zero for any value of r,

$$\therefore \quad a_{r+1} = a_r/(r+c+1) \qquad\qquad \text{IV}$$

Equation IV is the recurrence relation, and it is useful to derive equation III as a check on the algebraic derivation of equation IV.

By using the recurrence relation r times, the following expression can be obtained for the general term.

$$a_{r+1} = \frac{a_0}{(r+c+1)(r+c)(...)(c+1)}$$

or

$$a_n = \frac{a_0}{(n+c)(n+c-1)(...)(c+1)} \qquad\qquad \text{V}$$

The function $u(x,c)$ is now established by putting equation V into the general series (3.36).

$$u(x,c) = \sum_0^\infty \frac{a_0 x^{n+c}}{(n+c)(n+c-1)(...)(c+1)} \qquad\qquad \text{VI}$$

$$= a_0 x^c + \frac{a_0}{c+1} x^{c+1} + \frac{a_0}{(c+1)(c+2)} x^{c+2} + ...$$

When $c = 0$, $u(x,c)$ satisfies equation I and is the first solution,

$$y_1 = u(x,0) = a_0\left[1 + x + \frac{x^2}{2!} + \frac{x^3}{3!} + ...\right]$$

$$= a_0 e^x \qquad\qquad \text{VII}$$

To determine the second solution, substitute equation VI into the left-hand side of equation I.

$$\therefore \quad x\frac{d^2u}{dx^2} + (1-x)\frac{du}{dx} - u = a_0 c(c-1)x^{c-1} + a_0 cx^c + a_0 x^{c+1} + \ldots$$

$$+ a_0 cx^{c-1} + a_0 x^c + \frac{a_0}{c+1}x^{c+1} + \ldots$$

$$- a_0 cx^c - a_0 x^{c+1} - \frac{a_0}{c+1}x^{c+2} - \ldots$$

$$- a_0 x^c - \frac{a_0}{c+1}x^{c+1} - \frac{a_0}{(c+1)(c+2)}x^{c+2} - \ldots$$

$$= a_0 cx^{c-1}(c-1+1) + a_0 x^c(c+1-c-1) +$$

$$+ \frac{a_0}{c+1}x^{c+1}(c+1+1-c-1-1) + \ldots$$

$$= a_0 c^2 x^{c-1}$$

because all terms after the first are identically zero. This must necessarily be so because the terms in brackets are the recurrence relationships, and the first term is the left-hand side of the indicial equation II. The function $u(x,c)$ defined by equation VI thus satisfies the modified differential equation

$$x\frac{d^2u}{dx^2} + (1-x)\frac{du}{dx} - u = a_0 c^2 x^{c-1} \qquad \text{VIII}$$

Differentiating equation VIII partially with respect to c gives

$$x\frac{d^2}{dx^2}\left(\frac{\partial u}{\partial c}\right) + (1-x)\frac{d}{dx}\left(\frac{\partial u}{\partial c}\right) - \frac{\partial u}{\partial c} = a_0 c^2 x^{c-1}\ln x + 2a_0 cx^{c-1}$$

and taking the limit of the right-hand side of the equation as $c \to 0$,

$$x\frac{d^2}{dx^2}\left(\frac{\partial u}{\partial c}\right) + (1-x)\frac{d}{dx}\left(\frac{\partial u}{\partial c}\right) - \frac{\partial u}{\partial c} = 0$$

I.e. $y_2 = \partial u/\partial c$ also satisfies equation I when $c = 0$.

It has thus been shown in two alternative ways that the second solution of equation I is

$$y_2 = \frac{\partial}{\partial c}\left[a_0 \sum_0^\infty \frac{x^{n+c}}{(c+1)(c+2)(\ldots)(c+n)}\right]_{c=0} \qquad \text{IX}$$

The following two points of technique are useful in order to perform the required differentiation efficiently.

(i) $$x^{n+c} = e^{(n+c)\ln x} \qquad (3.44)$$

which may be verified by taking the logarithm of both sides.

(ii) If $$y = f_1(c) f_2(c) f_3(c)\ldots f_r(c) \qquad (3.45)$$

then $$\ln y = \ln f_1(c) + \ln f_2(c) + \ldots + \ln f_r(c)$$

Differentiating, and multiplying throughout by y,

$$\frac{dy}{dc} = y\left[\frac{f_1'(c)}{f_1(c)} + \frac{f_2'(c)}{f_2(c)} + \dots + \frac{f_r'(c)}{f_r(c)}\right] \tag{3.46}$$

where (') denotes differentiation with respect to c.

Continue the example by applying these principles to equation IX, taking $f_1(c) = 1/(c+1), \dots f_n(c) = 1/(c+n), f_{n+1}(c) = e^{(n+c)\ln x}$

$$\therefore \quad \frac{f_1'(c)}{f_1(c)} = \frac{-1}{c+1}, \quad \dots \frac{f_n'(c)}{f_n(c)} = \frac{-1}{c+n}, \quad \frac{f_{n+1}'(c)}{f_{n+1}(c)} = \ln x$$

$$\therefore \quad y_2 = \left[a_0\sum_0^\infty \frac{x^{n+c}}{(c+1)(c+2)(\dots)(c+n)}\left(\frac{-1}{c+1} - \frac{1}{c+2} - \dots - \frac{1}{c+n} + \ln x\right)\right]_{c=0}$$

$$= a_0\sum_0^\infty \frac{x^n}{n!}\ln x - a_0\sum_0^\infty \frac{x^n}{n!}\left(1 + \frac{1}{2} + \frac{1}{3} + \dots + \frac{1}{n}\right)$$

$$= a_0 e^x \ln x - a_0\sum_0^\infty \frac{x^n}{n!}\left(1 + \frac{1}{2} + \frac{1}{3} + \dots + \frac{1}{n}\right) \qquad\qquad \text{X}$$

Referring to equation VII, it can be seen that the second solution consists of the first solution multiplied by $\ln x$, added to a new series. This relationship always exists between the two solutions when the second solution is found by using the above method.

The complete solution of equation I is thus

$$y = Au(x, 0) + B(\partial u/\partial c)_{c=0}$$

$$= Ae^x + B\left[e^x \ln x - \sum_0^\infty \frac{x^n}{n!}\left(1 + \frac{1}{2} + \frac{1}{3} + \dots + \frac{1}{n}\right)\right] \qquad \text{XI}$$

3.5.3. *Case IIIa. Roots of Indicial Equation Differing by an Integer*

This case is very similar to Case II in that the second solution involves a partial differentiation with respect to c, thus generating a term $\ln x$. The function $u(x,c)$ has to be defined as before such that the recurrence relation is satisfied but not the indicial equation. The solution can be shown to take the form

$$y = Au(x, c_2) + B\frac{\partial}{\partial c}[(c - c_1)u(x, c)]_{c=c_1} \tag{3.47}$$

The reason for the above form of the second solution is best visualized by reference to an example.

Example 3

$$x(1-x)\frac{d^2y}{dx^2} + (2-5x)\frac{dy}{dx} - 4y = 0$$

With the usual series substitution (3.36) and following the same method as before, the indicial equation is

$$a_0 c(c-1) + 2a_0 c = 0 \qquad\qquad\qquad \text{II}$$

the first recurrence relation is

$$a_1(c+1) = a_0(c+2) \qquad\qquad \text{III}$$

and the general recurrence relation is

$$a_{r+1} = \frac{r+c+2}{r+c+1} a_r \qquad\qquad \text{IV}$$

The roots of the indicial equation are

$$c_1 = -1 \quad \text{or} \quad c_2 = 0.$$

As mentioned earlier in Section 3.5, when the roots of the indicial equation differ by an integer j, difficulties arise in the first recurrence relation in which a_j appears. In this example, $j = 1$, and equation III is the first equation in which a_1 occurs. When $c = 1$, equation III gives

$$a_1 0 = a_0$$

$$\therefore \quad a_1 = \infty$$

The series arising from $c = -1$ is thus of no value, but the series based on the larger root $c = 0$ is still valid. By successive use of the recurrence relation IV, the general term becomes

$$a_{r+1} = \frac{r+c+2}{c+1} a_0 \qquad\qquad \text{V}$$

and for the first solution with $c = 0$, this simplifies to

$$a_{r+1} = (r+2)a_0$$

$$\therefore \quad y_1 = a_0(1+2x+3x^2+...)$$

$$= a_0(1-x)^{-2} \qquad\qquad \text{VI}$$

by the binomial series (3.6).

Define the function $u(x,c)$ again, which satisfies the recurrence relation IV and its solution V, but not necessarily the indicial equation II.

$$u(x, c) = \sum_0^\infty \frac{n+c+1}{c+1} a_0 x^{n+c} \qquad\qquad \text{VII}$$

If this function is substituted into the left-hand side of the differential equation I, all terms cancel out as in Section 3.5.2 with the exception of the term identical with the indicial equation. Thus,

$$x(1-x)\frac{d^2u}{dx^2} + (2-5x)\frac{du}{dx} - 4u = a_0 c(c+1)x^{c-1} \qquad\qquad \text{VIII}$$

Whereas in example 2 the corresponding equation 2.VIII contained a squared term on the right-hand side, so that after differentiation a factor still remained in common with the indicial equation; here, this is not true of equation VIII. A similar behaviour can be obtained by artificially introducing a squared term into equation VIII by multiplying throughout by $(c+1)$. An alternative argument which determines the multiplying factor is available by inspection of equation VII. The factor $(c+1)$ makes $u(x,c)$ infinite, therefore transfer the awkward factor to the other side of the equation by multiplying throughout by it.

By a similar argument to that used in Section 3.5.2, it can be shown that the second solution takes the form

$$y_2 = \frac{\partial}{\partial c}\left[(c+1)u(x,c)\right]_{c=-1} \qquad \text{IX}$$

But, from equation VII

$$(c+1)u(x,c) = \sum_0^\infty (n+c+1)a_0 x^{n+c} \qquad \text{X}$$

$$\therefore \quad \frac{\partial}{\partial c}(c+1)u(x,c) = \sum_0^\infty a_0 x^{n+c}\left[(n+c+1)\ln x + 1\right]$$

$$\therefore \quad y_2 = a_0(\ln x)(1+2x+3x^2+...)+a_0(x^{-1}+1+x+...)$$

$$= \frac{a_0 \ln x}{(1-x)^2} + \frac{a_0}{x(1-x)} \qquad \text{XI}$$

Once again, the term multiplying $\ln x$ is the first solution. The complete solution of equation I is thus

$$y = \frac{A}{(1-x)^2} + \frac{B\ln x}{(1-x)^2} + \frac{B}{x(1-x)} \qquad \text{XII}$$

3.5.4. *Case IIIb. Roots of Indicial Equation Differing by an Integer*

There is just one further variation in the type of solution which can arise in the method of Frobenius. In the last example, equation III gave

$$a_1(c+1) = a_0(c+2)$$

and when $c = -1$, a_1 became infinite. Had the right-hand side also contained a factor $(c+1)$ this particular difficulty would not have arisen, equation III would have been automatically satisfied, and both parts of the solution would have 'been normal power series as in Case I. An example of this situation follows.

Example 4.

$$x\frac{d^2y}{dx^2} + (x-1)\frac{dy}{dx} - y = 0 \qquad \text{I}$$

With the usual series substitution (3.36) and following the same method as before, the indicial equation is

$$a_0 c(c-1) - a_0 c = 0 \qquad \text{II}$$

and the general recurrence relation is

$$a_{r+1}(r+c+1)(r+c-1) + a_r(r+c-1) = 0 \qquad \text{III}$$

Since the roots of equation II differ by 2, consider the first of equations III in which a_2 occurs. Viz.

$$a_2(c+2)c + a_1 c = 0 \qquad \text{IV}$$

When $c = 0$, the coefficient of a_2 in equation IV is zero as in Section 3.5.3, but both terms in equation IV are zero when $c = 0$, and a_2 remains indeterminate instead of infinite.

Therefore, if $c = 2$, equation III can be simplified by cancellation; but if $c = 0$, the term $(r+c-1)$ can only be cancelled if $r > 1$.

$$\therefore \quad a_{r+1}(r+c+1) = -a_r \quad \text{(unless } c = 0, \ r = 1) \qquad \text{V}$$

The first solution is given by $c = 2$, thus

$$a_{r+1}(r+3) = -a_r$$

and by successive substitution,

$$a_{r+1} = \frac{(-1)^{r+1} 2a_0}{(r+3)!}$$

$$\therefore \quad y_1 = \sum_0^\infty \frac{(-1)^n 2a_0}{(n+2)!} x^{n+2}$$

$$= 2a_0 \left(\frac{x^2}{2!} - \frac{x^3}{3!} + \frac{x^4}{4!} - \ldots \right)$$

$$= 2a_0(e^{-x} - 1 + x) \qquad \text{VI}$$

The second solution, when $c = 0$, becomes

$$y_2 = a_0 - a_0 x + a_2 x^2 - \frac{a_2 x^3}{3} + \frac{a_2 x^4}{3.4} - \ldots$$

$$= a_0(1-x) + 2a_2 \left(\frac{x^2}{2!} - \frac{x^3}{3!} + \frac{x^4}{4!} - \ldots \right)$$

$$= a_0(1-x) + 2a_2(e^{-x} - 1 + x) \qquad \text{VII}$$

All coefficients after the first two can be found in terms of a_2 and there are thus two arbitrary constants in the second solution making three in all. Inspection shows that the series associated with a_2 in equation VII is identical with the first solution as given by equation VI. One solution has thus been obtained twice, and in Case IIIb when a coefficient becomes indeterminate, the series obtained by using the smaller root is in fact the complete solution. The complete solution of equation I can therefore be written

$$y = A(. -x) + Be^{-x} \qquad \text{VIII}$$

where $A = a_0 - 2a_2$, and $B = 2a_2$ in equation VII.

3.5.5. Summary of the Method of Frobenius

The examples given above have been specially selected so that the series solutions could all be summed. The solutions can be checked quite easily by differentiation and substitution, thus demonstrating that the series method gives correct results. It must be emphasized that the methods of Chapter 2 should always be tried before resorting to the method of Frobenius. Too much time should not be devoted to trying to sum the series obtained because on many occasions the solution of problems of engineering importance will not be expressible in closed analytical form.

The method has only been described for expressing the solution as a series of powers of x. Solutions in powers of $(x-x_0)$ can also be obtained by moving the origin along the x axis to x_0 and then proceeding as before. The method will be applicable if the convergence conditions are satisfied at the new origin.

The differential equation

$$x^2\frac{d^2y}{dx^2} + xF(x)\frac{dy}{dx} + G(x)y = 0 \qquad (3.33)$$

can be solved by putting

$$y = \sum_0^\infty a_n x^{n+c} \qquad (a_0 \neq 0) \qquad (3.36)$$

if $F(x)$ and $G(x)$ can be expanded in a convergent series of non-negative powers of x for all $|x| < R$. The solution obtained will also be convergent for all $|x| < R$.

The indicial equation is found by equating the coefficients of the lowest power of x occurring in equation (3.33) after substituting equation (3.36). The recurrence relation is found by equating coefficients of x^{c+r} in the same equation. If the two roots of the indicial equation are $c = c_1$ and $c = c_2$ with $c_2 = c_1 + j$ and $j \geqslant 0$, then the following four cases arise.

Case I (j not an integer or zero). Two separate series of the form (3.36) are obtained, one for $c = c_1$ and the other for $c = c_2$. These two series added together with arbitrary constants give the complete solution.

Case II (j is zero). Define the function $u(x,c)$ which satisfies the recurrence relation but not necessarily the indicial equation. The solution then takes the form

$$y = Au(x, c_1) + B(\partial u/\partial c)_{c=c_1} \qquad (3.43)$$

Case IIIa (j is an integer). Find the first recurrence relation in which a_j appears. When $c = c_1$, the coefficient of a_j will be zero, and if the rest of the equation is not zero the solution takes the form

$$y = Au(x, c_2) + B\frac{\partial}{\partial c}[(c-c_1)u(x, c)]_{c=c_1} \qquad (3.47)$$

where $u(x,c)$ satisfies the recurrence relation but not necessarily the indicial equation.

Case IIIb (j is an integer). When $c = c_1$, the first recurrence relation in which a_j appears is identically zero leaving a_j indeterminate. The complete solution can be found in the form of equation (3.36) by putting $c = c_1$ when a_0 and a_j will be the two arbitrary constants.

3.5.6. *Illustrative Examples*

Example 5. Temperature Distribution in a Transverse Fin of Triangular Cross-section. The shape of the cooling fin is illustrated in Fig. 3.1 where the radius of the pipe (a) is 2 in, the radius of the rim of the fin (b) is 6 in, and the coordinate x (measured in feet) is measured inwards from the rim of the fin. There are two natural origins for the coordinate, but since the temperature distribution in the vicinity of the pipe axis is of no interest, the origin is taken on the rim instead. Assuming that the fin is thin, temperature

FIG. 3.1.   Transverse cooling fin

variations normal to the central plane of the fin will be neglected. The thermal conductivity of the fin (k) is 220 Btu/h ft² °F ft⁻¹, and the surface heat transfer coefficient (h) is 2 Btu/h ft² °F. Denoting temperature by T°F with T_A°F representing the air temperature, the heat balance can be taken as follows.
    The area available for heat conduction is

$$2\pi(b-x)(2x\tan\alpha) = 4\pi x(b-x)\tan\alpha \qquad\qquad \text{I}$$

Input $\qquad = -k4\pi x(b-x)\tan\alpha\dfrac{dT}{dx}$

Output $\qquad = -k4\pi x(b-x)\tan\alpha\dfrac{dT}{dx} + \dfrac{d}{dx}\left[-k4\pi x(b-x)\tan\alpha\dfrac{dT}{dx}\right]\delta x$

$\qquad\qquad + 2h2\pi(b-x)(\delta x\sec\alpha)(T-T_A)$

Accumulation $= 0$

Since Input $-$ Output $=$ Accumulation,

$$\frac{d}{dx}\left[k4\pi x(b-x)\tan\alpha\frac{dT}{dx}\right]\delta x - 2h2\pi(b-x)(\delta x\sec\alpha)(T-T_A) = 0$$

$$\therefore\quad k\sin\alpha\frac{d}{dx}\left[x(b-x)\frac{dT}{dx}\right] - h(b-x)(T-T_A) = 0 \qquad \text{II}$$

Putting $K = h/k\sin\alpha$, and $y = T-T_A$,

$$\therefore\quad x(b-x)\frac{d^2y}{dx^2} + (b-2x)\frac{dy}{dx} - K(b-x)y = 0 \qquad\qquad \text{III}$$

The appropriate boundary conditions are,

at $\qquad\qquad\qquad\qquad x=0, \quad y$ remains finite $\qquad\qquad\qquad$ IV

at $\qquad\qquad\qquad\qquad x=b-a, \qquad T=T_B$

$$\therefore\quad y = T_B - T_A \qquad\qquad\qquad\qquad\qquad\qquad \text{V}$$

where T_B is the temperature of the pipe contents.

Using the Frobenius substitutions (3.36), (3.37), and (3.38) in equation III gives

$$b \sum a_n(n+c)(n+c-1)x^{n+c-1} - \sum a_n(n+c)(n+c-1)x^{n+c} +$$
$$+ b \sum a_n(n+c)x^{n+c-1} - 2 \sum a_n(n+c)x^{n+c} - Kb \sum a_n x^{n+c} +$$
$$+ K \sum a_n x^{n+c+1} = 0 \qquad\qquad \text{VI}$$

The indicial equation obtained by equating coefficients of x^{c-1}, is

$$ba_0 c(c-1) + ba_0 c = 0 \qquad\qquad \text{VII}$$
$$\therefore \quad c^2 = 0$$

Equation III thus gives a Case II solution with equal roots. With the knowledge that the second solution will contain $\ln x$ which becomes infinite when $x = 0$ violating boundary condition IV, it may be concluded that the second solution has no physical significance in this example. Therefore it is only necessary to find the first solution with $c = 0$ and the remaining work can be simplified by omitting c.

Equating coefficients of the next power of x which is x^c,

$$ba_1 - Kba_0 = 0$$
$$\therefore \quad a_1 = Ka_0 \qquad\qquad \text{VIII}$$

The recurrence relation is

$$ba_{r+1}(r+1)r - a_r r(r-1) + ba_{r+1}(r+1) - 2a_r r - Kba_r + Ka_{r-1} = 0$$
$$\therefore \quad ba_{r+1}(r+1)^2 = a_r[r(r+1) + Kb] - Ka_{r-1} \qquad\qquad \text{IX}$$

This recurrence relation is different from all previous ones since it relates three of the original coefficients a_{r+1}, a_r, and a_{r-1}. It is thus difficult to determine a general formula for a_r in terms of a_0, although a solution may be possible by the methods of Chapter 9. Unless such a solution is possible, the second part of the complementary function in this example of equal roots cannot be found by the method of Section 3.5.3 even if it is required. The appropriate first solution can be found however on a term by term basis. Introducing the numerical values given in the problem, together with $T_A = 60$, $T_B = 212$, and $\alpha = 5°$ gives

$$K = 2/220 \times 0.0872 = 0.1043.$$

Equations VIII and IX become

$$a_1 = 0.1043a_0$$
$$a_{r+1}(r+1)^2 = a_r[2r(r+1) + 0.1043] - 0.2086a_{r-1} \qquad\qquad \text{X}$$
$$\therefore \quad a_2(2)^2 = 0.1043a_0(4.1043) - 0.2086a_0$$
$$= 0.2195a_0$$
$$\therefore \quad a_2 = 0.0549a_0$$

Using equation X again,

$$a_3(3)^2 = 0.0549a_0(12.1043) - 0.2086 \times 0.1043a_0$$
$$= 0.6424a_0$$
$$\therefore \quad a_3 = 0.0714a_0$$

etc.

It can be seen that the most important terms in equation X are the first two, and the later behaviour of the series will approximate to

$$a_{r+1}(r+1)^2 = 2a_r r(r+1)$$

$$\therefore \quad a_{r+1} = \frac{2r}{r+1} a_r \qquad \qquad \text{XI}$$

By Section 3.3, this approximate series has a radius of convergence of $\frac{1}{2}$ in agreement with the general statement of the convergence conditions related to equation (3.33). Because the fin is defined to occupy the range $0 \leqslant x \leqslant \frac{1}{3}$, the series solution is convergent throughout the fin.

Evaluating further coefficients from equation X gives

$$y = a_0(1+0\cdot1043x+0\cdot0549x^2+0\cdot0714x^3+0\cdot1068x^4+$$
$$+0\cdot171x^5+0\cdot285x^6+0\cdot488x^7+...) \qquad \text{XII}$$

Boundary condition V becomes;

at $\qquad \qquad \qquad x = \frac{1}{3}, \qquad y = 212-60 = 152$

$$\therefore \quad 152 = a_0(1+0\cdot0348+0\cdot0061+0\cdot0026+0\cdot0013+0\cdot0007+0\cdot0004)$$

$$\therefore \quad a_0 = 152/1\cdot0459 = 145\cdot3 \qquad \qquad \text{XIII}$$

Equation XII gives the temperature distribution throughout the fin, and equation XIII shows that the rim temperature is $205\cdot3°F$.

The rate of removal of heat by the fin can be calculated from the temperature gradient at the base. Thus

$$Q = k4\pi(b-a)a \tan \alpha \, (dT/dx)_{x=b-a}$$
$$= 1344(dT/dx)_{x=1/3}$$
$$= 1344(0\cdot1043+0\cdot0366+0\cdot0238+0\cdot0158+0\cdot0106+0\cdot0070+0\cdot0047+...)$$
$$= 285 \text{ Btu/h}$$

by differentiating equation XII, and using equation XI to estimate the continuation of the series to infinity.

Example 6. Tubular Gas Preheater. A supply of hot air is to be obtained by drawing cool air through a heated cylindrical pipe. The pipe is 4 in diameter and 4 ft long, and is maintained at a temperature $T_w = 600°F$ throughout its length. The properties of the air are:

Specific heat (C_p) $\qquad = 0\cdot24$ Btu/lb °F
Thermal conductivity $(k) = 0\cdot020$ Btu/h ft² °F ft^{-1}
Density (ρ) $\qquad \qquad = 0\cdot050$ lb/ft³
Flow rate (u) $\qquad \quad = 1000$ ft³/h
(the above are all mean values)
Inlet temperature $\qquad = 70°F$.

Overall heat transfer coefficient $(h) = 5x^{-\frac{1}{2}}$ Btu/h ft² °F where x is the distance measured in feet from the pipe inlet.

Assuming that heat transfer takes place by conduction within the gas in an axial direction, mass flow of the gas in an axial direction, and by the above variable heat transfer coefficient from the walls of the tube, find the temperature of the exit gas.

Solution

With the symbols given above, and illustrated in Fig. 3.2, the following heat balance can be established.

FIG. 3.2.   Gas preheater

	Input	Output
By conduction	$-kA\dfrac{dT}{dx}$	$-kA\dfrac{dT}{dx}+\dfrac{d}{dx}\left(-kA\dfrac{dT}{dx}\right)\delta x$
By mass flow	$u\rho C_p T$	$u\rho C_p\left(T+\dfrac{dT}{dx}\delta x\right)$
Wall heat transfer	$\pi dh(T_w-T)\,\delta x$	—

where A is the cross-sectional area of the pipe, and d its diameter. Since in steady state the accumulation is zero,

$$-kA\frac{dT}{dx}+u\rho C_p T+\pi dh(T_w-T)\,\delta x$$

$$=-kA\frac{dT}{dx}+\frac{d}{dx}\left(-kA\frac{dT}{dx}\right)\delta x+u\rho C_p\left(T+\frac{dT}{dx}\delta x\right)$$

$$\therefore\quad \pi dh(T_w-T)=-kA\frac{d^2T}{dx^2}+u\rho C_p\frac{dT}{dx} \qquad\qquad \text{I}$$

Rearranging,

$$\frac{d^2T}{dx^2}-\frac{u\rho C_p}{kA}\frac{dT}{dx}+\frac{\pi dh}{kA}(T_w-T)=0 \qquad\qquad \text{II}$$

Putting $t=T_w-T$,

$$\frac{d^2t}{dx^2}-\frac{u\rho C_p}{kA}\frac{dt}{dx}-\frac{4h}{kd}t=0 \qquad\qquad \text{III}$$

Inserting the numerical values,

$$\frac{d^2t}{dx^2}-6880\frac{dt}{dx}-3000x^{-\frac12}t=0 \qquad\qquad \text{IV}$$

Put $x = z^2$ to rationalize the coefficient of t,

$$\therefore \quad z\frac{d^2t}{dz^2} - (1+13760z^2)\frac{dt}{dz} - 12\,000z^2t = 0 \qquad \text{V}$$

If an attempt is made to solve this equation by the method of Frobenius, the results for the first few terms are,

$$c = 0 \quad \text{or 2 from the indicial equation}$$

Taking $$c = 2$$

$$a_1 = 0 \qquad\qquad a_3 = 800a_0$$

$$a_2 = 3440a_0 \qquad a_4 = 7{\cdot}9 \times 10^6 a_0$$

The coefficients are increasing at an alarming rate, yet a test of equation V shows that the series must be convergent. This is a case mentioned earlier where a convergent series is of no practical value since more than 100 terms would have to be calculated to determine even the first solution. The trouble arises because two of the coefficients in equation IV are much larger than the coefficient of d^2t/dx^2. The second derivative arises from the gas conduction term and if this is neglected, equation IV becomes

$$\frac{dt}{dx} + 0{\cdot}436x^{-\frac{1}{2}}t = 0 \qquad \text{VI}$$

which can be solved by separating the variables. Viz.

$$t = \alpha \exp\left(-0{\cdot}872x^{\frac{1}{2}}\right) \qquad \text{VII}$$

The boundary condition at $x = 0$, is $t = 600 - 70 = 530$.

$$\therefore \quad t = 530\exp\left(-0{\cdot}872x^{\frac{1}{2}}\right) \qquad \text{VIII}$$

$$\therefore \quad T = 600 - 530\exp\left(-0{\cdot}872x^{\frac{1}{2}}\right)$$

The exit gas temperature is therefore 507°F.

The approximation of neglecting the second differential term in equation IV can be checked by comparing the neglected term with one of the other terms. Differentiating VIII twice gives

$$\frac{dt}{dx} = -231{\cdot}1x^{-\frac{1}{2}}\exp\left(-0{\cdot}872x^{\frac{1}{2}}\right)$$

$$\frac{d^2t}{dx^2} = 231{\cdot}1(\tfrac{1}{2}x^{-3/2}+0{\cdot}436x^{-1})\exp\left(-0{\cdot}872x^{\frac{1}{2}}\right)$$

$$\therefore \quad \frac{d^2t}{dx^2}\bigg/6880\frac{dt}{dx} = \frac{\tfrac{1}{2}x^{-3/2}-0{\cdot}436x^{-1}}{6880x^{-\frac{1}{2}}}$$

$$= \frac{1}{13760x} + \frac{1}{15780x^{\frac{1}{2}}}$$

which is small except when x is small.

If $x = 10^{-3}$, the error ratio $= 7\tfrac{1}{2}\%$.

The error has thus been made over a negligible part of the pipe and this justifies the above result.

3.6. BESSEL'S EQUATION

The differential equation

$$x^2\frac{d^2y}{dx^2} + x\frac{dy}{dx} + (x^2 - k^2)y = 0 \tag{3.48}$$

is known as Bessel's equation of order k, where k is a positive or zero constant. This equation arises so frequently in practical problems that it has been studied in great detail and this section will be devoted to giving an outline of the derivation of the various solutions by using the method of Frobenius. Because the equation occurs so frequently, the series solutions have been standardized and tabulated† thus eliminating the necessity of working through the series solution for each individual problem. Many other second order differential equations can be reduced to Bessel's equation (3.48) by a suitable substitution, and they too can then be solved by using the standard tables.

Applying the method of Frobenius by putting

$$y = \sum_0^\infty a_n x^{n+c} \tag{3.36}$$

and its differential forms (3.37) and (3.38) into equation (3.48).

$$\sum_0^\infty a_n(n+c)(n+c-1)x^{n+c} + \sum_0^\infty a_n(n+c)x^{n+c} + (x^2-k^2)\sum_0^\infty a_n x^{n+c} = 0$$

The indicial equation is

$$a_0 c(c-1) + a_0 c - k^2 a_0 = 0$$

which has the two roots

$$c = k \text{ or } -k \tag{3.49}$$

The difference between the roots is thus $2k$, and the type of solution will depend upon the nature of k.

Equating coefficients of x^{c+1},

$$a_1(c+1)c + a_1(c+1) - k^2 a_1 = 0$$

$$\therefore \quad a_1(c+1+k)(c+1-k) = 0 \tag{3.50}$$

Because $c = \pm k$, and $k \geqslant 0$, then $c+1+k > 0$, but for the special case $k = \frac{1}{2}$, $c = -\frac{1}{2}$, $c+1-k = 0$. Therefore,

unless $\qquad k = \frac{1}{2}$ and $c = -\frac{1}{2}$, $\qquad a_1 = 0 \tag{3.51}$

The recurrence relation is obtained by equating coefficients of x^{c+r}.

$$a_r(r+c)(r+c-1) + a_r(r+c) - k^2 a_r + a_{r-2} = 0$$

$$\therefore \quad a_r(r+c)^2 - a_r k^2 = -a_{r-2} \tag{3.52}$$

$$\therefore \quad a_r = \frac{-a_{r-2}}{(r+c+k)(r+c-k)} \tag{3.53}$$

---

† For example, Jahnke and Emde, "Tables of Functions with Formulae and Curves," Dover Publications, New York. Or Watson, "Theory of Bessel Functions," Cambridge University Press (1922).

The first solution for $c = k$, will be normal in all cases and the recurrence relation becomes

$$a_r = \frac{-a_{r-2}}{r(r+2k)} \qquad (3.54)$$

Combining equations (3.51) and (3.53) gives

$$a_1 = a_3 = a_5 = \ldots = 0 \qquad (3.55)$$

and r can be replaced by $2m$ in the recurrence relation (3.54)

$$a_{2m} = \frac{-a_{2m-2}}{2m(2m+2k)}$$

Replacing m by $(m-1)$, $(m-2)$, etc., and making successive substitutions as before,

$$a_{2m} = \frac{(-1)^m a_0}{2^{2m} m!(m+k)(m+k-1)(\ldots)(k+1)}$$

$$= \frac{(-\tfrac{1}{4})^m a_0 \Gamma(k+1)}{m!\Gamma(m+k+1)}$$

where $\Gamma(k+1)$ is the Gamma function or generalized factorial whose properties will be discussed in Chapter 5.

The first solution of Bessel's equation is thus

$$y_1 = 2^k \Gamma(k+1)a_0 \sum_{m=0}^{\infty} \frac{(-1)^m(\tfrac{1}{2}x)^{2m+k}}{m!\Gamma(m+k+1)}$$

The Bessel function of the first kind of order k is defined as

$$J_k(x) = \sum_{m=0}^{\infty} \frac{(-1)^m(\tfrac{1}{2}x)^{2m+k}}{m!\Gamma(m+k+1)} \qquad (3.56)$$

Defining a new arbitrary constant, the first solution of equation (3.48) is thus

$$y_1 = AJ_k(x) \qquad (3.57)$$

The form of the second solution, for $c = -k$, depends on whether or not $2k$ is an integer, and the method of solution diverges into four channels corresponding with the cases of the method of Frobenius.

3.6.1. Case I ($2k$ is not an integer or zero)

In this case, the second solution is obtained from the first by replacing k in equation (3.56) by $-k$, giving the complete solution

$$y = AJ_k(x) + BJ_{-k}(x) \qquad (3.58)$$

3.6.2. Case II ($k = 0$)

Returning to the recurrence relation (3.53) and putting $k = 0$,

$$a_r = \frac{-a_{r-2}}{(r+c)^2}$$

Since $a_1 = 0$ from equation (3.51), r can be replaced by $2m$ again and the expression for the coefficient of the general term is

$$a_{2m} = \frac{(-1)^m a_0}{(2m+c)^2 (2m+c-2)^2 (...)(c+2)^2}$$

Defining $u(x,c)$ as given in Section 3.5.2,

$$u(x,c) = \sum_{m=0}^{\infty} \frac{(-1)^m a_0 x^{2m+c}}{(2m+c)^2 (2m+c-2)^2 (...)(c+2)^2} \tag{3.59}$$

Differentiating equation (3.59) with respect to c and putting $c = 0$ gives the second solution,

$$y_2 = \sum_{m=0}^{\infty} \frac{(-1)^m a_0 (\tfrac{1}{2}x)^{2m}}{(m!)^2} \left[\ln x - 1 - \frac{1}{2} - \frac{1}{3} - ... - \frac{1}{m} \right]$$

$$= a_0 \left[J_0(x) \ln x - \sum_{m=1}^{\infty} \frac{(-1)^m (\tfrac{1}{2}x)^{2m}}{(m!)^2} \left(1 + \frac{1}{2} + ... + \frac{1}{m} \right) \right]$$

The expression in brackets is the Neumann form of the second solution, but an alternative form named after Weber is more frequently used. The Weber form is obtained by adding $(\gamma - \ln 2) J_0(x)$ to the Neumann form and multiplying the result by $(2/\pi)$. Thus

$$y_2 = BY_0(x)$$

where

$$Y_0(x) = \frac{2}{\pi} [\ln(\tfrac{1}{2}x) + \gamma] J_0(x) - \frac{2}{\pi} \sum_{m=1}^{\infty} \frac{(-1)^m (\tfrac{1}{2}x)^{2m}}{(m!)^2} \left(1 + \frac{1}{2} + ... + \frac{1}{m} \right)$$

is the Weber form of the Bessel function of the second kind of order zero, and γ is Euler's constant which is defined by

$$\gamma = \lim_{m \to \infty} \left(1 + \frac{1}{2} + \frac{1}{3} + ... + \frac{1}{m} - \ln m \right) = 0{\cdot}5772...$$

The complete solution of equation (3.48) with $k = 0$ is thus

$$y = AJ_0(x) + BY_0(x) \tag{3.60}$$

3.6.3. *Case IIIa* (k *is an integer*)

2k is an even integer and the first recurrence relation in which a_{2k} appears is, from equation (3.52),

$$a_{2k}(2k+c)^2 - a_{2k} k^2 = -a_{2k-2}$$

or $$a_{2k}(k+c)(3k+c) = -a_{2k-2}$$

When $c = -k$, the left-hand side is zero but the right-hand side is not zero because a_{2k-2} is an even coefficient. The method for Case IIIa given in Section 3.5.4 must therefore be followed.

The eventual solution using

$$y_2 = \frac{\partial}{\partial c}[(c+k)u(x,c)]_{c=-k}$$

is

$$y_2 = BY_k(x) = \frac{2}{\pi}B[\ln\tfrac{1}{2}x+\gamma]J_k(x) - \frac{B}{\pi}\sum_{m=0}^{k-1}\frac{(k-m-1)!}{m!}(\tfrac{1}{2}x)^{2m-k} -$$

$$-\frac{B}{\pi}\sum_{m=0}^{\infty}\frac{(-1)^m(\tfrac{1}{2}x)^{2m+k}}{m!(m+k)!}\left[1+\frac{1}{2}+\ldots+\frac{1}{m}+1+\frac{1}{2}+\ldots\frac{1}{m+k}\right]$$

where γ is again Euler's constant, and the Weber form has been found by adding $a_0(\gamma-\ln 2)J_k(x)$ to the Neumann form and multiplying by $(2/\pi)$. $Y_k(x)$ is the Weber form of the Bessel function of the second kind of order k.

The complete solution of equation (3.48) is thus

$$y = AJ_k(x)+BY_k(x) \tag{3.61}$$

when k is an integer.

3.6.4. *Case IIIb* (2k is an odd integer)

The first recurrence relation in which a_{2k} appears is, from equation (3.52),

$$a_{2k}(k+c)(3k+c) = -a_{2k-2} \tag{3.62}$$

When $c = -k$, the left-hand side is zero, but the right-hand side is an odd coefficient and in all cases considered so far, the odd coefficients have been zero. This must now be investigated further. If $k = \tfrac{1}{2}$, equation (3.50) shows that a_1, the critical coefficient, is indeterminate and the solution follows Case IIIb giving two normal power series. If $k = 3/2$, the critical recurrence relation (3.62) becomes

$$a_3(\tfrac{3}{2}+c)(\tfrac{9}{2}+c) = -a_1$$

and since $a_1 = 0$, a_0 is indeterminate. Continuing this argument, a_{2k} will always be indeterminate if $2k$ is odd, and the solution again consists of two normal series.

$$y = AJ_k(x)+BJ_{-k}(x) \tag{3.63}$$

The general solution of Bessel's equation (3.48) can therefore be written

$$y = AJ_k(x)+BJ_{-k}(x) \tag{3.58, 63}$$

if k is not an integer or zero, or

$$y = AJ_k(x)+BY_k(x) \tag{3.60, 61}$$

if k is an integer or zero.

Examples of the use of the above Bessel functions occur quite frequently in chemical engineering when the problem involves partial differential equations, but their use in ordinary differential equations is rare in chemical engineering but more frequent in other branches of engineering. Rather than present an irrelevant example at this point, the reader is referred to Example 3 in Section 8.7.5 and Section 8.7.3, where the above solutions form one stage in the solution of certain partial differential equations.

3.6.5. *Modified Bessel's Equation*

Bessel's equation (3.48) has now been solved for all real values of x, and the solution given as the sum of two linearly independent functions of x each multiplied by an arbitrary constant. Two kinds of Bessel function have been defined both of which are needed to express the solution if k is an integer or zero, but two versions of only the first kind if k is not an integer or zero.

A further type of differential equation can be solved with the aid of Bessel functions; it is

$$x^2 \frac{d^2 y}{dx^2} + x \frac{dy}{dx} - (x^2 + k^2)y = 0 \qquad (3.64)$$

Equation (3.64) can be obtained from Bessel's equation (3.48) by replacing x with ix where $i = \sqrt{(-1)}$. The solution of equation (3.64) can thus be written

$$y = AJ_k(ix) + BJ_{-k}(ix) \qquad (3.65)$$

if k is not an integer or zero, or

$$y = AJ_k(ix) + BY_k(ix) \qquad (3.66)$$

if k is an integer or zero.

In Section 2.5.2 it was found that the solution of the second order linear differential equation with constant coefficients could be expressed more conveniently in terms of real trigonometric functions than complex exponential functions when the auxiliary equation had complex roots. Here, instead of using the Bessel functions of a complex variable, it is similarly convenient to define modified Bessel functions of a real variable so that the above solutions can be expressed in real form. The necessary definitions are

$$I_k(x) = e^{-\frac{1}{2}k\pi i} J_k(ix) \qquad (3.67)$$

$$= \sum_{m=0}^{\infty} \frac{(\frac{1}{2}x)^{2m+k}}{m!\,\Gamma(m+k+1)}$$

$$K_k(x) = e^{\frac{1}{2}(k+1)\pi i} \left[J_k(ix) + iY_k(ix) \right] \qquad (3.68)$$

$$= (-1)^{k+1} \left[\ln\left(\tfrac{1}{2}x\right) + \gamma \right] I_k(x) + \tfrac{1}{2} \sum_{m=0}^{k-1} \frac{(-1)^m (k-m-1)!}{m!} \left(\tfrac{1}{2}x\right)^{2m-k}$$

$$+ \tfrac{1}{2} \sum_{m=0}^{\infty} \frac{(-1)^k (\tfrac{1}{2}x)^{2m+k}}{m!(m+k)!} \left[1 + \frac{1}{2} + \dots + \frac{1}{m} + 1 + \frac{1}{2} + \dots + \frac{1}{m+k} \right]$$

The solution of equation (3.64) is thus

$$y = AI_k(x) + BI_{-k}(x) \qquad (3.69)$$

if k is not an integer or zero, or

$$y = AI_k(x) + BK_k(x) \qquad (3.70)$$

if k is an integer or zero.

$I_k(x)$ is called the modified Bessel function of the first kind of order k, and $K_k(x)$ is the modified Bessel function of the second kind of order k.

Example. Heat Loss Through Pipe Flanges. Two thin wall metal pipes of 1 in external diameter and joined by flanges $\frac{1}{2}$ in thick and 4 in diameter, are carrying steam at 250°F. If the conductivity of the flange metal $k = 220$ Btu/h ft^2 °F ft^{-1} and the exposed surfaces of the flanges lose heat to the surroundings at $T_1 = 60$°F according to a heat transfer coefficient $h = 2$ Btu/h ft^2 °F, find the rate of heat loss from the pipe, and the proportion which leaves the rim of the flange.

Solution. It is only necessary to consider one flange with one exposed circular face and an exposed rim. Because all dimensions are in inches, it is more convenient to use inches instead of feet for the length dimension, therefore take a radial co-ordinate r measured in inches from the axis of the pipe and consider the heat balance over an element of width δr, as shown in Fig. 3.3.

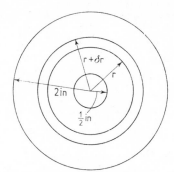

FIG. 3.3. Pipe flange

Input
$$= -2\pi\tfrac{1}{2}r\frac{k}{12}\frac{dT}{dr} = -\frac{\pi kr}{12}\frac{dT}{dr}$$

Output
$$= -\frac{\pi kr}{12}\frac{dT}{dr} + \frac{d}{dr}\left[-\frac{\pi kr}{12}\frac{dT}{dr}\right]\delta r + \frac{2\pi rh\,\delta r}{144}(T - T_1)$$

Accumulation $= 0$

The factors 12, and 144 are necessary because k and h are defined in terms of feet.

Simplification of the heat balance gives

$$r\frac{d^2T}{dr^2} + \frac{dT}{dr} - \frac{h}{6k}r(T - T_1) = 0 \qquad\qquad \text{I}$$

Putting $y = T - T_1$, and $x = r\sqrt{(h/6k)}$ gives the standard form of the equation,

$$x^2\frac{d^2y}{dx^2} + x\frac{dy}{dx} - x^2y = 0 \qquad\qquad \text{II}$$

Comparison with equation (3.64) shows that equation II is a modified Bessel equation of zero order. According to equation (3.70) the solution is thus

$$y = AI_0(x) + BK_0(x) \qquad \text{III}$$

The boundary conditions are,

at $\qquad\qquad\qquad r = \tfrac{1}{2}, \qquad T = 250 \qquad\qquad\qquad \text{IV}$

and at $\qquad\qquad r = 2, \qquad -\dfrac{k}{12}\dfrac{dT}{dr} = \dfrac{h}{144}(T - T_1) \qquad \text{V}$

where equation V states that the heat conducted through the metal to the rim must equal the heat lost from the rim surface to the surrounding air.

Changing the variables, and introducing the numerical values, equations IV and V become

at $\qquad\qquad\qquad x = 0\cdot0195, \qquad y = 190 \qquad\qquad \text{VI}$

and at $\qquad\qquad x = 0\cdot078, \qquad \dfrac{dy}{dx} = -0\cdot0195y \qquad\qquad \text{VII}$

Differentiating equation III, and using the properties (3.90), (3.91), (3.99), and (3.100), listed at the end of this chapter,

$$\frac{dy}{dx} = AI_1(x) - BK_1(x) \qquad \text{VIII}$$

Substituting equations VIII and III into equation VII gives

$$AI_1(0\cdot078) - BK_1(0\cdot078) = -0\cdot0195[AI_0(0\cdot078) + BK_0(0\cdot078)] \qquad \text{IX}$$

and substituting equation III into equation VI gives

$$AI_0(0\cdot0195) + BK_0(0\cdot0195) = 190 \qquad \text{X}$$

Finding the values of the various Bessel functions from tables† and solving equations IX and X gives

$$A = 186\cdot5, \qquad B = 0\cdot8636$$

Putting these values into equation III and reverting to the original variables gives the temperature distribution

$$T = 60 + 186\cdot5I_0(0\cdot039r) + 0\cdot8636K_0(0\cdot039r) \qquad \text{XI}$$

The heat conducted from the pipe by the flange is given by

$$\begin{aligned} Q_1 &= -\frac{\pi k}{24}\left(\frac{dT}{dr}\right)_{r=\frac{1}{2}} \\ &= 1\cdot127[BK_1(0\cdot0195) - AI_1(0\cdot0195)] \\ &= 47\cdot81\,\text{Btu/h} \end{aligned}$$

and the heat lost through the rim is given by

$$Q_2 = -\frac{\pi k}{6}\left(\frac{dT}{dr}\right)_{r=2}$$

† "British Association Mathematical Tables," Vol. VI. Cambridge University Press (1937).

$$= 4 \cdot 507 \left[BK_1(0 \cdot 078) - AI_1(0 \cdot 078) \right]$$

$$= 16 \cdot 62 \, \text{Btu/h}$$

Therefore, the pipe loses $47 \cdot 8$ Btu/h through each flange, and 35% of this is lost through the rim.

The above problem is similar to the problem of a flat circular cooling fin, which has been solved by Gardner† who presents solutions in the form of Bessel functions for the efficiencies of a variety of shapes of extended cooling surfaces.

3.7. Properties of Bessel Functions

Just as trigonometric functions have well known properties and relationships, so do Bessel functions, although these are not so widely known. Only a few of the more useful properties will be listed here, and the reader is referred to any of the specialized books on Bessel functions given at the end of the chapter, for a more comprehensive list. The formulae will be given in sections on limiting behaviour, differential properties, and integral properties.

3.7.1. *Behaviour Near the Origin*

As $x \to 0$, the Bessel function tends to the same limit as its leading term. $J_k(x)$ and $I_k(x)$ start at x^k and are therefore zero when x is zero for $k > 0$. Therefore,

when $\qquad k = 0, \qquad J_0(0) = I_0(0) = 1 \qquad\qquad (3.71)$

when $\qquad k > 0, \qquad \begin{cases} J_k(0) = I_k(0) = 0 & (3.72) \\ J_{-k}(0) = \pm I_{-k}(0) = \pm \infty & (3.73) \end{cases}$

The ambiguous sign is resolved in any particular case by reference to equations (3.56) or (3.67) where the sign is determined by the sign of $\Gamma(k+1)$ given in Section 5.3. In all physical cases, if $x = 0$ is a point in the system, no physical property can be infinite and the part of the solution containing $J_{-k}(x)$ or $I_{-k}(x)$ must be eliminated anyway. The above physical argument also applies to $Y_k(x)$ and $K_k(x)$ which are both infinite at the origin for all values of k. If k is not zero, the infinity is due to a negative power of x; if k is zero, the infinity is due to the term $\ln x$. Therefore, for all values of k,

$$- Y_k(0) = K_k(0) = \infty \qquad\qquad (3.74)$$

If the origin is a point in the calculation field, then $J_k(x)$ and $I_k(x)$ are the only physically permissible solutions.

3.7.2. *Asymptotic Behaviour for Large x*

If $x \gg k$, then the term k^2 in Bessel's equation (3.48) can be neglected in comparison with x^2 in the last term. Equation (3.48) becomes

$$x^2 \frac{d^2 d}{dx^2} + x \frac{dy}{dx} + x^2 y = 0 \qquad\qquad (3.75)$$

† Gardner, K. A. *Trans. A.S.M.E.* **67**, 621 (1945).

A substitution suggested by the first two terms is

$$z = x^{\frac{1}{2}}y \tag{3.76}$$

$$\therefore \quad \frac{dz}{dx} = x^{\frac{1}{2}}\frac{dy}{dx} + \frac{1}{2}x^{-\frac{1}{2}}y$$

$$\therefore \quad \frac{d^2z}{dx^2} = x^{\frac{1}{2}}\frac{d^2y}{dx^2} + x^{-\frac{1}{2}}\frac{dy}{dx} - \frac{1}{4}x^{-3/2}y$$

$$\therefore \quad x^{3/2}\frac{d^2z}{dx^2} = x^2\frac{d^2y}{dx^2} + x\frac{dy}{dx} - \frac{1}{4}y \tag{3.77}$$

Substituting (3.76) and (3.77) into equation (3.75) gives

$$x\frac{d^2z}{dx^2} + (\tfrac{1}{4}x^{-1}+x)z = 0$$

Again, $1/4x$ is small compared with x if $x \gg 1$.

$$\therefore \quad \frac{d^2z}{dx^2} + z = 0 \tag{3.78}$$

This is the equation of simple harmonic motion which has the solution

$$z = A\cos x + B\sin x$$

Substituting back into equation (3.76),

$$y = Ax^{-\frac{1}{2}}\cos x + Bx^{-\frac{1}{2}}\sin x \tag{3.79}$$

With the above simple treatment, it has been shown that for $x \gg 1$ and $x \gg k$, the Bessel functions behave as damped oscillations of period 2π. The evaluation of A and B to simulate the behaviour of the defined Bessel functions is an involved matching procedure, the result of which is

$$J_k(x) \simeq \sqrt{\frac{2}{\pi x}}\cos\left(x - \frac{\pi}{4} - \frac{k\pi}{2}\right) \tag{3.80}$$

$$Y_k(x) \simeq \sqrt{\frac{2}{\pi x}}\sin\left(x - \frac{\pi}{4} - \frac{k\pi}{2}\right) \tag{3.81}$$

A similar procedure may be adopted with equation (3.64) for the modified Bessel functions. The result is

$$I_k(x) \simeq \frac{1}{\sqrt{(2\pi x)}}e^x \tag{3.82}$$

$$K_k(x) \simeq \sqrt{\frac{\pi}{2x}}e^{-x} \tag{3.83}$$

Thus, $I_k(x)$ is the only Bessel function of the four which diverges to infinity as x increases; the other three decay to zero.

3.7.3. *Differential Properties*

By differentiating the series (3.56) term by term it can be shown that

$$x\frac{d}{dx}J_k(\alpha x) = kJ_k(\alpha x) - \alpha x J_{k+1}(\alpha x)$$

$$= \alpha x J_{k-1}(\alpha x) - kJ_k(\alpha x) \tag{3.84}$$

The corresponding formulae for the other Bessel functions are:

$$x\frac{d}{dx}Y_k(\alpha x) = kY_k(\alpha x) - \alpha x Y_{k+1}(\alpha x)$$

$$= \alpha x Y_{k-1}(\alpha x) - kY_k(\alpha x) \tag{3.85}$$

$$x\frac{d}{dx}I_k(\alpha x) = kI_k(\alpha x) + \alpha x I_{k+1}(\alpha x)$$

$$= \alpha x I_{k-1}(\alpha x) - kI_k(\alpha x) \tag{3.86}$$

$$x\frac{d}{dx}K_k(\alpha x) = kK_k(\alpha x) - \alpha x K_{k+1}(\alpha x)$$

$$= -\alpha x K_{k-1}(\alpha x) - kK_k(\alpha x) \tag{3.87}$$

3.7.4. *Integral Properties*

$$\int \alpha x^k J_{k-1}(\alpha x)\,dx = x^k J_k(\alpha x) \tag{3.88}$$

$$\int \alpha x^k Y_{k-1}(\alpha x)\,dx = x^k Y_k(\alpha x) \tag{3.89}$$

$$\int \alpha x^k I_{k-1}(\alpha x)\,dx = x^k I_k(\alpha x) \tag{3.90}$$

$$\int \alpha x^k K_{k-1}(\alpha x)\,dx = -x^k K_k(\alpha x) \tag{3.91}$$

The following integrals are needed for demonstrating the orthogonality of the Bessel functions (see Section 8.6). Since only $J_k(x)$ and $I_k(x)$ are finite at the origin and therefore the only functions of practical importance at the origin, the orthogonality integrals need only be quoted for these two functions.

$$\int_0^x J_k(\alpha x)J_k(\beta x)x\,dx = \frac{x}{\alpha^2 - \beta^2}\left[\alpha J_k(\beta x)J_{k+1}(\alpha x) - \beta J_k(\alpha x)J_{k+1}(\beta x)\right] \tag{3.92}$$

$$\int_0^x [J_k(\alpha x)]^2 x\,dx = \tfrac{1}{2}x^2\left[J_k^2(\alpha x) - J_{k-1}(\alpha x)J_{k+1}(\alpha x)\right] \tag{3.93}$$

$$\int_0^x I_k(\alpha x)I_k(\beta x)x\,dx = \frac{x}{\alpha^2 - \beta^2}\left[\alpha I_k(\beta x)I_{k+1}(\alpha x) - \beta I_k(\alpha x)I_{k+1}(\beta x)\right] \tag{3.94}$$

$$\int_0^x [I_k(\alpha x)]^2 x\,dx = \tfrac{1}{2}x^2\left[I_k^2(\alpha x) - I_{k-1}(\alpha x)I_{k+1}(\alpha x)\right] \tag{3.95}$$

3.7.5. *Bessel Functions of Negative Order*

Tables of Bessel functions are only given for zero and positive order, the negative order Bessel functions have to be evaluated using recursion formulae as follows. By rearranging equation (3.84).

$$\alpha x J_{k-1}(\alpha x) = 2k J_k(\alpha x) - \alpha x J_{k+1}(x) \tag{3.96}$$

Similar formulae can be obtained for the other Bessel functions by rearranging equations (3.85), (3.86), and (3.87). If the Bessel functions of order k and $k+1$ are known, the Bessel function of order $k-1$ can be calculated.

If k is also an integer, substitution into equation (3.56) and using the properties of the gamma function, Section 5.3, it can be shown that

$$J_{-k}(\alpha x) = (-1)^k J_k(\alpha x) \tag{3.97}$$

Similarly,

$$Y_{-k}(\alpha x) = (-1)^k Y_k(\alpha x) \tag{3.98}$$

$$I_{-k}(\alpha x) = I_k(\alpha x) \tag{3.99}$$

$$K_{-k}(\alpha x) = K_k(\alpha x) \tag{3.100}$$

which are only true for integer values of k.

3.7.6. *Bessel Functions of Half Integer Order*

Bessel's equations (3.48) can be solved analytically for the case $k = \frac{1}{2}$ by substituting

$$z = x^{\frac{1}{2}} y \tag{3.76}$$

as in Section 3.7.2. This gives

$$\frac{d^2 z}{dx^2} + z = 0$$

which has the solution

$$z = A \sin x + B \cos x$$

$$\therefore \quad y = (A \sin x + B \cos x)/x^{\frac{1}{2}}$$

Writing out the first few terms of the series for $J_{\frac{1}{2}}(x)$ from equation (3.56) it can be verified that

$$J_{\frac{1}{2}}(x) = \sqrt{\frac{2}{\pi x}} \sin x \tag{3.101}$$

and

$$J_{-\frac{1}{2}}(x) = \sqrt{\frac{2}{\pi x}} \cos x \tag{3.102}$$

Similarly, it can be shown that

$$I_{\frac{1}{2}}(x) = \sqrt{\frac{2}{\pi x}} \sinh x \tag{3.103}$$

and

$$I_{-\frac{1}{2}}(x) = \sqrt{\frac{2}{\pi x}} \cosh x \tag{3.104}$$

Equation (3.96) and the similar equation established from equation (3.86) allow the J or I functions of half integer order to be expressed in terms of trigonometric or hyperbolic functions.

Chapter 4

COMPLEX ALGEBRA

4.1. Introduction

In the following paragraphs, the algebra of complex numbers will be described and the principles and properties of a complex variable introduced.

The concepts of a complex number and a complex variable are utilized in many branches of applied mathematics and the simplest of these, the complex roots of a quadratic equation, have already been introduced in Chapter 2. It will be seen later that the basis of operational calculus is the integration of functions of complex variables. Consequently an understanding of the fundamental properties of complex quantities is considered essential for the appreciation of many mathematical methods employed in the solution of chemical engineering problems. However, complex numbers have no direct application in chemical engineering and the illustrative examples are necessarily of a pure mathematical nature.

4.2. The Complex Number

A complex number is an expression of the type $x + iy$, where both x and y are real numbers and the symbol

$$i = \sqrt{-1} \tag{4.1}$$

i is therefore not a real number and is defined as the fundamental "imaginary" number. The product iy will also be imaginary and every complex number will have a real part and an imaginary part. In the number $x + iy$, the real part is x and the imaginary part is y.

The algebraic operations of addition, subtraction, multiplication, and division can be performed on complex numbers by treating i as an unknown constant, and replacing (i^2) by (-1) on every occasion that it appears. Thus, if two complex numbers are represented by z_1 and z_2, where

$$z_1 = x_1 + iy_1 \quad \text{and} \quad z_2 = x_2 + iy_2 \tag{4.2}$$

then the addition of these two complex numbers is as follows.

$$z_1 + z_2 = x_1 + iy_1 + x_2 + iy_2$$
$$= (x_1 + x_2) + i(y_1 + y_2) \tag{4.3}$$

Subtraction gives

$$z_1 - z_2 = x_1 + iy_1 - x_2 - iy_2$$
$$= (x_1 - x_2) + i(y_1 - y_2) \tag{4.4}$$

Multiplication gives

$$z_1 z_2 = (x_1 + iy_1)(x_2 + iy_2)$$
$$= (x_1 x_2 - y_1 y_2) + i(x_1 y_2 + x_2 y_1) \qquad (4.5)$$

Division gives

$$\frac{z_1}{z_2} = \frac{x_1 + iy_1}{x_2 + iy_2} = \frac{x_1 + iy_1}{x_2 + iy_2} \cdot \frac{x_2 - iy_2}{x_2 - iy_2}$$
$$= \left(\frac{x_1 x_2 + y_1 y_2}{x_2^2 + y_2^2}\right) + i\left(\frac{y_1 x_2 - y_2 x_1}{x_2^2 + y_2^2}\right) \qquad (4.6)$$

The first three operations are quite straightforward but in the division operation the complex number was eliminated from the denominator by multiplying both numerator and denominator by a specially chosen complex number. This number which is obtained by reversing the sign of the imaginary part of the denominator, is called the "complex conjugate" of the denominator, and Section 4.6 is devoted to the further properties of conjugate numbers.

The two complex numbers z_1 and z_2 will be equal if their difference is zero, and by inspection of the subtraction operation (4.4) it can be seen that $z_1 - z_2 = 0$ only if $x_1 - x_2 = 0$ and $y_1 - y_2 = 0$. That is, z_1 and z_2 are only equal if their real and imaginary parts are separately equal.

In each of the algebraic operations presented in equations (4.3) to (4.6) the mathematical procedure was identical to that which would be followed if the same operation was being performed on a real number. The resulting number was in general complex containing both a real and an imaginary part; although either part could be zero.

4.3 THE ARGAND DIAGRAM

Early in the nineteenth century Argand suggested that a complex number could be represented by a line in a plane in much the same way as a vector is represented (c.f. Chapter 7). The value of the complex number could be expressed in terms of two axes of reference, and he suggested that one axis be called the real axis and the other axis arranged perpendicular to the first

FIG. 4.1. The Argand diagram

be called the imaginary axis. Then a complex number $z = x+iy$ could be represented by a line in the plane having projections x on the real axis and y on the imaginary axis. Such a line is illustrated in Fig. 4.1. Figure 4.1 is called the Argand diagram and the plane in which the line is drawn is called the Argand plane of z. The line OP represents the complex number $4+3i$ whose real part has a value of 4 and imaginary part 3. On the other hand, the line OQ represents the complex number $4i-3$ with real part -3 and imaginary part 4. The lengths of OP and OQ are equal but the complex numbers they represent are unequal because the real parts and the imaginary parts of each are different. This emphasizes the fact that any equation involving complex numbers is equivalent to two real equations obtained by separately equating the real and imaginary parts.

4.3.1 *Modulus and Argument*

For each of the complex numbers represented by the lines OP and OQ, the lengths of the lines are 5. That is,

$$\sqrt{4^2+3^2} = \sqrt{(-3)^2+4^2} = 5 \tag{4.7}$$

The value of the length of the line representing the complex number is called the "modulus" or "absolute value" of the number and is usually written in the alternative forms,

$$r = |z| = \operatorname{mod} z = \sqrt{x^2+y^2} \tag{4.8}$$

The inclination of the line representing the complex number to the positive real axis is called the "amplitude", "argument", or "phase" of z, and is usually written,

$$\theta = \operatorname{amp} z = \arg z = \tan^{-1}(y/x) \tag{4.9}$$

Solving equations (4.8) and (4.9) for x and y gives

$$x = r\cos\theta \quad \text{and} \quad y = r\sin\theta \tag{4.10}$$

From the above it can be seen that a complex number can be expressed in terms of cartesian co-ordinates as $x+iy$, or with the aid of equations (4.10) in polar co-ordinates as

$$z = r\cos\theta + ir\sin\theta = r(\cos\theta + i\sin\theta) = r\operatorname{cis}\theta \tag{4.11}$$

where cis θ is a convenient notation which should be read "$\cos\theta + i\sin\theta$".

4.4. Principal Values

When a complex number is expressed in polar co-ordinates, the principal value of θ is always implied unless otherwise stated. That is in Fig. 4.1,

$$\theta_P = \tan^{-1}(3/4) \quad = 37° = 0{\cdot}645 \,\text{radians}$$
$$\theta_Q = \tan^{-1}(-4/3) = 143° = 2{\cdot}495 \,\text{radians}$$

If the angle is not restricted to its principal value amp $(4+3i)$ would be equal to $(0{\cdot}645+2n\pi)$ radians, and amp $(4i-3)$ would be equal to $(2{\cdot}495+$

$2n\pi$) radians, where n could be zero or an integer. When the complex number is represented on the Argand diagram the principal value is the smaller of the two angles between the positive real axis and the line in question. The sign of the angle depends upon the sense of rotation from the positive real axis, and this implies that the principal value lies in the range $-\pi$ to $+\pi$ as shown in Fig. 4.2. It is sometimes more convenient to choose

Fig. 4.2.   Principal value of the argument

a different range of values for θ but the range is chosen here for consistency with the definitions to be used in the theory of complex variables at the end of this chapter.

4.5. Algebraic Operations on the Argand Diagram

In Section 4.2 the addition, subtraction, multiplication, and division of two complex numbers were carried out. If the Argand diagram describes all the properties of complex numbers it should be possible to carry out the above algebraic operations on the diagram. Thus consider Fig. 4.3a in which the complex numbers represented by the lines OP and OQ in Fig. 4.1 are redrawn. If z_3 is the sum of z_1 represented by OP and z_2 represented by OQ then,

$$z_3 = z_1 + z_2 = (x_1 + x_2) + i(y_1 + y_2)$$

or $$x_3 = x_1 + x_2 \quad \text{and} \quad y_3 = y_1 + y_2 \tag{4.12}$$

Equations (4.12) give the co-ordinates of z_3 on the Argand diagram as shown in Fig. 4.3a by the line OR. Using the same numerical values as before,

$$x_3 = 4 - 3 = 1 \quad \text{and} \quad y_3 = 3 + 4 = 7$$

$$\therefore \quad z_3 = x_3 + iy_3 = 1 + 7i \tag{4.13}$$

It is easily shown that the point R can be located geometrically by completing the parallelogram OPQR as in Fig. 4.3a.

In the same way, the subtraction of two complex numbers can be expressed in the form of the addition of z_1 to minus z_2 where

$$-z_2 = -(4i-3) = 3-4i \qquad (4.14)$$

By completing the parallelogram OPQ′T in Fig. 4.3b to locate the diagonal OT, the difference between the complex numbers z_1 and z_2 (i.e. $z_4 = z_1-z_2$)

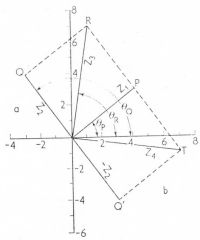

FIG. 4.3. Addition and subtraction on the Argand diagram

is obtained. The co-ordinates of z_4 can be verified algebraically as before, thus,

$$z_4 = z_1+(-z_2) = (4+3)+i(3-4) = 7-i.$$

From the elementary geometrical property of triangles that the sum of the absolute lengths of any two sides of a triangle must exceed the third side, there follows the important result,

$$|z_1+z_2| \leqslant |z_1|+|z_2| \qquad (4.15)$$

In order to illustrate multiplication and division on the Argand diagram, it is first necessary to show how the multiplication and division of two complex numbers are expressed in terms of polar coordinates. Thus

$$z_5 = z_1 z_2 = r_1 r_2(\cos\theta_1 + i\sin\theta_1)(\cos\theta_2 + i\sin\theta_2) \qquad (4.16)$$

$$= r_1 r_2[(\cos\theta_1\cos\theta_2 - \sin\theta_1\sin\theta_2)+i(\sin\theta_1\cos\theta_2 + \cos\theta_1\sin\theta_2)]$$

$$= r_1 r_2[\cos(\theta_1+\theta_2)+i\sin(\theta_1+\theta_2)]$$

or $\quad z_5 = r_5(\cos\theta_5 + i\sin\theta_5)$

where $\qquad\qquad\qquad r_5 = r_1 r_2 \quad$ and $\quad \theta_5 = \theta_1+\theta_2 \qquad (4.17)$

Therefore, to multiply two complex numbers, it is necessary to multiply the moduli and add the arguments. Hence the multiplication of two complex numbers can be expressed on an Argand diagram by multiplication of the two real numbers r_1 and r_2 to give the absolute length r_5, and drawing the line OU of length r_5 at an angle $(\theta_1 + \theta_2)$ with the positive real axis as illustrated in Fig. 4.4.

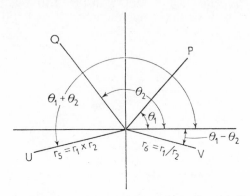

FIG. 4.4. Multiplication and division on the Argand diagram

The division of z_1 by z_2 can be expressed in terms of polar coordinates as follows.

$$\frac{z_1}{z_2} = \frac{r_1(\cos\theta_1 + i\sin\theta_1)}{r_2(\cos\theta_2 + i\sin\theta_2)}$$

$$= \frac{r_1(\cos\theta_1 + i\sin\theta_1)(\cos\theta_2 - i\sin\theta_2)}{r_2(\cos^2\theta_2 + \sin^2\theta_2)}$$

$$= \frac{r_1}{r_2}\left[\cos(\theta_1 - \theta_2) + i\sin(\theta_1 - \theta_2)\right] \tag{4.18}$$

where the denominator was again made real by multiplying numerator and denominator by the complex conjugate of the denominator.

Therefore, to divide two complex numbers it is necessary to divide the moduli and subtract the arguments. Hence the division of two complex numbers can be expressed on the Argand diagram by dividing the real number r_1 by the real number r_2, to give an absolute length of r_6, then drawing the line OV at an angle $(\theta_1 - \theta_2)$ with the positive real axis. This is illustrated in Fig. 4.4.

In the multiplication and division operations θ_1 and θ_2 were the principal values of the arguments of the numbers. However $(\theta_1 + \theta_2)$ and $(\theta_1 - \theta_2)$ need not be the principal values of the arguments of z_5 and z_6. Thus consider the complex numbers $z_1 = (3i - 4)$ and $z_2 = (i - 1)$ with arguments $\theta_1 = 143°$, and $\theta_2 = 135°$. By equation (4.5) $z_1 z_2 = 1 - 7i$, and $\theta_5 = \theta_1 + \theta_2 = 278°$. The principal value of the argument lying between $-180°$ and $+180°$ is $-82°$ and this value should be used in subsequent calculations unless there is some over-riding consideration (e.g. see Section 4.14.3).

It has been shown that it is possible to represent simple addition, subtraction, multiplication and division of two complex numbers, on the Argand diagram. Therefore it is obvious that by a series of geometric operations it is possible to describe any process involving complex numbers on an Argand diagram provided that they consist of a combination of the above four operations.

4.6. CONJUGATE NUMBERS

Two complex numbers such as $x+iy$ and $x-iy$ of which the real and imaginary parts are of equal magnitude, but in which the imaginary parts are of opposite sign are said to be conjugate numbers. On the Argand diagram they can be considered to be mirror images of each other in the real axis. Conjugate numbers have already been used in the definition of the division process. Usually, the conjugate of a complex number z is written as $\bar{z}$, and throughout this text conjugates of complex numbers will be written accordingly.

If a complex number possesses a conjugate, the imaginary part cannot be zero. However the sum and the product of a complex number with its conjugate are always real. Thus,

$$(x+iy)+(x-iy) = 2x \tag{4.19}$$

and
$$(x+iy)(x-iy) = x^2-(iy)^2 = x^2+y^2 \tag{4.20}$$

i.e. the final result is a real number since $i^2 = -1$. The division of a complex number by its conjugate will not produce a real number. These relations between sums and products can be extended to more than one complex number and its conjugate. Thus if w and z be two complex numbers whose conjugates are $\bar{w}$ and $\bar{z}$ respectively, let

$$w = r_1(\cos\theta + i\sin\theta) \tag{4.21}$$

then
$$\bar{w} = r_1(\cos\theta - i\sin\theta) \tag{4.22}$$

also let
$$z = r_2(\cos\phi + i\sin\phi) \tag{4.23}$$

then
$$\bar{z} = r_2(\cos\phi - i\sin\phi) \tag{4.24}$$

$$\therefore \quad w+z = r_1(\cos\theta + i\sin\theta)+r_2(\cos\phi + i\sin\phi)$$
$$= (r_1\cos\theta + r_2\cos\phi)+i(r_1\sin\theta + r_2\sin\phi) \tag{4.25}$$

$$\therefore \quad \overline{w+z} = (r_1\cos\theta + r_2\cos\phi)-i(r_1\sin\theta + r_2\sin\phi) \tag{4.26}$$

But
$$\bar{w}+\bar{z} = r_1(\cos\theta - i\sin\theta)+r_2(\cos\phi - i\sin\phi)$$
$$= (r_1\cos\theta + r_2\cos\phi)-i(r_1\sin\theta + r_2\sin\phi) \tag{4.27}$$

From equations (4.26) and (4.27)

$$\overline{w+z} = \bar{w}+\bar{z} \tag{4.28}$$

That is, the conjugate of the sum of two complex numbers is equal to the sum of the conjugates of the complex numbers. In fact this principle can be extended to any number of complex numbers.

In a similar manner it can be shown that if the complex number p is the product of $w\bar{z}$. That is

$$p = w\bar{z} \qquad (4.29)$$

$$\bar{p} = \bar{w}z \qquad (4.30)$$

Also if the complex number q is related to w and z by

$$q = w/z \qquad (4.31)$$

then

$$\bar{q} = \bar{w}/\bar{z} \qquad (4.32)$$

It is left to the reader to verify equations (4.29) to (4.32).

4.7. De Moivre's Theorem

This important theorem can be enunciated as follows: For all rational values of n, $\cos n\theta + i \sin n\theta$ is one of the values of $(\cos \theta + i \sin \theta)^n$. The proof of De Moivre's theorem depends on the value of n. That is, on whether n is a positive or negative integer, or a real fraction. Irrational numbers such as π are not included, but this is an academic restriction. The product of two complex numbers $z_1 z_2$ was shown to be

$$r_1 r_2 [\cos (\theta_1 + \theta_2) + i \sin (\theta_1 + \theta_2)]$$

in Section 4.5, and there it was stated that the algebraic process could be extended to evaluating multiple products. Hence,

$$z_1 z_2 z_3 = r_1 r_2 r_3 [\cos (\theta_1 + \theta_2) + i \sin (\theta_1 + \theta_2)] (\cos \theta_3 + i \sin \theta_3) \qquad (4.33)$$

$$= r_1 r_2 r_3 [\cos (\theta_1 + \theta_2) \cos \theta_3 - \sin (\theta_1 + \theta_2) \sin \theta_3 + $$
$$+ i \{\cos \theta_3 \sin (\theta_1 + \theta_2) + \sin \theta_3 \cos (\theta_1 + \theta_2)\}]$$

$$= r_1 r_2 r_3 [\cos (\theta_1 + \theta_2 + \theta_3) + i \sin (\theta_1 + \theta_2 + \theta_3)] \qquad (4.34)$$

The above algebraic operations can be extended to n complex numbers when it can be shown that

$$z_1 z_2 \dots z_n = r_1 r_2 \dots r_n [\cos (\theta_1 + \theta_2 + \dots + \theta_n) + i \sin (\theta_1 + \theta_2 + \dots \theta_n)] \qquad (4.35)$$

If $z_1 = z_2 = \dots = z_n$,
then equation (4.35) becomes

$$z^n = r^n (\cos \theta + i \sin \theta)^n = r^n (\cos n\theta + i \sin n\theta) \qquad (4.36)$$

or

$$(\cos \theta + i \sin \theta)^n = \cos n\theta + i \sin n\theta \qquad (4.37)$$

where n is a positive integer.

If n is a negative integer, say $-m$, then

$$(\cos \theta + i \sin \theta)^n = (\cos \theta + i \sin \theta)^{-m}$$

$$= \frac{1}{(\cos \theta + i \sin \theta)^m} \qquad (4.38)$$

But using De Moivre's theorem for a positive integer as given by equation (4.37),

$$\frac{1}{(\cos \theta + i \sin \theta)^m} = \frac{1}{\cos m\theta + i \sin m\theta} \qquad (4.39)$$

By a direct application of the division rule as given by equation (4.18),

$$\frac{1}{\cos m\theta + i \sin m\theta} = \cos(-m\theta) + i \sin(-m\theta) \tag{4.40}$$

Collecting together equations (4.38), (4.39), and (4.40), gives the required result,

$$(\cos\theta + i\sin\theta)^n = \cos n\theta + i\sin n\theta \tag{4.41}$$

which proves De Moivre's theorem for a negative integer.

Finally, if n is a fraction, say p/q, where p and q are both integers with q positive but p either positive or negative, then by De Moivre's theorem for an integer,

$$\left(\cos\frac{p}{q}\theta + i\sin\frac{p}{q}\theta\right)^q = \cos p\theta + i\sin p\theta$$

$$= (\cos\theta + i\sin\theta)^p \tag{4.42}$$

Taking the qth root of each side of equation (4.42) gives

$$\cos\frac{p}{q}\theta + i\sin\frac{p}{q}\theta = (\cos\theta + i\sin\theta)^{p/q} \tag{4.43}$$

Equation (4.43) proves De Moivre's theorem for fractional values of n; hence, the theorem is proved for all rational values of n.

4.8. The nth Roots of Unity

The nth root of a complex number z is $z^{1/n}$ which can be expressed in terms of polar coordinates, and it follows from De Moivre's theorem that

$$z^{1/n} = r^{1/n}(\cos\theta + i\sin\theta)^{1/n} = r^{1/n}\left[\cos\frac{\theta + 2s\pi}{n} + i\sin\frac{\theta + 2s\pi}{n}\right] \tag{4.44}$$

where the real number $s = 0, 1, 2, \ldots., (n-1)$.

Equation (4.44) expresses the nth root of any number z real or complex in its most general form, where the argument is not restricted to its principal value. Therefore, if $z = 1\cdot0$, $r = 1\cdot0$, and $\theta = 0$, the nth root of unity is

$$1^{1/n} = \cos\frac{2s\pi}{n} + i\sin\frac{2s\pi}{n} \tag{4.45}$$

or more specifically, by substituting values of s into equation (4.45) the nth roots of unity are:

$$\cos 0 + i\sin 0 = 1\cdot0, \ \cos\frac{2\pi}{n} + i\sin\frac{2\pi}{n}, \ \cos\frac{4\pi}{n} + i\sin\frac{4\pi}{n}, \ \ldots$$

$$\cos\frac{2(n-1)\pi}{n} + i\sin\frac{2(n-1)\pi}{n} \tag{4.46}$$

Inspection of equation (4.46) shows that all the n roots are different, and are situated at the n corners of a regular n-sided polygon centred at the origin.

De Moivre's theorem as expressed by equation (4.44) can be used to find the nth root of any complex number and this is illustrated in the following example.

Example. Find the square root of $4 + 3\sqrt{-5}$.
Using the equations (4.8) and 4.9) to express z in terms of polar coordinates gives

$$r^2 = 4^2 + (3\sqrt{5})^2 = 16 + 9 \times 5 = 61 \qquad\qquad \text{I}$$

$$\therefore \quad r = 7\cdot81 \quad \text{and} \quad r^{\frac{1}{2}} = 2\cdot795 \qquad\qquad \text{II}$$

$$\theta = \tan^{-1}(3\sqrt{5}/4) = \tan^{-1} 1\cdot6771 = 59^\circ\ 12' \qquad\qquad \text{III}$$

$$\therefore \quad \cos\tfrac{1}{2}\theta = 0\cdot8695, \quad \text{and} \quad \sin\tfrac{1}{2}\theta = 0\cdot4939 \qquad\qquad \text{IV}$$

Using equation (4.44), the two square roots of $4 + 3i\sqrt{5}$

are $\qquad\qquad \pm 2\cdot795(0\cdot8695 + 0\cdot4939i)$

or $\qquad\qquad \pm(2\cdot43 + 1\cdot38i) \qquad\qquad \text{V}$

4.9. Complex Number Series

If the complex number p_m can be expressed as

$$p_m = u_m + iv_m \qquad\qquad (4.45)$$

where both u_m and v_m are real, and if the complex number z_n is equal to the sum of n complex numbers p_m, then

$$z_n = \sum_{m=1}^{n} p_m = \sum_{m=1}^{n} u_m + i\sum_{m=1}^{n} v_m \qquad\qquad (4.46)$$

The summations $\sum u_m$ and $\sum v_m$ are both sums of real numbers and if

$$\sum_{m=1}^{n} u_m = x_n, \quad \text{and} \quad \sum_{m=1}^{n} v_m = y_n \qquad\qquad (4.47)$$

and as n tends to infinity both x_n and y_n tend to finite limits denoted by x and y respectively, then the two series in equation (4.47) are convergent. Their sum must therefore be convergent, or

$$z = \lim_{n \to \infty} z_n = \sum_{m=1}^{\infty} u_m + i\sum_{m=1}^{\infty} v_m = x + iy \qquad\qquad (4.48)$$

Therefore, for a complex series to be convergent, both the real part and the imaginary part of the series must each be convergent.

The convergence of complex series is usually discussed by referring to the associated series consisting of the absolute values of the individual terms. That is, the convergence of the series given by equation (4.46)

$$z_n = p_1 + p_2 + \ldots + p_n \qquad\qquad (4.46)$$

is discussed by referring to the series

$$S_n = |p_1| + |p_2| + \ldots + |p_n| \qquad\qquad (4.49)$$

If S_n tends to a finite limit S as $n \to \infty$, then the series (4.46) is said to be absolutely convergent. But equation (4.15) gives

$$|p_1 + p_2| \leqslant |p_1| + |p_2|$$

$$\therefore \quad |p_1 + p_2 + p_3| \leqslant |p_1| + |p_2| + |p_3|$$

etc.

$$\therefore \quad |z_n| \leqslant |p_1| + |p_2| + \cdots |p_n| \tag{4.50}$$

and it follows that if the series (4.46) is absolutely convergent, then it must also be convergent.

The convergence tests discussed in Chapter 3 are applicable to series of complex numbers and therefore need not be repeated here, but an invaluable result can be obtained from the exponential series as follows. The series for a complex exponent z was given in Chapter 3 as

$$e^z = 1 + z + \frac{z^2}{2!} + \cdots + \frac{z^n}{n!} + \cdots \tag{3.7}$$

which is convergent for all values of z. In particular, if $z = iy$, equation (3.7) becomes

$$e^{iy} = 1 + iy - \frac{y^2}{2!} - \frac{iy^3}{3!} + \frac{y^4}{4!} + \cdots \tag{4.51}$$

$$= \left(1 - \frac{y^2}{2!} + \frac{y^4}{4!} - \cdots\right) + i\left(y - \frac{y^3}{3!} + \frac{y^5}{5!} - \cdots\right) \tag{4.52}$$

Each of the series in equation (4.52) can be recognized by comparing with equations (3.10) and (3.11) in Chapter 3. Thus

$$e^{iy} = \cos y + i \sin y \tag{4.53}$$

or more generally

$$e^z = e^{x+iy} = e^x(\cos y + i \sin y) \tag{4.54}$$

Equation (4.53) can also be proved in the following neat fashion. Consider

$$f(y) = e^{-iy}(\cos y + i \sin y) \tag{4.55}$$

and differentiate with respect to y.

$$\therefore \quad \frac{df}{dy} = e^{-iy}(-\sin y + i \cos y) - ie^{-iy}(\cos y + i \sin y)$$

$$= e^{-iy}(-\sin y + i \cos y - i \cos y + \sin y)$$

$$= 0$$

Integrating,

$$\therefore \quad f(y) = A \, (\text{constant})$$

but when $y = 0$, equation (4.55) gives $f(y) = 1$.

$$\therefore \quad e^{-iy}(\cos y + i \sin y) = A = 1$$

Rearranging gives equation (4.53).

$$\cos y + i \sin y = e^{iy}$$

4.10. Trigonometrical—Exponential Identities

It has just been shown that

$$e^{iy} = \cos y + i \sin y \qquad (4.53)$$

and similarly it can be shown that

$$e^{-iy} = \cos y - i \sin y \qquad (4.56)$$

Addition of equations (4.53) and (4.56) gives

$$e^{iy} + e^{-iy} = 2 \cos y$$

or

$$\cos y = \frac{e^{iy} + e^{-iy}}{2} \qquad (4.57)$$

Subtraction of equation (4.56) from equation (4.53) gives

$$e^{iy} - e^{-iy} = 2i \sin y$$

or

$$\sin y = \frac{e^{iy} - e^{-iy}}{2i} \qquad (4.58)$$

The identities developed above between real trigonometrical functions and imaginary exponential functions can be extended to include hyperbolic functions. Thus, using equation (4.57) to find the cosine of a pure imaginary quantity,

$$\cos ix = \frac{e^{i^2 x} + e^{-i^2 x}}{2} = \frac{e^{-x} + e^{x}}{2}$$

which defines the hyperbolic cosine function,

$$\cos ix = \frac{e^{x} + e^{-x}}{2} = \cosh x \qquad (4.59)$$

Similarly,

$$\sin ix = \frac{e^{i^2 x} - e^{-i^2 x}}{2i} = i \frac{e^{x} - e^{-x}}{2} = i \sinh x \qquad (4.60)$$

which defines the hyperbolic sine function.

The above relationships can be extended to define a hyperbolic tangent function as,

$$\tan ix = \frac{\sin ix}{\cos ix} = \frac{i \sinh x}{\cosh x} = i \tanh x$$

$$\therefore \quad \tan ix = i \tanh x \qquad (4.61)$$

All properties of hyperbolic functions can be obtained from the corresponding trigonometrical identities by using equations (4.59), (4.60), and (4.61).

4.11. The Complex Variable

In the paragraphs above, the complex number z has been expressed in terms of the fixed real quantities x and y by the relation $z = x + iy$. If however the quantities x and y are variables, then so is z. In fact the quantity z

becomes a "complex variable", and since z is related to the variables x and y; the way in which z varies with x and y can be expressed by a curve in a plane having coordinates x and y. The plane is called the "z plane".

If the complex variable z is related functionally to another complex variable w so that

$$w = f(z) \qquad (4.62)$$

and the complex variable w can be expressed by the real quantities u and v so that $w = u+iv$, then when z varies in the z plane, w will follow a curve corresponding to equation (4.62) in the "w plane" whose coordinates are u and v. Since $z = x+iy$ and $w = u+iv$, u and v must be real functions of both x and y. This will become clear in the following example.

Example. If $z = x+iy$, and $w = u+iv$, where

$$w = z^2 \qquad \text{I}$$

express u and v in terms of x and y.

Substitute x, y, u, and v for w and z in equation I.

$$\therefore \quad u+iv = (x+iy)^2 = x^2+2ixy-y^2 \qquad \text{II}$$

Equating real and imaginary parts gives

$$u = x^2-y^2 \quad \text{and} \quad v = 2xy \qquad \text{III}$$

which determine u and v as functions of x and y.

Because the complex variable w has a functional relationship to z expressed by equation (4.62), derivatives of w with respect to z will exist provided that $f(z)$ is continuous in the region where the derivatives are required. Thus a complex variable $w = f(z)$ is said to be continuous at a point p if $f(p)$ has a finite value at $z = p$, and if the limit of $f(z)$ as z approaches p is $f(p)$. That is,

$$\lim_{z \to p} f(z) = f(p) \qquad (4.63)$$

If $f(z) = z^{-1}$ and the point p is the origin, the value of $f(z)$ at the origin depends upon the way in which the origin is approached. For instance, if z approaches zero along the positive real axis,

$$\lim_{x \to 0+} z^{-1} = \infty \qquad (4.64)$$

whereas if z approaches zero along the negative real axis,

$$\lim_{x \to 0-} z^{-1} = -\infty \qquad (4.65)$$

The limit of z^{-1} as z approaches zero does not therefore exist, and the function z^{-1} has a "singularity" at $z = 0$.

On the other hand, if $f(z) = z^4$, the function is continuous everywhere in the z plane but becomes infinite as z becomes infinite. Furthermore, z^4 has only one value at any given value of z and therefore it is said to be a "single valued" function. However, if w is related to z by $w = z^{\frac{1}{2}}$, w can have more than one value for each value of z, and w is then said to be a "many valued" function.

Difficulties can arise therefore in a number of ways when treating complex variables, but many of these can be resolved by confining the function to regions in the complex plane in which the functional relationships apply. This fact will be better understood later in the chapter.

4.12. DERIVATIVES OF A COMPLEX VARIABLE

Consider the complex number

$$w = f(z) \tag{4.62}$$

to be a continuous function, and let $w = u + iv$ and $z = x + iy$ as before. Then the partial derivative of w with respect to x can be obtained in two ways, thus

$$\frac{\partial w}{\partial x} = \frac{\partial u}{\partial x} + i\frac{\partial v}{\partial x} \tag{4.66}$$

and

$$\frac{\partial w}{\partial x} = \frac{df}{dz}\frac{\partial z}{\partial x} = \frac{df}{dz} \tag{4.67}$$

since $\partial z/\partial x = 1$. Equating these two expressions,

$$\frac{df}{dz} = \frac{\partial u}{\partial x} + i\frac{\partial v}{\partial x} \tag{4.68}$$

Similarly, differentiating w with respect to y gives

$$\frac{\partial w}{\partial y} = \frac{\partial u}{\partial y} + i\frac{\partial v}{\partial y} \tag{4.69}$$

and

$$\frac{\partial w}{\partial y} = \frac{df}{dz}\frac{\partial z}{\partial y} = i\frac{df}{dz} \tag{4.70}$$

since $\partial z/\partial y = i$.

$$\therefore \quad i\frac{df}{dz} = \frac{\partial u}{\partial y} + i\frac{\partial v}{\partial y} \tag{4.71}$$

Eliminating df/dz from equations (4.68) and (4.71) gives

$$i\frac{\partial u}{\partial x} - \frac{\partial v}{\partial x} = i\frac{df}{dz} = \frac{\partial u}{\partial y} + i\frac{\partial v}{\partial y} \tag{4.72}$$

Since u, v, x, and y are all real, the real and imaginary parts of equation (4.72) must be equated.

$$\therefore \quad \frac{\partial u}{\partial x} = \frac{\partial v}{\partial y} \quad \text{and} \quad \frac{\partial u}{\partial y} = -\frac{\partial v}{\partial x} \tag{4.73}$$

If equations (4.73) are satisfied, the derivative dw/dz becomes a unique single valued function which can be used in the mathematical solution of engineering problems. Hence the derivative of a complex variable has certain restrictions which derivatives of real variables do not have and these are described by equations (4.73). They are known as the "Cauchy-Riemann" conditions and they must be satisfied for the derivative of a complex number to have any meaning.

4.13. ANALYTIC FUNCTIONS

A function $w = f(z)$ of the complex variable $z = x + iy$ is called an analytic or regular function within a region R, if at all points z_0 in the region it satisfies the following conditions.

   (i) It is single valued in the region R.
   (ii) It has a unique finite value.
   (iii) It has a unique finite derivative at z_0 which satisfies the Cauchy-Riemann conditions.

Only functions which satisfy these conditions can be utilized in pure and applied mathematics, and therefore the whole of the following treatment will deal with analytic functions. However, when a mathematical analysis of an engineering problem involving complex functions is being undertaken, care should be exercised to confirm that the function satisfies the criteria stated above. The following examples illustrate the application of these rules.

Example 1.   If $w = z^3$, show that the function satisfies the Cauchy-Riemann conditions and state the region wherein the function is analytic.

$$w = z^3 = (x + iy)^3 = x^3 + 3ix^2y - 3xy^2 - iy^3$$

But $\qquad w = u + iv$, and equating real and imaginary parts,

$$u = x^3 - 3xy^2 \quad \text{and} \quad v = 3x^2y - y^3 \qquad\qquad \text{II}$$

$$\therefore \quad \frac{\partial u}{\partial x} = 3x^2 - 3y^2 \qquad \frac{\partial v}{\partial y} = 3x^2 - 3y^2 \qquad\qquad \text{III}$$

and $\qquad \dfrac{\partial u}{\partial y} = -6xy \qquad \dfrac{\partial v}{\partial x} = 6xy \qquad\qquad \text{IV}$

By inspection of equations III and IV it can be seen that the Cauchy-Riemann conditions (4.73) are satisfied. Furthermore, for all finite values of z, w is finite; hence the function $w = z^3$ is analytic in any region of finite size.

Example 2.   If $w = z^{-1}$, show that the function satisfies the Cauchy-Riemann conditions and state the region wherein the function is analytic.

$$w = \frac{1}{z} = \frac{1}{x + iy} = \frac{x - iy}{x^2 + y^2} \qquad\qquad \text{I}$$

$$\therefore \quad u = \frac{x}{x^2 + y^2} \quad \text{and} \quad v = \frac{-y}{x^2 + y^2} \qquad\qquad \text{II}$$

From equations II,

$$\frac{\partial u}{\partial x} = \frac{\partial v}{\partial y} = \frac{y^2 - x^2}{(x^2 + y^2)^2} \qquad \text{III}$$

and

$$\frac{\partial u}{\partial y} = -\frac{\partial v}{\partial x} = \frac{-2xy}{(x^2 + y^2)^2} \qquad \text{IV}$$

Equations III and IV show that the Cauchy-Riemann conditions are satisfied at a general point but consider the behaviour at the origin.

$\partial u/\partial x$ is obtained by keeping y constant, and to reach the origin, y must be constant at zero; hence equation II becomes

$$u = \frac{1}{x}$$

$$\therefore \quad \frac{\partial u}{\partial x} = \frac{-1}{x^2} \qquad \text{V}$$

which tends to negative infinity as x tends to zero through either positive or negative values.

Similarly, $\partial v/\partial y$ at the origin must be evaluated when $x = 0$. Equation II simplifies to

$$v = \frac{-1}{y}$$

$$\therefore \quad \frac{\partial v}{\partial y} = \frac{1}{y^2} \qquad \text{VI}$$

which tends to positive infinity as y tends to zero through either positive or negative values. Therefore, from equations V and VI, $\partial u/\partial x$ and $\partial v/\partial y$ diverge to opposite extremes at the origin, and one half of the Cauchy-Riemann conditions is not satisfied. It can be shown that the other half of the condition is satisfied, i.e.

$$\frac{\partial u}{\partial y} = -\frac{\partial v}{\partial x} = 0 \qquad \text{VII}$$

The Cauchy-Riemann conditions are not fully satisfied at the origin, w becomes infinite at the origin, and the function $w = z^{-1}$ is therefore analytic everywhere in the z plane with the exception of the one point $z = 0$.

4.14. SINGULARITIES

It has been shown in the examples above that the function $w = z^3$ is analytic everywhere except at $z = \infty$ whilst the function $w = z^{-1}$ is analytic everywhere except at $z = 0$. In fact no function except a constant is analytic throughout the complex plane, and every function of a complex variable has one or more points in the z plane where it ceases to be analytic. These points are called "singularities", and they may be classified as follows.

(a) Poles or unessential singularities.
(b) Essential singularities.
(c) Branch points.

The singularities (a) and (b) are characteristic of single valued functions whereas (c) arises with multivalued functions. Each will be discussed below.

4.14.1. *Poles or Unessential Singularities*

A pole is a point in the complex plane at which the value of a function becomes infinite. Thus $w = z^{-1}$ is infinite at $z = 0$, and therefore the function $w = z^{-1}$ is said to have a pole at the origin. However, in the neighbourhood of the origin, this function is finite and consequently analytic but at the pole it ceases to be analytic. The pole in $w = z^{-1}$ is said to be "first order" whilst the function $w = z^{-2}$ possesses a second order pole. The order of a pole is determined in the following manner.

If $w = f(z)$ becomes infinite at the point $z = a$, then define

$$g(z) = (z-a)^n f(z) \tag{4.74}$$

where n is an integer. If it is possible to find a finite value of n which makes $g(z)$ analytic at $z = a$, then the pole of $f(z)$ has been "removed" in forming $g(z)$. The order of the pole is defined as the minimum integer value of n for which $g(z)$ is analytic at $z = a$.

The function

$$w = \frac{1}{z^p(z-a)^q} \tag{4.75}$$

where p and q are both positive and finite, is a function containing multiple poles. That is, it contains a pole of order p at the origin, and a pole of order q at $z = a$. If either p or q is not an integer, the order of the pole is the next higher integer than p or q respectively.

4.14.2. *Essential Singularities*

Certain functions of complex variables have an infinite number of terms which all approach infinity as the complex variable approaches a specific value. These could be thought of as poles of infinite order, but as the singularity cannot be removed by multiplying the function by a finite factor, they cannot be poles. This type of singularity is called an essential singularity and is portrayed by functions which can be expanded in a descending power series of the variable. The classical example is $e^{1/z}$ which has an essential singularity at $z = 0$. Similarly the series

$$f(z) = \sum_{n=0}^{n=\infty} b_n(z-a)^{-n} \tag{4.76}$$

has an essential singularity at $z = a$.

Essential singularities can be distinguished from poles by the fact that they cannot be removed by multiplying by a factor of finite value. Thus consider the function

$$w = e^{1/z} \tag{4.77}$$

Using equation (3.7) to expand the exponential function,

$$w = 1 + \frac{1}{z} + \frac{1}{2!z^2} + \dots + \frac{1}{n!z^n} + \dots \tag{4.78}$$

Since w is infinite at the origin, try to remove the singularity by multiplying by z^p where p is some finite integer.

$$\therefore \quad z^p w = z^p + z^{p-1} + \frac{z^{p-2}}{2!} + \dots + \frac{z^{p-n}}{n!} + \dots \tag{4.79}$$

The series in equation (4.79) continues indefinitely and eventually n will be greater than p. Equation (4.79) thus consists of a finite number of positive powers of z, followed by an infinite number of negative powers of z. Since all terms of equation (4.79) are positive, then $z^p w \to \infty$ as $z \to 0$. It is therefore impossible to find a finite value of p which will remove the singularity in $e^{1/z}$ at the origin. The singularity is thus "essential".

Finally, it can be shown that the behaviour of a function in the neighbourhood of a pole and in the neighbourhood of an essential singularity is quite different. At a pole, the modulus of the function increases symmetrically about the pole to give an infinite pinnacle at the pole; whereas at an essential singularity, the function behaves very peculiarly. For example, Mclachlan[†] has shown that the function $e^{1/z}$ does not have the characteristics of a pole as z goes to zero. Thus for a fixed value of the argument of z in the range $0 < \theta < \frac{1}{2}\pi$ the modulus traces out a spiral of ever increasing radius in the w plane; whilst at $\theta = 0$ the function oscillates. This behaviour is most unlike that of a function near a pole.

4.14.3. Branch Points

The singularities described above arise from the non-analytic behaviour of single valued functions. However multivalued functions such as $w = z^{1/n}$ (where n is a positive integer) frequently arise in the solution of engineering problems. Therefore this type of function must be accommodated in the theory of complex variables. Thus consider the function

$$w = z^{\frac{1}{2}} \tag{4.80}$$

and let z vary in such a way that it follows a circular path whose centre is the origin. Converting to polar coordinates using equations (4.11) and (4.53),

$$z = r\, e^{i\theta} \tag{4.81}$$

where r is a constant and θ a variable. Substituting equation (4.81) into equation (4.80) gives

$$w = \sqrt{r}\, e^{\frac{1}{2}i\theta} \tag{4.82}$$

Hence, when the variable z makes one traverse of the circumference of the circle in the z plane, θ passes through 2π radians, but w with a constant modulus of $\sqrt{r}$ will only pass through π radians by equation (4.82). If z

† Mclachlan, N. W. "Complex Variable Theory and Transform Calculus," p. 16. Cambridge University Press (1955).

makes a second circuit of the circle in the z plane with θ changing from 2π to 4π, the function w will complete the circle as shown dotted in the w plane of Fig. 4.5. Consequently for any value of z represented by a point on the

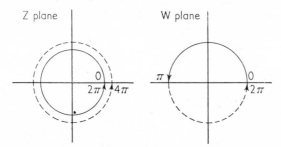

FIG. 4.5. Branch point of $w = z^{\frac{1}{2}}$ on the z and w complex planes

circumference of the circle in the z plane, there will be two corresponding values of w represented by points in the w plane. One value will be on the solid line semicircle where $0 < \frac{1}{2}\theta < \pi$, and the other will be on the dotted line semicircle where $\pi < \frac{1}{2}\theta < 2\pi$. Hence, by the simple expedient of restricting the values of θ to the range $0 \leqslant \theta < 2\pi$, the function w becomes single valued, and the Cauchy-Riemann conditions can be expressed as follows.

$$w = u + iv = \sqrt{r}\,e^{\frac{1}{2}i\theta}$$

$$\therefore \quad u = \sqrt{r}\cos\tfrac{1}{2}\theta \quad \text{and} \quad v = \sqrt{r}\sin\tfrac{1}{2}\theta$$

$$\therefore \quad \frac{\partial u}{\partial r} = \frac{1}{2\sqrt{r}}\cos\tfrac{1}{2}\theta \qquad \frac{\partial v}{\partial r} = \frac{1}{2\sqrt{r}}\sin\tfrac{1}{2}\theta$$

and

$$\frac{\partial u}{\partial \theta} = -\tfrac{1}{2}\sqrt{r}\sin\tfrac{1}{2}\theta \qquad \frac{\partial v}{\partial \theta} = \tfrac{1}{2}\sqrt{r}\cos\tfrac{1}{2}\theta$$

which gives

$$\frac{\partial u}{\partial r} = \frac{1}{r}\frac{\partial v}{\partial \theta} \quad \text{and} \quad \frac{\partial v}{\partial r} = -\frac{1}{r}\frac{\partial u}{\partial \theta} \qquad (4.83)$$

Equations (4.83) are the Cauchy-Riemann conditions in polar coordinates. The final step to equations (4.83) can only be made in this example if θ is restricted to the range $0 \leqslant \theta < 2\pi$.

The restriction which makes a multivalued function single valued within a given region enables these functions to be employed mathematically. The region where the function is single valued is called the "branch", and the particular value of z at which the function becomes infinite or zero is called the "branch point". In the example above, the origin is the branch point.

The function $w = z^{\frac{1}{2}}$ was multivalued because the contour followed by z enclosed the branch point at the origin. However this is a particular case, since the complex variable z may travel along any open curve in the z plane or any closed curve which may or may not enclose the branch point. Thus let the function $w = z^{\frac{1}{2}}$ follow the contour shown in Fig. 4.6 which does not enclose the branch point. On this occasion the angle θ, which is the argument of z, changes from θ_1 to θ_2 and back again to θ_1, and does not change by 2π radians in traversing the contour. Hence the function is single valued around the contour in Fig. 4.6 without any action being taken to restrict the

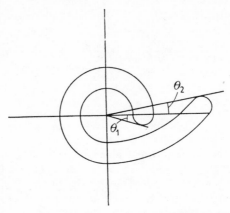

FIG. 4.6.   Contour of $w = z^{\frac{1}{2}}$ not enclosing branch point

values of θ. This shows that unless the contour of z encloses the branch point, the angle θ can only have one value at each point on the contour and this value cannot be altered by 2π by traversing the contour.

It has now been demonstrated that a function is only multivalued around closed contours which enclose the branch point, so it is only necessary to eliminate such contours and the function will become single valued. The simplest way of doing this is to erect a barrier from the branch point to infinity and not allow any curve to cross the barrier. With this convention, no curve can ever enclose the branch point and the function becomes single valued and therefore analytic for all permitted curves. The barrier must

FIG. 4.7.   Barrier erected to isolate branch point

start from the branch point but it can go to infinity in any direction in the z plane, and may be either curved or straight. In most normal applications the barrier is drawn along the negative real axis as shown in Fig. 4.7 so that it confines the function to the region in which the argument of z is within the range $-\pi < \theta < \pi$. This branch is then termed the "principal branch", and the correct name for the barrier is the "branch cut".

The above discussion refers to a single branch point at the origin. If the z plane contains only one branch point which is not at the origin, it is a simple matter to transfer the origin to the branch point. When the z plane contains more than one branch point, it is necessary to draw a branch cut from each branch point to infinity. There is much scope for choosing a suitable set of branch cuts in such cases but no new ideas are involved and this complication does not occur very often in practical applications.

4.15 INTEGRATION OF FUNCTIONS OF COMPLEX VARIABLES, AND CAUCHY'S THEOREM

The successive values of a complex variable z can be represented by a curve in the complex plane, and the function $w = f(z)$ will have a particular value at each point on this curve. Therefore the integral of $f(z)$ with respect to z is the sum of the products $f_M(z)\,\delta z$ along the curve in the complex plane, where $f_M(z)$ is the mean value of $f(z)$ in the length δz of the curve. I.e.

$$\lim_{\delta z \to 0} \sum f_M(z)\,\delta z = \int_C f(z)\,dz \qquad (4.83)$$

where the suffix C under the integral sign specifies the curve in the z plane along which the integration is performed. However, if $w = u + iv = f(z)$, and $z = x + iy$ are substituted into equation (4.83),

$$\int_C f(z)\,dz = \int_C (u + iv)(dx + i\,dy)$$

$$= \int_C (u\,dx - v\,dy) + i \int_C (v\,dx + u\,dy) \qquad (4.84)$$

Equation (4.84) expresses the integration of the complex function $w = f(z)$ with respect to z. If both w and z were real, the integral would become

$$\int_C u\,dx$$

since the values of v and y would be zero, which shows that the integration of real functions is a special case of a contour integration along the real axis.

4.15.1 *Cauchy's Theorem*

If any function is analytic within and upon a closed contour, the integral taken around the contour is zero.

The above theorem can be proved using a very concise procedure by referring to Stokes' theorem, which is

$$\int_C (P\,dx + Q\,dy) = \int\int_A \left(\frac{\partial Q}{\partial x} - \frac{\partial P}{\partial y}\right) dx\,dy \qquad (4.85)$$

where P and Q are functions of x and y, and the surface integral on the right hand side is taken over the area A enclosed by the closed contour C. Stokes' theorem will be proved in Section 7.7.4 to which the reader is referred.

If KLMN represents a closed curve in Fig. 4.8 and there are no singularities of $f(z)$ within or upon the contour, the value of the integral of $f(z)$

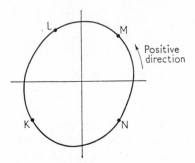

Fig. 4.8.   Contour integration of $f(z)$ around closed curve

around the contour is expressed by equation (4.84); and since the curve is closed, each integral on the right hand side of equation (4.84) can be restated as a surface integral using Stokes' theorem (4.85), thus

$$\int_C (u\,dx - v\,dy) = -\int\int_A \left(\frac{\partial v}{\partial x} + \frac{\partial u}{\partial y}\right) dx\,dy \qquad (4.86)$$

and

$$\int_C (v\,dx + u\,dy) = \int\int_A \left(\frac{\partial u}{\partial x} - \frac{\partial v}{\partial y}\right) dx\,dy \qquad (4.87)$$

But for an analytic function, by the Cauchy-Riemann conditions (4.73) each integral on the right hand side is zero.

$$\therefore \quad \int_C f(z)\,dz = 0 \qquad (4.88)$$

which proves Cauchy's theorem.

In Fig. 4.8, let the region of the complex plane within and upon the contour KLMN contain no singularities.   Therefore a function of z, $f(z)$ will be analytic within and upon the contour and Cauchy's theorem (4.88) is valid.   If now the integration of $f(z)$ is started at the point K on the contour and terminated at the point M, then the value of the integral along the curve KNM will be

$$\int_{KNM} f(z)\,dz \qquad (4.89)$$

This will be positive by the conventional order of the suffices of the integral corresponding with the description of the path of integration. If the integration is continued along MLK following the positive direction of the arrow in Fig. 4.8, the value of the second integral is

$$\int_{MLK} f(z)\,dz \tag{4.90}$$

However, the value of the integral around the closed contour KNMLK is zero by Cauchy's theorem and therefore

$$\int_{KNM} f(z)\,dz + \int_{MLK} f(z)\,dz = 0 \tag{4.91}$$

or reversing the order of the suffices of the second integral and therefore its sign,

$$\int_{KNM} f(z)\,dz = \int_{KLM} f(z)\,dz \tag{4.92}$$

That is, the value of an integral of $f(z)$ between two points in the complex plane is independent of the parth of integation, provided that the function is analytic everywhere within the region containing all of the paths.

Cauchy's theorem and its corollary that the value of the contour integral is independent of the path are of great value for the integration of complex functions of complex variables. The following examples indicate extensions of these ideas.

Example 1. Show that the value of $\int z^2\,dz$ between $z = 0$ and $z = 8+ 6i$ is the same whether the intregation is carried out along the path AB or around the path ACDB in Fig. 4.9.

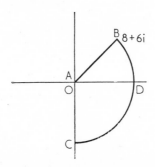

FIG. 4.9.   Two equivalent contours

The path AB is given by the equation

$$y = \tfrac{3}{4}x \qquad\qquad\qquad \text{I}$$

$$\therefore \quad z^2 = (x+\tfrac{3}{4}ix)^2 = \frac{7+24i}{16}x^2 \qquad\qquad \text{II}$$

and
$$dz = dx + \tfrac{3}{4}i\, dx \qquad\qquad\qquad \text{III}$$

$$\therefore \int_{0}^{8+6i} z^2\, dz = \int_{0}^{8} \frac{7+24i}{16} \cdot \frac{4+3i}{4} x^2\, dx \qquad\qquad \text{IV}$$

$$= \frac{-44+117i}{64} \left[\frac{x^3}{3}\right]_{0}^{8}$$

$$= \frac{-352+936i}{3} \qquad\qquad\qquad \text{V}$$

Consider the integration along the curve ACDB in parts.
(a) Along AC, $x = 0$ and thus $z = iy$.

$$\therefore \int_{0}^{-10i} z^2\, dz = -i \int_{0}^{-10} y^2\, dy = \left[-\frac{1}{3} i y^3\right]_{0}^{-10} = \frac{1000i}{3} \qquad \text{VI}$$

(b) The arc CDB is of constant radius 10, $\therefore z = 10e^{i\theta}$.

$$\therefore \int_{-10i}^{8+6i} z^2\, dz = \int_{-\frac{1}{2}\pi}^{\alpha} 100\, e^{2i\theta}\, 10i\, e^{i\theta}\, d\theta \qquad\qquad \text{VII}$$

where
$$\alpha = \tan^{-1}\tfrac{3}{4} = 36°\ 52'$$

$$\therefore \int_{-10i}^{8+6i} z^2\, dz = 1000i \left[\frac{1}{3i} e^{3i\theta}\right]_{-\frac{1}{2}\pi}^{\alpha}$$

$$= \frac{1000}{3}(\cos 3\alpha + i \sin 3\alpha - i)$$

$$= \frac{1000}{3}(-0{\cdot}352 + 0{\cdot}936i - i)$$

$$= \frac{-352-64i}{3} \qquad\qquad\qquad \text{VIII}$$

The complete integral round ACDB is the sum of equations VI and VIII which gives

$$\frac{-352+936i}{3}$$

as before. The integral of z^2 from $z = 0$ to $z = 8+6i$ is thus independent of the path taken.

Example 2. Evaluate $\int_{c} z^{-2}\, dz$ around a circle with its centre at the origin.

Let $z = r e^{i\theta}$, then $dz = ir e^{i\theta}\, d\theta$ since r is constant.

$$\therefore \quad \int_C \frac{dz}{z^2} = \int_0^{2\pi} \frac{ir\,e^{i\theta}\,d\theta}{r^2\,e^{2i\theta}} = \frac{i}{r} \int_0^{2\pi} e^{-i\theta}\,d\theta \qquad \text{I}$$

$$= \frac{i}{r}\left[\frac{e^{-i\theta}}{-i}\right]_0^2$$

$$= 0$$

That is, $\int_C z^{-2}\,dz = 0$ although the function is not analytic at the origin.

Similarly, $\int_C z^{-n}\,dz$ is always zero for any integer value of n other than unity.

Example 3. Evaluate $\int_C \frac{dz}{z}$ around a circle with its centre at the origin.

As in the previous example, put $z = r\,e^{i\theta}$ with r constant.

$$\therefore \quad \int_C \frac{dz}{z} = \int_0^{2\pi} \frac{ir\,e^{i\theta}\,d\theta}{r\,e^{i\theta}}$$

$$= i[\theta]_0^{2\pi}$$

$$= 2\pi i$$

This result is one of the fundamentals of contour integration.

4.15.2. *Cauchy's Integral Formula*

Consider Fig. 4.10 and let a complex function $f(z)$ be analytic upon and within the solid line contour C. Let a be a point within the closed contour

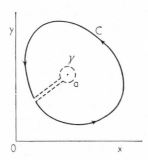

FIG. 4.10.   Integration contour for $\int \frac{f(z)}{z-a}\,dz$

such that $f(a)$ is not zero and define a new function $g(z)$ by

$$g(z) = \frac{f(z)}{z-a} \qquad (4.93)$$

This function is analytic within the contour C except at the point a where a simple pole will exist. If this pole is isolated by drawing a small circle γ around a and joining γ to C as shown dotted in Fig. 4.10, the value of the integral around the complete modified contour will be zero by Cauchy's theorem. The straight dotted lines joining the outside contour C and the inner circle γ are drawn very close together and their paths will be synonymous. Since integration along them will be in opposite directions and $g(z)$ is analytic in the region containing them, the net value of the integral along the straight dotted lines will be zero.

$$\therefore \quad \int_C \frac{f(z)\,dz}{z-a} - \int_\gamma \frac{f(z)\,dz}{z-a} = 0 \tag{4.94}$$

Let the value of $f(z)$ on γ be

$$f(z) = f(a) + \varepsilon \tag{4.95}$$

where ε is a small quantity.

$$\therefore \quad \int_C \frac{f(z)\,dz}{z-a} - \int_\gamma \frac{f(a)\,dz}{z-a} - \int_\gamma \frac{\varepsilon\,dz}{z-a} = 0 \tag{4.96}$$

Since $f(a)$ is constant, the second integral can be evaluated by putting $z = a + r\,e^{i\theta}$, and as θ varies by 2π radians the curve γ is described.

$$\therefore \quad \int_\gamma \frac{f(a)\,dz}{z-a} = if(a) \int_0^{2\pi} \frac{r\,e^{i\theta}\,d\theta}{r\,e^{i\theta}}$$

$$= 2\pi i f(a) \tag{4.97}$$

As the radius of the circle γ tends to zero, ε also tends to zero and the third integral in equation (4.96) becomes insignificant.

$$\therefore \quad f(a) = \frac{1}{2\pi i} \int_C \frac{f(z)\,dz}{z-a} \tag{4.98}$$

which is "Cauchy's Integral Formula". It permits the evaluation of a function at any point within a closed contour when the value of the function on the contour is known.

4.16. Laurent's Expansion and the Theory of Residues

The following section of complex variable theory is paramount to the understanding of the Laplace transformation and its effective application to chemical engineering problems. Laurent's expansion is an extension of Cauchy's integral formula for the case when $f(z)$ has a singularity at some point within the contour C.

For simplicity, take a coordinate system with its origin at the singularity of $f(z)$ and draw two concentric circles C_1 and C_2 centred at the origin so that $f(z)$ is analytic in the annulus between C_1 and C_2. This is illustrated in

Fig. 4.11 where the two circles are also joined by two straight dotted lines which connect the circular contours into one simple continuous closed curve. $f(z)$ is analytic within and upon the complete contour and thus

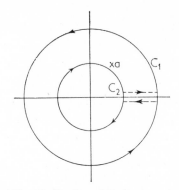

FIG. 4.11.   Verification of the Laurent theorem

Cauchy's integral formula is valid.   Therefore if a is located between C_1 and $\acute{C_2}$, and the two dotted lines are superposed, then

$$f(a) = \frac{1}{2\pi i} \int_{C_1} \frac{f(z)\,dz}{z-a} - \frac{1}{2\pi i} \int_{C_2} \frac{f(z)\,dz}{z-a} \qquad (4.99)$$

where the negative sign indicates that C_2 is described in a negative or clockwise direction.

In the first integral of equation (4.99), $|z| > |a|$ and $(z-a)^{-1}$ can be expanded by the binomial theorem in descending powers of z, thus

$$\frac{1}{z-a} = \frac{1}{z}\left(1 - \frac{a}{z}\right)^{-1} = \frac{1}{z} + \frac{a}{z^2} + \dots + \frac{a^n}{z^{n+1}} + \dots \qquad (4.100)$$

$$= \sum_{n=0}^{\infty} \frac{a^n}{z^{n+1}}$$

Similarly, on curve C_2, $|z| < |a|$ and $(z-a)^{-1}$ can be expanded by the binomial theorem in ascending powers of z, thus

$$\frac{-1}{z-a} = \frac{1}{a}\left(1 - \frac{z}{a}\right)^{-1} = \frac{1}{a} + \frac{z}{a^2} + \dots + \frac{z^{m-1}}{a^m} + \dots \qquad (4.101)$$

$$= \sum_{m=1}^{\infty} \frac{z^{m-1}}{a^m}$$

Substituting the expansions (4.100) and (4.101) into equation (4.99) gives

$$(a) = \frac{1}{2\pi i} \int_{C_1} \sum_{n=0}^{\infty} \frac{f(z)\,dz}{z^{n+1}} a^n + \frac{1}{2\pi i} \int_{C_2} \sum_{m=1}^{\infty} z^{m-1} f(z)\,dz\, a^{-m} \qquad (4.102)$$

If C is any simple continuous closed curve containing the origin with $f(z)$ analytic within and upon C with the exception of the singularity at the origin, then all integrals in equation (4.102) can be taken round the curve C instead of C_1 and C_2.

$$\therefore\ f(a) = \frac{1}{2\pi i} \sum_{n=0}^{\infty} \int_C \frac{f(z)\,dz}{z^{n+1}} a^n + \frac{1}{2\pi i} \sum_{m=1}^{\infty} \int_C z^{m-1} f(z)\,dz\,a^{-m} \qquad (4.103)$$

and putting $m = -n$, the two series can be combined to give

$$f(a) = \sum_{n=-\infty}^{\infty} b_n a^n \qquad (4.104)$$

where
$$b_n = \frac{1}{2\pi i} \int_C \frac{f(z)\,dz}{z^{n+1}} \qquad (4.105)$$

which is the Laurent expansion.

The group of terms for negative values of n is known as the "principal part" of the Laurent expansion near the singularity. If the singularity of $f(z)$ at the origin is a pole of order N, then the second series in equation (4.103) consists of a finite number of terms; because if $m > N$, the integrand consists of positive powers of z and the integrals are zero by Cauchy's theorem. Equation (4.104) can then be written

$$f(z) = \sum_{n=0}^{\infty} C_n z^n + \frac{B_1}{z} + \frac{B_2}{z^2} + \dots + \frac{B_N}{z^N} \qquad (4.106)$$

where $B_n = b_{-n}$ is given by equation (4.105), and a has been replaced in the expansion by z.

Equation (4.106) can be used to obtain the integral of $f(z)$ round any contour C enclosing the singularity as follows. The infinite series of positive powers of z is analytic within and upon C and the integral of these terms will be zero by Cauchy's theorem. Referring to Example 2 in Section 4.15.1, the integral of each of the other terms on the right hand side of equation (4.106) will also be zero except for the term (B_1/z). Example 3 of Section 4.15.1 shows that this integral will be $2\pi i B_1$, or

$$\int_C f(z)\,dz = 2\pi i B_1 \qquad (4.107)$$

Hence the value of the contour integral of a complex function is $2\pi i$ multiplied by the coefficient of z^{-1} in the Laurent expansion of the complex function. This coefficient is known as the "residue" of the function at the pole.

The above analysis is valid when the singularity is not at the origin, thus if the pole is at $z = z_0$, the Laurent expansion is obtained as a series of powers of $(z - z_0)$ and the residue of the function at z_0 is the coefficient of $(z - z_0)^{-1}$ in the Laurent expansion in the neighbourhood of z_0. If the Laurent expansion is valid near an essential singularity, the coefficient B_1 is still termed the residue at the singularity.

Example 1. Evaluate $\displaystyle\int_C \frac{e^z\, dz}{z^3}$ around a contour enclosing the origin.

Expanding the integrand gives

$$\frac{e^z}{z^3} = \frac{1}{z^3}\left[1 + z + \frac{z^2}{2!} + \dots\right] \qquad\qquad \text{I}$$

$$= \frac{1}{z^3} + \frac{1}{z^2} + \frac{1}{2z} + \dots \qquad\qquad \text{II}$$

Equation II is the Laurent expansion of e^z/z^3 near the origin and the coefficient of z^{-1} is $\tfrac{1}{2}$. Therefore the residue at the pole at the origin is $\tfrac{1}{2}$.

$$\therefore \quad \int_C \frac{e^z\, dz}{z^3} = 2\pi i(\tfrac{1}{2}) = \pi i \qquad\qquad \text{III}$$

Example 2. Evaluate $\displaystyle\int_C \frac{e^z\, dz}{(z-a)^3}$ around a circle centred at the origin.

If $|z| < |a|$, the function is analytic within the contour and

$$\int_C \frac{e^z\, dz}{(z-a)^3} = 0 \qquad\qquad \text{I}$$

by Cauchy's theorem.

If $|z| > |a|$, there is a pole of order 3 at $z = a$ within the contour. Therefore transfer the origin to $z = a$ by putting $\lambda = z - a$.
Then

$$\int_C \frac{e^z\, dz}{(z-a)^3} = \int_C \frac{e^{\lambda+a}\, d\lambda}{\lambda^3}$$

$$= e^a \int_C \left[\frac{1}{\lambda^3} + \frac{1}{\lambda^2} + \frac{1}{2!\lambda} + \frac{1}{3!} + \frac{\lambda}{4!} + \dots\right] d\lambda \qquad\qquad \text{II}$$

All integrals on the right hand side are zero except the third term which gives the residue $\tfrac{1}{2}\, e^a$

$$\therefore \quad \int_C \frac{e^{\lambda+a}\, d\lambda}{\lambda^3} = \int_C \frac{e^z\, dz}{(z-a)^3} = 2\pi i(\tfrac{1}{2}e^a) = \pi i\, e^a$$

4.16.1. *Evaluation of Residues without the Laurent Expansion*

With a large number of expressions encountered in applied science, the Laurent expansion is not immediately apparent to engineers. When this is the case, the following procedure is helpful. The complex function $f(z)$ can be expressed in terms of a numerator and a denominator if it has any singularities. That is

$$f(z) = \frac{F(z)}{g(z)} \tag{4.108}$$

and if a simple pole exists at $z = a$, then $(z-a)$ is a factor of $g(z)$ so that $g(z)$ can be written $(z-a)\,G(z)$ with $G(z)$ not zero at $z = a$. Furthermore, the Laurent expansion of $f(z)$ will exist even though it is not apparent, and therefore it can be written in the general form of equation (4.106),

$$f(z) = \frac{B_1}{z-a} + b_0 + b_1(z-a) + \ldots + b_n(z-a)^n + \ldots \tag{4.109}$$

Equation (4.109) has been terminated at the first inverse term because there is only a simple pole at $z = a$. Multiplying both sides by $(z-a)$ and then putting $z = a$ gives

$$B_1 = (z-a)f(z)\big|_{z=a} = F(a)/G(a) \tag{4.110}$$

which evaluates the residue at a simple pole. This is a very convenient method which will be illustrated by examples below, but certain points must be emphasized first. Thus in equation (4.108), $g(z)$ must contain one more factor $(z-a)$ than $F(z)$ for $f(z)$ to have a simple pole. Finally, if $g(z)$ has a number of factors so that

$$f(z) = \frac{F(z)}{(z-a_1)(z-a_2)(\ldots)(z-a_n)} \tag{4.111}$$

$f(z)$ will have a residue at each pole, $z = a_1, a_2, \ldots a_n$. Each residue can be evaluated independently by the method given above.

Example 3. Evaluate the residues of $\dfrac{z}{z^2+z-12}$

$$f(z) = \frac{z}{z^2+z-12} = \frac{z}{(z+4)(z-3)}$$

which has poles at $z = 3$ and $z = -4$.

Using equation (4.110), the residue at $z = 3$ is $3/7$; and the residue at $z = -4$ is $-4/(-7) = 4/7$.

The sum of the residues is

$$\tfrac{3}{7} + \tfrac{4}{7} = 1$$

Example 4. Evaluate the residues of $\dfrac{e^z}{z^2+w^2}$

$$f(z) = \frac{e^z}{(z+iw)(z-iw)} \qquad\qquad \text{I}$$

which has poles at $z = \pm iw$.
The residue at the pole $z = iw$ is

$$\frac{e^z}{z+iw} = \frac{e^{iw}}{2iw} \qquad\qquad \text{II}$$

The residue at the pole $z = -iw$ is

$$\frac{e^z}{z - iw} = \frac{-e^{-iw}}{2iw} \qquad \text{III}$$

The sum of the residues of $e^z/(z^2 + w^2)$ is

$$\frac{e^{iw} - e^{-iw}}{2iw} = \frac{\sin w}{w} \qquad \text{IV}$$

The above method of determining the residue of a function appears to depend on the factorization of the denominator. However, the method is generally applicable to the evaluation of the residue at a simple pole even when the denominator cannot be factorized. If $f(z)$ is expressed as in equation (4.108) and the denominator $g(z)$ does not factorize, the same procedure may still be followed. Thus the residue of $f(z)$ at $z = a$ is

$$B_1 = \frac{(z - a)F(z)}{g(z)}\bigg|_{z=a} = \frac{0}{0} \qquad (4.112)$$

which is indeterminate. Therefore, by L'Hôpital's rule, Section 3.3.8,

$$\frac{d(z - a)F(z)/dz}{dg(z)/dz} = \frac{F(z) + (z - a)F'(z)}{g'(z)}$$

$$\therefore \quad B_1 = \frac{F(a)}{g'(a)} \qquad (4.113)$$

where $g'(a)$ is the differential coefficient of $g(z)$ with respect to z, evaluated at $z = a$.

Example 5. Evaluate $\displaystyle\int_C \frac{e^z \, dz}{\sin nz}$ around a circle with centre at the origin and radius $|z| < \pi/n$.

The residue at the pole where $z = 0$ is given by equation (4.113) as

$$B_1 = \frac{e^z}{d \sin nz/dz}\bigg|_{z=0} = \frac{e^z}{n \cos nz}\bigg|_{z=0} = \frac{1}{n}$$

$$\therefore \quad \int_C \frac{e^z \, dz}{\sin nz} = 2\pi i \left(\frac{1}{n}\right) = \frac{2\pi i}{n}$$

4.16.2. *Evaluation of Residues at Multiple Poles*

If $f(z)$ has a pole of order n at $z = a$ and no other singularity, $f(z)$ can be written in the form

$$f(z) = \frac{F(z)}{(z - a)^n} \qquad (4.114)$$

where n is a finite integer, and $F(z)$ is analytic at $z = a$. $F(z)$ can be expanded by the Taylor series to give

$$F(z) = F(a) + (z - a)F'(a) + \frac{(z - a)^2}{2!}F''(a) + \dots + \frac{(z - a)^n}{n!}F^n(a) + \dots \quad (4.115)$$

Dividing throughout by $(z-a)^n$ gives

$$f(z) = \frac{F(a)}{(z-a)^n} + \frac{F'(a)}{(z-a)^{n-1}} + \dots + \frac{F^{n-1}(a)}{(n-1)!(z-a)} + \dots \qquad (4.116)$$

which is the Laurent expansion of $f(z)$ and therefore the residue at $z = a$ is the coefficient of $(z-a)^{-1}$ in equation (4.116). Therefore, the residue at a pole of order n situated at $z = a$ is given by

$$B_1 = \frac{1}{(n-1)!}\frac{d^{n-1}}{dz^{n-1}}[(z-a)^n f(z)] \qquad (4.117)$$

This reduces to equation (4.110) for a simple pole when $n = 1$.

Example 6.   Evaluate $\displaystyle\int_C \frac{\cos 2z\, dz}{(z-a)^3}$ around a circle of radius $|z| > |a|$.

$\dfrac{\cos 2z}{(z-a)^3}$ has a pole of order 3 at $z = a$, and the residue must be evaluated using equation (4.117).

$$\therefore \quad B_1 = \frac{1}{2!}\frac{d^2}{dz^2}\left[\frac{(z-a)^3 \cos 2z}{(z-a)^3}\right]_{z=a}$$

$$= \tfrac{1}{2}(-4\cos 2z)\big|_{z=a}$$

$$= -2\cos 2a$$

$$\therefore \quad \int_C \frac{\cos 2z\, dz}{(z-a)^3} = 2\pi i(-2\cos 2a) = -4\pi i\cos 2a$$

Chapter 5

FUNCTIONS AND DEFINITE INTEGRALS

5.1. INTRODUCTION

THE study of differential equations is one of the many branches of mathematics in which the object is to determine a functional relationship between two or more variables. The symbolism which is used to describe these functional relationships is largely a matter of convention; when a particular symbol is found convenient, it enters general usage and its properties are investigated. Elementary functions such as polynomials, powers, logarithms, exponentials, trigonometric and hyperbolic functions should be familiar to the reader already, and in Chapter 3 it was shown that the four kinds of Bessel function were useful for expressing the solutions of a particular class of differential equations. Other functions have been defined as the solutions of differential equations, and the Legendre polynomials which will be introduced in Chapter 8 is one such group.

Functions are also defined by integrals which cannot be evaluated in terms of the above elementary functions, and the purpose of this present chapter is to introduce some of these functions, enunciate their properties, and draw attention to their tabulated values as an aid to calculation. It will be shown that a variety of integrals can be expressed in terms of these new functions and thus be evaluated from tables.

Methods for evaluating some definite integrals by contour integration were presented in Chapter 4, and a further method by differentiating with respect to a parameter will be included in the present chapter

5.2 THE ERROR FUNCTION

This function which occurs in the theory of probability, distribution of residence times, conduction of heat, and diffusion of matter, is defined by the integral,

$$\operatorname{erf} x = \frac{2}{\sqrt{\pi}} \int_0^x e^{-z^2} \, dz \tag{5.1}$$

The error function is illustrated in Fig. 5.1 which shows erf x as the area beneath the curve and between the ordinates $z = 0$ and $z = x$ when $2/\sqrt{\pi}$ exp $(-z^2)$ is plotted against z. In equation (5.1), z is a "dummy variable" because it only enables the curve of Fig. 5.1 to be described and any variable would do this. The variable z is eliminated by the limits of integration thus

F   149

FIG. 5.1. The error function

leaving x as the only variable. The factor $2/\sqrt{\pi}$ is introduced for convenience so that

$$\text{erf } \infty = 1 \tag{5.2}$$

The truth of equation (5.2) can be proved by the following argument. To simplify the algebra, remove the normalizing factor $2/\sqrt{\pi}$ and consider two versions of the integral, thus

$$I = \int_0^R e^{-x^2}\,dx = \int_0^R e^{-y^2}\,dy \tag{5.3}$$

Considering that x and y are two independent cartesian coordinates, equation (5.3) can be written

$$I^2 = \int_0^R \int_0^R e^{-(x^2+y^2)}\,dx\,dy \tag{5.4}$$

which can be interpreted as a volume as shown in Fig. 5.2. If the variables

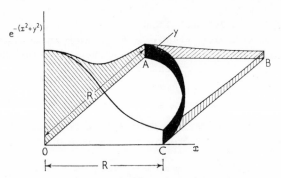

FIG. 5.2. Evaluation of erf ∞

x and y are changed to polar coordinates r and θ using the equations

$$x = r\cos\theta, \qquad y = r\sin\theta \tag{5.5}$$

then the element of area $(dx\,dy)$ has to be replaced by $(r\,dr\,d\theta)$. Also, the range of integration has to be altered from the square OABC, to the quadrant OAC which results in an error denoted by ε. Thus, equation (5.4) can be written

$$I^2 = \int_0^R \int_0^{\pi/2} e^{-r^2} r \, dr \, d\theta + \varepsilon \tag{5.6}$$

The volume represented by ε has a base area which is less than $\frac{1}{2} R^2$ and a maximum height of $\exp(-R^2)$. Thus

$$\varepsilon < \tfrac{1}{2} R^2 \exp(-R^2) \tag{5.7}$$

and as $R \to \infty$, $\varepsilon \to 0$.

Evaluating the double integral in equation (5.6) gives

$$I^2 = \tfrac{1}{4}\pi - \tfrac{1}{4}\pi \exp(-R^2) + \varepsilon \tag{5.8}$$

Therefore, as $R \to \infty$, $I^2 \to \tfrac{1}{4}\pi$. Comparing equations (5.1) and (5.3) gives the required result which is equation (5.2).

5.2.1. *Properties of the Error Function*

Differentiating equation (5.1) gives directly

$$\frac{d}{dx}\operatorname{erf} x = \frac{2}{\sqrt{\pi}} e^{-x^2} \tag{5.9}$$

Using this result to integrate equation (5.1) by parts gives

$$\int \operatorname{erf} x \, dx = x \operatorname{erf} x - \int x \frac{2}{\sqrt{\pi}} e^{-x^2} \, dx + C$$

$$= x \operatorname{erf} x + \frac{1}{\sqrt{\pi}} \exp(-x^2) + C \tag{5.10}$$

where C is the constant of integration. Equation (5.10) is sometimes tabulated under the symbol "ierf x" with $C = -1/\sqrt{\pi}$ so that ierf $0 = 0$.

Another related function which is sometimes tabulated is the complementary error function "erfc x". This is defined by the equation

$$\operatorname{erfc} x = 1 - \operatorname{erf} x$$

$$= \frac{2}{\sqrt{\pi}} \int_x^\infty e^{-z^2} \, dz \tag{5.11}$$

5.3. The Gamma Function

This is defined by the integral

$$\Gamma(n) = \int_0^\infty t^{n-1} e^{-t} \, dt \tag{5.12}$$

for positive values of n. t is again a dummy variable since the value of the definite integral is independent of t. The variable t is only used to describe the function to be integrated. As an illustration of this fact, take the special case $n = 1$, thus

$$\Gamma(1) = \int_0^\infty e^{-t}\, dt$$

$$\therefore \quad \Gamma(1) = 1 \tag{5.13}$$

which is independent of t.

The most important property of the gamma function can be derived by integrating equation (5.12) by parts.

$$\Gamma(n) = \int_0^\infty t^{n-1} e^{-t}\, dt$$

$$= [-t^{n-1} e^{-t}]_0^\infty + (n-1) \int_0^\infty t^{n-2} e^{-t}\, dt$$

$$\therefore \quad \Gamma(n) = (n-1)\Gamma(n-1) \tag{5.14}$$

since the first term is zero at both limits of integration provided that $n > 1$.

Repeated applications of equation (5.14) for integer values of n gives

$$\Gamma(n) = (n-1)(n-2)(...)(2)(1)\Gamma(1)$$

$$= (n-1)! \tag{5.15}$$

by using equation (5.13). The gamma function is thus a generalized factorial, and for positive integer values of n, the gamma function can be replaced by a factorial as given by equation (5.15). For non-integer values of n, the defining integral (5.12) has been evaluated numerically for $1 < n < 2$ and this table can be extended to all positive values of n by repeated use of equation (5.14).

The defining integral (5.12) is not valid for negative values of n, but the gamma function of a negative quantity can be found by using equation (5.14) to extend the definition. Thus, rearranging equation (5.14),

$$\Gamma(n-1) = \Gamma(n)/(n-1)$$

$$= \Gamma(n+1)/n(n-1) \tag{5.16}$$

etc.

This process can be repeated until the gamma function on the right hand side has an argument lying in the range 1 to 2. However, if n is zero or a negative integer, the gamma function becomes infinite. An example of this can be seen by putting $n = 1$ into equation (5.14), thus

$$\Gamma(1) = 0\Gamma(0) \tag{5.17}$$

But equation (5.13) shows that $\Gamma(1) = 1$. Therefore, $\Gamma(0)$ must be infinite to satisfy equation (5.17). It is obvious that the sequence of operations (5.16) will eventually involve $\Gamma(0)$ whenever n is a negative integer, and thus the gamma function is infinite for all negative integers.

Figure 5.3 shows how $\Gamma(n)$ varies with n. For negative values of n, $\Gamma(n)$ is alternatively positive and negative between successive integer values, and

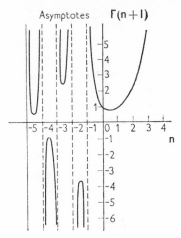

Asymptotes $\Gamma(n+1)$

FIG. 5.3.   The gamma function

for positive values of n the curve has a minimum value of $0\cdot8856$ at $n = 1\cdot4616$.

$\Gamma(\frac{1}{2})$ can also be evaluated analytically as follows. By definition, equation (5.12),

$$\Gamma(\tfrac{1}{2}) = \int_0^\infty t^{-\frac{1}{2}} e^{-t}\, dt \tag{5.18}$$

The negative square root can be removed by making the substitution $t = x^2$,

$$\therefore \quad dt = 2x\, dx.$$

$$\therefore \quad \Gamma(\tfrac{1}{2}) = \int_0^\infty x^{-1} e^{-x^2} 2x\, dx$$

$$= 2\int_0^\infty e^{-x^2}\, dx \tag{5.19}$$

Comparing equations (5.19) and (5.1) gives

$$\Gamma(\tfrac{1}{2}) = \sqrt{\pi}\,\operatorname{erf}\infty$$

and using equation (5.2) gives finally,

$$\Gamma(\tfrac{1}{2}) = \sqrt{\pi} \tag{5.20}$$

Other half integer gamma functions can be found using equations (5.14) and (5.16), as illustrated by the following examples.

Example 1.   Evaluate $\Gamma(3\frac{1}{2})$.

Successive application of equation (5.14) gives

$$\Gamma(3\tfrac{1}{2}) = \tfrac{5}{2}\Gamma(2\tfrac{1}{2})$$

$$= \tfrac{5}{2} \cdot \tfrac{3}{2} \cdot \tfrac{1}{2} \Gamma(\tfrac{1}{2})$$

$$= \tfrac{5}{2} \cdot \tfrac{3}{2} \cdot \tfrac{1}{2} \sqrt{\pi}$$

by equation (5.20).

$$\therefore \quad \Gamma(3\tfrac{1}{2}) = \tfrac{15}{8} \sqrt{\pi}$$

Example 2. Evaluate $\Gamma(-2\tfrac{1}{2})$.
Application of equation (5.16) gives

$$\Gamma(-2\tfrac{1}{2}) = \frac{-2}{5} \Gamma(-1\tfrac{1}{2})$$

$$= \frac{-2}{5} \cdot \frac{-2}{3} \cdot \frac{-2}{1} \Gamma(\tfrac{1}{2})$$

$$= \frac{-8}{15} \sqrt{\pi}$$

Example 3. Evaluate $\Gamma(3 \cdot 7)$.
Application of equation (5.14) gives

$$\Gamma(3 \cdot 7) = 2 \cdot 7 \Gamma(2 \cdot 7)$$

$$= 2 \cdot 7 (1 \cdot 7) \Gamma(1 \cdot 7)$$

$$= 4 \cdot 59 \Gamma(1 \cdot 7)$$

From tables, it can be found that

$$\Gamma(1 \cdot 7) = 0 \cdot 90864$$

$$\therefore \quad \Gamma(3 \cdot 7) = 4 \cdot 1707$$

5.4. THE BETA FUNCTION

This is yet another function which is defined by an integral, but the beta function contains two parameters instead of one, and the integral is taken between fixed finite limits. Viz.

$$B(p, q) = \int_0^1 t^{p-1} (1-t)^{q-1} \, dt \qquad (5.21)$$

Both p and q must be positive to ensure convergence of the integral at its limits.

An alternative form can be obtained for the defining integral by making the substitution $t = \sin^2 \theta$, $1 - t = \cos^2 \theta$, $\therefore dt = 2 \sin \theta \cos \theta d\theta$. Thus

$$B(p, q) = 2 \int_0^{\pi/2} \sin^{2p-1} \theta \cos^{2q-1} \theta \, d\theta \qquad (5.22)$$

By substituting $t = \cos^2 \theta$ in equation (5.21), an equation can be obtained which is similar to equation (5.22) but with p and q interchanged, thus showing that the beta function is symmetrical in its two arguments p and q.

A further useful substitution into equation (5.21) is

$$t = \frac{x}{1+x}, \qquad 1-t = \frac{1}{1+x}, \qquad dt = \frac{dx}{(1+x)^2},$$

which gives

$$B(p,q) = \int_0^\infty \frac{x^{p-1}\,dx}{(1+x)^{p+q}} \tag{5.23}$$

5.4.1. *Evaluation of* $B(1-q, q)$

For the special case $p+q = 1$, equation (5.23) becomes

$$B(1-q, q) = \int_0^\infty \frac{x^{-q}\,dx}{1+x} \tag{5.24}$$

This integral can be evaluated by contour integration using the methods developed in Chapter 4 as follows.

Consider integrating $z^{-q}/(1-z)$ round the contour shown in Fig. 5.4 where the complex z plane has a branch cut along the negative real axis

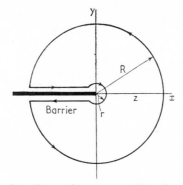

Fig. 5.4.   Integration contour of beta function

because q is not an integer. The contour consists of a circle C_R of large radius R described anti-clockwise, and a circle C_r of small radius r described clockwise. The two circles which cannot cross the branch cut, are joined on either side of the branch cut by straight lines. The only pole enclosed by this contour is at $z = 1$ (provided $r < 1 < R$) and the residue at this simple pole is unity by equation (4.113). Consider the four sections of the integral separately.

On C_R,

$$\left| \frac{1}{1-z} \right| < \frac{1}{R-1}, \quad \text{and if } q > 0,$$

$$\left| \int_{C_R} \frac{z^{-q}\,dz}{1-z} \right| < \frac{\pi R^{1-q}}{R-1} \to 0 \quad \text{as } R \to \infty \tag{5.25}$$

On C_r, $\left|\dfrac{1}{1-z}\right| < \dfrac{1}{1-r}$, and if $q < 1$,

$$\left|\int_{C_r} \frac{z^{-q}\,dz}{1-z}\right| < \frac{\pi r^{1-q}}{1-r} \to 0 \quad \text{as } r \to 0 \tag{5.26}$$

On the upper side of the branch cut where $z = x\,e^{i\pi}$ and x varies from R to r, the integral takes the form

$$\int_R^r \frac{x^{-q}\,e^{-iq\pi}}{1+x}\,dx \tag{5.27}$$

and on the lower side of the branch cut where $z = x\,e^{-i\pi}$ and x varies from r to R, the integral takes the form,

$$\int_r^R \frac{x^{-q}\,e^{iq\pi}}{1+x}\,dx \tag{5.28}$$

Putting these four parts of the contour integral together and equating them to $2\pi i$ (residue at $z = 1$) gives

$$(e^{iq\pi} - e^{-iq\pi})\int_0^\infty \frac{x^{-q}\,dx}{1+x} = 2\pi i \tag{5.29}$$

where the limits $r \to 0$ and $R \to \infty$ have been taken. Using equation (4.58) to introduce the trigonometrical function gives the result,

$$\int_0^\infty \frac{x^{-q}\,dx}{1+x} = \frac{\pi}{\sin q\pi} \tag{5.30}$$

Putting this value for the integral into equation (5.24) gives

$$B(1-q, q) = \frac{\pi}{\sin q\pi} \tag{5.31}$$

for $0 < q < 1$.

5.4.2. Relationship between Beta and Gamma Functions

Make the substitution $t = x^2$ in the definition of the gamma function (5.12)

$$\therefore \quad \Gamma(p) = 2\int_0^\infty x^{2p-1}\,e^{-x^2}\,dx \tag{5.32}$$

Define a second gamma function using a similar dummy variable y and consider the product of the two gamma functions.

$$\Gamma(p)\Gamma(q) = 4\int_0^\infty\int_0^\infty x^{2p-1}\,y^{2q-1}\,e^{-(x^2+y^2)}\,dx\,dy \tag{5.33}$$

This double integral can be evaluated as in Section 5.2 by changing to polar coordinates using equations (5.5). The transformation can be justified as before and equation (5.33) becomes

$$\Gamma(p)\Gamma(q) = 2 \int_0^{\pi/2} \cos^{2p-1}\theta \sin^{2q-1}\theta \, d\theta . 2 \int_0^{\infty} e^{-r^2} r^{2p+2q-1} \, dr \quad (5.34)$$

Comparing the first integral with equation (5.22), and the second integral with equation (5.32) shows that

$$\Gamma(p)\Gamma(q) = B(p,q)\Gamma(p+q) \quad (5.35)$$

for all positive values of p and q.

In the special case $p+q = 1$, using equations (5.13) and (5.31) proves the useful formula

$$\Gamma(q)\Gamma(1-q) = \pi/\sin q\pi \quad (5.36)$$

which is valid for $0 < q < 1$. Examination of Examples 1 and 2 in Section 5.3 indicates that equation (5.36) is valid for all values of q, although it is of no use for integer q.

5.5. OTHER TABULATED FUNCTIONS WHICH ARE DEFINED BY INTEGRALS

There are many other functions arising in engineering which cannot be integrated analytically in terms of elementary functions. Since the values of many integrals have been tabulated, much numerical work can be avoided if the integral to be evaluated can be altered to a form that is tabulated. This section contains primarily the definitions and terminology of some of these functions, and a description of their general behaviour. Their properties are neither so well known nor so important as those of the earlier functions in this chapter, nevertheless, a knowledge of the definitions is valuable particularly when using the Laplace Transform.

5.5.1. *The Elliptic Integral of the First Kind*

This is usually defined by

$$F(k,\phi) = \int_0^{\phi} \frac{d\Phi}{\sqrt{(1-k^2\sin^2\Phi)}} \quad (5.37)$$

where k is termed the "modulus" and ϕ the "amplitude". The integral occurs in the study of periodic motions when the amplitude is not small and the motion is not therefore simple harmonic. Hence the terminology for k and ϕ. The complete elliptic integral of the first kind is a function of k only and is defined by

$$F(k,\tfrac{1}{2}\pi) = K(k) \quad (5.38)$$

5.5.2. *The Elliptic Integral of the Second Kind*

This is defined in a similar manner by

$$E(k, \phi) = \int_0^\phi \sqrt{1 - k^2 \sin^2 \Phi}\, d\Phi \tag{5.39}$$

where again k is the modulus and ϕ the amplitude. This integral measures length round the arc of an ellipse from the minor axis, where ϕ is the complement of the normal parametric variable of an ellipse, and k is its eccentricity. The above connection with the geometry of the ellipse gives rise to the name "elliptic integral". The complete elliptic integral of the second kind is again defined as

$$E(k, \tfrac{1}{2}\pi) = E(k) \tag{5.40}$$

5.5.3. *The Sine, Cosine, and Exponential Integrals*

$$Si(x) = \int_0^x \frac{\sin t}{t}\, dt \tag{5.41}$$

$$Ci(x) = \int_\infty^x \frac{\cos t}{t}\, dt \tag{5.42}$$

$$Ei(x) = \int_{-\infty}^x \frac{e^t}{t}\, dt \tag{5.43}$$

$$-Ei(-x) = \int_x^\infty \frac{e^{-t}}{t}\, dt \tag{5.44}$$

Of this group of functions, only the sine integral remains finite at the origin. All of the other functions are infinite at the origin; also, $Ei(x)$ is infinite as $x \to \infty$, and $Ei(-x)$ is infinite as $x \to -\infty$.

Although the sine integral cannot be evaluated in terms of elementary functions, it is possible to evaluate $Si(\infty)$. The integrand of equation (5.41) is an even function, so that

$$Si(\infty) = \frac{1}{2} \int_{-\infty}^\infty \frac{\sin t}{t}\, dt \tag{5.45}$$

and integrating a suitable function round a closed contour in the complex plane, the integral can be evaluated.

An alternative and simpler method is to introduce a suitable parameter α and evaluate the integral as follows. Define

$$I(\alpha) = \int_0^\infty \frac{e^{-\alpha t} \sin t}{t}\, dt \tag{5.46}$$

and differentiate equation (5.46) with respect to α thus,

$$\frac{dI}{d\alpha} = -\int_0^\infty e^{-\alpha t} \sin t \, dt \tag{5.47}$$

Equation (5.47) can be integrated by parts twice, or a complex method can be adopted.

$$\frac{dI}{d\alpha} = -\operatorname{Im} \int_0^\infty e^{-\alpha t} e^{it} \, dt$$

$$= \operatorname{Im}\left[\frac{1}{\alpha-i} e^{-(\alpha-i)t}\right]_0^\infty$$

$$= -\operatorname{Im}\left[\frac{\alpha+i}{\alpha^2+1}\right]$$

$$= -\operatorname{Im}\left[\frac{\alpha}{\alpha^2+1} + i\frac{1}{\alpha^2+1}\right]$$

$$\therefore \quad \frac{dI}{d\alpha} = -\frac{1}{\alpha^2+1} \tag{5.48}$$

On integration, this yields

$$I = -\int \frac{d\alpha}{\alpha^2+1}$$

$$\therefore \quad I = A - \tan^{-1}\alpha \tag{5.49}$$

where A is an arbitrary constant which can be evaluated from a known result at any value of α. When $\alpha = \infty$, equation (5.46) shows $I(\alpha) = 0$.

$$\therefore \quad 0 = A - \tfrac{1}{2}\pi$$

Substituting this value of A into equation (5.49) gives

$$I(\alpha) = \tfrac{1}{2}\pi - \tan^{-1}\alpha \tag{5.50}$$

The infinite sine integral (5.45) is given by equation (5.46) with $\alpha = 0$, therefore from equation (5.50),

$$I(0) = \tfrac{1}{2}\pi$$

and

$$Si(\infty) = \int_0^\infty \frac{\sin t}{t} dt = \tfrac{1}{2}\pi \tag{5.51}$$

5.6. EVALUATION OF DEFINITE INTEGRALS

The method used above to evaluate $Si(\infty)$ is of wider application, particularly in some of the transform methods given in Chapter 8. It is often unnecessary to introduce a parameter such as α above, because a suitable parameter is already present within the integral. Consider the following examples of integrals of this type.

Example 1. Evaluate

$$I(\alpha) = \int_0^\infty \frac{\sin^2 \alpha x}{x^2} \, dx \qquad\qquad \text{I}$$

As in the standard functions earlier in this chapter, x is a dummy variable so that $I(\alpha)$ is a function of α only. Differentiate equation I with respect to α.

$$\therefore \quad \frac{dI}{d\alpha} = \int_0^\infty \frac{2 \sin \alpha x \cos \alpha x}{x} \, dx$$

$$= \int_0^\infty \frac{\sin 2\alpha x}{x} \, dx \qquad\qquad \text{II}$$

But with a simple change of variable ($t = 2\alpha x$), the integral in equation II is given by equation (5.51) as

$$Si(\infty) = \tfrac{1}{2}\pi$$

$$\therefore \quad \frac{dI}{d\alpha} = \tfrac{1}{2}\pi \qquad\qquad \text{III}$$

Integration of equation III gives

$$I = \tfrac{1}{2}\pi\alpha + A$$

where A is a constant of integration. As before, A can be evaluated by using the known result for any particular value of α. Thus if $\alpha = 0$, equation I gives, $I(\alpha) = 0$. Hence the final result,

$$I(\alpha) = \int_0^\infty \frac{\sin^2 \alpha x}{x^2} \, dx = \tfrac{1}{2}\pi\alpha \qquad\qquad \text{IV}$$

Example 2. Evaluate

$$I(\alpha) = \int_0^\infty e^{-x^2} \frac{\sin 2\alpha x}{x} \, dx \qquad\qquad \text{I}$$

This is a much more difficult example, however, following the same method and differentiating equation I with respect to α.

$$\therefore \quad \frac{dI}{d\alpha} = \int_0^\infty 2 e^{-x^2} \cos 2\alpha x \, dx \qquad\qquad \text{II}$$

The primary effect of this differentiation has been to remove the term x from the denominator of the integrand. A further differentiation will introduce a factor x into the numerator and facilitate an integration by parts, thus,

$$\frac{d^2I}{d\alpha^2} = -\int_0^\infty 4x\, e^{-x^2} \sin 2\alpha x \, dx \qquad \text{III}$$

$$= \left[2e^{-x^2} \sin 2\alpha x - \int 4\alpha\, e^{-x^2} \cos 2\alpha x \, dx \right]_0^\infty \qquad \text{IV}$$

On the right hand side of equation IV, the first term vanishes at both limits, and the second term is a constant multiple of the right hand side of equation II. Therefore,

$$\frac{d^2I}{d\alpha^2} = -2\alpha \frac{dI}{d\alpha} \qquad \text{V}$$

The dependent variable does not occur explicitly in equation V and the method of Section 2.4.1 can be used. Thus, put

$$p = \frac{dI}{d\alpha} \qquad \text{VI}$$

separate the variables, and obtain the solution for p in terms of α. Viz.

$$p = A\, e^{-\alpha^2} \qquad \text{VII}$$

where A is the constant of integration which can be evaluated for the special case $\alpha = 0$, when equation II gives

$$p = \frac{dI}{d\alpha} = \sqrt{\pi}\, \text{erf}\, \infty = \sqrt{\pi}$$

$$\therefore \quad p = \frac{dI}{d\alpha} = \sqrt{\pi}\, e^{-\alpha^2} \qquad \text{VIII}$$

Integrating again with respect to α, and using equation (5.1),

$$I = \tfrac{1}{2}\pi\, \text{erf}\, \alpha + B \qquad \text{IX}$$

where B, the constant of integration, can be evaluated by using equation I when $\alpha = 0$. Thus,

if $\qquad\qquad \alpha = 0, I = 0; \therefore B = 0.$

The evaluation of the integral in equation I is thus

$$I(\alpha) = \int_0^\infty e^{-x^2} \frac{\sin 2\alpha x}{x} \, dx = \tfrac{1}{2}\pi\, \text{erf}\, \alpha \qquad \text{X}$$

The above method consists essentially of finding a differential equation V which the given integral satisfies, solving the differential equation and hence obtaining an alternative form for the solution. This process will inevitably introduce arbitrary constants of integration and these must be evaluated by referring to the original integral which is the desired particular solution of the differential equation.

In the first example, the integral was shown to be a solution of the simple first order differential equation III; and in the previous section, $Si(\infty)$ was shown to be a solution of equation (5.48). In all three cases therefore, the method is the same but the details are different. It is not always possible to find a suitable differential equation; for example the gamma function defined by equation (5.12) does not satisfy any differential equation with rational coefficients. Nevertheless, the above method and the method of contour integration are two advanced techniques which will successfully evaluate many definite integrals.

Tables of the functions discussed in this chapter are readily available in:—

Dwight, H. B. "Mathematical Tables" (2nd Ed.), Dover (1958).
Jahnke, E. and Emde, F. "Tables of Functions" (4th Ed.), Dover (1945).
"Standard Mathematical Tables" (11th Ed.), Chemical Rubber Publishing Company (1957).

An index of published tables has been compiled by Fletcher, Miller and Rosenhead.†

† Fletcher, A., Miller, J. C. P. and Rosenhead, L. "An Index of Mathematical Tables," Scientific Computing Services, London (1946).

Chapter 6

THE LAPLACE TRANSFORMATION

6.1. INTRODUCTION

THE Laplace transformation is the name given to a particular "operational method" of solving differential equations. Essentially, an operational method is a technique whereby an ordinary differential equation is converted into an equivalent algebraic form which can be solved by the laws of elementary algebra. The method will also convert a partial differential equation into an equivalent easily solvable ordinary differential equation. There are many such operational methods but the Laplace transformation is a particularly useful mathematical tool for solving engineering problems because the boundary conditions are introduced into the equation prior to its solution.

The application of operational methods for the solution of engineering problems was first made by Heaviside (1850–1925), and although his methods were largely intuitive they were successful. This stimulated the interest of other mathematicians who developed the theoretical basis of Heaviside's methods and extended them into what is known as the Laplace transformation. The essential features of the method and its application to the solution of chemical engineering problems involving ordinary differential equations are presented in the following sections, although the methods of Chapter 2 are normally used for solving these problems. The most useful applications of the Laplace transformation, to partial differential equations and difference-differential equations, will be given in Chapters 8 and 9 respectively.

6.2. THE LAPLACE TRANSFORM

If $f(t)$ is a continuous function of an independent variable t for all values of t greater than zero, then the integral with respect to t of the product of $f(t)$ with e^{-st} between the limits 0 and ∞ is defined as the Laplace transform of $f(t)$. I.e.

$$\int_0^\infty e^{-st} f(t)\, dt = \mathscr{L}[f(t)] \tag{6.1}$$

For the present, the only conditions that will be placed on the integral in equation (6.1) are that the parameter s must be large enough to make the integral convergent at the upper limit, and t must be positive.

The Laplace transform of a function can be denoted by placing "$\mathscr{L}$" before the function as shown in equation (6.1). To be exact, this signifies that the operation of the Laplace transformation has been carried out on the function $f(t)$ and the modern practice is to write $\bar{f}(s)$ for the transform of the function to imply the connection between $f(t)$ and its transform $\bar{f}(s)$. Thus

$$\mathscr{L}[f(t)] = \bar{f}(s) \tag{6.2}$$

To familiarize the reader with the method, the Laplace transforms of some simple functions will now be derived. Thus if $f(t) = 1$, then

$$\mathscr{L}[1] = \int_0^\infty 1\,e^{-st}\,dt = \left[\frac{e^{-st}}{-s}\right]_0^\infty = \frac{1}{s} \tag{6.3}$$

or $\bar{f}(s) = 1/s$.

From equation (6.3) it can be seen that the Laplace transform of a constant K is

$$\mathscr{L}[K] = K\mathscr{L}[1] = K/s \tag{6.4}$$

since the constant can be inside or outside the integral in equation (6.3). This simple result follows from the fact that the Laplace transformation is a linear operation.

To illustrate the procedure further, let the Laplace transform of t^n be required. Thus

$$\mathscr{L}[t^n] = \int_0^\infty t^n e^{-st}\,dt \tag{6.5}$$

The integration variable in equation (6.5) can be changed by putting

$$z = st$$

$$\therefore \quad dz = s\,dt$$

$$\therefore \quad \mathscr{L}[t^n] = s^{-n-1}\int_0^\infty z^n e^{-z}\,dz \tag{6.6}$$

Comparing equation (6.6) with the definition of the gamma function, equation (5.12), gives

$$\mathscr{L}[t^n] = \Gamma(n+1)/s^{n+1} \tag{6.7}$$

If n is a positive integer, the property of the gamma function given by equation (5.15) shows that

$$\mathscr{L}[t^n] = n\,!/s^{n+1} \tag{6.8}$$

Finally, let $f(t) = e^{at}$; and the Laplace transform of this function is

$$\bar{f}(s) = \int_0^\infty e^{at}e^{-st}\,dt = \int_0^\infty e^{-(s-a)t}\,dt = \frac{1}{s-a} \tag{6.9}$$

In the same way the Laplace transforms of other simple functions can be obtained. Some simple transforms are shown in Table 6.1, and the reader is encouraged to verify each of the examples given. A more complete table of Laplace transforms is given at the end of the book.

TABLE 6.1. *Elementary Transforms*

$f(t)$	$\bar{f}(s)$
K	K/s
t^n	$\dfrac{n!}{s^{n+1}}$ (n an integer)
t^n	$\dfrac{\Gamma(n)}{s^{n+1}}$ (n not an integer)
e^{at}	$\dfrac{1}{s-a}$
$\sin \alpha t$	$\dfrac{\alpha}{s^2+\alpha^2}$
$\cos \alpha t$	$\dfrac{s}{s^2+\alpha^2}$
$\sqrt{t}$	$\dfrac{1}{2}\sqrt{\dfrac{\pi}{s^3}}$
$\dfrac{1}{\sqrt{t}}$	$\sqrt{\dfrac{\pi}{s}}$

6.2.1. *Laplace Transforms of Derivatives*

The method given in Section 6.2 for determining the Laplace transform of a function can be applied to the differential coefficient of any continuous function. Thus let the derivative of a function be $df(t)/dt$, then the Laplace transform of this derivative is

$$\int_0^\infty \frac{df(t)}{dt} e^{-st}\, dt = [f(t)\, e^{-st}]_0^\infty - s \int_0^\infty f(t)\, e^{-st}\, dt \qquad (6.10)$$

and since the Laplace transform of $f(t)$ is $\bar{f}(s)$, equation (6.10) becomes

$$\mathcal{L}\left[\frac{df(t)}{dt}\right] = s\,\bar{f}(s) - f(0) \qquad (6.11)$$

Similarly, the second derivative of a function $d^2f(t)/dt^2$ can be converted to its Laplace transform by the same procedure to give

$$\mathcal{L}\left[\frac{d^2f(t)}{dt^2}\right] = s^2\bar{f}(s) - sf(0) - f'(0) \qquad (6.12)$$

where $f(0)$ and $f'(0)$ are the values of the function and its derivative when the independent variable is zero.

Finally the integration processes described above can be extended to finding the Laplace transform of an nth order derivative of a function. The result is

$$\mathscr{L}\left[\frac{d^n f(t)}{dt^n}\right] = s^n \bar{f}(s) - [s^{n-1} f(0) + s^{n-2} f'(0) \ldots + s f^{(n-2)}(0) + f^{(n-1)}(0)] \qquad (6.13)$$

where $f'(0)$, $f^2(0)$ ..... $f^{(n-1)}(0)$ are the values of the first, second, up to the $(n-1)$th derivative of the function when the independent variable is zero.

The Laplace transforms of the different order derivatives presented above are only valid for continuous functions. If the function undergoes a step-change in the range in which the independent variable is being considered, each of the equations (6.11) to (6.13) have to be modified. This will be considered later, in Section 6.5.

Equations (6.11) to (6.13) introduce the fundamental operational properties of the Laplace transformation. These are the properties that introduce the boundary conditions $f(0)$, $f'(0)$, etc. into the problem before solution of the equation. At the same time, the differential equation is reduced to an algebraic equation in terms of the operator s. However, it should be noted that the operation described is only applicable to "initial value" problems. That is, the value of the function and its derivatives must be known when the independent variable is zero. This becomes apparent by inspection of the transforms of the derivatives.

Finally, equation (6.13) can be utilized to find the Laplace transform of a function without carrying out the integration procedure, and to illustrate the method, the Laplace transform of $\sin \alpha t$ will be evaluated.

Let
$$f(t) = \sin \alpha t$$

Then
$$f'(t) = \alpha \cos \alpha t$$

and
$$f''(t) = -\alpha^2 \sin \alpha t$$

Also
$$f(t)\big|_{t=0} = \sin \alpha t \big|_{t=0} = 0$$

and
$$f'(t)\big|_{t=0} = \alpha \cos \alpha t \big|_{t=0} = \alpha$$

Since
$$\mathscr{L}[f''(t)] = s^2 \bar{f}(s) - s f(0) - f'(0) \qquad (6.12)$$

$$\therefore \quad -\mathscr{L}[\alpha^2 \sin \alpha t] = s^2 \mathscr{L}[\sin \alpha t] - 0 - \alpha$$

or
$$\mathscr{L}[\sin \alpha t] = \frac{\alpha}{s^2 + \alpha^2} \qquad (6.14)$$

Equation (6.14) gives the expression for the transform that is reported in Table 6.1.

6.2.2. The Shifting Theorem

This theorem is most valuable in obtaining the transform of an exponential type of function and also in carrying out the inverse transformation which will be described later. The shifting theorem may be enunciated as follows:

If the Laplace transform of $f(t)$ is $\bar{f}(s)$, then the Laplace transform of $e^{-\alpha t} f(t)$ is $\bar{f}(s+\alpha)$, where α is a finite constant. That is, the multiplication of $f(t)$ by $e^{-\alpha t}$ in effect shifts the origin of s to $(s+\alpha)$.

This theorem can be proved by carrying out the integration procedure on the general function $f(t)$, but it will be more illuminating to verify it by applying the theorem to the following example.

Example. Determine the Laplace transform of $e^{-\alpha t} \cos \beta t$.

In Table 6.1, if $f(t) = \cos \beta t$, then $\bar{f}(s) = s/(s^2 + \beta^2)$.

Therefore, by the shifting theorem

$$\mathscr{L}[e^{-\alpha t} \cos \beta t] = \frac{s+\alpha}{(s+\alpha)^2 + \beta^2} \qquad \text{I}$$

which is the desired result. However, this will be verified by integration. Thus

$$\int_0^\infty e^{-\alpha t} \cos \beta t\, e^{-st}\, dt = \mathscr{R} \int_0^\infty e^{-\alpha t}\, e^{i\beta t}\, e^{-st}\, dt \qquad \text{II}$$

$$= \mathscr{R} \int_0^\infty e^{-(\alpha+s-i\beta)t}\, dt$$

$$= \mathscr{R} \left[\frac{e^{-(\alpha+s-i\beta)t}}{-(\alpha+s-i\beta)} \right]_0^\infty$$

$$= \mathscr{R}\left[1/(\alpha+s-i\beta) \right]$$

Using the division rule for complex numbers, and discarding the imaginary part confirms the result given in equation I.

6.3. THE INVERSE TRANSFORMATION

In order that the operational method of the Laplace transformation can be exploited for the solution of engineering problems, it must be convenient to convert the transform back to a function of the independent variable. That is, it is necessary to perform the operation

$$\mathscr{L}^{-1}[\bar{f}(s)] = f(t) \qquad (6.15)$$

in order to complete the solution of the problem. On occasion this can be done by inspection, by looking up the function corresponding to the transform in a table of Laplace transforms, such as the one reproduced at the end of this book. Some manipulation of the constants is often necessary as illustrated by the following example.

Example 1. Find the inverse transform of $s/(s^2 - 2s + 5)$. Completing the square of the denominator in an attempt to find factors gives

$$\bar{f}(s) = \frac{s}{(s-1)^2 + 4} \qquad \text{I}$$

Applying the shifting theorem,

$$\bar{f}(s+1) = \frac{s+1}{s^2 + 2^2} \qquad \text{II}$$

But the right hand side of equation II is the sum of transforms number 15 and 16 at the end of the book.

$$\therefore \quad e^{-t}f(t) = \cos 2t + \tfrac{1}{2}\sin 2t$$

$$\therefore \quad f(t) = e^{t}(\cos 2t + \tfrac{1}{2}\sin 2t) \qquad\qquad \text{III}$$

is the inverse transform of $\bar{f}(s) = s/(s^2 - 2s + 5)$.

6.3.1. *Inverting the Transform Using Partial Fractions*

The Laplace transform of a function is an expression involving the parameter s which may be very complex. When the expression is of the form

$$\bar{f}(s) = \frac{\theta(s)}{\phi(s)} \qquad\qquad (6.16)$$

where $\theta(s)$ and $\phi(s)$ are polynomials in s, and $\phi(s)$ is of higher degree than $\theta(s)$, $f(s)$ can be expanded into its partial fractions. If the complex roots of $\phi(s)$ are also resolved, then all terms in the resolution must be of the type $1/(s-a)^n$ with n an integer and a a real or complex constant. The inversion of $\bar{f}(s)$ is then simply a case of repeated application of transform number 10 in the tables, viz.

If
$$(s) = \frac{1}{(s-a)^n}$$

then
$$f(t) = \frac{1}{(n-1)!}\,t^{n-1}e^{at}$$

For use with partial fractions, this transform pair is well worth remembering. Alternatively, transform number 3 can be memorized and the shifting theorem applied to it. The following example illustrates this technique.

Example 2. Determine $f(t)$ if $\bar{f}(s) = 1/(s+a)(s+b)^2$.

Expanding by partial fractions gives

$$(s) = \frac{1}{(s+a)(s+b)^2} = \frac{A}{s+a} + \frac{B}{s+b} + \frac{C}{(s+b)^2}$$

$$\therefore \quad A(s+b)^2 + B(s+a)(s+b) + C(s+a) = 1 \qquad\qquad \text{II}$$

Evaluating C by putting $s = -b$ gives

$$C = 1/(a-b) \qquad\qquad \text{III}$$

Evaluating A by putting $s = -a$ gives

$$A = 1/(a-b)^2 \qquad\qquad \text{IV}$$

Evaluating B by equating coefficients of s^2 in equation II gives

$$B = -1/(a-b)^2 \qquad\qquad \text{V}$$

$$\therefore \quad (a-b)^2\bar{f}(s) = \frac{1}{s+a} - \frac{1}{s+b} + \frac{a-b}{(s+b)^2} \qquad\qquad \text{VI}$$

Inverting the right hand side of equation IV term by term using transform number 10 (or special cases 8 and 9) gives

$$(a-b)^2 f(t) = e^{-at} - e^{-bt} + (a-b)t\,e^{-bt} \qquad\qquad \text{VII}$$

$$\therefore\quad f(t) = \mathscr{L}^{-1}\left[\frac{1}{(s+a)(s+b)^2}\right] = \frac{e^{-bt} + [(a-b)t-1]\,e^{-bt}}{(a-b)^2} \qquad \text{VIII}$$

The expansion of the transform by the use of partial fractions is quickly and conveniently accomplished when the denominator contains only simple roots; but when the denominator contains a repeated root of high order, resolution of the coefficients is a lengthy, time-consuming process. However, the evaluation of coefficients by the theory of residues is much more straightforward and is recommended under such circumstances. This method is discussed in Section 6.8 where it is shown to be the most powerful method of obtaining the inverse transform.

6.3.2. *Application to the Solution of Ordinary Differential Equations*

The primary application of the Laplace transformation is the provision of a powerful operational method for removing derivatives from an equation. Therefore, before proceeding further with the properties of the transformation, the operational characteristics will be applied to the solution of ordinary differential equations in order to illustrate the technique. The method depends on the fact that an ordinary differential equation can be converted into an equivalent algebraic equation called the "subsidiary equation" in which the Laplace transform operator s is the independent variable. The procedure is illustrated by the following example.

Example 3. Solve $\dfrac{d^2y}{dt^2} + 4y = 3$, where $y(0) = y'(0) = 1$.

Using equation (6.12) to transform the derivative gives

$$\mathscr{L}\left[\frac{d^2y}{dx^2}\right] = s^2\bar{y}(s) - s - 1 \qquad\qquad \text{I}$$

and transforming the constant using tables gives

$$\mathscr{L}[3] = 3/s \qquad\qquad \text{II}$$

Substituting these transforms into the differential equation gives the subsidiary equation

$$s^2\bar{y}(s) - s - 1 + 4\bar{y}(s) = 3/s \qquad\qquad \text{III}$$

Solving the algebraic equation III for $\bar{y}(s)$ gives

$$\bar{y}(s) = \frac{s}{s^2+4} + \frac{1}{s^2+4} + \frac{3}{s(s^2+4)} \qquad\qquad \text{IV}$$

Inverting equation IV term by term, using transforms number 16, 15, and

19 respectively from the table at the back of the book gives

$$y = \cos 2t + \tfrac{1}{2}\sin 2t + \tfrac{3}{4}(1 - \cos 2t) \qquad \text{V}$$

which will simplify to

$$y = \tfrac{1}{2}\sin 2t + \tfrac{1}{4}\cos 2t + \tfrac{3}{4} \qquad \text{VI}$$

6.4. Properties of the Laplace Transformation

Before further application of the Laplace transformation to the solution of engineering problems is made, some of its most important properties will be discussed, so that this operational method can be applied to the solution of more complicated problems.

6.4.1. *Differentiation of the Transform with Respect to the Operator s*

If $f(t)$ is a continuous function of the independent variable t, and its Laplace transform is $\bar{f}(s)$, then differentiation of the transform with respect to s corresponds to multiplying the function by $-t$.

This property can be proved as follows.

$$\bar{f}(s) = \int_0^\infty f(t)\,e^{-st}\,dt \qquad (6.17)$$

by definition, and differentiating equation (6.17) with respect to s gives

$$\frac{d}{ds}[\ (s)] = \int_0^\infty -tf(t)\,e^{-st}\,dt \qquad (6.18)$$

But the integral in equation (6.18) is the Laplace transform of $-tf(t)$ by the definition (6.1). Hence the property is proved.

6.4.2. *The Laplace Transform of the Integral of a Function*

If $f(t)$ is an integrable function of the independent variable t and its Laplace transform is $\bar{f}(s)$, then division of $\bar{f}(s)$ by s corresponds to integration of $f(t)$ between the limits 0 and t.

The above property can be verified most easily by showing that the converse is true. Thus

$$\mathscr{L}\left[\int_0^t f(t)\,dt\right] = \int_0^\infty \left[\int_0^t f(t)\,dt\right]e^{-st}\,dt \qquad (6.19)$$

The right hand side can be integrated by parts by letting

$$u = \int_0^t f(t)\,dt$$

and then

$$du = f(t)\,dt$$
$$dv = e^{-st}\,dt$$

so that

$$v = -e^{-st}/s$$

Substitution of these parts into equation (6.19) gives

$$\mathscr{L}\left[\int_0^t f(t)\,dt\right] = -\left[\frac{e^{-st}}{s}\int_0^t f(t)\,dt\right]_0^\infty + \frac{1}{s}\int_0^\infty f(t)\,e^{-st}\,dt \qquad (6.20)$$

The first term is zero at the upper limit because of the exponential term, and zero at the lower limit because of the range of integration. Therefore

$$\mathscr{L}\left[\int_0^t f(t)\,dt\right] = \frac{1}{s}\bar{f}(s) \qquad (6.21)$$

The results of Sections 6.4.1 and 6.4.2 are of great value in the solution of engineering problems. They find extensive use in the solution of differential equations with variable coefficients and the method of solution will be illustrated by the next example.

Example. Using the data given below obtain a preliminary estimate of the diameter of the tubes to be installed in a fixed bed catalytic reactor which is to be used for the synthesis of vinyl chloride from acetylene and hydrogen chloride. The tubes are to contain the mercuric chloride catalyst deposited on 0·1 inch particles of carbon and the heat of the reaction is to be employed to generate steam at 250°F for the remainder of the process. To do this, the temperature of the inside surface of the tubes should be constant at 300°F.

Effective thermal conductivity of bed $(k_E) = 4\cdot0\,\dfrac{\text{Btu}}{\text{h ft}^2\,{}°\text{F/ft}}$

Heat of reaction at bed temperature $(\Delta H) = 46{,}200$ Btu/lb mole†

Bulk density of bed (ρ) $\qquad\qquad = 18$ lb/ft^3.

The rate of reaction is a function of temperature, concentration and the various adsorption coefficients‡, but for the preliminary estimate assume that the rate of reaction can be expressed as

$$r = r_0\,(1+AT)\text{ lb moles/h lb catalyst.}$$

where $r_0 = 0\cdot12$, $A = 0\cdot024$, and T is the temperature in degrees Fahrenheit above a datum of 200°F.

The maximum allowable catalyst temperature to ensure a satisfactory life is 485°F (that is, $T = 285$).

Solution

Consider Fig. 6.1, which illustrates the following additional symbols describing the process.

$G =$ Flow rate in lb/h ft^2 of reactor section.
$R =$ Tube radius in ft.
$x =$ Radial coordinate.

† Calculated from heats of formation, etc. (negative sign omitted for convenience).
‡ Wesselhoft, R. D., Woods, J. M. and Smith, J. M. *A.I.Ch.E.J.* **5**, 361 (1959).

z = Axial coordinate from inlet.

C_p = Heat capacity of the gas in Btu/lb °F.

FIG. 6.1.   Fixed bed reactor

Taking a heat balance over the element illustrated in Fig. 6.1 gives

$$\text{Input} = -2\pi x\, k_E \frac{\partial T}{\partial x} \delta z + 2\pi x \delta x\, G\, C_p T + 2\pi x \delta x \delta z\, \rho \Delta H r$$

$$\text{Output} = -2\pi x\, k_E \frac{\partial T}{\partial x} \delta z + \frac{\partial}{\partial x}\left[-2\pi x\, k_E \frac{\partial T}{\partial x} \delta z \right] \delta x +$$

$$+ 2\pi x \delta x\, G\, C_p \left(T + \frac{\partial T}{\partial z} \delta z \right) \qquad \text{II}$$

Accumulation = 0, because the process is at steady state.

But,   Input − Output = Accumulation   (1.25)

and dividing throughout by $2\pi\, k_E\, x \delta x \delta z$ gives

$$\frac{\partial^2 T}{\partial x^2} + \frac{1}{x}\frac{\partial T}{\partial x} - \frac{GC_p}{k_E}\frac{\partial T}{\partial z} + \frac{\rho \Delta H r}{k_E} = 0 \qquad \text{III}$$

Equation III is a well known partial differential equation expressing the relationship between the temperature and the dimensions of the reactor. If for the preliminary estimate, it is assumed that the temperature of the bed reaches a maximum at all radii, at the same distance z from the reactor entrance; then at this radial section of the bed $\partial T/\partial z$ will be zero even though the actual temperatures will vary with x. The temperature will be a maximum at the tube axis and this must not exceed 485°F. Hence at the tube axis $\partial T/\partial x$ will be zero also, but will have a finite value at all radii greater than zero. Hence the partial differential equation III becomes an ordinary differential equation at this particular value of z. That is

$$\frac{d^2T}{dx^2} + \frac{1}{x}\frac{dT}{dx} + \frac{\rho\Delta H r_0}{k_E}(1+AT) = 0 \qquad\qquad \text{IV}$$

Equation IV can be easily converted to a Bessel equation of zero order and solved by the method given in Chapter 3, but on this occasion it will be solved using the Laplace transformation. The equation can be rewritten

$$x\frac{d^2T}{dx^2} + \frac{dT}{dx} + \frac{\rho\Delta H r_0}{k_E}(1+AT)x = 0 \qquad\qquad \text{V}$$

Using equations (6.12) and (6.18)

$$\mathscr{L}\left[x\frac{d^2T}{dx^2}\right] = -\frac{d}{ds}[s^2\bar{T}(s) - sT(0) - T'(0)]$$

$$= -s^2\bar{T}'(s) + 2s\bar{T}(s) - T(0) \qquad\qquad \text{VI}$$

and using equation (6.11)

$$\mathscr{L}\left[\frac{dT}{dx}\right] = s\bar{T}(s) - T(0) \qquad\qquad \text{VII}$$

Also,

$$\mathscr{L}\left[\frac{\rho\Delta H r_0}{k_E}x\right] = \frac{\rho\Delta H r_0}{k_E s^2} \qquad\qquad \text{VIII}$$

and using equation (6.18) again,

$$\mathscr{L}\left[\frac{\rho\Delta H r_0 A}{k_E}xT\right] = -\frac{\rho\Delta H r_0 A}{k_E}\bar{T}'(s) \qquad\qquad \text{IX}$$

Substituting the transforms VI, VII, VIII, and IX for the equivalent terms in equation V and simplifying gives

$$\frac{d\bar{T}}{ds} + \frac{s}{s^2+Q}\bar{T} = -\frac{P}{s^2(s^2+Q)} \qquad\qquad \text{X}$$

where $Q = \rho\Delta H r_0 A/k_E$, and $P = \rho\Delta H r_0/k_E$. Equation X can be solved by using an integrating factor as shown in Section 2.3.4 giving the result

$$\bar{T}(s) = \frac{K}{\sqrt{(s^2+Q)}} - \frac{P}{Qs} \qquad\qquad \text{XI}$$

This can be inverted using the tables, numbers 55 and 1.

$$\therefore \quad T = KJ_0(x\sqrt{Q}) - \frac{1}{A} \qquad\qquad \text{XII}$$

where K is the arbitrary constant of integration which can be evaluated as follows.

When $\qquad x = 0, \quad J_0(x\sqrt{Q}) = 1, \quad$ and $\quad T = 285$

$$\therefore \quad 285 = K - 1/A \qquad\qquad \text{XIII}$$

but
$$A = 0 \cdot 024$$
$$\therefore \quad 1/A = 41 \cdot 7, \quad \text{and} \quad K = 326 \cdot 7$$

Now
$$Q = \frac{18 \times 46\,200 \times 0 \cdot 12 \times 0 \cdot 024}{4 \cdot 0} = 599$$
$$\therefore \quad \sqrt{Q} = 24 \cdot 5$$

and equation XII becomes

$$T = 326 \cdot 7 J_0(24 \cdot 5x) - 41 \cdot 7 \qquad\qquad \text{XIV}$$

At the boundary, $x = R$, $T = 100$;

$$\therefore \quad 100 = 326 \cdot 7 J_0(24 \cdot 5R) - 41 \cdot 7$$

or
$$J_0(24 \cdot 5R) = 0 \cdot 4337$$

Use of a table of Bessel functions gives

$$24 \cdot 5R = 1 \cdot 64$$

or
$$R = 0 \cdot 80 \text{ inches}$$

For safety, the diameter of the tubes that would be installed in the reactor should be less than $1 \cdot 60$ in, as for this diameter the cooling rate would be just sufficient to prevent the temperature of the catalyst at the centre of the tube exceeding 485°F. Hence tubes of diameter $1 \cdot 50$ in would be recommended.

6.5. The Step Functions

It is possible for chemical engineering processes and equipment to undergo sudden changes in their operating conditions; for example the steam supply could suddenly change, or a vacuum pump or compressor could fail. It is desirable to be able to predict what effects these sudden changes will have on the process and quality of the product; and this can be accomplished by means of the step functions which will be considered below.

6.5.1. *The Unit Step Function*

This is illustrated in Fig. 6.2, which shows that the value of the function

Fig. 6.2. The unit step function

is zero for values of the independent variable less than b, and unity for values of the independent variable greater than b. The Laplace transform of the unit step function can be obtained in the usual way by integration.

Thus

$$\mathscr{L}[S_b(t)] = \int_0^b 0\,e^{-st}\,dt + \int_b^\infty 1.\,e^{-st}\,dt = e^{-bs}/s \qquad (6.22)$$

If the value of b is zero, the transform would reduce to $1/s$ which is the transform of unity. Thus multiplication of the transform of unity by e^{-bs} indicates that the function is zero over the interval 0 to b and unity for values of t greater than b. This concept can be extended to any other functions which are zero for specific intervals or which undergo sudden changes as illustrated by the unit impulse function below.

6.5.2. *The Unit Impulse Function*

The unit step function was characterized by having zero value for all values of the independent variable less than b, and a value of unity for values of t between b and infinity. If the value of this function is suddenly reduced to zero when the value of the independent variable is $(b+c)$ the function will appear as an impulse when plotted as shown in Fig. 6.3.

FIG. 6.3.   The unit impulse function

Furthermore, if the height of the impulse between b and $(b+c)$ is $1/c$, the area beneath the curve will be unity. As $c\to0$, the area will remain constant at unity, and this limit defines the unit impulse function as

$$I(t-b) = \lim_{c\to0}\left[S_b(t) - S_{b+c}(t)\right]/c \qquad (6.23)$$

Taking the Laplace transform of both sides, using equation (6.22) gives

$$\mathscr{L}[I(t-b)] = \lim_{c\to0}\left[\frac{e^{-bs} - e^{-(b+c)s}}{cs}\right] \qquad (6.24)$$

By L'Hôpital's rule, Section 3.3.8, this limit becomes

$$\mathscr{L}[I(t-b)] = e^{-bs} \qquad (6.25)$$

Frequently, the unit impulse function is called the "Dirac delta function" and is written $\delta(t-b)$. It expresses the rate of change of the unit step function.

6.5.3. *The Staircase Function*

This is shown in Fig. 6.4 where it can be seen that the function is formed by the successive addition of unit step functions at 0, b, $2b$, $3b$, ... etc.

FIG. 6.4.   The staircase function

Hence the Laplace transform of the staircase function is obtained by adding together the transforms of each step function. Thus

$$\mathscr{L}[S(b,t)] = \frac{1}{s} + \frac{e^{-bs}}{s} + \frac{e^{-2bs}}{s} + \ldots + \frac{e^{-nbs}}{s} + \ldots$$

$$= (1 + e^{-bs} + e^{-2bs} + \ldots e^{-nbs} + \ldots)/s \qquad (6.26)$$

The infinite series in equation (6.26) is a geometrical progression which can be summed to give the result

$$\mathscr{L}[S(b,t)] = \frac{1}{s(1 - e^{-bs})} \qquad (6.27)$$

Use will be made of these functions later in the text but the use of the unit step function will be illustrated by the following example.

Example. A control valve of the type shown in Fig. 6.5 is actuated by air pressure ranging from 3 to 15 lb/in^2 gauge operating on a 16-in diameter diaphragm whose effective area is equivalent to 100 square inches.   The

FIG. 6.5.   Control valve

effective dead weight of the moving parts of the valve, allowing for the friction in the gland, etc., is estimated to be 300 lb weight, the stiffness of the spring is 600 lb/in and the damping constant is estimated to be 17·0 lb sec/in.   If the total lift of the valve is 2·0 in, predict the response of the valve if the controlling air pressure suddenly changes from 6 lb/in^2 to 12 lb/in^2 gauge.

Solution

A force balance on the valve is

Input force $= \Delta P\, A\, S_0(t)$

Output force

(a) to overcome inertia of movable parts $= m\dfrac{d^2x}{dt^2}$.

(b) to overcome resistance of spring $\quad= kx.$

(c) to overcome damping resistance $\quad= c\dfrac{dx}{dt}$.

Therefore at equilibrium

$$m\frac{d^2x}{dt^2} + c\frac{dx}{dt} + kx = \Delta PAS_0(t) \qquad\qquad \text{I}$$

Let $\alpha = c/2m\omega$ where $\omega = \sqrt{k/m}$
Then equation I becomes

$$\frac{d^2x}{dt^2} + 2\alpha\omega\frac{dx}{dt} + \omega^2 x = \frac{\Delta PA}{m}S_0(t) \qquad\qquad \text{II}$$

The Laplace transform of equation II is

$$(s^2 + 2\alpha\omega s + \omega^2)\bar{x} = \frac{\Delta PA}{ms} + sx(0) + 2\alpha\omega x(0) + x'(0) \qquad \text{III}$$

In order to ease the calculations, let the origin of x be changed so that an air pressure of 6 lb/in^2 corresponds to $x = 0$,

$$\therefore \quad x(0) = x'(0) = 0$$

and therefore

$$\bar{x} = \frac{\Delta PA}{ms(s^2 + 2\alpha\omega s + \omega^2)} \qquad\qquad \text{IV}$$

The inverse transform of equation IV can be obtained by partial fractions as

$$x = \frac{\Delta PA}{k}\left[1 - \frac{e^{-\alpha\omega t}}{\sqrt{(1-\alpha^2)}}\cos\left(\omega t\sqrt{1-\alpha^2} - \phi\right)\right] \qquad \text{V}$$

where

$$\tan\phi = \alpha/\sqrt{1-\alpha^2} \qquad\qquad \text{VI}$$

x can now be evaluated as a function of t by using the data given in the problem. Thus

$$\Delta PA/k = 1$$

$$m = 300 \text{ lb dead weight} = \frac{300}{32\times 12} = 0\cdot781 \text{ lb sec}^2/\text{in}$$

$$\omega = \sqrt{\frac{k}{m}} = \sqrt{\frac{600}{0\cdot781}} = 27\cdot72$$

$$\alpha = \frac{c}{2m\omega} = \frac{17\cdot0}{2\times 0\cdot781\times 27\cdot72} = 0\cdot393$$

$$\therefore \quad \sqrt{1-\alpha^2} = 0\cdot920$$

$$\therefore \quad \tan\phi = \frac{0\cdot393}{0\cdot920} = 0\cdot427$$

$$\therefore \quad \phi = 0\cdot404 \text{ radians}$$

Substituting these values into equation V gives Table 6.2 and hence Fig. 6.6. Because x is measured from the top of the valve, Fig. 6.6 has been drawn to show valve opening X.

TABLE 6.2. *Evaluation of Equation V*

ωt	$\dfrac{e^{-0\cdot393\omega t}}{0\cdot92}$	$\cos(0\cdot92\omega t - 0\cdot404)$	x	X
0	1·0870	0·9196	0·000	1·500
1	0·7337	0·8698	0·362	1·138
2	0·4953	0·1346	0·933	0·567
3	0·3343	−0·7075	1·237	0·263
4	0·2257	−0·9910	1·224	0·276
5	0·1523	−0·4939	1·075	0·425
6	0·1028	0·3929	0·960	0·540
7	0·0694	0·9697	0·933	0·567
8	0·0469	0·7819	0·963	0·537
9	0·0316	−0·0220	1·007	0·493
10	0·0214	−0·5883	1·013	0·487

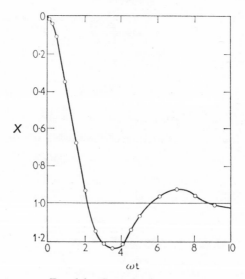

FIG. 6.6. Control valve response

Therefore, the response of the valve is $10/27\cdot72 = 0\cdot36$ sec. That is, in $0\cdot36$ sec the position of the valve alters by one inch and has stabilized at its new position.

6.6. CONVOLUTION

It frequently happens in solving problems by the Laplace transformation that the final transform of the equation is a product of two easily identifiable transforms, but these are difficult to resolve in the form of a summation. When this arises, the inverse transformation can be accomplished by the method of "convolution".

Space does not permit the derivation of the convolution integral, and therefore only the mechanics of its use will be explained. Any reader interested in the derivation is advised to consult Thomson† or Churchill‡. Thus if the transform of the equation is $\bar{f}(s)$ and this is composed of the factors $\bar{g}(s)$ and $\bar{h}(s)$ whose inverse transforms are recognizable from Laplace transform tables, the inverse transform of $\bar{f}(s)$ is obtained as follows.

Let the inverse transform of $\bar{g}(s)$ be $g(t)$, and the inverse transform of $\bar{h}(s)$ be $h(t)$.
Then since

$$\bar{f}(s) = \bar{g}(s)\,\bar{h}(s) \tag{6.28}$$

$$f(t) = \mathscr{L}^{-1}[\bar{g}(s)\bar{h}(s)] = \int_0^t g(\tau)\,h(t-\tau)\,d\tau = \int_0^t h(\tau)g(t-\tau)\,d\tau \tag{6.29}$$

Equation (6.29) gives the convolution integral of $f(t)$ and implies its symmetry. The convolution integral is frequently given the shorthand form

$$f(t) = g(t)\,h^*(t) \tag{6.30}$$

The use of the convolution integral to find an inverse transform will be illustrated in the next example.

Example. Find the inverse transform of $\dfrac{s^2}{(s^2+1)^2}$.

Transform number 16 in the tables shows that if

$$\bar{g}(s) = \bar{h}(s) = \frac{s}{s^2+1}$$

then
$$g(t) = h(t) = \cos t$$

Therefore, by the convolution integral (6.29),

$$f(t) = \int_0^t \cos\tau\cos(t-\tau)\,d\tau \qquad\qquad \text{I}$$

$$= \tfrac{1}{2}\int_0^t \left[\cos t + \cos(2\tau - t)\right]d\tau \qquad\qquad \text{II}$$

† Thomson, W. T. "Laplace Transformation." Longmans Green & Co.
‡ Churchill, R. V. "Operational Mathematics." McGraw Hill Book Co.

$$f(t) = \tfrac{1}{2}\left[\tau\cos t + \tfrac{1}{2}\sin(2\tau - t)\right]_0^t$$

$$= \tfrac{1}{2}(t\cos t + \tfrac{1}{2}\sin t + \tfrac{1}{2}\sin t) \qquad\qquad \text{III}$$

$$= \tfrac{1}{2}(t\cos t + \sin t) \qquad\qquad \text{IV}$$

The answer given by equation IV checks with the answer given directly in the tables number 23.

6.7. Further Elementary Methods of Inversion

Three further methods for finding the inverse Laplace transform will be given in this section. These methods will often yield answers more quickly than either partial fractions or convolution, and they can also be used when previous methods fail.

6.7.1. *Using the Properties of the Transformation*

It was shown in Section 6.4.2 that dividing the transform of a function $f(t)$ by s was equivalent to integrating the function between the limits 0 and t. Thus the power of s in the denominator of $\bar{f}(s)$ can be increased in an integral manner by successive applications of equation (6.21) as illustrated in the next example. When this process is combined with the shifting theorem (Section 6.2.2), a powerful method of inversion results.

Example 1. Find $f(t)$ if $\bar{f}(s) = 1/s^2(s+a)$.

Transform number 8 shows that if $\bar{f}_1(s) = 1/(s+a)$, then $f_1(t) = e^{-at}$. Application of equation (6.21) gives

$$\bar{f}_2(s) = \frac{1}{s}\bar{f}_1(s) = \frac{1}{s(s+a)}$$

$$\therefore \quad f_2(t) = \int_0^t e^{-at}\,dt$$

$$= \frac{1-e^{-at}}{a} \qquad\qquad \text{II}$$

A further application of equation (6.21) to this result gives

$$\bar{f}_3(s) = \frac{1}{s}\bar{f}_2(s) = \frac{1}{s^2(s+a)} \qquad\qquad \text{III}$$

$$\therefore \quad \bar{f}_3(t) = \int_0^t (1-e^{-at})\frac{dt}{a}$$

$$= \frac{1}{a}\left[t + \frac{e^{-at}}{a}\right]_0^t$$

$$= \frac{1}{a^2}(at + e^{-at} - 1) \qquad\qquad \text{IV}$$

Therefore, if $\text{\j}(s) = \bar{f}/s^2(s+a)$, then

$$f(t) = (e^{-at} + at - 1)/a^2 \qquad\qquad \text{V}$$

6.7.2. *Expansion in a Descending Power Series*

It will be noted in the tables that as $|s| \to \infty$, then $\bar{f}(s) \to 0$ for every transform pair, although an application of L'Hôpital's rule is often necessary to show this. The first seven transforms in the table also give an inversion for any negative power of s; and hence, if $\bar{f}(s)$ can be expanded in a series containing only negative powers of s, these first few transforms will determine a series form for $f(t)$.

An ascending power series will always contain positive powers of the variable after a certain stage, so that to restrict the series to negative powers, a descending power series of s must be used. Inspection of transform numbers 1 to 7 shows that the termwise inversion will lead to an ascending power series in t. Referring back to Section 3.3, if this series has a finite radius of convergence, then the result will only be valid for small values of t. Hence, the initial behaviour of a system can be determined by inverting the first few terms of such a power series expansion. The method of obtaining the series will be illustrated by the following examples.

Example 2. Determine $f(t)$ if $\bar{f}(s) = \ln[1+(a/s)^2]$.

The logarithmic expansion (3.8) applied to $\bar{f}(s)$ gives a series of descending powers of s, viz.

$$\bar{f}(s) = \frac{a^2}{s^2} - \frac{a^4}{2s^4} + \frac{a^6}{3s^6} - \cdots$$

Transforming each term separately using number 3, gives

$$f(t) = a^2 t - \frac{a^4 t^3}{2.3!} + \frac{a^6 t^5}{3.5!} - \cdots \qquad \text{II}$$

$$= \frac{2}{t}\left[\frac{(at)^2}{2!} - \frac{(at)^4}{4!} + \frac{(at)^6}{6!} - \cdots\right] \qquad \text{III}$$

The series in equation III can be recognized (equation (3.11)) giving the result

$$f(t) = \frac{2}{t}(\cos at - 1) \qquad \text{IV}$$

which confirms transform number 105 in the tables.

Example 3. Determine $f(t)$ if $\bar{f}(s) = 1/s^{\frac{1}{2}}(s+a^2)$.

In order to obtain a descending power series, s must be considered to be large so that the term $(s+a^2)$ must be rearranged in the following manner before the binomial theorem can be applied. Thus

$$(s) = \frac{1}{s^{3/2}}\left(1 + \frac{a^2}{s}\right)^{-1} \qquad \text{I}$$

$$= \frac{1}{s^{3/2}}\left(1 - \frac{a^2}{s} + \frac{a^4}{s^2} - \frac{a^6}{s^3} + \cdots\right)$$

$$= \frac{1}{s^{1\frac{1}{2}}} - \frac{a^2}{s^{2\frac{1}{2}}} + \frac{a^4}{s^{3\frac{1}{2}}} - \frac{a^6}{s^{4\frac{1}{2}}} + \cdots \qquad \text{II}$$

G

Applying transform number 6 to each term of equation II gives

$$f(t) = \frac{2t^{\frac{1}{2}}}{\sqrt{\pi}} - \frac{2^2 t^{1\frac{1}{2}}}{1.3\sqrt{\pi}} + \frac{2^3 t^{2\frac{1}{2}}}{1.3.5\sqrt{\pi}} - \frac{2^4 t^{3\frac{1}{2}}}{1.3.5.7\sqrt{\pi}} + \cdots$$

$$= 2\sqrt{\frac{t}{\pi}} \left[1 - \frac{2t}{1.3} + \frac{(2t)^2}{1.3.5} - \frac{(2t)^3}{1.3.5.7} + \cdots \right] \qquad \text{III}$$

Equation III is likely to be a more useful inversion formula for the given transform than that shown in the tables as number 41.

6.7.3. *Other Series Expansions*

It is more convenient on occasions to expand $\bar{f}(s)$ in descending powers of $(s+a)$ and apply the shifting theorem; and many other expansions are also possible in terms of a wide variety of functions. The only restriction on any series expansion is that it should be convergent for sufficiently large values of s, and the following example illustrates such an expansion in terms of exponential functions.

Example 4. In a note published by T. Wood†, the following transform requires inversion

$$\bar{f}(s) = \frac{1}{s + \alpha + \beta e^{-as}} \qquad \text{I}$$

Following the method given in the publication, equation I can be rearranged as

$$\bar{f}(s) = \frac{1}{s+\alpha} \left[1 + \frac{\beta}{s+\alpha} e^{-as} \right]^{-1} \qquad \text{II}$$

Provided $\beta e^{-as} < s+\alpha$ III

equation II can be expanded using the binomial theorem. But for sufficiently large values of s, equation III will be satisfied, therefore the expansion will be valid. Thus

$$\bar{f}(s) = \sum_{n=0}^{\infty} \frac{\beta^n}{(s+\alpha)^{n+1}} e^{-nas} \qquad \text{IV}$$

Inverting term by term using transform number 63 and the shifting theorem gives

$$f(t) = \sum_{n=0}^{\infty} \frac{(\beta z)^n}{n!} e^{-\alpha z} S_{na}(t) \qquad \text{V}$$

where $z = t - na$

6.8. INVERSION OF THE LAPLACE TRANSFORM BY CONTOUR INTEGRATION

In the above theory of the Laplace transformation, the various methods given for the inversion of the transform to regenerate a function of the

† Wood, T. *Nature*, **191**, 589 (1961).

independent variable depended on the resolution of the transform into partial fractions, or modification of the transforms appearing in the tables by using convolution or the shifting theorem. These methods are usually adequate for solving problems involving ordinary differential equations, but often fail when applied to complex transforms resulting from the solution of partial differential equations. These complex transforms can be inverted by means of a contour integral, and the following section will explain this method in preparation for its application to the solution of partial differential equations in Chapter 8.

The basis of the inversion of a transform by contour integration is the Mellin-Fourier theorem, which may be formally stated by the following expressions without placing any restrictions on the functions. Thus if

$$\bar{f}(s) = \int_0^\infty e^{-st} f(t)\, dt$$

$$\text{then} \qquad f(t) = \frac{1}{2\pi i} \lim_{\beta \to \infty} \int_{\alpha-i\beta}^{\alpha+i\beta} e^{st} \bar{f}(s)\, ds \tag{6.31}$$

where α is a constant greater than the real part of any singularity in the transform $\bar{f}(s)$.

The Mellin-Fourier theorem is frequently referred to simply as the inversion theorem and it can be deduced directly from Fourier's integral theorem which is comprehensively dealt with in most university texts in mathematics. Thus Fourier's integral theorem can be expressed

$$f(t) = \frac{1}{2\pi} \int_{-\infty}^\infty e^{i\lambda t} \int_{-\infty}^\infty e^{-i\lambda t} f(t)\, dt\, d\lambda \tag{6.32}$$

where $f(t)$ is any function of t, periodic or otherwise.

In applied mathematics, t cannot be less than zero and therefore let $f(t) = 0$ for $t < 0$, in which case equation (6.32) becomes

$$f(t) = \frac{1}{2\pi} \int_{-\infty}^\infty e^{i\lambda t} \int_0^\infty e^{-i\lambda t} f(t)\, dt\, d\lambda \tag{6.33}$$

Put $i\lambda = s - \alpha$, where α is chosen to ensure convergence of the first integral

$$\therefore \quad f(t) = \frac{1}{2\pi i} \int_{\alpha-i\infty}^{\alpha+i\infty} e^{st} e^{-\alpha t} \int_0^\infty e^{-st} e^{\alpha t} f(t)\, dt\, ds \tag{6.34}$$

$$\therefore \quad e^{\alpha t} f(t) = \frac{1}{2\pi i} \int_{\alpha-i\infty}^{\alpha+i\infty} e^{st} \int_0^\infty e^{-st} [e^{\alpha t} f(t)]\, dt\, ds \tag{6.35}$$

which is equivalent to equation (6.31) applied to $e^{\alpha t} f(t)$.

Therefore, the Mellin-Fourier integral theorem provides a method of obtaining the inverse transform directly by integration in the complex plane along a line parallel to the imaginary axis, and at distance α along the positive real axis from the origin. The value of this integral may be obtained as follows. Consider the contour shown in Fig. 6.7 where the arc of the circle of radius R encloses all the singularities. The integral around this contour is the sum of the integrals along the straight path AB from $-i\beta$ to $+i\beta$, and around the arc BCA. The integration path from A to B as $\beta \to \infty$ is known as the "first Bromwich path". Expressed symbolically,

$$\int\limits_{ABCA} e^{st}\,\bar{f}(s)\,ds = \int\limits_{\alpha-i\beta}^{\alpha+i\beta} e^{st}\bar{f}(s)\,ds + \int\limits_{BCA} e^{st}\bar{f}(s)\,ds \qquad (6.36)$$

If equation (6.36) is to be of any value, the last integral must vanish as $R \to \infty$. The condition for this will now be established.

On the arc BDCEA, $|s| = R$ and it will be assumed that $|\bar{f}(s)| < \varepsilon$ for all points on the arc.

$$\therefore \quad \int\limits_{DCE} e^{st}\bar{f}(s)\,ds < \varepsilon \int\limits_{DCE} e^{st}\,ds \qquad (6.37)$$

Because e^{st} is analytic everywhere except at infinity, the integral on the right hand side of equation (6.37) will have the same value for all paths between $s = -iR$ and $s = iR$.

$$\therefore \quad \int\limits_{DCE} e^{st}\bar{f}(s)\,ds < \varepsilon \left[\frac{e^{st}}{t}\right]_{-iR}^{iR} = \frac{2i\varepsilon}{t}\sin Rt \qquad (6.38)$$

Along the arc BD, $|\bar{f}(s)| < \varepsilon$, $|e^{st}| \leqslant e^{\alpha t}$, and it is certainly true that the length of the integration path is less than 2α.

$$\therefore \quad \int\limits_{BD} e^{st}\bar{f}(s)\,ds < \varepsilon e^{\alpha t}\,2\alpha \qquad (6.39)$$

Similarly, the integral along the arc EA can be shown to be less than $2\alpha\varepsilon e^{\alpha t}$. Adding these results together,

$$\int\limits_{BCA} e^{st}\bar{f}(s)\,ds < \varepsilon\left(4\alpha e^{\alpha t} + \frac{2i}{t}\sin Rt\right) \qquad (6.40)$$

As $R \to \infty$, $\beta \to \infty$, but $\sin Rt \leqslant 1$. Therefore the term in the brackets in equation (6.40) remains finite as $R \to \infty$. If $\varepsilon \to 0$ as $R \to \infty$, then

$$\int\limits_{BCA} e^{st}\bar{f}(s)\,ds \to 0 \quad \text{as } R \to \infty \qquad (6.41)$$

Therefore, provided $|\bar{f}(s)| \to 0$ as $|s| \to \infty$ in the left hand side half plane, the last integral in equation (6.36) can be neglected and this gives

$$f(t) = \frac{1}{2\pi i}\int\limits_{\alpha-i\infty}^{\alpha+i\infty} e^{st}\bar{f}(s)\,ds = \frac{1}{2\pi i}\int\limits_{ABCA} e^{st}\bar{f}(s)\,ds \qquad (6.42)$$

The evaluation of the integrals in equation (6.42) depends on the type of singularity of $\bar{f}(s)$.

6.8.1. *Inversion when the Singularities are Poles*

In this case, the last integral in equation (6.42) can be evaluated by the theory of residues given in Section 4.16. Thus

$$(t) = \frac{1}{2\pi i} \int_{Br_1} e^{st} \bar{f}(s)ds = \frac{1}{2\pi i} \int_{ABCA} e^{st} \bar{f}(s)ds = \sum (\text{residues of } e^{st} \bar{f}(s)) \qquad (6.43)$$

Example 1. Find the inverse transform of $\dfrac{2s+1}{s(s^2+1)}$ by contour integration.

The given function has three simple poles, at $s = 0$, i, and $-i$. Using equation (4.110) to evaluate each residue separately gives:

Residue at $s = 0$,

$$\rho_0 = \lim_{s \to 0} \left[\frac{(2s+1)s}{s(s^2+1)} \right] e^{st} = 1 \qquad \qquad \text{I}$$

Residue at $s = i$,

$$\rho_i = \lim_{s \to i} \left[\frac{(2s+1)(s-i)}{s(s-i)(s+i)} \right] e^{st} = \frac{1+2i}{-2} e^{it} \qquad \text{II}$$

Residue at $s = -i$,

$$\rho_{-i} = \lim_{s \to -i} \left[\frac{(2s+1)(s+i)}{s(s-i)(s+i)} \right] e^{st} = \frac{1-2i}{-2} e^{-it} \qquad \text{III}$$

$$\therefore \quad f(t) = \rho_0 + \rho_i + \rho_{-i} = 1 - \frac{e^{it}+e^{-it}}{2} - i(e^{it}-e^{-it}) \qquad \text{IV}$$

$$\therefore \quad f(t) = 1 - \cos t + 2 \sin t \qquad \qquad \text{V}$$

6.8.2. *Inversion when the Singularity is a Branch Point*

In Section 4.14.3 it was shown that the path of a contour integral cannot cross a "barrier" erected from a branch point, and the integration path must consequently be modified to exclude this point. If the Laplace transform $\bar{f}(s)$ contains such a branch point at the origin, and the branch cut follows the negative real axis, then the integration path of Fig. 6.7 must be modified as shown in Fig. 6.8. On the assumption that this transform does not contain

FIG. 6.7. Contour integration of equation (6.31)

FIG. 6.8. Contour integration along second Bromwich path

other singularities, the value of the integral around the closed contour
ABCPQRDA is zero by Cauchy's theorem. Furthermore, as $\beta \to \infty$, the value
of the integral around the arcs BCP and RDA is zero. The value of the
integral along the first Bromwich path is thus equivalent to the value along
the path RQP which is called the "second Bromwich path", or

$$f(t) = \frac{1}{2\pi i} \int_{RQP} e^{st} \bar{f}(s) ds = \frac{1}{2\pi i} \int_{Br_2} e^{st} \bar{f}(s) ds \qquad (6.44)$$

Example 2. Evaluate the inverse transform of $1/s\sqrt{s+1}$.

In Section 6.4.2 it was shown that division of a transform by s corres-
ponded to integrating the function between the limits 0 and t. Therefore let

$$\frac{df(t)}{dt} = \mathscr{L}^{-1}\left[\frac{1}{\sqrt{s+1}}\right] \qquad \text{I}$$

The inversion of equation I can be done directly from the tables, but here it
will be inverted by contour integration. Since the function has no poles but
a branch point at $s = -1$, the origin will be moved to the branch point
by putting $\lambda = s+1$, and equation (6.44) will be applied. Thus

$$\frac{df(t)}{dt} = \frac{1}{2\pi i} \int_{Br_2} \frac{e^{(\lambda-1)t} d\lambda}{\sqrt{\lambda}} \qquad \text{II}$$

Br_2 for this function is as illustrated in Fig. 6.8 and the value of the integral
along the arcs is zero. The integral along RQP will now be evaluated in
three parts as follows.

i. *Integration along RQ.* The line RQ is defined by $\lambda = x e^{-i\pi}$ with x
varying from ∞ to 0.

$$\therefore \quad \lambda = x e^{-i\pi} = x(\cos \pi - i \sin \pi) = -x \qquad \text{III}$$

$$\therefore \quad d\lambda = -dx$$

$$\therefore \quad \sqrt{\lambda} = x^{\frac{1}{2}} e^{-\frac{1}{2}\pi i} = -i\sqrt{x} \qquad \text{IV}$$

$$\therefore \quad \int_{RQ} \frac{e^{(\lambda-1)t}}{\sqrt{\lambda}} d\lambda = -i e^{-t} \int_{\infty}^{0} \frac{e^{-xt}}{\sqrt{x}} dx = i e^{-t} \int_{0}^{\infty} x^{-\frac{1}{2}} e^{-xt} dx \qquad \text{V}$$

ii. *Integration around the circle Q of radius δ*

Let $\lambda = \delta e^{i\theta}$ where θ varies from $-\pi$ to π.

$$\therefore \quad d\lambda = i \delta e^{i\theta} d\theta \qquad \text{VI}$$

$$\therefore \quad \sqrt{\lambda} = \delta^{\frac{1}{2}} e^{\frac{1}{2}i\theta} \qquad \text{VII}$$

$$\therefore \quad \int_{Q} \frac{e^{(\lambda-1)t}}{\sqrt{\lambda}} d\lambda = \lim_{\delta \to 0} i e^{-t} \delta^{\frac{1}{2}} \int_{-\pi}^{\pi} e^{\delta(\cos\theta + i\sin\theta)t + \frac{1}{2}i\theta} d\theta = 0 \qquad \text{VIII}$$

iii. *Integration along QP.* By the same procedure as in part (i), the value of this integral is

$$\int_{QP} \frac{e^{(\lambda-1)t}}{\sqrt{\lambda}}\, d\lambda = i\,e^{-t}\int_0^\infty x^{-\frac{1}{2}}\,e^{-xt}\,dx \qquad \text{IX}$$

Adding together equations V, VIII and IX and substituting into equation II gives

$$\frac{df(t)}{dt} = \frac{2i\,e^{-t}}{2\pi i}\int_0^\infty x^{-\frac{1}{2}}\,e^{-xt}\,dx \qquad \text{X}$$

The integral in equation X can be evaluated by putting $xt = \alpha^2$.

$$\therefore \quad \frac{df(t)}{dt} = \frac{2e^{-t}}{\pi\sqrt{t}}\int_0^\infty e^{-\alpha^2}\,d\alpha \qquad \text{XI}$$

$$= e^{-t}/\sqrt{\pi t}$$

by equation (5.2). Integrating gives

$$f(t) = \frac{1}{\sqrt{\pi}}\int_0^t t^{-\frac{1}{2}}\,e^{-t}\,dt \qquad \text{XII}$$

$$\therefore \quad f(t) = \mathscr{L}^{-1}\left[\frac{1}{s\sqrt{s+1}}\right] = \mathrm{erf}\sqrt{t} \qquad \text{XIII}$$

The last few stages of this calculation involve the properties of the error function from Chapter 5.

6.8.3. *Inversion when there are Both Poles and a Branch Point*

When there are pole singularities in addition to the branch point, equation (6.44) is still applicable but the contour Br_2 must be modified to exclude

FIG. 6.9. Modification of Br_2 for poles and a branch point

all of the singularities. This is done by drawing a circle around each singularity and connecting it to the main contour with a pair of parallel coincident straight lines. Figure 6.9 shows the case of a branch point at the origin and two poles which are self-conjugate. Br_2 is the curve GFEDC and the Mellin-Fourier integral is evaluated as follows.

By Cauchy's theorem, the integral of $e^{st} \bar{f}(s)$ round the closed curve ABCDEFGA is zero. The parts of this contour which have been drawn with dotted lines make no contribution to the integral; the sections BC and GA because of equation (6.41), and the pairs of parallel lines because they are coincident and are traversed in opposite directions. Thus,

$$\int_{Br_1} e^{st}\bar{f}(s)\,ds = \int_{GFEDC} e^{st}\bar{f}(s)\,ds$$

The circles enclosing the poles at D and F are both described in the positive (anticlockwise) direction and make a contribution $2\pi i$ (residue at the pole) towards the integral along Br_2.

Hence, the transform can be inverted by adding $2\pi i$ times the sum of the residues at all of the poles of $e^{st}\,\bar{f}(s)$, to the piecewise integration along GEC as for an ordinary branch cut without poles. That is,

$$f(t) = \frac{1}{2\pi i} \int_{Br_2} e^{st}\bar{f}(s)\,ds = \int_{GEC} e^{st}\bar{f}(s)\,ds + \sum (\text{residues of } e^{st}\bar{f}(s)) \qquad (6.45)$$

Equation (6.45) summarizes the method of inversion of the Laplace transform by contour integration. To use it, if $\bar{f}(s)$ does not contain a branch point, the integral along GEC will be zero and equation (6.45) simplifies to equation (6.43), but in general the full equation (6.45) is needed. The integral along GEC can always be performed in a piecewise manner as in Example 2 above, and the residues of $\bar{f}(s)\,e^{st}$ can always be found by the methods given in Section 4.16. Thus any transform can be inverted provided the conditions for equation (6.41) are satisfied. That is, $|\bar{f}(s)| \to 0$ as $|s| \to \infty$. As mentioned at the start of Section 6.7.2 this condition is invariably satisfied, and it is true to say that any transform arising in connection with a physically reasonable problem will satisfy this condition so that the solution can be found in principle by the method of residues.

6.9. Application of the Laplace Transform to Automatic Control Theory

The study or design of automatic control systems for chemical processes requires setting up differential equations that will predict the dynamic behaviour of a piece of equipment, and in particular the response of the equipment to sudden changes. The example in Section 6.5 predicting the response of the control valve to a sudden change in air pressure illustrates how these problems can be solved by means of the Laplace transformation. However, let it be assumed that a simple automatic control system is described by the linear differential equation

$$A\frac{d^2y}{dt^2} + B\frac{dy}{dt} + Cy = f(t) \qquad (6.46)$$

The Laplace transform of this equation is

$$\bar{y}(s) = \frac{\bar{f}(s)}{As^2 + Bs + C} + \frac{(As + B)y(0) + Ay'(0)}{As^2 + Bs + C} \qquad (6.47)$$

where $y(0)$ and $y'(0)$ are the values of the measured variable, i.e. temperature, pressure, at a time $t = 0$. $\bar{y}(s)$ is called the "response transform". The first transform on the right of equation (6.47) is the transform of the steady state solution after the change, and the last term on the right is the transform of the transient solution. That is, the first term on the right is characteristic of the control system and the last term is characteristic of the initial disturbance. Furthermore the denominator of the terms on the right hand side of equation (6.47) determines the way in which the system reaches its new equilibrium position and therefore $\left[\dfrac{1}{As^2 + Bs + C} \right]$ is the important group in automatic control theory and is called the "transfer function".

The transfer function is defined as the response of a control system to a disturbance of unit impulse from the steady state condition. Therefore referring to equation (6.47) it will be appreciated that the origin of y can be chosen so that $y(0)$ and $y'(0)$ are both zero when $t = 0$. The transfer function is now characterized by

$$\frac{\bar{y}(s)}{\bar{f}(s)} = \frac{1}{As^2 + Bs + C} \qquad (6.48)$$

which defines it as the ratio of the Laplace transform of the response variable to the Laplace transform of the disturbing variable. In addition, since this ratio is equal to the reciprocal of the transform of the differential equation describing the system, it can be evaluated only for equations that can be transformed. However, this need not be a serious restriction because in many cases an approximate subsidiary equation can be found without undue simplification; on other occasions it may be necessary to obtain the transfer function experimentally because of the complexity of the control system.

The transfer function describing a part of, or the complete control system is usually inserted into a "block diagram". Such diagrams are used extensively in automatic control theory to depict the action of the variables involved. They are similar to energy flow diagrams but the arrowed lines to and from the different blocks indicate input and output signals. A typical block diagram of an automatic control system is illustrated in Fig. 6.10b. The corresponding process diagram depicting an electrical heating coil installed in a stirred tank through which a liquid to be heated is passed, is shown in Fig. 6.10a.

In Fig. 6.10b the circle represents an algebraic operation and the two plus signs imply that the output signal $f(t)$ is obtained by summing the outputs from the two transfer functions. Each transfer function is enclosed in a rectangle, and the transfer function together with its block is called a dynamic function because it indicates a rate of change. In the particular example it indicates a rate of heat input.

FIG. 6.10.   Block diagram of electrical heating process

The only rules to be remembered in the construction of block diagrams are

(a) Only one line may enter, and only one line may leave a block representing a dynamic function.

(b) Only two lines may enter and one line leave a circle representing an algebraic operation.

(c) If a control system is described by one or more linear differential equations, the dynamic functions and algebraic operations can be rearranged without altering the controlability of the process.

For further details of these points the reader is advised to consult "Automatic Process Control", by Eckman†, as the present text is only concerned with the mathematical background.   However, it is possible to rearrange, or combine the transfer functions of a series of controlled elements in such a way that the whole process may be represented by blocks whose transfer functions have poles or zeros that are easily identified.   This is very important in the analysis of systems containing a large number of variables because the roots of the transformed equation in the denominator of the transfer function may not be easily obtained if its degree is high.

6.9.1. *Control Systems*

Chemical processes are controlled by either the "open loop" or "closed loop" control system, and in all but the most simple cases, closed loop control is employed.   Thus in the open loop system the composition of a stream may be controlled as shown in Fig. 6.11a by proportioning the flow of A by means of the flow meter in the line through which the liquid B passes, and the flow controller is only able to take a preset action according to the signal it receives from this meter.   Any other changes in the process conditions, such as the concentration of A or B prior to mixing, will have no effect on the controller, and will lead to deviations from the chosen position. If, however, a detecting device such as a *p*H meter is placed in the product line as shown in Fig. 6.11b so that the concentration of A in B can be

† Eckman, D. P. "Automatic Process Control." Wiley & Sons, New York (1958).

FIG. 6.11.   Open and closed loops

measured, and a signal representing the measured concentration changes fed back to the controller, the possible deviation can be corrected. That is "feedback" is an essential feature of a closed loop system.

A block diagram of a closed loop system is illustrated in Fig. 6.12 in which the transfer functions of the different elements depicting the controlling means have been grouped together in the combined transfer function $\bar{G}_1(s)$, whilst the transfer function of the feedback element (i.e. the measuring

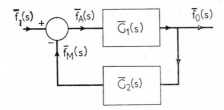

FIG. 6.12.   Typical closed loop block diagram

element) is shown in the block $\bar{G}_2(s)$. Thus, making use of the rules for dynamic and algebraic functions, the subsidiary equations for different parts of this control process can be written as

$$\bar{f}_M(s) = \bar{G}_2(s)\bar{f}_0(s) \tag{6.49}$$

$$\bar{f}_A(s) = \bar{f}_1(s) - \bar{f}_M(s) = \bar{f}_1(s) - \bar{G}_2(s)\bar{f}_0(s) \tag{6.50}$$

$$\bar{f}_0(s) = \bar{G}_1(s)\bar{f}_A(s) = \bar{G}_1(s)[\bar{f}_1(s) - \bar{G}_2(s)\bar{f}_0(s)] \tag{6.51}$$

$$\therefore \quad \bar{f}_0(s) = \frac{\bar{G}_1(s)\bar{f}_1(s)}{1 + \bar{G}_1(s)\,\bar{G}_2(s)} \tag{6.52}$$

Inverting equation (6.52) gives the value of the output from the controlled process as a function of time. That is,

$$f_0(t) = \frac{1}{2\pi i} \int_{Br_1} \frac{\bar{G}_1(s)\bar{f}_1(s)\,e^{st}\,ds}{1 + \bar{G}_1(s)\,\bar{G}_2(s)} \tag{6.53}$$

If the Laplace transform of the function describing the control system does not contain any singularities other than poles, the value of the integral can be obtained from equation (6.43) as

$$_0(t) = \sum \left[\text{residues of} \frac{\bar{G}_1(s)\bar{f}_1(s)\,e^{st}}{1+\bar{G}_1(s)\,\bar{G}_2(s)} \right] \qquad (6.54)$$

and the behaviour of the control system, after being subjected to a disturbance, can be predicted.

6.9.2. *Control Sytem Stability*

To be useful, a control system must be stable and some indication of this may be obtained by inspection of the residues in equation (6.54). Thus if any of the poles of the numerator or zeros of the denominator have positive real parts, then $f_0(t)$ will contain a term $e^{\alpha t}$ which will increase to infinity as the time t increases and hence lead to instability. Consequently, all of the relevant poles and zeros must have negative real parts so that any disturbance will decay exponentially with time and the control system will be stable. This implies that all of the poles of the integrand of equation (6.53) must be in the left half of the s plane for the system to be stable.

If in addition there are poles on the imaginary axis, the control system will fluctuate indefinitely, whilst a pole at the origin, associated with other poles in the negative half plane, indicates that the system will fluctuate about a new position after a disturbance. This means that the control system will experience an "offset".

6.9.3. *Stability Criteria*

The transfer functions describing a control system may be very complicated, containing numerous poles and zeros, with the result that the procedure of evaluating the residues is very lengthy and time-consuming. Consequently some "short cut" methods, indicating whether or not a control system will be stable, have been devised. These will not reveal the extent of the instability but for obvious reasons this is not necessary. Neither will these methods indicate the sensitivity of a control system to a disturbance; for a control system could be mathematically stable but functionally useless because the time required to attain steady state could be very large.

Two methods extensively used to test the stability of a control system are those of Routh and Hurwitz, and Nyquist. Essentially the Routh-Hurwitz criteria of stability has its basis in matrix theory which will be treated in Chapter 12; here it will suffice to explain the mechanics of the method so that the section will be complete in itself. Thus let the denominator be expressed in the form of a polynomial, viz.

$$1+\bar{G}_1(s)\,\bar{G}_2(s) = p_0 s^n + p_1 s^{n-1} + \dots + p_n = 0 \qquad (6.55)$$

The stability of the control system will depend upon the roots of the subsidiary equation (6.55) and it can be assessed as follows. The system will be unstable if

(a) the coefficients in equation (6.55) vary in sign,

(b) some coefficients are zero.

Both of these conditions can be assessed by inspection. However, they must be further tested by "Routh's Rules" for the assessment of the number of roots of an equation that have positive real parts. Routh proposed that the coefficients of terms in an equation be arranged into test functions R_i as follows. Thus in relation to equation (6.55)

$$R_0 = p_0$$
$$R_1 = p_1$$
$$R_2 = p_2 - \frac{p_0 p_3}{p_1}$$
$$R_3 = \frac{p_1 p_2 p_3 - p_0 p_3^2 - p_1^2 p_4 + p_0 p_1 p_5}{p_1 p_2 - p_0 p_3}$$

etc.

Routh's test functions can be conveniently expressed in terms of "test determinants" which are more rational expressions for the test functions. They are

$$\Delta_0 = p_0 \qquad \Delta_1 = p_1 \qquad \Delta_2 = \begin{vmatrix} p_1 & p_0 \\ p_3 & p_2 \end{vmatrix}$$

$$\Delta_3 = \begin{vmatrix} p_1 & p_0 & 0 \\ p_3 & p_2 & p_1 \\ p_5 & p_4 & p_3 \end{vmatrix} \qquad \Delta_4 = \begin{vmatrix} p_1 & p_0 & 0 & 0 \\ p_3 & p_2 & p_1 & p_0 \\ p_5 & p_4 & p_3 & p_2 \\ p_7 & p_6 & p_5 & p_4 \end{vmatrix}$$

In these determinants it will be noticed that the order of the determinant is the same as the suffix of Δ with the exception that Δ_0 is of first order. In addition, the elements of each determinant are arranged in ascending order down the diagonals, and in descending order horizontally from left to right. The determinants are related to the test functions as follows.

$$R_0 = \Delta_0$$
$$R_1 = \Delta_1$$
$$R_2 = \Delta_2/\Delta_1$$
$$R_3 = \Delta_3/\Delta_2$$
$$...R_n = \Delta_n/\Delta_{n-1}$$

In fact,
$$R_n = \Delta_n/\Delta_{n-1} = p_n$$

The necessary and sufficient condition for the control system to be stable is that all of the test functions, or all of the test determinants shall be positive.

Example 1. The denominator of the complete transfer function of a control system can be represented by

$$5s^4 + 3(\alpha-1)s^3 + 2\alpha s^2 + (\alpha-2)s - (\alpha-3) = 0 \qquad \text{I}$$

Discuss the stability of the system.

Inspection of equation I shows that if α is less than 2, then p_3 is negative; and if α is greater than 3, then p_4 is negative. Hence the system may be stable if α has values between 2 and 3. This will be confirmed using Routh's test functions which are:

$$R_0 = 5$$

$$R_1 = 3(\alpha - 1)$$

$$R_2 = 2\alpha - \frac{5(\alpha - 2)}{3(\alpha - 1)}$$

$$R_3 = \frac{3(\alpha - 1)(2\alpha)(\alpha - 2) - 5(\alpha - 2)^2 + 9(\alpha - 1)^2(\alpha - 3)}{6\alpha(\alpha - 1) - 5(\alpha - 2)}$$

and $R_4 = p_4 = 3 - \alpha$

These can be simplified to give

$$R_0 = 5 \qquad\qquad\qquad \text{II}$$

$$R_1 = 3(\alpha - 1) \qquad\qquad \text{III}$$

$$R_2 = \frac{6\alpha^2 - 11\alpha + 10}{3(\alpha - 1)} \qquad\qquad \text{IV}$$

$$R_3 = \frac{15\alpha^3 - 68\alpha^2 + 95\alpha - 47}{6\alpha^2 - 11\alpha + 10} \qquad\qquad \text{V}$$

$$R_4 = 3 - \alpha \qquad\qquad\qquad \text{VI}$$

The quadratic in the numerator of R_2 and the denominator of R_3 has complex roots and is therefore positive for all real values of α. Hence, provided $1 < \alpha < 3$, R_0, R_1, R_2, and R_4 must be positive. It is now necessary to determine if there are any values of α within this range that make the numerator of R_3 positive. Denote this numerator by $f(\alpha)$.

$$\therefore \quad f(\alpha) = 15\alpha^3 - 68\alpha^2 + 95\alpha - 47 \qquad\qquad \text{VII}$$

To form an idea of the shape of this function it can be differentiated, viz.

$$\frac{df}{d\alpha} = 45\alpha^2 - 136\alpha + 95 \qquad\qquad \text{VIII}$$

Equation VIII has zeros at $\alpha = 1 \cdot 10$ and $\alpha = 1 \cdot 93$. The first corresponds to a maximum and the second to a minimum. Substitution into equation VII shows that

if $\alpha = 1 \cdot 10, \quad f(\alpha) = -4 \cdot 8 \qquad\qquad \text{IX}$

Since this is a maximum of $f(\alpha)$, $f(\alpha)$ must be negative for all $\alpha < 1 \cdot 93$. The available range of values for α is now restricted to the original range $2 < \alpha < 3$ approximately and choosing a few values in this range gives

$$\alpha = 2 \qquad f(\alpha) = -9 \cdot 0$$

$$\alpha = 2 \cdot 5 \qquad f(\alpha) = -0 \cdot 125$$

$$\alpha = 3 \qquad f(\alpha) = 31 \cdot 0$$

Therefore $\alpha = 2\cdot5$ is an approximate root of equation VII with $f(\alpha) = 0$. This value can be improved by the method to be given in Chapter 11, thus proving that the system described by equation I is stable for

$$2\cdot503 < \alpha < 3\cdot0 \qquad\qquad \text{X}$$

6.9.4. *The Nyquist Diagram*

The Nyquist criteria of stability makes use of the complex character of the Laplace parameter s, and the fact that the denominator of an unstable control loop transfer function will have roots with positive real parts situated in the right half of the s plane. Hence if the contour of integration of equation (6.54) is drawn in this part of the s plane as shown in Fig. 6.13, it

Fig. 6.13.   Nyquist contour

will enclose all of the zeros and poles of $1+\ _1(s)\ _2(s)$ with positive real parts. Furthermore, it can be shown that within any closed contour

$$\begin{bmatrix} \text{Number} \\ \text{of zeros} \end{bmatrix} - \begin{bmatrix} \text{Number} \\ \text{of poles} \end{bmatrix} = \frac{1}{2\pi}\begin{bmatrix} \text{Change in arg of} \\ \text{function around contour} \end{bmatrix} \qquad (6.56)$$

Nyquist stated that $[\mathrm{Arg}\,\bar{f}(s)/2\pi]$ was equal to the number of times the contour encircled the origin of $\bar{f}(s)^C$. If this is N, the number of zeros is Z, and the number of poles is P, then equation (6.56) becomes

$$Z - P = N \qquad\qquad (6.57)$$

In these equations, an nth order zero or pole is considered to be n zeros or poles of first order.

Nyquist used equation (6.57) to restate the stability requirement of equation (6.54). A control system is stable if there are no zeros of the function $[1+\bar{G}_1(s)\,\bar{G}_2(s)]$ in the positive half plane, and this means that if the sum of the number of encirclements of the origin of this function and the number of poles enclosed by the contour is zero then the control system is stable. The Nyquist diagram consists of plotting the "transfer locus" of $[\bar{G}_1(s)\,\bar{G}_2(s)]$ as s traverses the contour of Fig. 6.13. The origin of the function $[1+\bar{G}_1(s)\,\bar{G}_2(s)]$ is $(-1,0)$ and provided $|\bar{G}_1(s)\,\bar{G}_2(s)|\to0$ as $|s|\to\infty$ the infinite semicircle can be ignored. The poles of $\bar{G}_1(s)$ and $\bar{G}_2(s)$

have to be located in any case thus determining P, and the number of times the point $(-1, 0)$ is enclosed by the transfer locus determines N and the Nyquist criteria can be applied. Usually it is only necessary to plot the transfer locus of $s = i\omega$ for $0 < \omega < \infty$ because the locus between 0 and $-\infty$ is just its reflection in the real axis.

The Nyquist criteria can be applied by plotting the function $[\bar{G}_1(s)\ \bar{G}_2(s)]$ from arbitrarily chosen values of ω between 0 and ∞, or by plotting directly experimental phase and magnitude data. Since it is not essential to factorize the open loop transfer function in order to obtain the number of poles, the stability of the system can be assessed by using the value of N obtained from the transfer locus and the value of P obtained by inspection. Unless $Z = P + N = 0$, then the control system is unstable. These principles will now be illustrated by an example.

Example 2. Estimate the stability of an automatic control system whose combined transfer function is

$$\bar{G}_1(s)\ \bar{G}_2(s) = 9/(10s + 1)^3 \qquad\qquad \text{I}$$

Put
$$s = i\omega$$

then
$$\frac{9}{(10i\omega + 1)^3} = \frac{9}{(10i\omega + 1)^3}\frac{(1 - 10i\omega)^3}{(1 - 10i\omega)^3} \qquad\qquad \text{II}$$

$$= \frac{9(1 - 300\omega^2)}{(1 + 100\omega^2)^3} - i\left[\frac{9(30\omega - 1000\omega^3)}{(1 + 100\omega^2)^3}\right] \qquad\qquad \text{III}$$

In equation III the function has been separated into its real and imaginary parts. These are the coordinates of the transfer function in the Nyquist diagram and Table 6.3 shows the evaluation of them.

The final two columns of Table 6.3 are plotted in Fig. 6.14 to form the

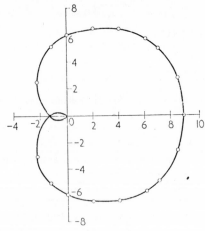

Fig. 6.14. Stability diagram for the transfer function $\dfrac{9}{(10s + 1)^3}$

TABLE 6.3. Transfer Locus of $9/(10s+1)^3$

ω	ω^2	ω^3	$9(1-300\omega^2)$	$(1+100\omega^2)^3$	$9(30\omega-1000\omega^3)$	$\dfrac{9(1-300\omega^2)}{(1+100\omega^2)^3}$	$\dfrac{9(30\omega-1000\omega^3)}{(1+100\omega^2)^3}$
0	0	0	9·00	1·00	0·00	9·00	0·00
0·01	1×10^{-4}	1×10^{-6}	8·73	1·03	2·69	8·48	2·61
0·02	4×10^{-4}	8×10^{-6}	7·92	1·12	5·33	7·08	4·76
0·03	9×10^{-4}	27×10^{-6}	6·57	1·30	7·85	5·05	6·03
0·04	16×10^{-4}	64×10^{-6}	4·68	1·56	10·23	3·00	6·56
0·05	25×10^{-4}	$1\cdot25\times10^{-4}$	2·25	1·96	12·37	1·15	6·30
0·06	36×10^{-4}	$2\cdot16\times10^{-4}$	−0·72	2·51	14·25	−0·28	5·68
0·07	49×10^{-4}	$3\cdot43\times10^{-4}$	−4·23	3·30	15·9	−1·28	4·81
0·08	64×10^{-4}	$5\cdot12\times10^{-4}$	−8·3	4·41	17·0	−1·88	3·85
0·10	0·0100	0·0010	−18	8·0	18·0	−2·25	2·25
0·15	0·0225	0·0034	−52	34·5	10·1	−1·50	0·29
0·20	0·0400	0·0080	−99	125	−18·0	−0·79	−0·15
0·25	0·0625	0·0156	−160	380	−72·9	−0·42	−0·19
0·4	0·16	0·064	−423	4920	−468	−0·09	−0·09
0·8	0·64	0·512	−1719	275000	−4392	−0·01	−0·01

Nyquist diagram for the transfer function $9/(10s+1)^3$. This function does not have any poles in the right half plane as can be seen by inspection; however, the transfer locus encircles the point $(-1, 0)$ twice.

$$\therefore \quad N = 2 \qquad\qquad\qquad \text{IV}$$

Therefore, by equation (6.57)

$$Z = N + P = 2$$

and the control system is unstable.

In the example given, the Laplace transform could have been inverted and the stability checked as a function of time just as rapidly as Table 6.3 and Fig. 6.14 were prepared. However, it must be remembered that with an actual control system, the transfer function would be very complicated, and it would then be advantageous to prepare the transfer locus and use the Nyquist criteria to test stability.

Chapter 7

VECTOR ANALYSIS

7.1. INTRODUCTION

IN Chapter 4 it was shown that a complex number consisted of two independent parts, a real part and an imaginary part. The one symbol z was used to represent a combination of two symbols x and y so that manipulations with a single symbol were much quicker than the corresponding elementary operations on the separate variables. It is natural to enquire whether this principle can be extended so that more than two variables can be combined into a single symbol thus shortening the work in multi-variable systems. The Argand diagram is a plane, two-dimensional representation of the two parts of a complex number which lie along two orthogonal axes, and a natural extension is to represent three parts of a "number" along three orthogonal axes in three-dimensional space. This new type of "number" is a vector.

Further extensions of this idea cannot be visualized, but any number of variables can be grouped into a single symbol in two ways; the first, by means of matrices, will be discussed in Chapter 12, and the second using tensors will be described briefly here. Tensors are introduced to indicate a general type of number of which vectors are a special case. The two variables which are combined in a complex number are distinguished as a real part and an imaginary part, and the principal difference between tensors and matrices is the labelling and ordering of the many distinct parts. The ordinary operations of arithmetic have to be restricted in the study of complex numbers by defining principal values, giving a special rule for division, etc. With vectors, the restrictions are more severe as will be shown in the following sections of this chapter.

The symbolism and operations of vector analysis constitute a powerful shorthand method for describing complex problems and expressing equations in general terms. For example, in Section 1.8, the steady state temperature distribution in a cylindrical conductor was shown to satisfy the equation

$$\frac{d^2T}{dr^2} + \frac{1}{r}\frac{dT}{dr} = 0 \tag{7.1}$$

It is a simple matter to show that the corresponding temperature distribution in a flat conductor with insulated edges satisfies the equation

$$\frac{d^2T}{dx^2} = 0 \tag{7.2}$$

Both of the above equations relate to the one process, heat transfer, but to systems having different geometrical shapes. The utility of vector analysis is that the following equation in vector form will represent all steady state heat conduction processes with constant thermal conductivity in any number of dimensions and for any shape of solid. Thus

$$\nabla^2 T = 0 \qquad (7.3)$$

The rules of vector analysis are explained in the earlier sections of this chapter, so that the second half of the chapter can be devoted to the use and interpretation of Hamilton's operator (∇) which is the fundamental symbol of this compact notation.

Vector equations are usually used to describe general processes such as the above, but when a particular example is considered, the vector form (7.3) is expanded into the appropriate particular form (7.1) or (7.2) and the completion of the problem is outside the domain of vector analysis. It is thus difficult to find chemical engineering examples which use vector methods exclusively, and this chapter is primarily a service chapter for the later parts of the book.

7.2. TENSORS

The notation of tensors can be introduced by referring to complex numbers. The complex number z can be written in the alternative ways

$$z = x + iy = z_1 + iz_2 \qquad (7.4)$$

where z_m is referred to as a tensor of first rank because one suffix m is needed to specify it. It is understood that the subscript m takes either of two values, 1 for the real part and 2 for the imaginary part. A more general tensor z_m can have more than two parts if m is allowed to have more than two values. The resulting parts z_1, z_2, z_3, ... etc., are all independent of one another just as z_1 and z_2 are independent in equation (7.4). By reference to the Argand diagram this can be interpreted as extending the number of dimensions of the system. If m is restricted to three values, the system is three-dimensional and can be illustrated diagrammatically, whereas if m takes values greater than three, systems of higher dimensions can be described but not visualized pictorially.

The notion of a tensor can be further generalized by using more than one subscript, thus z_{mn} is a tensor of second rank in which both m and n can take integer values within the dimensions of the system. For instance, in three dimensions the tensor z_{mn} represents the nine quantities z_{11}, z_{12}, z_{13}, z_{21}, z_{22}, z_{23}, z_{31}, z_{32}, z_{33}, whilst in four dimensions, z_{mn} represents sixteen quantities. For a clearer distinction between the first and second subscript, the one index is sometimes raised to the position of a superscript, thus z_m^n. The symbolism for the general tensor is now obvious, it consists of a main symbol such as z with any number of associated indices which may be subscripts or superscripts. Each index is allowed to take any integer value up to the chosen dimensions of the system. The number of indices associated with the tensor is called the "rank" of the tensor.

7.2.1. *Tensors of Zero Rank, Scalars*

If the tensor has no index, then it only consists of one quantity independent of the number of dimensions of the system. The value of this quantity is independent of the complexity of the system, possesses magnitude only and is called a "scalar". No direction can be associated with a scalar since direction can only be specified in a system of known dimensionality. All physical properties are examples of scalars. For example, density, mass, specific heat, coefficient of viscosity, diffusion coefficient, thermal conductivity, etc. Other examples are the scalar point functions such as temperature, concentration, and pressure which are all signified by a number which may vary with position but not depend upon direction. Energy and time are also scalars.

It is worth noting that the coefficient of viscosity for a non-newtonian fluid may be defined as a vector quantity if its value at a point is related to a specified direction. Normally, however, the coefficient depends upon the state of the fluid at the point rather than the point itself.

7.2.2. *Tensors of First Rank, Vectors*

When the tensor has a single subscript it consists of as many elements as the number of dimensions of the system. For practical purposes this number is three and the tensor has three elements which are normally called components. The tensor of first rank is alternatively named a "vector". Vectors have both magnitude and direction and can be represented in three dimensions by a straight line in space. The most common examples of vectors are force, velocity, momentum, angular velocity, weight, and area.

The above classification of scalars and vectors should help to clear some common misconceptions about the nature of the properties listed. For instance, mass is a scalar and depends only upon the substance involved and not upon its environment, whereas weight is a force resulting from the action of gravity upon the mass. Weight is thus a vector since it acts in a direction chosen by the gravitational field in which the scalar mass is situated. Newton's second law of motion is a vector equation relating the two vectors force and acceleration by means of a proportionality constant, mass.

Pressure is a scalar quantity because it acts equally in all directions and thus has no special direction. Scalar pressure becomes vector force when a surface is defined to sustain the pressure; the direction of the force vector is associated with the orientation of the surface and thus surface area is a vector quantity.

The results of various products between vectors and scalars will be better understood later in this chapter when multiplication of vectors has been defined, especially the reasons why momentum is a vector, whereas energy is a scalar.

7.2.3. *Tensors of Second Rank*

The one tensor of second rank which occurs frequently in engineering is the stress tensor. This of course has a double subscript and has both a magnitude and two directions associated with it. In three dimensions the stress tensor consists of nine quantities which can be arranged in a matrix form thus,

$$T_{mn} = \begin{bmatrix} T_{11} & T_{12} & T_{13} \\ T_{21} & T_{22} & T_{23} \\ T_{31} & T_{32} & T_{33} \end{bmatrix} \qquad (7.5)$$

The physical interpretation is as follows. Take three cartesian coordinate axes x, y, z, and define an elementary rectangular box of dimensions δx, δy, δz. There are three typical faces to the box each having a normal parallel to one of the coordinate axes. Each face of this box has a force acting upon it, and this force can be resolved into three components parallel to the three axes. This is illustrated in Fig. 7.1 for two of the faces where the normal

FIG. 7.1.   The stress tensor

components have been labelled with p and the shear components with τ. To distinguish between these various forces it is necessary to specify both the direction of the plane and the line of action. The nine elements of the stress tensor (7.5) can be associated with these individual forces by using the first subscript to denote the plane and the second subscript to denote the direction of the force. Thus

$$T_{mn} = \begin{bmatrix} p_{xx} & \tau_{xy} & \tau_{xz} \\ \tau_{yx} & p_{yy} & \tau_{yz} \\ \tau_{zx} & \tau_{zy} & p_{zz} \end{bmatrix} \qquad (7.6)$$

where the subscripts 1, 2, 3 have been replaced by x, y, z to restrict the tensor to three dimensions. τ_{xy} is read as "the shear force on the x facing plane acting in the y direction". It can be seen that one component of the force on a plane acts in the normal direction whilst the other two are shear forces along the surface. The forces illustrated in the diagram are the forces acting on the element, and the reaction forces exerted by the element on neighbouring elements are obviously all reversed in direction. For this reason, the components of stress acting on a plane facing in a positive axis direction (e.g. ABED) all act in the positive direction of the corresponding axis; whereas the components acting on a plane facing in a negative direction (e.g. OABC) all act in the negative direction of the corresponding axis. It is to be noted that the repeated suffix gives the normal forces, and the unlike suffices denote the shear forces. Also, the normal forces include the pressure, but with reversed sign because the force due to pressure acts inwards towards the element.

Tensor calculus, which is a specialized field of mathematics, has little direct application to chemical engineering at present since chemical engineers confine their attention to three dimensions. Consequently, only the above special kinds of tensor (scalar and vector) which have physical interpretations will be considered in this chapter. If the reader is interested in the manipulation of tensors he is referred to Craig or Sokolnikoff[†].

In the subsequent discussion, all quantities will be referred to as either vectors or scalars and all further remarks will apply to three dimensions. The subscripts will be labelled by the coordinate variables rather than by numbers for extra clarity. Bold face type will be used for vectors, and ordinary type for scalars.

7.3. Addition and Subtraction of Vectors

Any vector can be represented geometrically by a straight line with an arrow, the length of the line representing the magnitude of the vector and the direction of the line as indicated by the arrow representing the direction of the vector. The addition of two vectors is defined geometrically by the well-known "triangle of forces". The start of the line representing the second vector is superimposed on the end of the line representing the first

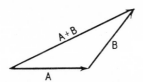

Fig. 7.2. Addition of vectors

vector. The sum of the two vectors is represented by the line joining the start of the first vector to the end of the second vector as illustrated in Fig. 7.2.

The product of two scalars is obtained according to the rules of ordinary arithmetic, and to multiply a vector by a scalar, the magnitude of the vector is multiplied by the scalar and the direction remains unchanged. Multiplication of a vector by a negative number also involves reversing the direction

† Craig, H. V. " Vector and Tensor Analysis." McGraw-Hill (1943).
Sokolnikoff, I. S. " Tensor Analysis." Wiley and Sons (1951).

of the vector. Thus to subtract one vector from another it is only necessary to reverse the direction of the vector to be subtracted and add the other to it as illustrated in Fig. 7.3.

FIG. 7.3.   Subtraction of vectors

7.3.1. *Components*

The process of addition described above can be reversed allowing a vector to be resolved into equivalent constituent parts called "components". If all components of a vector are added together using the above rule, the original vector is returned. A vector can be resolved into components in an infinite variety of ways but the resolution into components in three specified non-coplanar directions is unique. This fundamental property is ultilized by defining a coordinate system referred to three mutually orthogonal axes. Define the three cartesian coordinate axes x, y, z as shown in Fig. 7.4, and

FIG. 7.4.   Resolving into components

represent the vector A by a line starting from the origin. Complete the rectangular box which has edges parallel to the axes, and the vector A as diagonal, and denote the edges of the box by the vectors A_x, A_y, A_z. The subscripts denote the directions of the vectors and it is obvious that all parallel edges have the same length and are denoted by the same vector. Applying the rule of addition twice it can be seen that

$$A = A_x + A_y + A_z \qquad (7.7)$$

Since vectors are frequently resolved into components along the co-ordinate axes, it is convenient to define a set of unit vectors having unit magnitudes and the directions of the coordinate axes. Any vector can then be expressed as the sum of scalar multiples of these unit vectors. The standard set of unit vectors which define the cartesian coordinate system is

i, j, k in the x, y, z directions respectively. Equation (7.7) can now be re-written as

$$A = A_x i + A_y j + A_z k \qquad (7.8)$$

where A_x, A_y, A_z are the scalar lengths of the edges of the box, and the unit vectors i, j, k define the directions. Two applications of the theorem of Pythagoras in Fig. 7.4 shows that the magnitude of A, which is denoted by $|A|$ or A by analogy with complex numbers, is given by

$$|A| = \sqrt{(A_x^2 + A_y^2 + A_z^2)} \qquad (7.9)$$

or the squared magnitude of a vector is equal to the sum of the squares of its three mutually orthogonal components.

7.3.2. Position Vectors

The position of a point in space can be specified relative to an origin by defining the vector joining the origin to the point. Such a vector is called a "position vector". The above definition of position is independent of any coordinate system and only requires the definition of an origin. An analogy which may be helpful in grasping this point is the reply to a stranger who asks for directions to a particular destination. If the reply given is "travel 500 yards in a NNE direction", then a complete coordinate system is implicitly involved; whereas if the information is given in the form of an arm pointing out the direction with the instruction "travel 500 yards over there", the arm is a vector indicating direction and the spoken instruction gives the magnitude. The first reply presupposes that both parties can locate the exact northerly direction, which is unlikely, while the second reply is much more direct and useful.

A vector defining the position of a point is usually given the symbol r which can be resolved into components in the same way as any other vector once a coordinate system has been defined. Thus

$$r = x + y + z \qquad (7.10)$$

or
$$r = xi + yj + zk \qquad (7.11)$$

The point can therefore be specified by its coordinates either by equation (7.10) in a vector form, or by equation (7.11) in a scalar form. The latter is more usual and it is implied that x is measured in a direction defined by i and similarly for y and z. Thus when a point is specified by (x, y, z) it is vitally important that the order of the coordinates should not be disturbed.

Returning to the addition of two vectors A and B, and referring to Fig. 7.5, it can be seen that the sum of the vectors can be obtained by summing the separate components. Thus if

$$A = A_x i + A_y j + A_z k \qquad (7.12)$$

and
$$B = B_x i + B_y j + B_z k \qquad (7.13)$$

then
$$A + B = (A_x + B_x)i + (A_y + B_y)j + (A_z + B_z)k \qquad (7.14)$$

also
$$A - B = (A_x - B_x)i + (A_y - B_y)j + (A_z - B_z)k \qquad (7.15)$$

For two vectors to be equal, their difference must be zero, and from equation (7.15), A can only equal B if

$$A_x - B_x = 0, \qquad A_y - B_y = 0, \quad \text{and } A_z - B_z = 0 \qquad (7.16)$$

Thus a single vector equation represents three simultaneous scalar equations.

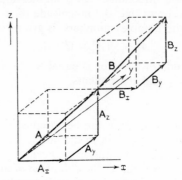

FIG. 7.5.   Addition of vectors by components

7.3.3. *Properties of Addition*

Both the associative law and the commutative law of algebra are valid for the addition of vectors. That is,

$$A + (B + C) = (A + B) + C \qquad (7.17)$$

and

$$A + B = B + A \qquad (7.18)$$

The distributive law is also valid for the multiplication of the sum of two vectors by a scalar. Thus

$$m(A + B) = mA + mB \qquad (7.19)$$

There is no divergence therefore from the normal rules of algebra when addition and subtraction of vectors is considered.

7.3.4. *Geometrical Applications*

In general, two vectors are sufficient to define a plane, and if a linear relationship exists between three vectors then they must be coplanar. This is obvious from the rule of addition because when two of the vectors have been added together, they must have the same direction as the third vector.

Example 1. If A and B are two position vectors, find the equation of the straight line passing through the end points of A and B.

Referring to Fig. 7.6 where the origin is O and C is the position vector of any other point on the line through A and B, the vector joining A to B is $B - A$. Similarly, the vector joining B to C is $C - B$. If ABC is to be a straight line, then these two vectors have the same direction and can only differ in magnitude. Therefore

$$C - B = m(B - A) \qquad\qquad\qquad \text{I}$$

where m is a variable scalar and C is the variable vector. Equation I can be rearranged to give

$$C = (m+1)B - mA \qquad\qquad \text{II}$$

or $\qquad\qquad mA - (m+1)B + C = 0 \qquad\qquad \text{III}$

Equation II is the standard equation of a straight line with m the independent

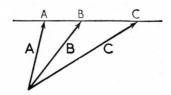

FIG. 7.6.   Equation of a straight line

variable, and C the dependent variable. Equation III is in the form of a linear relationship between three vectors, the general form of which is

$$pA + qB + rC = 0 \qquad\qquad \text{IV}$$

Comparison of equations III and IV shows that equation III is the special case in which $p+q+r = 0$. Thus the general result that if three position vectors are related by a linear equation then they are coplanar. If the sum of the three coefficients is also zero, then the end points of the vectors are colinear.

Example 2.   Prove that the medians of a triangle are concurrent.

Figure 7.7 illustrates the problem with reference to the triangle ABC, where L, M, N are the mid-points of the sides. It is assumed that BM and AL intersect at P and that CN does not necessarily pass through P.

FIG. 7.7.   Medians of a triangle

Taking C as origin, and denoting the position vectors of A and B by A and B, then the equations of the lines BM and AL can be written as follows using the results of Example 1. Thus the equation of the line through B and M is

$$\alpha = (s+1)B - s(\tfrac{1}{2}A) \qquad\qquad \text{I}$$

and as the parameter s varies, the vector α determines the various points along the line BM. Similarly, the equation of AL is

$$\alpha' = (t+1)A - t(\tfrac{1}{2}B) \qquad\qquad \text{II}$$

Since P is the point of intersection of AL and BM, the position vector of P is given by $\alpha = \alpha'$, or

$$(s+1)B - \tfrac{1}{2}sA = (t+1)A - \tfrac{1}{2}tB \qquad\qquad \text{III}$$

$$\therefore \quad (t+1+\tfrac{1}{2}s)A = (s+1+\tfrac{1}{2}t)B \qquad\qquad \text{IV}$$

Equation IV relates two vectors which have different directions and the equality can only be satisfied by both vectors having zero magnitude.

$$\therefore \quad t+1+\tfrac{1}{2}s = 0 \quad \text{and } s+1+\tfrac{1}{2}t = 0 \qquad\qquad \text{V}$$

The solution of equations V is

$$s = t = -\tfrac{2}{3}$$

and the vector CP becomes $\tfrac{1}{3}(B+A)$ from equation I.

The vector CN is the sum of the vectors along CB and BN; and thus the position vector of N is given by

$$B + \tfrac{1}{2}(A-B) = \tfrac{1}{2}(A+B)$$

Therefore the vectors CN and CP have the same direction $(A+B)$ and thus CN must pass through P

Example 3. *Generalized Vector Method for Stagewise Processes.* It has been shown by Lemlich and Leonard[†] that many of the existing difference point constructions for determining the number of theoretical steps in a stagewise process are variations of a more general vector method. They have also shown that the comprehensive vector method suggests many hitherto untried constructions and this example from their work derives the standard rectangular diagram from the general vector diagram.

In any stagewise process there is more than one property to be conserved and for the purpose of this example it will be assumed that the three properties, enthalpy (H), total mass flow (M), and mass flow of one component (C) are conserved. Instead of considering three separate scalar balances, one vector balance can be taken by using a set of cartesian coordinates in the following manner. Using x to measure M, y to measure H, and z to measure C, then any process stream can be represented by a vector thus,

$$OM = M_1 i + H_1 j + C_1 k \qquad\qquad \text{I}$$

where OM is the vector illustrated in Fig. 7.8. Similarly, a second stream can be represented by

$$ON = M_2 i + H_2 j + C_2 k \qquad\qquad \text{II}$$

and using vector addition,

$$OR = OM + ON = (M_1 + M_2)i + (H_1 + H_2)j + (C_1 + C_2)k \qquad\qquad \text{III}$$

Thus OR which represents the sum of the two streams, must be a constant vector for the three properties to be conserved within the system. Hence,

† Lemlich, R. and Leonard, R. A. *A.I.Ch.E.J.* **8**, 214 (1962)

to perform a calculation, when either of the streams OM or ON is determined, the other is obtained by subtraction from the constant OR. It will now be shown that the intersection of these vectors with the plane $x = 1$, as illustrated in Fig. 7.8, gives the usual enthalpy–concentration diagram for the Ponchon-Savarit method.

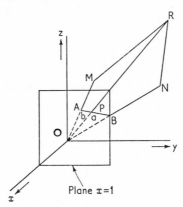

FIG. 7.8. Representation of a stagewise process

The constant line OR will cross the plane $x = 1$ at point P which will be a fixed point. The variable vectors OM and ON will also cross the plane at A and B respectively, and since OMRN is a parallelogram, APB will be a straight line. Let

$$\frac{AP}{PB} = \frac{b}{a} \qquad\qquad \text{IV}$$

as illustrated in Fig. 7.8. Then by the triangle rule of addition,

$$aOA = aOP + aPA = aOP + \frac{ab}{a+b}BA \qquad\qquad \text{V}$$

and

$$bOB = bOP + bPB = bOP + \frac{ab}{a+b}AB \qquad\qquad \text{VI}$$

Adding the extreme parts of equations V and VI gives

$$aOA + bOB = (a+b)OP \qquad\qquad \text{VII}$$

Because equation IV only defines a ratio between a and b, the magnitude of a can now be chosen so that

$$aOA = OM \qquad\qquad \text{VIII}$$

Since OB is in the same direction as ON and OP is in the same direction as OR, it can be proved in a similar manner to that used in Example 2 that equations III and VII are now identical, i.e.

$$bOB = ON \qquad\qquad \text{IX}$$

and

$$(a+b)OP = OR \qquad\qquad \text{X}$$

Using similar triangles and equations I and VIII, the x component of OM can be written in two equivalent ways.

$$a = M_1 \qquad\qquad \text{XI}$$

Similarly,
$$b = M_2 \qquad\qquad \text{XII}$$

and substituting into equation IV gives

$$\frac{AP}{PB} = \frac{M_2}{M_1} \qquad\qquad \text{XIII}$$

the normal lever law.

Using equations I, II, III, VIII, IX, X, XI, and XII, the coordinates of points A, B, and P can be determined as

point A is $\quad \left(1, \ \dfrac{H_1}{M_1}, \ \dfrac{C_1}{M_1}\right)$

point B is $\quad \left(1, \ \dfrac{H_2}{M_2}, \ \dfrac{C_2}{M_2}\right)$

point C is $\quad \left(1, \ \dfrac{H_1+H_2}{M_1+M_2}, \ \dfrac{C_1+C_2}{M_1+M_2}\right)$

Comparing these with the original interpretation of the coordinate axes, the appropriate two-dimensional coordinates are the enthalpy, and the mass fraction of the important component.

Thus the normal constructions in the enthalpy-concentration diagram are valid as a special case of a more general vector method. By taking the intersections of the vectors with different planes, different two-dimensional diagrams can be obtained. If the chosen plane is symmetrically inclined to all axes, then the familiar triangular diagram is obtained. The work of Lemlich and Leonard is extended to these cases and also to four dimensions. Suggested extension to higher orders is difficult to visualize and matrix methods may be more appropriate. The example is, however, sufficient indication of the generality of the vectorial approach which gives a clearer insight into the connection between related problems.

7.4. MULTIPLICATION OF VECTORS

In multiplication, the first serious divergence from normal algebra arises because it is necessary to define two distinct kinds of multiplication. Two physical situations in which the interplay of two vectors gives rise to the result, are firstly, the work done by a force during a displacement when both the force and the displacement are vectors; and secondly, the moment of a force about an origin, when both the force and the position vector of its point of application must be specified. These two interactions between vectors are fundamentally different as will be shown in the present section.

7.4.1. *Scalar or Dot Product*

The scalar product of two vectors is defined as the product of the magnitude of the one vector with the magnitude of the component of the other vector resolved along it. This product is signified by placing a dot between the vectors to be multiplied together. Symbolically,

$$A . B = |A| |B| \cos \theta = B . A \qquad (7.20)$$

where θ is the angle between the vectors as shown in Fig. 7.9. The result of the operation is a scalar quantity, hence the name for the product.

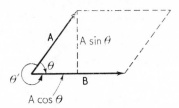

FIG. 7.9.   Scalar and vector products

One physical interpretation of this product is the calculation giving the work done by a force during a displacement. The fundamental definition of the work done is the magnitude of the force multiplied by the distance moved by its point of application in the direction of the force. Alternatively, the work done is the displacement multiplied by the component of the force causing the displacement. That these two alternatives are equivalent is obvious from the definition, equation (7.20). Work and hence energy are thus scalar quantities which arise from the multiplication of two vectors.

When a vector is multiplied by itself in this fashion, the scalar result can be written in the equivalent forms

$$A . A = A^2 = A^2 \qquad (7.21)$$

The inverse process to multiplication, division, is not uniquely defined for the following reason. If an equation such as

$$A . B = 0 \qquad (7.22)$$

is satisfied, then any of the following three conclusions can be drawn.

(a) The vector A is zero.
(b) The vector B is zero.
(c) $\theta = 90°$, and A and B are mutually perpendicular.

The third possibility arises in equation (7.20) because $\cos \theta$ may be zero. It is therefore possible for the scalar product of two vectors to be zero when both vectors are finite. Division thus has no meaning, for if equation (7.22) could be divided by a non-zero A, the inevitable conclusion would be that B is zero which is not necessarily true.

7.4.2. *Vector or Cross Product*

Referring to Fig. 7.9 again in which θ is the angle between the two vectors A and B, then the vector product of A and B is defined by

$$A \wedge B = |A| |B| \sin \theta \, n \qquad (7.23)$$

where the symbol ($\wedge$) is used to denote a vector product. n is a unit vector along the normal to the plane containing A and B and its positive direction is determined as follows. The right hand screw rule is applied to the sense of rotation from A to B in measuring the angle θ, thus defining the positive direction of n. Referring to Fig. 7.9, this rule indicates that n acts into the plane of the paper, thus $A \wedge B$ is also a vector into the plane of the paper. This definition is unique, because if θ were described in the opposite sense as indicated by θ', the positive direction of n would be reversed, the sign of $\sin \theta$ would also be reversed, and the vector $A \wedge B$ would still act into the plane of the paper. However, the vector $B \wedge A$ has the same magnitude as $A \wedge B$ but the direction of n is reversed due to describing θ by moving from B to A. Hence

$$A \wedge B = -B \wedge A \qquad (7.24)$$

and the order of terms in the product is important. The magnitude of the vector product of A and B is equal to the area of the parallelogram formed by A and B. This is also illustrated in Fig. 7.9 which shows the base of the parallelogram of length B, and height $A \sin \theta$, giving an area of $AB \sin \theta$ or $|A| |B| \sin \theta$.

The moment of a force is defined by a vector product in the following manner. If there is a force F acting at a point P with position vector r relative to an origin O as illustrated in Fig. 7.10, then the moment of F about O is defined by

$$L = r \wedge F \qquad (7.25)$$

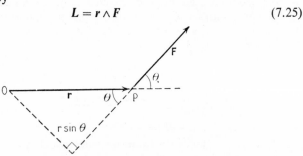

FIG. 7.10.   Moments of a force

In order to define the positive normal n, the vectors r and F must have a common origin. If P is taken as this origin and the right hand screw rule applied to equation (7.25) then n is seen to act out of the plane of the paper. Using the fundamental definition of L as the product of the force and the perpendicular distance of the origin from the line of action of the force gives

$$|L| = |F| r \sin \theta$$

which checks with equation (7.25) and the definition (7.23). The direction of the vector L which is outwards from the plane of the paper also corresponds with the fundamental definition of a moment.

Again, vector division is impossible, since if

$$A \wedge B = 0 \qquad (7.26)$$

then either

(a) The vector A is zero
(b) The vector B is zero
or (c) θ is zero, and the vectors A and B are parallel.

7.4.3. *Properties of Multiplication*

Although the associative, distributive, and commutative laws are valid for the addition and subtraction of vectors, these rules need to be considered more carefully with respect to products. It has already been shown in equation (7.20) that the commutative law is valid for the scalar product, whereas equation (7.24) shows that the commutative law is not valid for the vector product. That is,

$$A \cdot B = B \cdot A \qquad (7.20)$$

but

$$A \wedge B = -B \wedge A \qquad (7.24)$$

The order of terms in a vector product can only be altered if the sign is reversed.

The distributive law is unreservedly valid for all vector products. That is,

$$A \cdot (B+C) = A \cdot B + A \cdot C \qquad (7.27)$$

$$A \wedge (B+C) = A \wedge B + A \wedge C \qquad (7.28)$$

The associative law is simplified by the convention that two vectors without an operating sign between them have no meaning, thus reducing the need for brackets. For example, the following terms can only be evaluated in the one particular order indicated by brackets on the right hand side of each equation.

$$A \cdot B\, C \cdot D = (A \cdot B)(C \cdot D) \qquad (7.29)$$

$$A \cdot B\, C = (A \cdot B)C \qquad (7.30)$$

$$A \wedge B \cdot C = (A \wedge B) \cdot C \qquad (7.31)$$

In equations (7.29) and (7.30) each dot product yields a scalar which can be treated as any other scalar, so that equation (7.29) is a product of two scalars, and in equation (7.30) the magnitude of the vector C is increased by the scalar multiplier $(A.B)$. In equation (7.31) the vector product must be taken first because a vector product cannot be formed between the vector A and the scalar $(B.C)$. Brackets are usually essential when more than one vector product is involved, and then the associative law is not valid because

$$A \wedge (B \wedge C) \neq (A \wedge B) \wedge C$$

as will be shown in Section 7.4.6.

H

7.4.4. *Unit Vector Relationships*

It is frequently useful to resolve vectors into components along the axial directions in terms of the unit vectors i, j and k. All operations are then performed on the unit vectors and the results of products between them are all standard. Since by definition, i, j and k are mutually orthogonal, the angle θ in the definitions of the two products must be either 0 or $\pi/2$ and because

$$\sin 0 = 0 \quad \text{and} \quad \cos \pi/2 = 0$$

the following results are true.

$$i.j = j.k = k.i = 0 \tag{7.32}$$

and

$$i \wedge i = j \wedge j = k \wedge k = 0 \tag{7.33}$$

Because i, j and k have unit magnitude,

$$i.i = j.j = k.k = 1 \tag{7.34}$$

By the definition of the vector product in Section 7.4.2, $i \wedge j$ is a vector normal to the plane of i and j and hence must lie in the k direction. A convention is now needed which determines whether $i \wedge j$ is in the positive or negative k direction. If $i \wedge j = k$, the set of axes is said to be "right handed", since k is defined by the right hand screw rule from the vector product of i and j; whereas if $i \wedge j = -k$, the set of axes is left handed. It is normal to use a right handed set of axes and it can easily be verified that

$$i \wedge j = k, \quad j \wedge k = i, \quad k \wedge i = j \tag{7.35}$$

and

$$j \wedge i = -k, \quad k \wedge j = -i, \quad i \wedge k = -j \tag{7.36}$$

The use of these relationships is illustrated by the straightforward application to the simple products of the two vectors

$$A = A_x i + A_y j + A_z k \tag{7.12}$$

and

$$B = B_x i + B_y j + B_z k \tag{7.13}$$

Thus,

$$A.B = (A_x i + A_y j + A_z k).(B_x i + B_y j + B_z k)$$
$$= A_x B_x + A_y B_y + A_z B_z \tag{7.37}$$

and

$$A \wedge B = (A_x i + A_y j + A_z k) \wedge (B_x i + B_y j + B_z k)$$
$$= A_x(B_y k - B_z j) + A_y(B_z i - B_x k) + A_z(B_x j - B_y i)$$

using equations (7.32) to (7.36). Rearrangement of the last line gives

$$A \wedge B = i(A_y B_z - A_z B_y) + j(A_z B_x - A_x B_z) + k(A_x B_y - A_y B_x) \tag{7.38}$$

Equation (7.38) can be written in a more useful and compact form by expressing the right hand side as a determinant. The evaluation of determinants is considered in elementary mathematical texts, thus

$$A \wedge B = \begin{vmatrix} i & j & k \\ A_x & A_y & A_z \\ B_x & B_y & B_z \end{vmatrix} \tag{7.39}$$

7.4.5. *Scalar Triple Product*

Because $A \wedge B$ is a vector, further products can be taken with a third vector. The scalar product of $A \wedge B$ with C is best considered geometrically as shown in Fig. 7.11, where θ is the usual angle between the two vectors $(A \wedge B)$ and C. By definition,

$$A \wedge B . C$$

is a scalar whose magnitude is the magnitude of $(A \wedge B)$ multiplied by the component of the vector C resolved along $(A \wedge B)$. But the magnitude of $(A \wedge B)$ is the area of the parallelogram formed on A and B, and since the

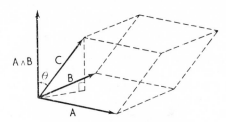

Fig. 7.11.   Scalar triple product

vector $(A \wedge B)$ must be perpendicular to the plane of A and B, then the resolved part of C along $(A \wedge B)$ must equal the height of the parallelepiped as shown in Fig. 7.11. The magnitude of $A \wedge B . C$ is thus the volume of the parallelepiped with edges parallel to A, B, and C. The result is positive or negative according as θ is acute or obtuse. Since the volume of a parallel-epiped can be expressed as the product of any base with the corresponding height, and the order of vectors in a dot product is irrelevant, the scalar triple product can be written in six equivalent ways, thus

$$A \wedge B . C = A . B \wedge C = B \wedge C . A = B . C \wedge A = C \wedge A . B = C . A \wedge B$$
$$= [A, B, C] \qquad (7.40)$$

where the three vectors remain in the cyclic order A, B, C and the positions of the dot and cross are arbitrary. The other six ways of writing this triple product have the same numerical value as the expressions in (7.40) but have the opposite sign due to reversing the order of terms in the vector product. Thus

$$[A, B, C] = -[A, C, B] \qquad (7.41)$$

7.4.6. *Vector Triple Product*

The vector product of $A \wedge B$ with a third vector C can be taken, but in this case the order of multiplication and position of brackets is of vital importance. Referring to Fig. 7.11 again, it can be seen that the vector $A \wedge B$ is perpendicular to the plane of A and B. When the further vector product with C is taken, the resulting vector must be perpendicular to $A \wedge B$ and hence in the plane of A and B. The resulting vector triple pro-duct can therefore be resolved into components along A and B, thus

$$(A \wedge B) \wedge C = mA + nB \qquad (7.42)$$

where m and n are scalar constants to be determined. Multiplying throughout equation (7.42) by C using a scalar product gives

$$C.(A \wedge B) \wedge C = mC.A + nC.B \qquad (7.43)$$

Considering $A \wedge B$ as a combined vector, the left hand side of equation (7.43) is a scalar triple product with the vector C appearing twice. Hence the left hand side is zero.

$$\therefore \quad mC.A + nC.B = 0$$

or $$m = \alpha C.B \quad \text{and} \quad n = -\alpha C.A \qquad (7.44)$$

which is equivalent. Substituting equations (7.44) into (7.42) gives

$$(A \wedge B) \wedge C = \alpha[(C.B)A - (C.A)B] \qquad (7.45)$$

Since each term in equation (7.45) contains the three vectors, α must be just a number. Also, because equation (7.45) is valid for any vectors A, B, and C, it must be valid for a particular set of values for A, B, and C. Thus letting $A = i$, $B = C = j$, and using equations (7.35) and (7.36) gives

$$(A \wedge B) \wedge C = (i \wedge j) \wedge j$$
$$= k \wedge j$$
$$= -i$$

But using equations (7.32) and (7.34),

$$C.B = j.j = 1$$
$$C.A = j.i = 0$$

Using these results in equation (7.45) gives

$$-i = \alpha i$$
$$\therefore \quad \alpha = -1$$

and $$(A \wedge B) \wedge C = (A.C)B - (B.C)A \qquad (7.46)$$

Similarly it can be shown that

$$A \wedge (B \wedge C) = (A.C)B - (A.B)C \qquad (7.47)$$

In order to remember equations (7.46) and (7.47) the following rule is helpful.

The terms appearing outside the brackets on the right-hand side are the terms appearing inside the brackets on the left-hand side. The positive term is the dot product of the extreme vectors multiplied by the central vector.

7.5. DIFFERENTIATION OF VECTORS

If a vector r is a function of a scalar variable t (say time), then when t varies by an increment δt, r will vary by an increment δr. Just as in ordinary calculus, δr is a variable associated with r but it need not have either the same magnitude or direction as **r**. If **δr** tends to zero as δt tends to zero, then

$$\lim_{\delta t \to 0} \frac{\delta r}{\delta t} = \frac{dr}{dt} \tag{7.48}$$

defines the first derivative of **r** with respect to t.

If **r** is interpreted as a position vector resolved into its components, then

$$r = xi + yj + zk \tag{7.11}$$

and

$$\delta r = \delta x i + \delta y j + \delta z k$$

$$\therefore \quad \frac{\delta r}{\delta t} = \frac{\delta x}{\delta t}i + \frac{\delta y}{\delta t}j + \frac{\delta z}{\delta t}k$$

and taking the limit as $\delta t \to 0$,

$$\frac{dr}{dt} = \frac{dx}{dt}i + \frac{dy}{dt}j + \frac{dz}{dt}k \tag{7.49}$$

Differentiation of a vector with respect to a scalar is thus similar to ordinary differentiation and the rules as applied to products of vectors are unchanged, viz.

$$\frac{d}{dt}(A.B) = A.\frac{dB}{dt} + \frac{dA}{dt}.B \tag{7.50}$$

$$\frac{d}{dt}(A \wedge B) = A \wedge \frac{dB}{dt} + \frac{dA}{dt} \wedge B \tag{7.51}$$

As t varies, the end point of the position vector **r** will trace out a curve in space. Taking s as a variable measuring length along this curve, the differentiation process can be performed with respect to s thus,

$$\frac{dr}{ds} = \frac{dx}{ds}i + \frac{dy}{ds}j + \frac{dz}{ds}k \tag{7.52}$$

Applying equation (7.9),

$$\left|\frac{dr}{ds}\right| = \sqrt{\left(\frac{dx}{ds}\right)^2 + \left(\frac{dy}{ds}\right)^2 + \left(\frac{dz}{ds}\right)^2}$$

$$= \frac{\sqrt{(dx)^2 + (dy)^2 + (dz)^2}}{ds}$$

But,

$$(ds)^2 = (dx)^2 + (dy)^2 + (dz)^2$$

Therefore, dr/ds is a unit vector in the direction of the tangent to the curve. A further useful result can be obtained as follows.

$$\frac{d}{dt}(A^2) = \frac{d}{dt}(A.A) = 2A.\frac{dA}{dt}$$

If A is a vector of constant magnitude but variable direction, then A^2 will be a constant.

$$\therefore \quad A \cdot \frac{dA}{dt} = 0 \tag{7.53}$$

and the vector dA/dt is perpendicular to A. An example of this is uniform motion in a circle when the acceleration is perpendicular to the instantaneous velocity.

It has been shown above that dr/ds is a unit vector and hence differentiating again with respect to s and using equation (7.53), then d^2r/ds^2 must be perpendicular to the tangent dr/ds. The direction of d^2r/ds^2 is the normal to the curve, and the two vectors defined as the tangent and normal define what is called the "osculating plane" of the curve.

7.5.1. *Partial Differentiation of Vectors*

Temperature is a scalar quantity which can depend in general upon three coordinates defining position and a fourth independent variable time. An increment δT can arise from an increment in any of the four independent variables, or from a combination of such increments. The increment δT arising from a single space increment, say δx, can be expressed as a ratio to δx and in the limit as $\delta x \to 0$, the ratio becomes a derivative. This particular derivative is denoted by $\partial T/\partial x$ which implies that the other independent variables remain constant during the limiting process, and in this respect, $\partial T/\partial x$ is a "partial derivative". $\partial T/\partial x$ is the temperature gradient in the x direction and is a vector quantity; similarly, $\partial T/\partial y$ and $\partial T/\partial z$ are also vector gradients. As will be shown in the next section, these three vectors can be compounded into a single generalized vector gradient. The other partial derivative with respect to time, $\partial T/\partial t$ is a scalar rate of change.

A dependent variable such as temperature, having the properties described above, is called a "scalar point function" and the system of variables is frequently called a "scalar field". There are many scalar point functions and amongst those of interest to chemical engineers are temperature, concentration, and pressure. In chemical engineering, there are other dependent variables which are vectorial in nature, and vary with position. Examples are velocity, heat flow rate, and mass transfer rate, which are called "vector point functions" and they constitute "vector fields". A familiar illustration of a two-dimensional vector field is the disposition of iron filings showing the field strength of a magnet. The differentiation of vector point functions will be discussed in the next section.

7.6. HAMILTON'S OPERATOR ∇

Returning to the consideration of temperature as a function of the three space variables, it was shown in Section 7.5.1 that the three partial derivatives of the temperature were vector gradients. If these three vector components are added together, there results a single vector gradient

$$i\frac{\partial T}{\partial x} + j\frac{\partial T}{\partial y} + k\frac{\partial T}{\partial z} = \nabla T \tag{7.54}$$

which defines the operator ∇ for determining the complete vector gradient of a scalar point function. The operator ∇ is pronounced "del" or "nabla", and the vector ∇T is often written "grad T" for obvious reasons.

∇ can operate upon any scalar quantity as above and yield a vector gradient. Written out in an abstract manner,

$$\nabla = i\frac{\partial}{\partial x} + j\frac{\partial}{\partial y} + k\frac{\partial}{\partial z} \tag{7.55}$$

The nature of ∇T can be further illustrated by taking a scalar product of ∇T with an infinitesimal increment dr in the position vector r. Thus

$$dr.\nabla T = (i\,dx + j\,dy + k\,dz).\left(i\frac{\partial T}{\partial x} + j\frac{\partial T}{\partial y} + k\frac{\partial T}{\partial z}\right) \tag{7.56}$$

and using the properties of products of unit vectors (7.32) and (7.34), this simplifies to

$$dr.\nabla T = \frac{\partial T}{\partial x}dx + \frac{\partial T}{\partial y}dy + \frac{\partial T}{\partial z}dz \tag{7.57}$$

Comparing equation (7.57) with equation (8.9) from the next chapter, it can be seen that

$$dr.\nabla T = dT \tag{7.58}$$

If vector division were possible (which it is not) then equation (7.58) could be rearranged to show that ∇T is the ratio of dT to dr, which is the generalized first derivative of a scalar variable with respect to an independent vector variable. The expression dT/dr does not exist to represent this quantity, but ∇T is the vector equivalent of the generalized gradient.

The physical interpretation of ∇T can be found by taking a variable position vector r to describe an isothermal surface.

$$T(x, y, z) = C$$

With this definition of r, for any increment dr, the corresponding increment dT will be zero because dr lies on the isothermal surface. But equation (7.58) shows that

$$dr.\nabla T = dT = 0$$

and thus ∇T must be perpendicular to dr. Since the vector dr can lie in any direction in the tangent plane to the isothermal at r, and ∇T can only have one value at a point r, then ∇T must be perpendicular to the tangent plane at r. This direction is the line of most rapid change of T. Thus ∇T is a vector in the direction of the most rapid change of T, and its magnitude is equal to this rate of change.

7.6.1. *Divergence of a Vector*, $\nabla.A$

Because the operator ∇ is of vector form, a scalar product can be obtained between ∇ and any vector A, with the interpretation that ∇ is to be treated as a vector as far as the product with A is concerned, and as a differential operator upon everything which follows it. Thus, if A is resolved into components, then

$$\nabla . A = \left(i \frac{\partial}{\partial x} + j \frac{\partial}{\partial y} + k \frac{\partial}{\partial z} \right) . (A_x i + A_y j + A_z k)$$

Since i, j and k are constant both in magnitude and direction, the differential operators only take effect upon A_x, A_y, and A_z. Using the unit vector relationships (7.32) and (7.34), therefore

$$\nabla . A = \frac{\partial A_x}{\partial x} + \frac{\partial A_y}{\partial y} + \frac{\partial A_z}{\partial z} \tag{7.59}$$

Equation (7.59) has been obtained by abstract manipulations, but the operation (∇.) on a vector has an important physical interpretation.

The continuity equation expressing the law of conservation of material within a flowing fluid will be derived in Chapter 8 as

$$\frac{\partial}{\partial x} (\rho u) + \frac{\partial}{\partial y} (\rho v) + \frac{\partial}{\partial z} (\rho w) + \frac{\partial \rho}{\partial t} = 0 \tag{7.60}$$

where ρ is the density, and

$$u = ui + vj + wk \tag{7.61}$$

is the velocity. Multiplying equation (7.61) by ρ and applying the operator (∇.) to the result using equation (7.59) gives the first three terms of equation (7.60). Thus

$$\nabla . \rho u + \frac{\partial \rho}{\partial t} = 0 \tag{7.62}$$

is the vector form of the continuity equation. The physical interpretation of equation (7.62) is as follows. $d\rho/\partial t$ is the rate of change of mass contained in unit volume, or the rate of accumulation of mass per unit volume. Using the general conservation law (1.25), then $\nabla . \rho u$ must equal the output less the input, which is the net rate of mass flow from unit volume. In general, $\nabla . A$ is the net flux of A per unit volume at the point considered, counting vectors into the volume as negative, and vectors out of the volume as positive.

If a tubular element of volume is taken such that the vectors of the field A lie in the curved surface of the tubular element, then the only flux of A within the element must enter and leave at the ends of the tube. If $\nabla . A$ is positive, then the flux leaving the one end must exceed the flux entering at the other end. In this respect the tubular element is divergent in the direction of flow. For this reason, the operation ∇. is frequently called the "divergence" and is written

$$\nabla . A = \operatorname{div} A \tag{7.63}$$

7.6.2. Curl or Rotation of a Vector, $\nabla \wedge A$.

A further differential function can be obtained using Hamilton's operator by taking a vector product between the operator and another vector. Expanding into components and using equation (7.39) to express the vector product gives

$$\nabla \wedge A = \begin{vmatrix} i & j & k \\ \dfrac{\partial}{\partial x} & \dfrac{\partial}{\partial y} & \dfrac{\partial}{\partial z} \\ A_x & A_y & A_z \end{vmatrix} = \operatorname{curl} A = \operatorname{rot} A \qquad (7.64)$$

The physical interpretation of the operator ($\nabla \wedge$) can be explained by referring to Fig. 7.12. For simplicity, it is assumed that the z component of velocity (w) is zero and that the flow is two-dimensional. This implies that all partial derivatives with respect to z are zero, and equation (7.64) simplifies to

$$\nabla \wedge u = \begin{vmatrix} i & j & k \\ \dfrac{\partial}{\partial x} & \dfrac{\partial}{\partial y} & 0 \\ u & v & 0 \end{vmatrix} = k \left(\dfrac{\partial v}{\partial x} - \dfrac{\partial u}{\partial y} \right) \qquad (7.65)$$

In Fig. 7.12, an element of fluid is defined from an origin O by taking increments δx and δy along the axes. Using Taylor's theorem, the y component of velocity at A and the x component of the velocity at B will be as shown.

FIG. 7.12. Curl of a velocity vector

The side OA of the fluid element is rotating in addition to its lateral and ongitudinal motion, and its angular velocity is $\partial v/\partial x$ as may be seen from the diagram. This rotation is in an anti-clockwise direction and by the right-hand screw rule acts in the positive k direction. Thus the angular velocity of OA is $k \dfrac{\partial v}{\partial x}$.

Similarly, the angular velocity of OB is $- k \dfrac{\partial u}{\partial y}$.

The angular velocity of the fluid element is the average of these two values, and denoting the angular velocity by ωk, then

$$\omega k = \tfrac{1}{2} \left(\dfrac{\partial v}{\partial x} - \dfrac{\partial u}{\partial y} \right) k \qquad (7.66)$$

Comparing equations (7.65) and (7.66) shows that

$$\nabla \wedge \boldsymbol{u} = 2\omega \boldsymbol{k} = \zeta \qquad (7.67)$$

which defines ζ, the "vorticity" of the fluid element. The vorticity is thus twice the angular velocity of the fluid element and this explains why $(\nabla \wedge)$ is called the "rotation" or "curl" operation.

7.7. Integration of Vectors and Scalars

In ordinary integration with respect to a single independent variable, the value of an integral depends upon the limits of integration only, because only one path of integration is possible. When alternative paths are available in two or more dimensions, the value of an integral depends upon both the limits and the path. It was shown in Section 4.16.1 that for an analytic function of a complex variable, the path of integration was irrelevant. These properties will now be generalized for three dimensions by using vectors.

7.7.1. *Line Integrals*

An arbitrary path of integration can be specified by defining a variable position vector $\boldsymbol{r}$ such that its end point sweeps out the curve between P and Q as shown in Fig. 7.13. A vector A can be integrated between two fixed

Fig. 7.13.   Line integrals

points P and Q along the curve $\boldsymbol{r}$ by summing the components of A resolved along the curve. This integral can be written

$$\int_{P}^{Q} A.d\boldsymbol{r} = \int_{P}^{Q} (A_x\,dx + A_y\,dy + A_z\,dz) \qquad (7.68)$$

by the definition of scalar products and resolution into components.

If the integral in equation (7.68) is to depend on P and Q but not upon the path $\boldsymbol{r}$, then the integrand must be the differential of some function ϕ, i.e.

$$A.d\boldsymbol{r} = d\phi \qquad (7.69)$$

But using equation (7.58),

$$d\boldsymbol{r}.\nabla\phi = d\phi \qquad (7.70)$$

$$\therefore \quad (A - \nabla\phi).d\boldsymbol{r} = 0 \qquad (7.71)$$

by subtraction of equations (7.69) and (7.70). Since the result is to be independent of the path of integration, dr can have any direction at a point, and $(A - \nabla\phi)$ cannot be perpendicular to all directions. Hence,

$$A - \nabla\phi = 0 \tag{7.72}$$

This means that if a vector field A can be expressed as the gradient of a scalar field ϕ, then the line integral of the vector A between any two points P and Q is independent of the path taken.

If ϕ is a single valued function, then the order of differentiation of ϕ with respect to any two variables is immaterial. Thus

$$\frac{\partial}{\partial y}(A_x) = \frac{\partial}{\partial y}\left(\frac{\partial\phi}{\partial x}\right) = \frac{\partial}{\partial x}\left(\frac{\partial\phi}{\partial y}\right) = \frac{\partial}{\partial x}(A_y) \tag{7.73}$$

But the k component of $\nabla \wedge A$ from equation (7.64) is

$$k\left(\frac{\partial A_y}{\partial x} - \frac{\partial A_x}{\partial y}\right)$$

which is zero by equation (7.73). Similarly, all three components of $\nabla \wedge A$ are zero if equation (7.72) is satisfied.

Hence the general result that the line integral of equation (7.68) is independent of the path of integration if $\nabla \wedge A = 0$. Also, if this is true, then A can be represented as the gradient of some scalar point function ϕ.

An example of the use of line integrals is the following. If the vector field A is a force field so that a particle at a point r experiences a force A, then the work done in moving the particle a distance δr from r is defined as the displacement times the component of force opposing the displacement. Therefore, the incremental work done (δW) is given by

$$\delta W = A . \delta r \tag{7.74}$$

Referring to Fig. 7.13, the total work done in moving the particle from P to Q is the sum of the increments along the path. As the size of the increments tends to zero, the sum becomes an integral, or

$$W = \int_P^Q A . dr \tag{7.75}$$

When this work done is independent of the path of the particle from P to Q, the force field A is said to be "conservative", and the results just enunciated are valid. Such a force field can be represented by the gradient of a scalar function. When a scalar point function is used to represent a vector field, it is called a "potential" function. Thus, the gravitational force field is represented by a gravitational potential function (potential energy), the electrostatic force field by an electric potential, and a magnetic force field by a magnetic potential. A further useful potential function will be introduced in Section 7.10.2.

7.7.2. *Vector Area and Surface Integrals*

An element of surface has its area defined as a vector by reference to its boundary. The magnitude of the area is defined as the maximum projected area of the element, and the direction of the vector is normal to this plane of projection. The direction of the positive normal is determined by the right-hand screw rule applied to the sense of describing the boundary of the element as illustrated in Fig. 7.14.

FIG. 7.14.   Vector area

When two adjacent elements of area are added together, their separate vector areas are defined so that the directions of tracing the common part of the boundary are opposite, so that the combined area is traced out by ignoring the common boundary. Since areas are thus defined as vectors, the vector rule of addition must be applied. Hence it can be seen that the vector area of any closed figure must be zero, because the projected area on any plane is doubly described, one clockwise and the other anticlockwise leading to complete cancellation.

When discussing line integrals above, the infinitesimal dr was a vector and the type of product with the vector A had to be specified. To integrate a vector over a surface, it is also necessary to specify the type of product, and although the dot product is used again, the physical interpretation is different. If there is a vector field denoted by A and the element of surface is denoted by $dS = n\, dS$ where n is the unit vector normal to the surface element, then the surface integral is usually defined as

$$\int A \cdot dS = \int A \cdot n\, dS \qquad (7.76)$$

When A is a force field, the above integral gives the total force acting on the surface, so that if the surface is closed, the integral gives the resultant force on the body due to the integrated effect over the surface. If the vector A is replaced by the velocity vector u, then the surface integral defined by equation (7.76) gives the net volumetric flow across the surface.

It is possible to integrate a cross product between A and dS, but this has very little practical value and is usually ignored.

7.7.3. *Volume Integrals*

The element of volume $dx\, dy\, dz$ is usually denoted by $d\sigma$ so that its shape is not restricted in any way. Although both the elements of length (dr) and surface (dS) are vectors, the element of volume $(d\sigma)$ is a scalar quantity, and thus there is no cause to specify any type of multiplication.

There are relationships between these three types of integration and the following sub-sections will be devoted to them. If the three integrals are considered in terms of cartesian coordinates, it can be seen that a surface integration involves two linear integrations, whilst a volume integration involves three linear integrations. It seems obvious therefore that any relationship between the different types of integration will involve a number of linear differentiations to match the orders. If these general ideas can be assimilated, the following relationships may appear to be more logical.

7.7.4. *Stokes' Theorem*

Consider any continuous surface S having elements dS defined in the usual way and denote by C the curve describing the boundary of the surface S. The positive direction of the curve C is related to the positive direction of the normal vector n as given in the definition of vector area in Section 7.7.2. Stokes' theorem states that if there is a vector field A then the line integral of A taken round C is equal to the surface integral of $\nabla \wedge A$ taken over S. Symbolically,

$$\int_C A.dr = \int_S \nabla \wedge A.dS = \int_S n.\nabla \wedge A \, dS \qquad (7.77)$$

It can now be seen that the result of Section 7.7.1 is a special case of the above theorem. That is, if $\nabla \wedge A = 0$, then the line integral of A around any closed curve is zero. Equation (7.77) is much more general than this previous result, and is frequently used in vector analysis. Similar results are available for other line and surface integrals but they are of rarer occurrence. The formulae are:

$$\int U \, dr = \int n \wedge \nabla U \, dS \qquad (7.78)$$

$$\int A.dr = \int n \wedge \nabla.A \, dS \qquad (7.79)$$

$$-\int A \wedge dr = \int (n \wedge \nabla) \wedge A \, dS \qquad (7.80)$$

where all line integrals are taken along the curve C which defines the boundary of the surface S over which the surface integrals are taken. The negative sign is necessary in equation (7.80) because the vector A has been moved from the first to the last term of a vector product so that it follows the operator ∇.

Stokes' theorem can be applied to a two-dimensional system by putting

$$A = P i + Q$$

where P and Q are functions of x and y only and the elementary length

$$dr = dx \, i + dy \, j$$

The normal to the xy plane is in the z direction, hence

$$n \, dS = dx \, dy \, k$$

and using equation (7.64) gives

$$\nabla \wedge A = k \left(\frac{\partial Q}{\partial x} - \frac{\partial P}{\partial y} \right)$$

Putting these various forms into equation (7.77) and simplifying gives

$$\int_C (P\,dx + Q\,dy) = \iint_S \left(\frac{\partial Q}{\partial x} - \frac{\partial P}{\partial y}\right) dx\,dy \qquad (7.81)$$

which was used in Section 4.15 to prove Cauchy's theorem.

7.7.5. Gauss' Divergence Theorem

When the continuity equation was considered in Section 7.6.1 it was shown that $\nabla.\rho u$ is the net rate of mass flow from unit volume. It was also stated in Section 7.7.2 that the surface integral of the velocity vector u gives the net volumetric flow across the surface. If these two ideas are now combined by applying them to a closed surface S enclosing a volume σ, the following result is obtained by equating the two expressions for the mass flow rate.

$$\int_S \rho u\,.dS = \int_\sigma \nabla.\rho u\,d\sigma \qquad (7.82)$$

Equation (7.82) is valid for any vector A giving

$$\int_S A\,.dS = \int_\sigma \nabla.A\,d\sigma \qquad (7.83)$$

which is the "divergence theorem".

Again, this equation can be extended to other products giving the set of formulae

$$\int n\,U\,dS = \int \nabla U\,d\sigma \qquad (7.84)$$

$$\int n\,.A\,dS = \int \nabla.A\,d\sigma \qquad (7.85)$$

$$\int n \wedge A\,dS = \int \nabla \wedge A\,d\sigma \qquad (7.86)$$

where the surface integrals are taken over the surface S enclosing the volume σ over which the volume integrals are taken.

7.7.6. Green's Theorem

If U and V are two continuous, differentiable scalar point functions, then an application of Gauss' divergence theorem (7.83) to the function $U\nabla V$ gives

$$\int_S U\nabla V\,.dS = \int_\sigma \nabla.(U\nabla V)\,d\sigma \qquad (7.87)$$

The right-hand side can be expanded as the derivative of a product, thus

$$\nabla.(U\ V) = (\nabla U).(\nabla V) + U\nabla^2 V \qquad (7.88)$$

Substituting equation (7.88) into equation (7.87) and rearranging gives

$$\int \nabla U\,.\nabla V\,d\sigma = \int U\nabla V\,.dS - \int U\nabla^2 V\,d\sigma \qquad (7.89)$$

Interchanging U and V throughout the above argument gives

$$\int \nabla U\,.\nabla V\,d\sigma = \int V\nabla U\,.dS - \int V\nabla^2 U\,d\sigma \qquad (7.90)$$

Equating equations (7.89) and (7.90) and rearranging the integrals gives

$$\int (U\nabla V - V\nabla U).d\mathbf{S} = \int (U\nabla^2 V - V\nabla^2 U)\,d\sigma \qquad (7.91)$$

Equations (7.89, 90, 91) are known as various forms of "Green's theorem". As will be appreciated in the next chapter, the differential equation

$$\nabla^2 V = \nabla.\nabla V = 0 \qquad (7.92)$$

is of frequent occurrence, and equation (7.91) can be very useful for dealing with such systems. It is of even more use in the theory of electricity and magnetism because both the electric and magnetic potentials satisfy equation (7.92).

7.8. STANDARD IDENTITIES

Any of the following equations can be verified quite easily by using the formulae given in the earlier parts of this chapter, but it is useful to have the following list available for reference purposes. This first group of equations arises from differentiating various products.

$$\nabla.UA = U\nabla.A + A.\nabla U \qquad (7.93)$$

$$\nabla \wedge UA = U\nabla \wedge A - A \wedge \nabla U \qquad (7.94)$$

$$\nabla.A \wedge B = B.\nabla \wedge A - A.\nabla \wedge B \qquad (7.95)$$

$$\nabla \wedge (A \wedge B) = B.\nabla A + A\nabla.B - A.\nabla B - B\nabla.A \qquad (7.96)$$

In the derivation of the next useful formula, the dual nature of ∇ causes some difficulty in the notation, but if it is understood that when no symbol follows ∇, the symbol immediately preceding it is to be differentiated, then the intermediate steps can be followed.

$$A \wedge (\nabla \wedge B) = A.B\nabla - A.\nabla B \qquad (7.97)$$

$$B \wedge (\nabla \wedge A) = B.A\nabla - B.\nabla A \qquad (7.98)$$

and $$\nabla A.B = B.A\nabla + A.B\nabla \qquad (7.99)$$

Eliminating the two expressions on the right-hand side of equation (7.99) and rearranging gives the required formula; the notation now being normal.

$$\nabla A.B = A.\nabla B + B.\nabla A + A \wedge (\nabla \wedge B) + B \wedge (\nabla \wedge A) \qquad (7.100)$$

If now $B = A$, equation (7.100) gives

$$\tfrac{1}{2}\nabla A^2 = A.\nabla A + A \wedge (\nabla \wedge A) \qquad (7.101)$$

The next group of formulae is intended to simplify expressions involving second derivatives.

$$\nabla \wedge (\nabla \wedge A) = \nabla\nabla.A - \nabla^2 A \qquad (7.102)$$

$$\nabla \wedge \nabla.A = \nabla.\nabla \wedge A = 0 \qquad (7.103)$$

$$\nabla \wedge \nabla U = 0 \qquad (7.104)$$

These last two equations are only valid when the order of differentiation is not important in the second mixed derivative.

7.9. CURVILINEAR COORDINATE SYSTEMS

So far in this chapter, vector equations have been developed which are independent of the coordinate system used. Position vectors only require an origin to be defined as stated in Section 7.3.2 and thus the vector equations are very general. On occasions, a vector relationship has been illustrated by resolving the vectors into a cartesian coordinate system by using the unit vectors i, j, and k. This particular set consists of unit vectors which remain constant in both magnitude and direction, but in many problems the cartesian set of coordinates is not the most convenient. Both cylindrical polar coordinates and spherical polar coordinates are frequently used in chemical engineering problems and it is therefore necessary to be able to express a vector relationship in terms of other coordinate systems. Books devoted to vector analysis† invariably derive the necessary equations for a general coordinate system and the reader is referred to these, but all of the necessary equations will be developed here for spherical polar coordinates, and quoted for cylindrical polar coordinates. One important point which must be accepted here is that in any coordinate system other than cartesian, the unit vectors are variable in direction. For example, when a radial coordinate is used, the value of the variable increases in opposite directions at the opposite ends of a diameter, and comparing the two positions the unit radial vector is also reversed. Hence extra terms arise as a result of differentiating the unit vectors.

7.9.1. *Spherical Polar Coordinates*

These can be defined relative to the cartesian coordinate system as illustrated in Fig. 7.15. The radial distance of the point P from the origin O

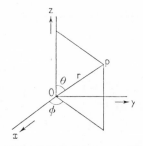

FIG. 7.15.   Spherical polar coordinates

is denoted by r, the polar angle of OP relative to the z axis is denoted by θ, and the azimuthal angle of the plane containing OP and the z axis relative to the xz plane is denoted by ϕ. Care must be taken to ensure that (r, θ, ϕ) is a right-handed set of coordinates as further illustrated in Fig. 7.16. The

† Weatherburn, C. E. " Advanced Vector Analysis." Bell & Sons, London (1951).

volume element is defined by taking increments δr, $\delta\theta$, and $\delta\phi$ in the coordinates as before, but now, the edges of the element are in general curved and their lengths are not equal to the simple increments. If a set of unit vectors

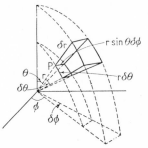

FIG. 7.16.   Volume element in spherical polar coordinates

a, *b*, *c* are defined at the point P, then the incremental position vector δr describing a general displacement from P can be written

$$\delta r = \delta r\, a + r\,\delta\theta\, b + r\sin\theta\,\delta\phi\, c \qquad (7.105)$$

It is now possible to expand Hamilton's operator (∇) in terms of the new coordinate system. Equation (7.58) gives the general result that

$$dr.\nabla \equiv d \qquad (7.106)$$

Equation (7.105) gives an expression for *dr* in the limit as $\delta r \to 0$, and the expression for (∇) which satisfies the identity (7.106) is

$$\nabla = a\frac{\partial}{\partial r} + \frac{b}{r}\frac{\partial}{\partial\theta} + \frac{c}{r\sin\theta}\frac{\partial}{\partial\phi} \qquad (7.107)$$

The various differential operations, grad, div, and curl, can now be expressed in terms of spherical polar coordinates by using this identity. The gradient of a scalar point function U, is simply obtained by placing U after each term in equation (7.107). Thus

$$\nabla U = a\frac{\partial U}{\partial r} + \frac{b}{r}\frac{\partial U}{\partial\theta} + \frac{c}{r\sin\theta}\frac{\partial U}{\partial\phi} \qquad (7.108)$$

Before developing expressions for the divergence and curl of a general vector, it is necessary to determine them for the unit vectors *a*, *b*, and *c*. Putting $U = \theta$ in equation (7.108) gives

$$\nabla\theta = b/r \qquad (7.109)$$

because r, θ and ϕ are independent. Substituting into equation (7.104) gives

$$0 = \nabla\wedge\nabla\theta = \nabla\wedge(b/r)$$

$$= \frac{1}{r}(\nabla\wedge b) - b\wedge\nabla\left(\frac{1}{r}\right)$$

$$= \frac{1}{r}(\nabla\wedge b) - b\wedge a\frac{\partial}{\partial r}\left(\frac{1}{r}\right) \qquad (7.110)$$

where equation (7.108) has been used again in the last line. Provided (r, θ, ϕ) and hence (a, b, c) is a right-handed set of axes, equation (7.110) can be simplified and rearranged as follows.

$$0 = \frac{1}{r}(\nabla \wedge b) + c \, (-1/r^2)$$

$$\therefore \quad \nabla \wedge b = c/r \tag{7.111}$$

Similarly, it can be shown that

$$\nabla \wedge a = 0 \tag{7.112}$$

$$\nabla \wedge c = (a \cot \theta - b)/r \tag{7.113}$$

To find the divergence of the unit vectors, the above expressions are used in conjunction with equation (7.95). Thus

$$\nabla . a = \nabla . (b \wedge c)$$

$$= c . \nabla \wedge \quad - b . \nabla \wedge c$$

$$= \frac{1}{r} + \frac{1}{r}$$

$$\therefore \quad \nabla . a = 2/r \tag{7.114}$$

Similarly, $\qquad\qquad \nabla . b = (\cot \theta)/r \tag{7.115}$

$$\nabla . c = 0 \tag{7.116}$$

Assuming that the vector A can be resolved into components in terms of a, b, and c as

$$A = A_r a + A_\theta b + A_\phi c \tag{7.117}$$

and using the above seven equations, therefore

$$\nabla . A = \frac{2A_r}{r} + \frac{A_\theta \cot \theta}{r} + \frac{\partial A_r}{\partial r} + \frac{1}{r}\frac{\partial A_\theta}{\partial \theta} + \frac{1}{r \sin \theta}\frac{\partial A_\phi}{\partial \phi}$$

$$\therefore \quad \nabla . A = \frac{1}{r^2}\frac{\partial}{\partial r}(r^2 A_r) + \frac{1}{r \sin \theta}\frac{\partial}{\partial \theta}(A_\theta \sin \theta) + \frac{1}{r \sin \theta}\frac{\partial A_\phi}{\partial \phi} \tag{7.118}$$

and $\qquad \nabla \wedge A = \frac{c}{r}A_\theta + \frac{a \cot \theta - b}{r}A_\phi - \frac{c}{r}\frac{\partial A_r}{\partial \theta} + \frac{b}{r \sin \theta}\frac{\partial A_r}{\partial \phi} + c\frac{\partial A_\theta}{\partial r} -$

$$- \frac{a}{r \sin \theta}\frac{\partial A_\theta}{\partial \phi} - b\frac{\partial A_\phi}{\partial r} + \frac{1}{r}\frac{\partial A_\phi}{\partial \theta}$$

$$\therefore \quad \nabla \wedge A = \frac{a}{r \sin \theta}\left[\frac{\partial}{\partial \theta}(A_\phi \sin \theta) - \frac{\partial A_\theta}{\partial \phi}\right] +$$

$$+ \frac{b}{r \sin \theta}\left[\frac{\partial A_r}{\partial \phi} - \sin \theta \frac{\partial}{\partial r}(rA_\phi)\right] + \frac{c}{r}\left[\frac{\partial}{\partial r}(rA_\theta) - \frac{\partial A_r}{\partial \theta}\right] \tag{7.119}$$

By applying equation (7.118) to the expansion of ∇U as given by equation (7.108), the following expression for $\nabla^2 U$ can be obtained.

$$\nabla^2 U = \frac{1}{r^2}\frac{\partial}{\partial r}\left(r^2\frac{\partial U}{\partial r}\right) + \frac{1}{r^2\sin\theta}\frac{\partial}{\partial\theta}\left(\sin\theta\frac{\partial U}{\partial\theta}\right) + \frac{1}{r^2\sin^2\theta}\frac{\partial^2 U}{\partial\phi^2} \qquad (7.120)$$

The expansion of $\nabla^2 A$ is more complicated than equation (7.120) and is not usually given as a standard formula. It can be obtained however by expanding equation (7.102) by two applications of equation (7.119) and one application of each of equations (7.118) and (7.108).

7.9.2. *Cylindrical Polar Coordinates*

Following the same procedure as above, the following formulae can be derived for cylindrical polar coordinates (ω, ϕ, z) which are defined as

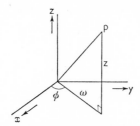

FIG. 7.17. Cylindrical polar coordinates

illustrated in Fig. 7.17. z is one of the cartesian coordinates, and ϕ is the same azimuthal angle as for spherical polar coordinates.

$$d\mathbf{r} = \delta\omega\mathbf{a} + \omega\delta\phi\mathbf{b} + \delta z\mathbf{c} \qquad (7.121)$$

$$U = \mathbf{a}\frac{\partial U}{\partial\omega} + \frac{\mathbf{b}}{\omega}\frac{\partial U}{\partial\phi} + \mathbf{c}\frac{\partial U}{\partial z} \qquad (7.122)$$

$$\nabla.A = \frac{1}{\omega}\frac{\partial}{\partial\omega}(\omega A_\omega) + \frac{1}{\omega}\frac{\partial A_\phi}{\partial\phi} + \frac{\partial A_z}{\partial z} \qquad (7.123)$$

$$\nabla\wedge A = \mathbf{a}\left[\frac{1}{\omega}\frac{\partial A_z}{\partial\phi} - \frac{\partial A_\phi}{\partial z}\right] + \mathbf{b}\left[\frac{\partial A_\omega}{\partial z} - \frac{\partial A_z}{\partial\omega}\right] + \mathbf{c}\left[\frac{\partial A_\phi}{\partial\omega} - \frac{1}{\omega}\frac{\partial A_\omega}{\partial\phi}\right] \qquad (7.124)$$

$$\nabla^2 U = \frac{1}{\omega}\frac{\partial}{\partial\omega}\left(\omega\frac{\partial U}{\partial\omega}\right) + \frac{1}{\omega^2}\frac{\partial^2 U}{\partial\phi^2} + \frac{\partial^2 U}{\partial z^2} \qquad (7.125)$$

Again, $\nabla^2 A$ must be evaluated by using equations (7.102, 122, 123, 124).

7.10. THE EQUATIONS OF FLUID FLOW

One of the most important applications of vector analysis in chemical engineering is to the study of fluid flow. As stated previously, velocity is a vector quantity, and in a moving fluid the velocity is a vector point function.

Ignoring the heating effect due to the friction in a moving fluid, and assuming that no mass transfer is taking place, there are nine scalar variables related by the fluid flow equations. There are three coordinates and time which are the four independent variables; and in addition to the three velocity components there are pressure and density making five dependent variables. It will be assumed that the fluid is newtonian so that the coefficient of viscosity remains constant. Five equations are needed because there are five dependent variables, and one of these, the continuity equation (7.62) has already been mentioned. A second equation is the equation of state relating the density to the pressure which leaves three further equations to be supplied. Instead of treating the three velocity components separately, the use of a single vector velocity variable will reduce the requirement to one vector equation and this is how vector analysis effects a simplification. This equation is obtained by applying Newton's second law of motion to a fluid element. That is, the external forces, the pressure forces, and the viscous forces are combined and equated to the product of the mass of the element and its acceleration. The details of the derivation are given in many books devoted to fluid flow† and in any text book devoted to theoretical hydrodynamics.

For an incompressible fluid, the equation of motion can be written

$$\frac{\partial u}{\partial t} + u.\nabla u = -\frac{1}{\rho}\nabla p + \nu\nabla^2 u + F \qquad (7.126)$$

which is known as the "Navier-Stokes equation". The advantage of the above vector form is that the five terms can be easily identified as: time dependent, inertial, pressure, viscous, and external force terms respectively. The continuity equation for such an incompressible fluid is the following simplified version of equation (7.62).

$$\nabla.u = 0 \qquad (7.127)$$

F representing the external forces is usually due to gravity and gives rise to the hydrostatic pressure in the system, and if this is the case, F can be expressed as the gradient of a scalar point function and combined with the pressure term. It will therefore be ignored in the remainder of this work.

There is no general method of solution for the system of equations (7.126) and (7.127) and most attempts have centred on either of two simplifying assumptions. These theories will now be considered separately.

7.10.1. *Stokes' Approximation*

If it is assumed that the fluid velocity is everywhere small, the inertia term in equation (7.126) can be omitted. Without this term, the system of equations is linear and can therefore be solved. To find out under what conditions the approximation is justified, it is convenient to express the equations in dimensionless form by taking the ratio of all lengths to some

† For example, Knudsen, J. G. and Katz, D. L. "Fluid Dynamics and Heat Transfer." McGraw-Hill (1958). Lamb, H. "Hydrodynamics." Cambridge University Press (1895). Milne-Thompson, L. M. "Theoretical Hydrodynamics" (2nd edition). Macmillan (1949).

characteristic length (L) and the ratio of all velocities to some characteristic velocity (U). Denoting the dimensionless variables by ('), equation (7.126) becomes

$$\frac{L}{U}\frac{\partial \boldsymbol{u}'}{\partial t} + \boldsymbol{u}'.\nabla \boldsymbol{u}' = -\frac{1}{\rho U^2}\nabla p + \frac{\nu}{LU}\nabla^2 \boldsymbol{u}' \qquad (7.128)$$

In this dimensionless equation, three dimensionless groups have arisen: Ut/L, which is the dimensionless time, $2p/\rho U^2$, the dimensionless pressure coefficient, and LU/ν, the Reynolds number. It is conventional to introduce a factor of 2 into the pressure coefficient and sometimes into the Reynolds number, although in the latter case a convenient characteristic length is often defined to include this factor.

The approximation of neglecting the inertia term in comparison with the viscous term can now be interpreted as assuming that the Reynolds number is small compared with unity. Returning to the dimensional equation (7.126) and making the approximation gives

$$\frac{\partial \boldsymbol{u}}{\partial t} = -\frac{1}{\rho}\nabla p + \nu\nabla^2 \boldsymbol{u} \qquad (7.129)$$

Without vectors, the system of equations (7.127) and (7.129) would contain four dependent variables, and a lengthy piece of algebra would be required to find a single differential equation involving only one dependent variable. However, a simple vector method is available. Operating on equation (7.129) with (∇.) gives

$$\frac{\partial}{\partial t}(\nabla.\boldsymbol{u}) = -\frac{1}{\rho}\nabla^2 p + \nu\nabla^2\nabla.\boldsymbol{u} \qquad (7.130)$$

But the continuity equation (7.127) shows that $\nabla.\boldsymbol{u} = 0$.

$$\therefore \quad \nabla^2 p = 0 \qquad (7.131)$$

and the pressure distribution can be found in general terms. Unfortunately, the boundary conditions usually govern the velocity and not the pressure, and thus equation (7.131) is not really useful. Hence, operating upon equation (7.129) with ($\nabla \wedge$) gives

$$\frac{\partial}{\partial t}(\nabla \wedge \boldsymbol{u}) = -\frac{1}{\rho}\nabla \wedge \nabla p + \nu\nabla^2\nabla \wedge \boldsymbol{u}$$

Now equation (7.67) defines the vorticity of the fluid by

$$\nabla \wedge \boldsymbol{u} = \zeta \qquad (7.67)$$

and equation (7.104) shows that the pressure term is identically zero. Hence

$$\frac{\partial \zeta}{\partial t} = \nu\nabla^2\zeta \qquad (7.132)$$

which is analogous to the heat conduction or mass transfer equation, except that equation (7.132) is a vector equation whereas both of the others are scalar equations.

Equation (7.132) will now be put into a simpler form for the special case of fluid flow with an axis of symmetry by introducing the stream function ψ so that the continuity equation (7.127) is automatically satisfied. Taking spherical polar coordinates and assuming that the problem has an axis of symmetry (the z axis) then from any point P, curves Q_1 and Q_2 can be drawn to a point on the z axis as illustrated in Fig. 7.18. By rotating the plane of the diagram about the z axis, the curves Q_1 and Q_2 become surfaces. Now the total volume of fluid crossing the surface Q_1 from right to left must equal the volume crossing Q_2 in the same direction. Also, because there is no flow across the axis of symmetry, there will be an equal volumetric flow across any other surface such as Q_3. This volumetric flow is denoted by $2\pi\psi$ where ψ is Stokes' stream function. This definition shows that $\psi = 0$ at all points on the z axis, and elsewhere it is a scalar point function.

FIG. 7.18.   Stokes stream function, axi-symmetrical flow

It should be noted that the above definition of ψ is related to a direction in Fig. 7.18 and in a generalized non-symmetrical system, a vector stream function can be defined by

$$\boldsymbol{u} = \nabla \wedge \boldsymbol{\Psi} \tag{7.133}$$

but the specialized scalar stream function will be used here.

Taking a small displacement from P in each of the coordinate directions, it can be shown that

$$u = \frac{-1}{r^2 \sin\theta} \frac{\partial\psi}{\partial\theta}, \qquad v = \frac{1}{r\sin\theta} \frac{\partial\psi}{\partial r} \tag{7.134}$$

where u and v are respectively the r and θ components of the velocity $\boldsymbol{u}$. Putting equations (7.134) into equation (7.118) shows that the continuity equation is satisfied. The vorticity can be expressed in terms of the stream function by substituting equations (7.134) into equation (7.119). Thus

$$\boldsymbol{\zeta} = \nabla \wedge \boldsymbol{u} = \frac{c}{r}\left[\frac{\partial}{\partial r}\left(\frac{1}{\sin\theta}\frac{\partial\psi}{\partial r}\right) - \frac{\partial}{\partial\theta}\left(\frac{-1}{r^2\sin\theta}\frac{\partial\psi}{\partial\theta}\right)\right]$$

$$= \frac{c}{r\sin\theta}\left[\frac{\partial^2\psi}{\partial r^2} + \frac{\sin\theta}{r^2}\frac{\partial}{\partial\theta}\left(\frac{1}{\sin\theta}\frac{\partial\psi}{\partial\theta}\right)\right] \tag{7.135}$$

$$\therefore \quad \zeta r \sin\theta = c E^2 \psi \tag{7.136}$$

where E^2 is the differential operator in the brackets of equation (7.135). Equation (7.136) shows that the vorticity has a component in the ϕ direction only and the scalar symbol ζ can be used to represent this component.

Applying equation (7.119) to the vorticity gives

$$\nabla \wedge \zeta = \frac{a}{r\sin\theta}\frac{\partial}{\partial\theta}(\zeta\sin\theta) - \frac{b}{r}\frac{\partial}{\partial r}(\zeta r) \qquad (7.137)$$

Using equation (7.119) again gives

$$\nabla \wedge (\nabla \wedge \zeta) = \frac{c}{r}\left[-\frac{\partial^2}{\partial r^2}(\zeta r) - \frac{\partial}{\partial\theta}\left\{\frac{1}{r\sin\theta}\frac{\partial}{\partial\theta}(\zeta\sin\theta)\right\}\right] \qquad (7.138)$$

Combining equations (7.127, 102, 132, 138) and assuming that the flow is steady (i.e. $\partial\zeta/\partial t = 0$) gives

$$\frac{\partial^2}{\partial r^2}(\zeta r) + \frac{1}{r}\frac{\partial}{\partial\theta}\left\{\frac{1}{\sin\theta}\frac{\partial}{\partial\theta}(\zeta\sin\theta)\right\} = 0$$

which can be rearranged to give

$$E^2(\zeta r\sin\theta) = 0$$

or
$$E^4\psi = 0 \qquad (7.139)$$

which is the fourth order linear scalar partial differential equation describing the steady axi-symmetrical flow of an incompressible fluid at low Reynolds numbers.

The above equation will be solved in Section 8.5.4 for the case of flow past a solid sphere.

7.10.2. *The Ideal Fluid Approximation*

It is assumed in this case that the viscosity of the fluid is small, i.e. that the Reynolds number is large. Thus, neglecting the viscous term in equation (7.126) gives

$$\frac{\partial u}{\partial t} + u.\nabla u = -\frac{1}{\rho}\nabla p \qquad (7.140)$$

Using equation (7.101) to alter the form of the middle term and rearranging gives

$$\nabla\left(\tfrac{1}{2}u^2 + \frac{p}{\rho}\right) = u \wedge (\nabla \wedge u) - \frac{\partial u}{\partial t} \qquad (7.141)$$

If the flow is steady, and the vorticity is zero, then the right-hand side of equation (7.141) vanishes and the equation reduces to Bernoulli's theorem.

$$p + \tfrac{1}{2}\rho u^2 = \text{const.} \qquad (7.142)$$

From the above analysis it can be seen that Bernoulli's theorem is only strictly true when the laminar flow is steady, incompressible, inviscid, and irrotational.

Applying the operator $(\nabla \wedge)$ to equation (7.141) and using the property (7.104) to simplify the left-hand side gives

$$0 = \nabla \wedge (u \wedge \zeta) - \frac{\partial\zeta}{\partial t}$$

and expanding the vector triple product and remembering that

$$\nabla . \zeta = \nabla . \nabla \wedge u = 0$$

gives
$$\frac{\partial \zeta}{\partial t} + u . \nabla \zeta = 0 \qquad (7.143)$$

Equation (7.143) shows that the substantive derivative (see Section 8.2.3) of the vorticity is zero. This means that the vorticity of any fluid element remains constant, and if the fluid motion has been started from rest, then the vorticity will be zero everywhere for all time. Thus, for a fluid motion started from rest, the vorticity is zero and the flow is irrotational.

$$\therefore \quad \nabla \wedge u = 0 \qquad (7.144)$$

However, it was shown in Section 7.7.1 that if the curl of a vector is zero, then the vector itself can be expressed as the gradient of a scalar point function called a potential function. Thus, for an inviscid irrotational fluid, the velocity can be expressed as the gradient of the "velocity potential" ϕ. Thus

$$u = -\nabla \phi \qquad (7.145)$$

Combining equation (7.145) with the continuity equation (7.127) shows that the velocity potential satisfies Laplace's equation

$$\nabla^2 \phi = 0 \qquad (7.146)$$

This second order linear partial differential equation will also be solved in Section 8.5.4 for the case of ideal fluid flow past a solid sphere.

It is possible to express ideal fluid flow in terms of the stream function ψ, and in the axi-symmetrical case equation (7.136) becomes

$$E^2 \psi = 0 \qquad (7.147)$$

because the flow is irrotational. Although the stream function representation is valid for both Stokes' flow and ideal fluid flow, the velocity potential can only be used in ideal fluid flow. In viscous flow, equation (7.144) is not valid, the system is not conservative, and energy is dissipated by the action of viscosity. Therefore, for comparison of the two solutions, both must be expressed in terms of the stream function.

7.11. Transport of Heat, Mass, and Momentum

The partial differential equation which governs heat transfer will be derived from first principles in the next chapter, but here it will be derived by a vector method for comparison. The rate of flow of heat per unit area at any point is proportional to the temperature gradient at that point; the constant of proportionality being the thermal conductivity. Using the generalized gradient from Section 7.6 gives

$$\frac{\partial Q}{\partial t} = -k\nabla T \qquad (7.148)$$

The definition of the divergence operator in Section 7.6.1 shows that $\nabla . Q$ is the net flow of heat from unit volume. However, the total heat content of unit volume is $\rho C_p T$ where C_p is the specific heat, and the conservation law states that heat can only leave at the expense of the remaining contents. Thus

$$-\frac{\partial}{\partial t}(\rho C_p T) = \frac{\partial}{\partial t}(\nabla.\mathbf{Q}) \tag{7.149}$$

Since space derivatives and time derivatives are independent, they are commutable. Hence, operating upon equation (7.148) with (∇.), assuming that the physical properties remain constant, and substituting into equation (7.149) gives

$$\frac{\partial T}{\partial t} = \frac{k}{C_p \rho} \nabla^2 T$$

or

$$\frac{\partial T}{\partial t} = \alpha \nabla^2 T \tag{7.150}$$

where α is the "thermal diffusivity".

In the transport of mass by molecular diffusion the equation analogous to (7.148) is

$$\frac{\partial N}{\partial t} = -D\nabla c \tag{7.151}$$

where N is the molar flux density, D is the diffusivity, and c is the molar concentration. Following the same argument as for heat transfer, it can be shown that

$$\frac{\partial c}{\partial t} = D\nabla^2 c \tag{7.152}$$

Equations (7.150) and (7.152) have been derived for systems without bulk motion, if a bulk flow is included in the derivation the time derivatives have to be replaced by the substantive time derivatives (see Section 8.2.3) and collecting the equations (7.126, 150, 152) together, the equations governing the transport processes are

$$\frac{\partial T}{\partial t} + \mathbf{u}.\nabla T = \alpha \nabla^2 T \tag{7.153}$$

$$\frac{\partial c}{\partial t} + \mathbf{u}.\nabla c = D\nabla^2 c \tag{7.154}$$

$$\frac{\partial \mathbf{u}}{\partial t} + \mathbf{u}.\nabla \mathbf{u} = \nu\nabla^2\mathbf{u} - \frac{1}{\rho}\nabla p + F \tag{7.155}$$

These equations are seen to be very similar in vector form, yet equation (7.155) is quite different, having two extra terms, and being the only vector equation. The analogy between heat and mass transfer however is complete if α and D have the same value. These points are discussed more fully in the literature.†

† Klinkenberg, A. and Mooy, H. H. *Chem. Engng Prog.*, **44**, 17 (1948). Garner, F. H., Jenson, V. G. and Keey, R. B. *Trans. Instn Chem. Engrs*, **37**, 191 (1959).

Chapter 8

PARTIAL DIFFERENTIATION AND PARTIAL
DIFFERENTIAL EQUATIONS

8.1. INTRODUCTION

AFTER showing how conservation laws and rate equations could be used to derive algebraic equations in Chapter 1, the method was extended to systems described by an independent variable, either a distance or time. Thus ordinary differential equations were derived by considering the equilibrium of an infinitesimal element and using Taylor's theorem to introduce the derivative. In this chapter, problems requiring the specification of more than one independent variable will be considered. An example of such a problem is the change of the temperature distribution within a system as the steady state condition is approached; when the temperature is a function both of position and time. The differentiation process can be performed relative to an incremental change in the space variable giving a temperature gradient, or with respect to an increment of the time variable giving a rate of temperature rise. These two first derivatives of the temperature have to be distinguished from each other, and the first part of this chapter clarifies the meaning of a derivative in a multi-variable system.

The formulation of partial differential equations follows the same rules as given in Chapter 1, but the formulation of boundary conditions requires more attention. The second half of this chapter is devoted to the solution of partial differential equations by three methods. Studying the boundary conditions will often suggest a special kind of solution and this is the first method. The more fundamental methods of separation of variables and operators form the major part of this chapter and in chemical engineering there are probably more examples of the use of these methods than any other mathematical method.

In difficult problems, such as fluid flow, it is often advisable to formulate the problem in cartesian coordinates or find the vector form of the differential equation directly. The vector equation can then be expanded into a coordinate system which better suits the shape of the boundaries of the problem. For example, it is easier to specify a spherical surface by $r = a$ in spherical polar coordinates than by $x^2 + y^2 + z^2 = a^2$ in cartesian coordinates. Thus it can be seen that in problems involving more than one independent variable, the boundary conditions play an important part in determining the coordinate system for the problem.

It will be shown later that the boundary conditions also influence the choice of method of solution. Therefore the boundary conditions are more important in the study of partial differential equations than ordinary differential equations.

8.2. Interpretation of Partial Derivatives

Figure 8.1 shows curves of the system

$$u = f(x, y) \tag{8.1}$$

plotted with u as a parameter. At each point in the xy plane, a value of u can be calculated from equation (8.1) and each curve is obtained by connecting points with equal values of u. Thus Fig. 8.1 can be interpreted as a

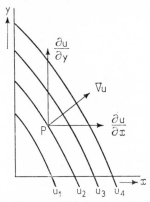

FIG. 8.1.   First partial derivatives of $u = f(x, y)$

contour map where u represents height measured perpendicularly to the xy plane. If x is allowed to vary whilst y remains constant, then in general u will also vary and the derivative of u with respect to x will be the rate of change of u relative to x, or the gradient in the chosen direction. This derivative is written

$$\left(\frac{\partial u}{\partial x}\right)_y \tag{8.2}$$

where y is placed outside the brackets to imply that y must be held constant while the derivative is being evaluated.

Similarly, the gradient along a line parallel to the y axis (x held constant) is written

$$\left(\frac{\partial u}{\partial y}\right)_x \tag{8.3}$$

In Chapter 7 it was shown that ∇u is a vector along the line of greatest slope and has a numerical value equal to that slope. This vector is also illustrated in Fig. 8.1. In the present case, z is not a relevant variable and equation (7.54) gives

$$\nabla u = i\frac{\partial u}{\partial x} + j\frac{\partial u}{\partial y} = \text{grad } u \tag{8.4}$$

the gradient in the x direction can be reclaimed from equation (8.4) by taking the scalar product (Section 7.4.1) with the unit vector i in the x direction. Thus

$$i.\nabla u = \partial u/\partial x \tag{8.5}$$

Using the appropriate unit vector the gradient can be found in any direction.

If δr is an incremental displacement from P so that

$$\delta r = i\,\delta x + j\,\delta y \tag{8.6}$$

then u will change by $(\partial u/\partial x)\delta x$ due to the change in x, and by $(\partial u/\partial y)\delta y$ due to the change in y provided δx and δy are small.

$$\therefore \quad \delta u = \left(\frac{\partial u}{\partial x}\right)\delta x + \left(\frac{\partial u}{\partial y}\right)\delta y \tag{8.7}$$

and in the limit as $\delta x \to dx$ and $\delta y \to dy$, $\delta u \to du$ where

$$du = \left(\frac{\partial u}{\partial x}\right)dx + \left(\frac{\partial u}{\partial y}\right)dy \tag{8.8}$$

is called the "total differential" of u.

In general, if u is a function of many variables $x_1, x_2, x_3, \ldots x_n$, then

$$du = \left(\frac{\partial u}{\partial x_1}\right)dx_1 + \left(\frac{\partial u}{\partial x_2}\right)dx_2 + \ldots + \left(\frac{\partial u}{\partial x_n}\right)dx_n \tag{8.9}$$

which is the fundamental equation of partial differentiation.

It will be noted that while a partial differential coefficient such as $(\partial u/\partial x_1)$ is being evaluated, all other independent variables, $x_2, x_3, \ldots x_n$ must be held constant. These other variables should be placed outside the brackets enclosing the derivative but in most cases it is obvious which variables must be held constant and they are omitted for brevity.

8.2.1. *Relationships between Partial Derivatives*

Returning to functions of one independent variable

$$y = f(x) \tag{8.10}$$

then dy, the infinitesimal change in y, is related to dx by

$$dy = \left(\frac{d_y}{dx}\right)dx \tag{8.11}$$

Sometimes, y is not given as an explicit function of x such as equation (8.10) but as an implicit function thus

$$g(x, y) = 0 \tag{8.12}$$

Considering g as a third variable temporarily, equation (8.9) can be used to give

$$dg = \left(\frac{\partial g}{\partial x}\right) dx + \left(\frac{\partial g}{\partial y}\right) dy = 0 \qquad (8.13)$$

where dg must equal zero to satisfy equation (8.12). By rearranging equation (8.13) an expression for dy can be obtained and compared with equation (8.11) to give

$$\frac{df}{dx} = -\frac{(\partial g/\partial x)}{(\partial g/\partial y)} = \frac{dy}{dx} \qquad (8.14)$$

One important fact concerning partial derivatives is evident from equation (8.14); the symbol "∂g" cannot be cancelled out because at least a sign mistake would be caused. Thus the two parts of the ratio defining a partial derivative can never be separated and considered alone. This is in marked contrast to ordinary derivatives where the infinitesimals dx, dy can be treated separately. To demonstrate the truth of equation (8.14), consider the following example.

Example 1. If $x^2 + y^2 = a^2$, find dy/dx.

The above equation can be solved for y giving

$$y = (a^2 - x^2)^{\frac{1}{2}} \qquad\qquad \text{I}$$

Differentiating in the usual way,

$$\frac{dy}{dx} = \frac{\frac{1}{2}(-2x)}{(a^2 - x^2)^{\frac{1}{2}}} = \frac{-x}{(a^2 - x^2)^{\frac{1}{2}}} \qquad\qquad \text{II}$$

Alternatively, the original equation can be written

$$g(x, y) = x^2 + y^2 - a^2 = 0 \qquad\qquad \text{III}$$

Differentiating equation III partially with respect to x keeping y constant gives

$$\frac{\partial g_1}{\partial x} = 2x \qquad\qquad \text{IV}$$

Similarly,

$$\frac{\partial g}{\partial y} = 2y \qquad\qquad \text{V}$$

Substituting the values given by equations IV and V into equation (8.14) gives

$$\frac{dy}{dx} = -\frac{2x}{2y}$$

and eliminating y by using equation I,

$$\frac{dy}{dx} = \frac{-x}{(a^2 - x^2)^{\frac{1}{2}}} \qquad\qquad \text{VI}$$

Thus, equations II and VI are identical, illustrating the validity of equation (8.14).

The above ideas can be readily extended to functions of two independent variables by generalizing equation (8.12) to

$$z = g(x, y) \tag{8.15}$$

and hence

$$dz = \left(\frac{\partial g}{\partial x}\right) dx + \left(\frac{\partial g}{\partial y}\right) dy \tag{8.16}$$

Equation (8.15) can also be put into the implicit form

$$F(x, y, z) = 0 \tag{8.17}$$

and thus

$$dF = \left(\frac{\partial F}{\partial x}\right) dx + \left(\frac{\partial F}{\partial y}\right) dy + \left(\frac{\partial F}{\partial z}\right) dz = 0 \tag{8.18}$$

Rearranging equation (8.18) gives

$$dz = -\frac{(\partial F/\partial x)}{(\partial F/\partial z)} dx - \frac{(\partial F/\partial y)}{(\partial F/\partial z)} dy \tag{8.19}$$

and comparing equations (8.16) and (8.19) gives

$$\frac{\partial g}{\partial x} = -\frac{\partial F/\partial x}{\partial F/\partial z}, \quad \frac{\partial g}{\partial y} = -\frac{\partial F/\partial y}{\partial F/\partial z} \tag{8.20}$$

Considering the manner in which a partial derivative is obtained, it is clear that

$$\left(\frac{\partial g}{\partial x}\right)\left(\frac{\partial x}{\partial g}\right) = 1 \tag{8.21}$$

and eliminating $(\partial F/\partial z)$ from the two equations (8.20) gives

$$\left(\frac{\partial g}{\partial x}\right)\left(\frac{\partial y}{\partial g}\right) = \left(\frac{\partial F}{\partial x}\right)\left(\frac{\partial y}{\partial F}\right) \tag{8.22}$$

If z is held constant in equation (8.18), then $dz = 0$ and

$$\frac{\partial y}{\partial x} = -\frac{(\partial F/\partial x)}{(\partial F/\partial y)} \tag{8.23}$$

Equating (8.22) and (8.23) and rearranging gives

$$\left(\frac{\partial g}{\partial x}\right)\left(\frac{\partial y}{\partial g}\right)\left(\frac{\partial x}{\partial y}\right) = -1 \tag{8.24}$$

or using the symmetrical version of equation (8.15), viz. (8.17), equation (8.24) can be written

$$\left(\frac{\partial z}{\partial x}\right)\left(\frac{\partial y}{\partial z}\right)\left(\frac{\partial x}{\partial y}\right) = -1 \tag{8.25}$$

giving further indication that partial derivative signs cannot be cancelled out.

8.2.2. *Changing the Independent Variables*

Referring to equation (8.15) where x and y are the two independent variables, it may be desired to change to new independent variables u and v where the old and new variables are related by

$$\left. \begin{aligned} x &= \phi\,(u,v) \\ y &= \psi\,(u,v) \end{aligned} \right\} \qquad (8.26)$$

Applying the general formula (8.9) to equations (8.26) gives

$$\left. \begin{aligned} dx &= \frac{\partial \phi}{\partial u}\,du + \frac{\partial \phi}{\partial v}\,dv \\[2mm] dy &= \frac{\partial \psi}{\partial u}\,du + \frac{\partial \psi}{\partial v}\,dv \end{aligned} \right\} \qquad (8.27)$$

which can be substituted into equation (8.16), thus

$$dz = \left(\frac{\partial g}{\partial x}\right)\left[\frac{\partial \phi}{\partial u}\,du + \frac{\partial \phi}{\partial v}\,dv\right] + \left(\frac{\partial g}{\partial y}\right)\left[\frac{\partial \psi}{\partial u}\,du + \frac{\partial \psi}{\partial v}\,dv\right] \qquad (8.28)$$

The partial derivative of z with respect to u is obtained by keeping v constant, and hence $dv = 0$ in equation (8.28).

$$\frac{\partial z}{\partial u} = \frac{\partial g}{\partial x}\frac{\partial \phi}{\partial u} + \frac{\partial g}{\partial y}\frac{\partial \psi}{\partial u}$$

or using the alternative nomenclature to clarify the equation,

$$\frac{\partial z}{\partial u} = \frac{\partial z}{\partial x}\frac{\partial x}{\partial u} + \frac{\partial z}{\partial y}\frac{\partial y}{\partial u} \qquad (8.29)$$

Similarly,

$$\frac{\partial z}{\partial v} = \frac{\partial z}{\partial x}\frac{\partial x}{\partial v} + \frac{\partial z}{\partial y}\frac{\partial y}{\partial v} \qquad (8.30)$$

Equations (8.29) and (8.30) can be extended to any number of independent variables. Thus if

$$z = f(x_1, x_2, x_3, \ldots x_n)$$
$$x_1 = g_1(u_1, u_2, u_3, \ldots u_m)$$
$$x_2 = g_2(u_1, u_2, u_3, \ldots u_m)$$
$$\text{etc.}$$

then

$$\frac{\partial z}{\partial u_1} = \frac{\partial z}{\partial x_1}\frac{\partial x_1}{\partial u_1} + \frac{\partial z}{\partial x_2}\frac{\partial x_2}{\partial u_1} + \cdots + \frac{\partial z}{\partial x_n}\frac{\partial x_n}{\partial u_1} \qquad (8.31)$$

The number of variables m need not be the same as the original number of variables n, but $m = n$ is the usual case.

8.2.3. *Independent Variables not Truly Independent*

On occasions there are restricting relationships between the basic independent variables. For instance, the composition of the vapour leaving a binary liquid is a function of temperature, pressure, and liquid composition; which are three independent variables. However, a restriction that the liquid is boiling is frequently applied and this gives a further equation relating temperature to pressure and liquid composition. This case can be stated symbolically thus,

$$y = f(x, T, P) \tag{8.32}$$

$$T = g(x, P) \tag{8.33}$$

Applying equation (8.9) to both of these gives

$$dy = \frac{\partial f}{\partial x}\,dx + \frac{\partial f}{\partial T}\,dT + \frac{\partial f}{\partial P}\,dP \tag{8.34}$$

and

$$dT = \frac{\partial g}{\partial x}\,dx + \frac{\partial g}{\partial P}\,dP \tag{8.35}$$

Substituting for dT from equation (8.35) into (8.34) and rearranging gives

$$dy = \left(\frac{\partial f}{\partial x} + \frac{\partial f}{\partial T}\frac{\partial g}{\partial x}\right)dx + \left(\frac{\partial f}{\partial P} + \frac{\partial f}{\partial T}\frac{\partial g}{\partial P}\right)dP \tag{8.36}$$

and here it is not advisable to replace $(\partial g/\partial x)$ with $(\partial T/\partial x)$ because the latter term is ambiguous. It could be obtained from equation (8.32) at constant y and P, or from equation (8.33) at constant P, yielding different results. If the data is collected at constant pressure, $dP = 0$, and equation (8.36) becomes

$$\left(\frac{\partial y}{\partial x}\right)_P = \frac{\partial f}{\partial x} + \frac{\partial f}{\partial T}\frac{\partial g}{\partial x} \tag{8.37}$$

or

$$\left(\frac{\partial y}{\partial x}\right)_P = \left(\frac{\partial y}{\partial x}\right)_{P,\,T} + \left(\frac{\partial y}{\partial T}\right)_{x,\,P}\left(\frac{\partial T}{\partial x}\right)_P \tag{8.38}$$

where the derivatives with one variable held constant are obtained from equation (8.33), and the others from equation (8.32).

The above system is sometimes studied at constant temperature which precludes the elimination of dT between equations (8.34) and (8.35) because $dT = 0$. However, a similar method will show that

$$\left(\frac{\partial y}{\partial x}\right)_T = \left(\frac{\partial y}{\partial x}\right)_{P,\,T} + \left(\frac{\partial y}{\partial P}\right)_{x,\,T}\left(\frac{\partial P}{\partial x}\right)_T \tag{8.39}$$

A further case of interest in chemical engineering is when a fluid property (e.g. temperature T) is a function of three coordinates (x, y, z) and time (t). The temperature increment determined from equation (8.9) is

$$dT = \left(\frac{\partial T}{\partial x}\right)dx + \left(\frac{\partial T}{\partial y}\right)dy + \left(\frac{\partial T}{\partial z}\right)dz + \left(\frac{\partial T}{\partial t}\right)dt \tag{8.40}$$

If a path is traversed across the system so that x, y, and z become functions of time only, equation (8.40) can be divided by dt to give

$$\frac{dT}{dt} = \left(\frac{\partial T}{\partial x}\right)\frac{dx}{dt} + \left(\frac{\partial T}{\partial y}\right)\frac{dy}{dt} + \left(\frac{\partial T}{\partial z}\right)\frac{dz}{dt} + \left(\frac{\partial T}{\partial t}\right) \qquad (8.41)$$

where dx/dt, etc., are the velocity components which determine the progress along the path and dT/dt is the "total time derivative" of the temperature.

A special case of equation (8.41) is when the path of a fluid element is traversed so that $dx/dt = u$, $dy/dt = v$, and $dz/dt = w$, are the components of fluid velocity. The total time derivative is then given the special symbol D/Dt named the "substantive derivative". Thus

$$\frac{DT}{Dt} = \left(\frac{\partial T}{\partial x}\right)u + \left(\frac{\partial T}{\partial y}\right)v + \left(\frac{\partial T}{\partial z}\right)w + \frac{\partial T}{\partial t} \qquad (8.42)$$

or in vector form,

$$\frac{DT}{Dt} = \frac{\partial T}{\partial t} + \boldsymbol{u}.\nabla T \qquad (8.43)$$

The distinction between DT/Dt and $\partial T/\partial t$ can be clarified by considering a heat exchanger operating at steady state. At any fixed point in the exchanger the temperature of the fluid passing the point is constant, thus $\partial T/\partial t = 0$, since by definition this derivative is taken at fixed values of the coordinate variables. However, any element of fluid undergoes a temperature rise or fall as it passes through the exchanger, and as far as the fluid element is concerned $DT/Dt \neq 0$. Thus it is important to distinguish between the equilibrium of an element of space and the equilibrium of an element of fluid.

An example of the use of equation (8.41) is the rule for differentiating a product. Thus if

$$y = uv \qquad (8.44)$$

where u and v are functions of x only, application of equation (8.41) gives

$$\frac{dy}{dx} = \frac{\partial y}{\partial u}\frac{du}{dx} + \frac{\partial y}{\partial v}\frac{dv}{dx}$$

Evaluating the partial derivatives by differentiating equation (8.44),

$$\frac{dy}{dx} = v\frac{du}{dx} + u\frac{dv}{dx} \qquad (8.45)$$

8.3. FORMULATING PARTIAL DIFFERENTIAL EQUATIONS

The method whereby a physical situation can be represented by a partial differential equation was described in Section 1.13 although the details were only described for ordinary differential equations. The first difficulty in describing the model is determining the number of independent variables needed to specify the system. The normal maximum number is four; three coordinates defining position, and time. If the problem contains either a

I

plane of symmetry or a line of symmetry, one coordinate can be dispensed with in the appropriate coordinate system. Cartesian or cylindrical polar coordinates are suitable in cases of plane symmetry, whereas either cylindrical or spherical polar coordinates are suitable for describing axial symmetry.

In Chapter 1 the space element was defined by the two planes at x and $x + \delta x$, whereas in the general three-dimensional case the space element is defined by taking an increment in each of the coordinate directions. The relevant conservation law is still applied to this new space element but the inventory of inputs and outputs must include the behaviour at all six faces of the space element, and not just two of the faces. The space element in spherical polar coordinates has already been illustrated in Fig. 7.16 where it can be seen that each face of the element is defined by keeping one of the coordinate variables constant, and each edge of the element is defined by keeping two coordinates constant. Thus, a version of Taylor's theorem can be applied along each edge of the element, and the value of the dependent variable can be established at each corner of the space element in terms of its value at one corner and the three partial derivatives constituting the Laplace operator.

These ideas can be better understood from actual examples, and in the following sub-sections a few of the more common partial differential equations will be derived. The first derivation will be given in full to clarify the method, but the later derivations will include many of the short cuts anticipating the result.

8.3.1. *Unsteady State Heat Conduction in One Dimension*

Figure 8.2 illustrates a section of a flat wall of thickness L ft whose height and length are both large compared with L. If the temperature distribution is uniform throughout the wall at zero time and heat is supplied at a fixed

FIG. 8.2. One dimensional heat transfer

rate per unit area to the one surface, it is required to determine the temperature as a function of position and time.

Since the original temperature is uniform, and every part of each wall surface is subjected to the same conditions, no heat will travel parallel to the surface and the temperature will be constant in any plane parallel to the surface. Thus the temperature distribution can be specified in terms of a single coordinate denoted by x in Fig. 8.2, and the discussion can be restricted to a section of unit area through the wall. Considering the thermal equilibrium of a slice of the wall between a plane at distance x from the heated surface and a parallel plane at $x + \delta x$ from the same surface gives the following balance, where T is the temperature and k is the thermal conductivity.

Rate of heat input at distance x and time t is $-k \dfrac{\partial T}{\partial x}$.

Rate of heat input at distance x and time $t + \delta t$ is

$$-k \frac{\partial T}{\partial x} + \frac{\partial}{\partial t}\left(-k\frac{\partial T}{\partial x}\right)\delta t$$

This second rate is obtained by applying Taylor's theorem as in Chapter 1 and considering that x is a constant. Similarly, two output rates can be determined from the corresponding input rates by applying Taylor's theorem at constant t and variable x, thus:

Rate of heat output at distance $x + \delta x$ and time t is

$$-k \frac{\partial T}{\partial x} + \frac{\partial}{\partial x}\left(-k\frac{\partial T}{\partial x}\right)\delta x$$

Rate of heat output at distance $x + \delta x$ and time $t + \delta t$ is

$$-k \frac{\partial T}{\partial x} + \frac{\partial}{\partial t}\left(-k\frac{\partial T}{\partial x}\right)\delta t + \frac{\partial}{\partial x}\left[-k\frac{\partial T}{\partial x} + \frac{\partial}{\partial t}\left(-k\frac{\partial T}{\partial x}\right)\delta t\right]\delta x$$

Heat content of the element at time t is $\rho C_p T\, \delta x$

Heat content of the element at time $t + \delta t$ is $\rho C_p\left(T + \dfrac{\partial T}{\partial t}\delta t\right)\delta x$

$\therefore$ accumulation of heat in time δt is $\rho C_p \dfrac{\partial T}{\partial t}\delta t\,\delta x$

Taking average input and output rates during the time interval δt gives
Heat input $=$

$$= \left[-k\frac{\partial T}{\partial x} + \tfrac{1}{2}\frac{\partial}{\partial t}\left(-k\frac{\partial T}{\partial x}\right)\delta t\right]\delta t$$

Heat output $=$

$$= \left\{-k\frac{\partial T}{\partial x} + \frac{\partial}{\partial x}\left(-k\frac{\partial T}{\partial x}\right)\delta x + \tfrac{1}{2}\frac{\partial}{\partial t}\left[-k\frac{\partial T}{\partial x} + \frac{\partial}{\partial x}\left(-k\frac{\partial T}{\partial x}\right)\delta x\right]\delta t\right\}\delta t$$

Using the general conservation law (1.25), and cancelling some terms for simplicity,

$$-\left[\frac{\partial}{\partial x}\left(-k\frac{\partial T}{\partial x}\right)\delta x + \tfrac{1}{2}\frac{\partial^2}{\partial t\,\partial x}\left(-k\frac{\partial T}{\partial x}\right)\delta x\,\delta t\right]\delta t = \rho C_p \frac{\partial T}{\partial t}\delta t\,\delta x$$

Dividing throughout by $\delta x \delta t$ and assuming that k is constant gives

$$k\frac{\partial^2 T}{\partial x^2} + \tfrac{1}{2}k\frac{\partial^3 T}{\partial x^2 \partial t}\delta t = \rho C_p\frac{\partial T}{\partial t} \tag{8.46}$$

Taking the limit of equation (8.46) as $\delta t \to 0$, the central term vanishes, and introducing the thermal diffusivity (α) as in equation (7.150) gives

$$\alpha\frac{\partial^2 T}{\partial x^2} = \frac{\partial T}{\partial t} \tag{8.47}$$

which is the required equation. It can also be obtained directly from the vector equation (7.150) by expanding (∇^2) in cartesian coordinates and deleting all y and z derivatives.

In the above derivation, it will be seen that the same equation (8.47) results if the simple input and output rates at time t are used without the added complication of using average rates. This simplification is consistent with the findings of Chapter 1, but until the reader is confident about which simplifications are justified and which are not, he is advised to allow for all possible correction terms as above. Care must be taken in each term to write down the correct number of infinitesimals (δx, δt), since these govern which terms are rejected in the step from equation (8.46) to (8.47). The boundary conditions will be derived separately in Section 8.4, and next an equation relating to unsteady state axi-symmetrical diffusion will be derived.

8.3.2. *Mass Transfer with Axial Symmetry*

A spray column is to be used for extracting one component from a binary mixture which forms the rising continuous phase. In order to estimate the transfer coefficient it is desired to study the detailed concentration distribution around an individual droplet of the spray.

To confine attention to a single droplet, a spherical polar coordinate

FIG. 8.3.   Mass transfer with axial symmetry

system is taken with its origin at the centre of the droplet. During its fall through the column, the droplet moves into contact with liquid of stronger composition so that allowance must be made for the time variation of the system. The concentration will also be a function of both the radial coordinate (r) and the angular coordinate (θ) but will not depend upon ϕ due to the symmetry provided that the z axis is vertical. Denoting concentration by c, diffusivity by D and the r and θ components of the continuous phase velocity by u and v respectively, a material balance can be taken over the element ABCD shown in Fig. 8.3. The element is defined in the normal manner by allowing one independent variable to vary at a time, and the diagram shows a section through what is in fact a ring-shaped element, symmetrical about the z axis.

$$\text{Area of face AB is } 2\pi r^2 \sin\theta\, \delta\theta \tag{8.48}$$

$$\text{Area of face AD is } 2\pi r \sin\theta\, \delta r \tag{8.49}$$

$$\text{Volume of element is } 2\pi r^2 \sin\theta\, \delta\theta\, \delta r \tag{8.50}$$

Material is transferred across each surface of the element by two mechanisms, bulk flow and molecular diffusion. Thus the transfer rates at each surface can be written as follows.

$$\text{Input rate across AB} = \left(uc - D\frac{\partial c}{\partial r} \right) 2\pi r^2 \sin\theta\, \delta\theta$$

$$\text{Input rate across AD} = \left(vc - \frac{D}{r}\frac{\partial c}{\partial \theta} \right) 2\pi r \sin\theta\, \delta r$$

It should be noted that the concentration gradient in the θ direction is $\dfrac{1}{r}\dfrac{\partial c}{\partial \theta}$ as obtained from the expansion of ∇c in spherical polar coordinates, equation (7.108). The output rates across CD and BC are obtained from the corresponding input rates by using Taylor's theorem as in Chapter 1.

Output rate across CD =

$$= \left(uc - D\frac{\partial c}{\partial r} \right) 2\pi r^2 \sin\theta\, \delta\theta + \frac{\partial}{\partial r}\left[\left(uc - D\frac{\partial c}{\partial r} \right) 2\pi r^2 \sin\theta\, \delta\theta \right] \delta r$$

Output rate across BC =

$$= \left(vc - \frac{D}{r}\frac{\partial c}{\partial \theta} \right) 2\pi r \sin\theta\, \delta r + \frac{\partial}{\partial \theta}\left[\left(vc - \frac{D}{r}\frac{\partial c}{\partial \theta} \right) 2\pi r \sin\theta\, \delta r \right] \delta\theta$$

Accumulation rate =

$$= 2\pi r^2 \sin\theta\, \delta r\, \delta\theta \frac{\partial c}{\partial t}$$

Using the general conservation law (1.25) and cancelling the obvious terms gives

$$-\frac{\partial}{\partial r}\left[\left(uc - D\frac{\partial c}{\partial r} \right) 2\pi r^2 \sin\theta\, \delta\theta \right] \delta r -$$

$$-\frac{\partial}{\partial \theta}\left[\left(vc - \frac{D}{r}\frac{\partial c}{\partial \theta} \right) 2\pi r \sin\theta\, \delta r \right] \delta\theta = 2\pi r^2 \sin\theta\, \delta r\, \delta\theta \frac{\partial c}{\partial t}$$

250 MATHEMATICAL METHODS IN CHEMICAL ENGINEERING

Dividing throughout by the volume of the element (8.50),

$$\frac{\partial c}{\partial t} = -\frac{1}{r^2}\frac{\partial}{\partial r}\left(r^2 uc - r^2 D\frac{\partial c}{\partial r}\right) - \frac{1}{r\sin\theta}\frac{\partial}{\partial\theta}\left[\left(vc - \frac{D}{r}\frac{\partial c}{\partial\theta}\right)\sin\theta\right] \quad (8.51)$$

Differentiating the products and separating the velocity terms from the diffusion terms gives

$$\frac{\partial c}{\partial t} + u\frac{\partial c}{\partial r} + \frac{v}{r}\frac{\partial c}{\partial\theta} + c\left[\frac{1}{r^2}\frac{\partial}{\partial r}(r^2 u) + \frac{1}{r\sin\theta}\frac{\partial}{\partial\theta}(v\sin\theta)\right]$$
$$= \frac{D}{r^2}\frac{\partial}{\partial r}\left(r^2\frac{\partial c}{\partial r}\right) + \frac{D}{r^2\sin\theta}\frac{\partial}{\partial\theta}\left(\sin\theta\frac{\partial c}{\partial\theta}\right) \quad (8.52)$$

But the term in square brackets is the expression for ∇.**u** given by equation (7.118) and is thus zero because of the continuity equation.

$$\therefore \quad \frac{\partial c}{\partial t} + u\frac{\partial c}{\partial r} + \frac{v}{r}\frac{\partial c}{\partial\theta} = \frac{D}{r^2}\frac{\partial}{\partial r}\left(r^2\frac{\partial c}{\partial r}\right) + \frac{D}{r^2\sin\theta}\frac{\partial}{\partial\theta}\left(\sin\theta\frac{\partial c}{\partial\theta}\right) \quad (8.53)$$

which is the expansion of equation (7.120) in spherical polar coordination.

8.3.3. *The Continuity Equation*

This important yet simple equation expresses the fact that in a flowing fluid the mass of the fluid is conserved. Figure 8.4 shows a rectangular element of space the lengths of whose edges parallel to the three cartesian

Fig. 8.4. Volume element in cartesian coordinates

axes are δx, δy, and δz. The components of the fluid velocity are denoted by u, v and w as shown, and the density of the fluid by ρ. The positive directions of u, v, and w must be the same as the positive directions of the axes so that fluid is considered to enter the element through faces ABCD, ABFE, and ADHE, and leave through the other three faces.

The rate at which fluid enters through face ABCD is proportional to the area of the face $(\delta y\delta z)$, the fluid density (ρ), and the velocity component (u) perpendicular to the face. Strictly, the velocity component only has the value u at the point A, and the velocity through the face will vary slightly from u. This is a small correction which will disappear at the end of the derivation and it will be ignored. If the reader wishes to check the above statement, all velocity components can be considered as values averaged over the relevant face, and when the limit is taken as the size of the element shrinks to zero, each average velocity tends to its point value at A. Thus

$$\text{Input rate through ABCD} = \rho u \, \delta y \, \delta z$$
$$\text{,, \quad ,, \quad ,, \quad ADHE} = \rho v \, \delta x \, \delta z$$
$$\text{,, \quad ,, \quad ,, \quad ABFE} = \rho w \, \delta x \, \delta y$$

Once again, the output rates are obtained from the corresponding input rates by applying Taylor's theorem. Thus

$$\text{Output rate through EFGH} = \rho u \, \delta y \, \delta z + \frac{\partial}{\partial x}(\rho u \, \delta y \, \delta z) \, \delta x$$

$$\text{,, \quad ,, \quad ,, \quad BCGF} = \rho v \, \delta x \, \delta z + \frac{\partial}{\partial y}(\rho v \, \delta x \, \delta z) \, \delta y$$

$$\text{,, \quad ,, \quad ,, \quad CDHG} = \rho w \, \delta x \, \delta y + \frac{\partial}{\partial z}(\rho w \, \delta x \, \delta y) \, \delta z$$

The mass of fluid contained in the element at time t is $\rho \delta x \, \delta y \, \delta z$.

$\therefore$ rate of increase of mass contained in element is $\dfrac{\partial}{\partial t}(\rho \delta x \, \delta y \, \delta z)$.

Because

$$\text{Input} - \text{Output} = \text{Accumulation}$$

$$\therefore \quad -\frac{\partial}{\partial x}(\rho u) \, \delta x \, \delta y \, \delta z - \frac{\partial}{\partial y}(\rho v) \, \delta x \, \delta y \, \delta z - \frac{\partial}{\partial z}(\rho w) \, \delta x \, \delta y \, \delta z = \frac{\partial \rho}{\partial t} \, \delta x \, \delta y \, \delta z$$

$$(8.54)$$

where the obvious terms have been cancelled. Dividing by the volume of the element gives

$$\frac{\partial}{\partial x}(\rho u) + \frac{\partial}{\partial y}(\rho v) + \frac{\partial}{\partial z}(\rho w) + \frac{\partial \rho}{\partial t} = 0 \qquad (8.55)$$

Taking the limit of equation (8.55) as the size of the element tends to zero leaves it unaltered, because all surplus terms have been ignored at an earlier stage in anticipation of this result.

Each term of equation (8.55) can be differentiated as a product and rearranged to give

$$\rho \frac{\partial u}{\partial x} + \rho \frac{\partial v}{\partial y} + \rho \frac{\partial w}{\partial z} + u \frac{\partial \rho}{\partial x} + v \frac{\partial \rho}{\partial y} + w \frac{\partial \rho}{\partial z} + \frac{\partial \rho}{\partial t} = 0 \qquad (8.56)$$

Since ρ is a function of x, y, z, and t, its substantive derivative can be taken as in equation (8.42), thus

$$\frac{D\rho}{Dt} = u \frac{\partial \rho}{\partial x} + v \frac{\partial \rho}{\partial y} + w \frac{\partial \rho}{\partial z} + \frac{\partial \rho}{\partial t} \qquad (8.57)$$

Combining equations (8.56) and (8.57) gives

$$\frac{1}{\rho}\frac{D\rho}{Dt} + \frac{\partial u}{\partial x} + \frac{\partial v}{\partial y} + \frac{\partial w}{\partial z} = 0 \tag{8.58}$$

which is the required continuity equation for a compressible fluid.

8.4. BOUNDARY CONDITIONS

In the last section the differential equation was found by taking a balance over an arbitrary element within the region of interest. The boundary conditions can always be obtained in a similar manner by considering the equilibrium of the particular element which contains the boundary. The variety of possible boundary conditions is quite small and sub-sections are devoted to each of four types. These results should be committed to memory, thus dispensing with the necessity for a detailed derivation on each occasion.

In the study of ordinary differential equations with only one independent variable, the boundary is defined by one particular value of the independent variable and the condition is stated in terms of the behaviour of the dependent variable at the boundary point. In the study of partial differential equations, each boundary is still defined by giving a particular value to just one of the independent variables. The boundary condition must then specify the behaviour of the dependent variable as a function of all of the other independent variables. There are three types of boundary condition arising in practice for which analytical solutions are sometimes possible and these are considered separately below. The more complicated integro-differential type of boundary condition is also derived, but problems in which they are involved are usually intractable by analytical methods. The discussion will be confined to heat transfer but the methods are generally applicable.

8.4.1. *First Type, Function Specified*

If values of the dependent variable itself are given at all points on a particular boundary, then the condition is said to be of the first type. Considering time dependent heat transfer in one dimension as in Section 8.3.1, the temperature will be a function of both x and t, thus the boundaries will be defined as either fixed values of x or fixed values of t. Two boundary conditions of the first type for this problem are:

(i) at $\qquad\qquad t = 0, \qquad T = f(x) \qquad\qquad$ (8.59)

(ii) at $\qquad\qquad x = 0, \qquad T = g(t) \qquad\qquad$ (8.60)

Equation (8.59) gives the temperature at all values of x for one value of t, whilst equation (8.60) restricts the behaviour of the temperature at all times at one value of x.

In the case of steady heat conduction in a cylindrical conductor of finite size, it is usual to use cylindrical polar coordinates so that $z = \pm a$ defines the end faces and $r = r_0$ defines the curved surface. Hence both boundaries are defined by keeping one of the independent variables constant, and conditions of the first type take the form

at $\qquad\qquad\qquad z = a, \qquad T = f(r, \theta)$ $\qquad\qquad$ (8.61)

at $\qquad\qquad\qquad r = r_0, \qquad T = g(z, \theta)$ $\qquad\qquad$ (8.62)

Due to the axial symmetry in this problem, temperature will not be a function of θ and equations (8.61) and (8.62) can be simplified, but in the corresponding unsteady state problem there will be a θ dependence and also a t dependence. The use of cartesian coordinates is not convenient in the above problem because the description of the boundaries is not so simple and all of the coordinates vary on the curved surface.

8.4.2. *Second Type, Derivative Specified*

The position of the boundary will still be defined as above by keeping one independent variable constant, but instead of giving the direct behaviour of the dependent variable, its derivative is restricted by a boundary condition of the second type. This situation occurs with radiant heating or cooling of a surface, electrical heating of a surface, or the special case of a thermally insulated surface. It can be seen in these cases that the heat flow rate is known but not the surface temperature. Because the heat flow rate is related to the temperature gradient, this boundary condition is of the second type, and two examples will now be considered.

Example 1.   A rectangular block of metal is subject to temperature variation in all directions, but the surface at $x = 0$ is thermally insulated. Express this condition by an equation.

It is convenient to use cartesian coordinates in this problem, and the boundary condition is derived by considering the infinitesimal element

FIG. 8.5.   Boundary element

residing at the boundary as shown in Fig. 8.5. Heat can only pass through the faces of the element by conduction, and the rates can be found for five of the surfaces using the same method as that used to determine the differential equation for a general volume element.

Input rate through   ADHE $= -k\dfrac{\partial T}{\partial y}\delta x\,\delta z$

Output rate through BCGF $= -k\dfrac{\partial T}{\partial y}\delta x\,\delta z + \dfrac{\partial}{\partial y}\left(-k\dfrac{\partial T}{\partial y}\delta x\,\delta z\right)\delta y$

Input rate through   ABFE $= -k\dfrac{\partial T}{\partial z}\delta x\,\delta y$

Output rate through DCGH $= -k\dfrac{\partial T}{\partial z}\delta x\,\delta y + \dfrac{\partial}{\partial z}\left(-k\dfrac{\partial T}{\partial z}\delta x\,\delta y\right)\delta z$

Output rate through EFGH $= -k\dfrac{\partial T}{\partial x}\delta y\,\delta z + \dfrac{\partial}{\partial x}\left(-k\dfrac{\partial T}{\partial x}\delta y\,\delta z\right)\delta x$

Because the face at $x = 0$ is thermally insulated, the heat input rate through ABCD must be zero. The rate of accumulation of heat within the element is $\rho C_p \dfrac{\partial T}{\partial t}\delta x\,\delta y\,\delta z$ as before, and completing the balance gives (after some cancellation)

$$k\frac{\partial^2 T}{\partial y^2}\delta x\,\delta z\,\delta y + k\frac{\partial^2 T}{\partial z^2}\delta x\,\delta y\,\delta z + k\frac{\partial T}{\partial x}\delta y\,\delta z +$$

$$+ k\frac{\partial^2 T}{\partial x^2}\delta y\,\delta z\,\delta x = \rho C_p\frac{\partial T}{\partial t}\delta x\,\delta y\,\delta z \qquad\qquad \text{I}$$

Due to the third term in this equation, it is only possible to cancel out $\delta y\delta z$ giving

$$k\left(\frac{\partial^2 T}{\partial y^2} + \frac{\partial^2 T}{\partial z^2} + \frac{\partial^2 T}{\partial x^2}\right)\delta x + k\frac{\partial T}{\partial x} = \rho C_p\frac{\partial T}{\partial t}\delta x \qquad\qquad \text{II}$$

Taking the limit as the size of the element shrinks to zero, results in all of the terms of equation I tending to zero with one exception. Thus equation I becomes

$$\frac{\partial T}{\partial x} = 0 \quad \text{at } x = 0 \qquad\qquad \text{III}$$

and this is the required boundary condition.

Example 2.   A cylindrical furnace is lined with two uniform layers of insulating brick of different physical properties. What boundary conditions should be imposed at the junction between the layers?

Figure 8.6 illustrates the problem, where a denotes the radius of curvature of the boundary between the layers, and the element is considered to lie across the boundary as shown. The symbols T, k, C_p, and ρ will be used for the temperature, conductivity, specific heat, and density of the layers, and a subscript 1 or 2 will distinguish between the layers. Due to axial symmetry, no heat will flow across the faces of the element given by $\theta = $ constant, but allowances will be made for heat flow in the z direction.

One boundary condition, which is of the first type, is that the temperature must be continuous across the boundary. That is,

at $\qquad\qquad\qquad\qquad r = a, \qquad T_1 = T_2 \qquad\qquad\qquad\qquad$ I

The second boundary condition is that the law of conservation of heat must be satisfied for the element shown in Fig. 8.6. The rate of flow of heat just

FIG. 8.6.   Section through cylindrical element at boundary

inside the boundary of the first layer is $-k_1 a\theta\,\delta z\,\dfrac{\partial T_1}{\partial r}$, and using Taylor's theorem, the rate of flow of heat into the element across the face CD is

$$-k_1 r\,\theta\,\delta z\,\frac{\partial T_1}{\partial r} - \tfrac{1}{2}\delta r\,\frac{\partial}{\partial r}\left(-k_1 r\,\theta\,\delta z\,\frac{\partial T_1}{\partial r}\right)$$

which must be evaluated at $r = a$.

$\therefore$ Input across CD =

$$= -k_1 a\,\theta\,\delta z\,\frac{\partial T_1}{\partial r} + \tfrac{1}{2}k_1\,\theta\,\delta r\delta z\,\frac{\partial}{\partial r}\left(r\,\frac{\partial T_1}{\partial r}\right)\Bigg|_a$$

Similarly,

Output across AB =

$$= -k_2 a\,\theta\,\delta z\,\frac{\partial T_2}{\partial r} - \tfrac{1}{2}k_2\,\theta\,\delta r\delta z\,\frac{\partial}{\partial r}\left(r\,\frac{\partial T_2}{\partial r}\right)\Bigg|_a$$

The heat flow rates in the z direction can be written:

Input at face (z) =

$$= -\tfrac{1}{2}a\,\theta\,\delta r\,\frac{\partial}{\partial z}(k_1 T_1 + k_2 T_2)$$

Output at face $(z + \delta z)$ =

$$= -\tfrac{1}{2}a\,\theta\,\delta r\,\frac{\partial}{\partial z}(k_1 T_1 + k_2 T_2) + \frac{\partial}{\partial z}\left[-\tfrac{1}{2}a\,\theta\,\delta r\,\frac{\partial}{\partial z}(k_1 T_1 + k_2 T_2)\right]\delta z$$

Accumulation within the element =

$$= \tfrac{1}{2}\rho_1 C_{p1}\,a\,\theta\,\delta r\delta z\,\frac{\partial T_1}{\partial t} + \tfrac{1}{2}\rho_2 C_{p2}\,a\,\theta\,\delta r\delta z\,\frac{\partial T_2}{\partial t}$$

Completing the heat balance and cancelling the obvious terms gives

$$-k_1 a \theta \delta z \frac{\partial T_1}{\partial r} + \tfrac{1}{2} k_1 \theta \delta r \delta z \frac{\partial}{\partial r}\left(r \frac{\partial T_1}{\partial r}\right) + k_2 a \theta \delta z \frac{\partial T_2}{\partial r} +$$

$$+ \tfrac{1}{2} k_2 \theta \delta r \delta z \frac{\partial}{\partial r}\left(r \frac{\partial T_2}{\partial r}\right) + \tfrac{1}{2} a \theta \delta r \delta z \frac{\partial^2}{\partial z^2}(k_1 T_1 + k_2 T_2)$$

$$= \tfrac{1}{2} a \theta \delta r \delta z \frac{\partial}{\partial t}(\rho_1 C_{p1} T_1 + \rho_2 C_{p2} T_2) \qquad \text{II}$$

Dividing by $a\theta\delta z$ gives

$$-k_1 \frac{\partial T_1}{\partial r} + \tfrac{1}{2} k_1 \frac{\delta r}{a} \frac{\partial}{\partial r}\left(r \frac{\partial T_1}{\partial r}\right) + k_2 \frac{\partial T_2}{\partial r} + \tfrac{1}{2} k_2 \frac{\delta r}{a} \frac{\partial}{\partial r}\left(r \frac{\partial T_2}{\partial r}\right) +$$

$$+ \tfrac{1}{2} \delta r \frac{\partial^2}{\partial z^2}(k_1 T_1 + k_2 T_2)$$

$$= \tfrac{1}{2} \delta r \frac{\partial}{\partial t}(\rho_1 C_{p1} T_1 + \rho_2 C_{p2} T_2) \qquad \text{III}$$

In the limit as $\delta r \to 0$, most of the terms in equation III disappear leaving

$$k_1 \frac{\partial T_1}{\partial r} = k_2 \frac{\partial T_2}{\partial r} \qquad \text{IV}$$

which is the second boundary condition.

These examples, particularly the second one, show that most of the effects which give rise to important terms in the differential equation are not important in the consideration of boundary conditions. The boundary condition IV does not include any terms describing either the variation of temperature with movement in the z direction, or the variation with time, or even the curvature of the boundary. All of these terms disappeared in the final limiting step from equation III.

Incidentally, the differential equation can also be derived from equation III by moving the element into either layer when all subscripts can be removed and a must be replaced by r. The two terms $(k\,\partial T/\partial r)$ will cancel out, followed by cancellation throughout by (δr); the limiting process will then yield the general differential equation

$$\frac{1}{r} \frac{\partial}{\partial r}\left(r \frac{\partial T}{\partial r}\right) + \frac{\partial^2 T}{\partial z^2} = \frac{\rho C_p}{k} \frac{\partial T}{\partial t} \qquad \text{V}$$

for heat conduction in cylindrical polar coordinates with axial symmetry.

8.4.3. *Third Type, Mixed Conditions*

This type of boundary condition consists of those in which the derivative of the dependent variable is related to the boundary value of the dependent variable by a linear equation. The most usual case of this is when the surface rate of heat loss is governed by a heat transfer coefficient. Referring back to Fig. 8.5, if the surface ABCD at $x = 0$ is cooling to surroundings at a temperature (T_0) through a gas film giving a resistance which can be expressed in terms of a heat transfer coefficient (h), the boundary condition can be stated thus.

Rate at which heat is removed from the surface $= h(T-T_0)$ per unit area. Also, the rate at which heat is conducted to the surface internally $= k\partial T/\partial x$ per unit area. These two rates must be equal, and hence

$$k\frac{\partial T}{\partial x} = h(T-T_0) \tag{8.63}$$

The above derivation assumes that curvature, time, and other space variations do not affect the balance, thus using the results of the previous section.

Equation (8.63) is true for any surface which faces in the negative direction of the x axis, but the sign of the left-hand side must be reversed if the surface faces in the positive direction. The signs must not be changed according to whether the surface is being heated or cooled. The only negative signs arise from the following two considerations,

(i) the heat conduction equation contains a negative sign by definition. (cf. equation (1.48)).

(ii) the outward normal from the surface may be in the negative coordinate direction.

Equation (8.63) contains both of these negative signs and is correct as written.

8.4.4. *Integro-Differential Boundary Condition*

This type of boundary condition arises most frequently in the study of mass transfer when the material crossing the boundary either enters or leaves a restricted volume and contributes to a modified driving force. Thus consider the following example.

Example 3. A solute is to be leached from a collection of porous spheres by stirring them as a suspension in a solvent. What is the correct boundary condition at the surface of one of the spheres?

The rate at which material diffuses to the surface of a porous sphere of radius a is $-4\pi a^2 D \dfrac{\partial c}{\partial r}\Big|_a$, where D is an effective diffusivity, and c is the concentration within the sphere. If V is the volume of solvent and C is the concentration in the bulk of the solvent, then

$$V\frac{\partial C}{\partial t} = -4N\pi a^2 D \frac{\partial c}{\partial r}\Big|_a \qquad\qquad \text{I}$$

where N is the number of spheres. For continuity of concentration, $c = C$ at $r = a$, and equation I must be integrated to determine C. Hence the boundary condition takes the form:

at $\qquad\qquad r = a, \qquad c = -\int_0^t \frac{4N\pi D a^2}{V}\frac{\partial c}{\partial r}\Big|_a dt \qquad\qquad \text{II}$

8.4.5. *Initial Value and Boundary Value Problems*

So far, the different types of boundary condition have been classified but the number of conditions required for the solution of a particular problem has not been defined. For ordinary differential equations, it was stated that the number of boundary conditions was equal to the order of the differential equation, but no corresponding rule has yet been discovered for partial differential equations. It is possible, however, to give a guiding hint which will help in the more usual problems.

Considering any one independent variable, say x, and assuming that the dependent variable is a function of x only so that all derivatives with respect to the other variables are zero, then the partial differential equation becomes an ordinary differential equation in terms of x. This simplified problem will require as many boundary conditions as its order and these must be given at fixed values of x. This number of boundary conditions is frequently the same as the number required by the corresponding partial differential equation at fixed values of x. Treating the other independent variables in the same manner gives the number of conditions needed at the boundaries of the other variables. Thus, for the equation of heat conduction in one dimension derived in Section 8.3.1,

$$\alpha \frac{\partial^2 T}{\partial x^2} = \frac{\partial T}{\partial t} \tag{8.47}$$

this rule states that two boundary conditions are needed at fixed values of x, and one at a fixed value of t. This rule cannot be relied upon in every case but is meant as a guide for common problems. For example, if it is applied to equation (8.55) it indicates that one boundary condition is required at fixed t, two at fixed r, and two at fixed θ, and yet it is not normally necessary to specify any conditions at fixed θ except that the solution should repeat itself at intervals of 2π.

The boundary conditions lead to an important classification of partial differential equations as follows. When only one condition is needed in a particular variable it is specified at one fixed value of that variable, whereas when two or more conditions are needed, they can all be specified at one value of the variable, or some can be specified at one value and the rest at another value. In the latter case, conditions are established at both ends of a range of values of an independent variable and the range is said to be "closed" by conditions at the beginning and the end of the range. Alternatively, if only one condition is stated, or all conditions are stated at one fixed value of the variable, then the behaviour of the dependent variable is restricted at the beginning of a range but no end is specified and the range is said to be "open" as far as that independent variable is concerned. If the range is closed for every independent variable, the problem is alternatively named a "boundary value" or "jury" problem. If the range of any independent variable is open, the problem is called an "initial value" or "marching" problem. This classification affects the choice of a method of solution. Thus the method of the Laplace transform, to be given in Section 8.8, can only be applied to initial value problems because the variable removed by the transformation must have an open range. When numerical methods are considered in Chapter 11 it will be seen that the calculation techniques are quite different depending on whether the problem is initial value or boundary value and that the methods are not interchangeable.

8.5. Particular Solutions of Partial Differential Equations

The general solution of a partial differential equation is not often possible, but when the boundary conditions are taken into account useful particular solutions can often be found. The methods given in this section for finding such particular solutions are the simplest to follow but the most difficult to initiate. In Section 8.7, the more powerful method of separation of variables will be described, but again the resultant expression is a collection of particular solutions which become of general use only when the conditions given in Section 8.6 are satisfied.

The other methods using various transforms are treated in Sections 8.8 and 8.9 and they will determine general solutions for particular combinations of boundary conditions classified in Section 8.4. However, a partial differential equation cannot be reduced to an ordinary differential equation by using the Laplace transform, which is the most useful of the many transform methods, unless all variables except one have open ranges. Thus the most that can be obtained in nearly all cases is a particular solution or a combination of particular solutions, and very rarely can a general solution be obtained. The particular solutions are complete and valid, and will satisfy practical requirements but an individual solution has to be obtained for each problem.

8.5.1. *Compounding the Independent Variables into One Variable*

It is always possible to make a simple change of variables by replacing one variable with a new variable, but there are exceptional cases in which the elimination of one variable by substitution results in the disappearance of a second variable from the problem. The basis of the present method is to look for this possibility and hence reduce a partial differential equation in two independent variables to an ordinary differential equation.

Consider for example the one dimensional heat conduction equation derived in Section 8.3.1.

$$\alpha \frac{\partial^2 T}{\partial x^2} = \frac{\partial T}{\partial t} \tag{8.47}$$

It is assumed that the solution of equation (8.47) can be written

$$T = f(q) \tag{8.64}$$

where

$$q = xt^n \tag{8.65}$$

n is any unknown constant, and q is the new variable. Equation (8.64) can be differentiated partially with respect to both x and t as follows.

$$\frac{\partial T}{\partial x} = \frac{df}{dq}\frac{\partial q}{\partial x} = t^n \frac{d_f}{dq} \tag{8.66}$$

$$\therefore \quad \frac{\partial^2 T}{\partial x^2} = t^{2n} \frac{d^2 f}{dq^2} \tag{8.67}$$

and

$$\frac{\partial T}{\partial t} = \frac{df}{dq}\frac{\partial q}{\partial t} = nxt^{n-1} \frac{df}{dq} \tag{8.68}$$

Substituting equations (8.67) and (8.68) into equation (8.47),

$$\alpha\, t^{2n} \frac{d^2 f}{dq^2} = nxt^{n-1} \frac{df}{dq} \tag{8.69}$$

Using equation (8.65) to eliminate x from equation (8.69) gives

$$\alpha\, t^{2n} \frac{d^2 f}{dq^2} = nqt^{-1} \frac{df}{dq} \tag{8. 0}$$

The above steps are valid for any constant value of n, and in particular they are true for

$$n = -\tfrac{1}{2} \tag{8.71}$$

With this value of n, equation (8.70) becomes independent of t giving the ordinary differential equation

$$\alpha \frac{d^2 f}{dq^2} = -\tfrac{1}{2}q \frac{df}{dq} \tag{8.72}$$

The dependent variable does not occur explicitly in equation (8.72) and hence it can be solved by the method given in Section 2.4.1 after one stage of integration,

$$\frac{df}{dq} = A\, e^{-q^2/4\alpha} \tag{8.73}$$

where A is a constant of integration. A further integration of equation (8.73) gives

$$f = B\operatorname{erf}(q/2\sqrt{\alpha}) + C$$

or

$$T = B\operatorname{erf}(x/2\sqrt{\alpha t}) + C \tag{8.74}$$

where B and C are arbitrary constants.

The kind of situation of which equation (8.74) is the solution can be found by putting $x = 0$ or $t = 0$ and determining the boundary conditions satisfied by equation (8.74).

If $x = 0,$ $T = C$

and if $t = 0,$ $T = B + C$

Thus equation (8.74) describes the temperature distribution as a function of time within a semi-infinite slab of material which is cooled on one surface. The initial temperature throughout the slab is uniform at $B + C$, and C is the temperature of the exposed face. This is the only situation described by equation (8.74); any other type of boundary condition is incompatible with the equation. The above method thus determines a particular solution which will probably not satisfy the required boundary conditions, and therefore the method is not very valuable.

8.5.3. *Superposition of Solutions*

It was shown in Section 2.5 that the complementary function of a linear ordinary differential equation could be added to the particular integral and the combination still satisfied the differential equation. Thus for any linear ordinary differential equation in which each term contains the dependent variable, solutions can be superposed. It will now be shown that the principle of superposition can be applied to linear partial differential equations provided that every term contains the dependent variable.

Taking the general linear partial differential equation of second order in two independent variables

$$f_1 \frac{\partial^2 u}{\partial x^2} + f_2 \frac{\partial^2 u}{\partial x \partial y} + f_3 \frac{\partial^2 u}{\partial y^2} + f_4 \frac{\partial u}{\partial x} + f_5 \frac{\partial u}{\partial y} + f_6 u = 0 \qquad (8.75)$$

where f_n are functions of x and y, and assuming that $u = u_1$ and $u = u_2$ are two different particular solutions of equation (8.75), then the sum

$$u_3 = u_1 + u_2 \qquad (8.76)$$

will also be a solution. Differentiating equation (8.76) gives

$$\left. \begin{aligned}
\frac{\partial u_3}{\partial x} &= \frac{\partial u_1}{\partial x} + \frac{\partial u_2}{\partial x} \\[2mm]
\frac{\partial^2 u_3}{\partial x^2} &= \frac{\partial^2 u_1}{\partial x^2} + \frac{\partial^2 u_2}{\partial x^2} \\[2mm]
\frac{\partial^2 u_3}{\partial x \partial y} &= \frac{\partial^2 u_1}{\partial x \partial y} + \frac{\partial^2 u_2}{\partial x \partial y} \\[2mm]
\text{etc.}
\end{aligned} \right\} \qquad (8.77)$$

Putting $u = u_3$ into equation (8.75) by using the set of equations (8.77) it can be seen that $u = u_3$ is also a solution when u_1 and u_2 are solutions. This is only true when the dependent variable u occurs once and once only in each term of the partial differential equation, and the above argument can obviously be extended to any number of independent variables and equations of any order. Thus the important result emerges, that for a linear partial differential equation, an infinite number of particular solutions can be added together to give a further solution.

One particular solution of the heat conduction equation was found in Section 8.5.1, and using the same symbols, a more basic particular solution can be found by differentiating equation (8.47) with respect to x. Thus

$$\alpha \frac{\partial^2}{\partial x^2} \left(\frac{\partial T}{\partial x} \right) = \frac{\partial}{\partial t} \left(\frac{\partial T}{\partial x} \right)$$

which shows that T can be replaced by $\partial T/\partial x$ to give a further particular solution of equation (8.47). Combining equations (8.65, 66, 71, 73) gives

$$\frac{\partial T}{\partial x} = A\,t^{-\frac{1}{2}}e^{-x^2/4\alpha t}$$

$$\therefore\quad T = A\,t^{-\frac{1}{2}}e^{-x^2/4\alpha t} \tag{8.78}$$

is also a solution of equation (8.47).

Considering unit cross-sectional area of a semi-infinite slab of density ρ and specific heat C_p occupying all space for positive x values, then the total heat content of the slab at any fixed time t is given by

$$H = \int_0^\infty \rho C_p T\,dx \tag{8.79}$$

Using the temperature distribution given by equation (8.78),

$$\therefore\quad H = \rho C_p A\,t^{-\frac{1}{2}}\int_0^\infty e^{-x^2/4\alpha t}\,dx$$

Because H is being evaluated at constant t, all of the present calculations are performed with t constant. Changing variables by putting $x = 2z\sqrt{\alpha t}$ so that $dx = 2\,dz\sqrt{\alpha t}$, hence

$$H = 2\rho C_p A\sqrt{\alpha}\int_0^\infty e^{-z^2}\,dz \tag{8.80}$$

The above integral has been evaluated in Section 5.2.

$$\therefore\quad H = \rho C_p\,A\sqrt{\alpha\pi}$$

$$= kA\sqrt{\pi/\alpha} \tag{8.81}$$

because $\quad\quad\quad \alpha = k/\rho C_p \tag{7.150}$

Equation (8.81) shows that the amount of heat in the slab remains constant for all time.

The initial temperature distribution is determined by taking the limit, as $t\to0$, of equation (8.78). L'Hôpital's rule cannot be used because the exponent cannot be expanded by Taylor's theorem in positive powers of t. However, it can be proved that an exponential function tends to its limit more rapidly than any finite power of the variable tends to its limit, but the proof is not elementary. Equation (8.78) thus shows that when $t = 0$, $T = 0$ for all values of x except $x = 0$. At $x = 0$, the exponential factor is unity for all time so that as $t\to0$, $T\to\infty$. Hence the heat content as given by equation (8.81) is initially concentrated at the face $x = 0$, and as time progresses it is all conducted into the slab according to equation (8.78). The following example illustrates the superposition of solutions of this type.

Example 1. Heat is supplied at a fixed rate Q Btu/h ft^2 to one face of a large rectangular slab of density ρ lb/ft^3, specific heat C_p Btu/lb °F, and conductivity k Btu/h ft^2 °F ft^{-1}, find the variation of surface temperature with time during the early stages after exposure.

The physical picture of the above situation is that heat is arriving at the surface and then being conducted into the slab according to equation (8.78) so that the temperature distribution at any time t is the accumulated effect of the heat entering the surface between zero time and time t. Thus let τ be a new time variable within the range $0 < \tau < t$ so that during a time increment $\delta\tau$, a quantity of heat $Q\delta\tau$ will be received by the surface. At time t, this heat will have been conducted into the slab for $(t-\tau)$ hours and its distribution will be given by equation (8.78) as

$$\delta T = A(t-\tau)^{-\frac{1}{2}} e^{-x^2/4\alpha(t-\tau)} \qquad\qquad \text{I}$$

Using equation (8.81)

$$Q\delta\tau = kA\sqrt{\pi/\alpha}$$

$$\therefore \quad \delta T = \frac{Q}{k}\sqrt{\frac{\alpha}{\pi}}(t-\tau)^{-\frac{1}{2}} e^{-x^2/4\alpha(t-\tau)}\delta\tau \qquad\qquad \text{II}$$

Equation II gives the part of the temperature distribution at time t which is the result of the heat absorbed by the surface between time τ and $\tau+\delta\tau$. Hence the total temperature distribution can be obtained by adding together all of these temperature increments and taking the limit as $\delta\tau \to 0$. Thus

$$T = \frac{Q}{k}\sqrt{\frac{\alpha}{\pi}}\int_0^t (t-\tau)^{-\frac{1}{2}} e^{-x^2/4\alpha(t-\tau)}\,d\tau \qquad\qquad \text{III}$$

Equation III can be integrated in terms of the error function by making the substitution $t-\tau = 1/z^2$, but as the temperature variation at the surface is all that is required by the problem, x can be put equal to zero in equation III giving the surface temperature

$$T_s = \frac{Q}{k}\sqrt{\frac{\alpha}{\pi}}\int_0^t (t-\tau)^{-\frac{1}{2}}\,d\tau$$

$$= \frac{2Q}{k}\sqrt{\frac{\alpha t}{\pi}} \qquad\qquad \text{IV}$$

Other problems can be solved by this method, but if Q is a function of time it must remain inside the integral in equation III as $Q(\tau)$.

8.5.3. *The Method of Images*

The solutions of the conduction equation considered so far have only applied to a semi-infinite body. It is possible to extend the solutions to finite media for two types of boundary condition. Firstly, if one plane surface is insulated or the finite body has a plane of symmetry, and secondly if the boundary condition is of the first type.

Example 2. Consider a wall of thickness $2L$ ft with a uniform initial temperature throughout, and let both faces be suddenly raised to the same higher temperature. Find the temperature distribution as a function of time.

Taking an x coordinate measured from one face of the slab, the initial uniform temperature as the datum and considering unit cross-sectional area, the differential equation is again

$$\alpha \frac{\partial^2 T}{\partial x^2} = \frac{\partial T}{\partial t} \qquad\qquad \text{I}$$

and the boundary conditions are

at $\qquad\qquad\qquad t = 0, \qquad T = 0 \qquad\qquad\qquad \text{II}$

at $\qquad\qquad\qquad x = 0, \qquad T = T_0 \qquad\qquad\qquad \text{III}$

at $\qquad\qquad\qquad x = L, \qquad \dfrac{\partial T}{\partial x} = 0 \qquad\qquad\qquad \text{IV}$

The last condition takes advantage of the symmetry of the problem so that no heat crosses the central plane. According to Section 8.5.1, the solution which satisfies conditions II and III for an infinite slab is

$$T_1 = T_0 - T_0 \operatorname{erf}(x/2\sqrt{\alpha t})$$
$$= T_0 \operatorname{erfc}(x/2\sqrt{\alpha t}) \qquad\qquad \text{V}$$

This is satisfactory for small values of t, but as soon as the temperature at $x = L$ starts to rise, equation IV is violated. Since the system is symmetrical, the insulated face at $x = L$ is equivalent to another heated face at $x = 2L$ (this in fact returns to the original problem). But equation V gives the temperature distribution as a function of distance x from any heated face. The distance of a point in the body from the second heated face is $(2L - x)$, and hence the temperature distribution resulting from the heat entering the face at $x = 2L$ is given by

$$T_2 = T_0 \operatorname{erfc}[(2L - x)/2\sqrt{\alpha t}] \qquad\qquad \text{VI}$$

by analogy with equation V. The combined solution becomes

$$T_3 = T_0 \operatorname{erfc}(x/2\sqrt{\alpha t}) + T_0 \operatorname{erfc}[(2L - x)/2\sqrt{\alpha t}] \qquad\qquad \text{VII}$$

The solution T_3 satisfies equation IV but as t increases further, the second part of equation VII violates equation III. If a heated face at $x = 2L$ causes the temperature at $x = 0$ to rise at a certain rate, then a correspondingly cooled surface at $x = 2L$ will cause a corresponding fall rate at $x = 0$. The temperature distribution caused by such a cooled face at $x = 2L$ is given by

$$T_4 = -T_0 \operatorname{erfc}[(2L + x)/2\sqrt{\alpha t}] \qquad\qquad \text{VIII}$$

which can be added to equation VII to satisfy equation III again. Thus

$$T_5 = T_0 \operatorname{erfc}(x/2\sqrt{\alpha t}) + T_0 \operatorname{erfc}[(2L - x)/2\sqrt{\alpha t}] - T_0 \operatorname{erfc}[(2L + x)/2\sqrt{\alpha t}] \qquad \text{IX}$$

The distribution given by equation IX now violates equation IV again but a further reflection at the plane $x = L$ gives

$$T_6 = -T_0 \operatorname{erfc}\left[(4L-x)/2\sqrt{\alpha t}\right] \qquad \text{X}$$

which can be added to equation IX. This process can be continued indefinitely, by treating each face at $x = 0$ and $x = L$ like a perfectly reflecting mirror so that any source to the left of $x = L$ possesses a corresponding image source to the right of $x = L$. Also, any source to the right of $x = 0$ must have a corresponding image sink to the left of $x = 0$. Thus the insulated face (or plane of symmetry) acts as a perfect reflector as far as sources and sinks are concerned, and the constant temperature face acts as a reflector which interchanges sources and sinks upon reflection. The complete solution is thus

$$T = T_0 \sum_{n=0}^{\infty} (-1)^n \{ \operatorname{erfc}\left[(x+2nL)/2\sqrt{\alpha t}\right] + \operatorname{erfc}\left[(2nL+2L-x)/2\sqrt{\alpha t}\right] \} \qquad \text{XI}$$

This method of images was originally developed to solve linear problems in electricity and magnetism, but it can be applied to any problem involving the solution of a linear partial differential equation where superposition of solutions is permissible and the boundary conditions are of the first type, or of second type with vanishing derivative.

It is possible to extend this image principle to cylindrical and spherical boundaries but this is rather more complicated and so specialized that the method will not be considered here.

8.5.4. *Particular Solution Suggested by the Boundary Conditions*

Because all boundary conditions are specified at a fixed value of one independent variable but over a range of values of the other variables, a functional form frequently appears in the statement of a boundary condition. If the particular solution required is to satisfy such a condition, it is reasonable to suppose that the particular solution may have a similar functional form. This is especially true in classical hydrodynamics and the following examples illustrate the technique applied to the problem of incompressible fluid flow round a spherical obstacle using each of the approximations to the Navier-Stokes equation (7.126) given in Section 7.10.

Example 3. *Ideal Fluid Flow Round a Sphere.* In Section 7.10.1 it was shown that when the viscous terms were neglected in the equation of fluid motion, a velocity potential (ϕ) could be defined so that

$$\boldsymbol{u} = -\nabla\phi \qquad \text{I}$$

and
$$\nabla^2\phi = 0 \qquad \text{II}$$

It is convenient to use spherical polar coordinates for the present problem and there is no dependence on the azimuthal angle and hence no ambiguity over the meaning of the symbol ϕ. Using equation (7.120), equation II can be written

$$\frac{1}{r^2}\frac{\partial}{\partial r}\left(r^2\frac{\partial\phi}{\partial r}\right) + \frac{1}{r^2\sin\theta}\frac{\partial}{\partial\theta}\left(\sin\theta\frac{\partial\phi}{\partial\theta}\right) = 0 \qquad \text{III}$$

If the radius of the sphere is a, and the fluid flows with velocity U_0 along the axis of symmetry $\theta = 0$ towards the origin at the centre of the sphere as shown in Fig. 8.7, the boundary conditions can be written:

at $\qquad\qquad r = a, \qquad u = 0$ $\qquad\qquad\qquad\qquad\qquad\qquad$ IV

as $\qquad\qquad r \to \infty, \qquad u \to -U_0 \cos\theta, \qquad v \to U_0 \sin\theta$ $\qquad\qquad$ V

where u and v are the r and θ components of the velocity $\boldsymbol{u}$ respectively.

FIG. 8.7.   Flow round a sphere

Equation IV prohibits flow through the surface of the sphere, and equation V states that the flow at a large distance from the obstacle, in any direction, is undisturbed parallel flow. In order to solve equation III for these boundary conditions, equations V must be expressed in terms of ϕ by substituting into equation I. Thus

$$-\frac{\partial\phi}{\partial r} = -U_0\cos\theta$$

$$-\frac{1}{r}\frac{\partial\phi}{\partial\theta} = U_0\sin\theta$$

$$\therefore\quad \phi = U_0 r\cos\theta$$

$$\therefore \text{ as } r\to\infty, \qquad \phi \to U_0 r\cos\theta \qquad\qquad\qquad \text{VI}$$

Boundary condition VI suggests trying a particular solution of the form

$$\phi = f(r)\cos\theta \qquad\qquad\qquad\qquad \text{VII}$$

in the partial differential equation III. Thus

$$\cos\theta\frac{\partial}{\partial r}\left(r^2\frac{\partial f}{\partial r}\right) + \frac{f}{\sin\theta}\frac{\partial}{\partial\theta}\left(\sin\theta\frac{\partial\cos\theta}{\partial\theta}\right) = 0 \qquad\qquad \text{VIII}$$

Performing the differentiations with respect to θ and replacing the partial derivatives with respect to r with ordinary derivatives,

$$\cos\theta\frac{d}{dr}\left(r^2\frac{df}{dr}\right) - \frac{f}{\sin\theta}(2\sin\theta\cos\theta) = 0$$

$$\therefore\quad r^2\frac{d^2f}{dr^2} + 2r\frac{df}{dr} - 2f = 0 \qquad\qquad\qquad\qquad \text{IX}$$

Equation IX is independent of θ, and since it is both linear and homogeneous it can be solved by the methods of Sections 2.4 and 2.5. The result is

$$f = Ar + B/r^2 \qquad\qquad \text{X}$$

Substituting into equation VII gives the solution

$$\phi = (Ar + B/r^2)\cos\theta$$

To satisfy condition VI, $A = U_0$,

$$\therefore \quad \phi = (U_0 r + B/r^2)\cos\theta \qquad\qquad \text{XI}$$

But $u = -\partial\phi/\partial r$ from equation I, therefore boundary condition IV becomes

at $\qquad\qquad r = a, \quad u = -(U_0 - 2B/r^3)\cos\theta = 0$

$$\therefore \quad B = \tfrac{1}{2}U_0 a^3 \qquad\qquad \text{XII}$$

Combining equations XI and XII gives

$$\phi = U_0\left(r + \frac{a^3}{2r^2}\right)\cos\theta \qquad\qquad \text{XIII}$$

which satisfies the boundary conditions IV and VI and the differential equation III and is thus the solution. The stream function form of equation XIII is

$$\psi = \tfrac{1}{2}U_0 r^2\left(1 - \frac{a^3}{r^3}\right)\sin^2\theta \qquad\qquad \text{XIV}$$

which can be checked by differentiating equations XIII and XIV and comparing the two expressions for each velocity component.

It is worth noting that the θ component of velocity does not vanish at the surface of the sphere. That is,

$$v = -\frac{1}{r}\frac{\partial\phi}{\partial\theta} = \frac{3}{2}U_0\sin\theta \qquad\qquad \text{XV}$$

which means that there is slipping at the surface of the sphere. This is not physically reasonable and is caused by neglecting the viscous term in the equation of motion. The difficulty can be overcome by assuming that there is a thin layer of fluid near any boundary in which viscous effects are important, and this is the basis of Prandtl's "boundary layer theory". The reader is referred to Goldstein or Schlichting† for further details.

Example 4. *Viscous Flow Round a Sphere.* The simplified equation of motion describing this problem in terms of the stream function is

$$E^4\psi = 0 \qquad\qquad \text{I}$$

where the operator E^2 is defined by equation (7.135) in spherical polar coordinates as

$$E^2\psi = \frac{\partial^2\psi}{\partial r^2} + \frac{\sin\theta}{r^2}\frac{\partial}{\partial\theta}\left(\frac{1}{\sin\theta}\frac{\partial\psi}{\partial\theta}\right) \qquad\qquad \text{II}$$

† Goldstein, S. " Modern Developments in Fluid Dynamics," Vol. I. Oxford University Press (1938). Schlicting, H. " Boundary Layer Theory " (translated from German), 4th edition. McGraw-Hill.

The boundary condition for large values of r in terms of the stream function is:

as $$r \to \infty, \qquad \psi \to \tfrac{1}{2}U_0 r^2 \sin^2 \theta \qquad\qquad\qquad \text{III}$$

The boundary conditions at the surface of the sphere of radius a which impose conditions of zero slip are:

at $$r = a, \qquad u = 0, \qquad v = 0$$

or at $$r = a, \qquad \frac{\partial \psi}{\partial r} = 0, \qquad \frac{\partial \psi}{\partial \theta} = 0 \qquad\qquad \text{IV}$$

Equation III suggests trying the particular solution

$$\psi = f(r)\sin^2 \theta \qquad\qquad\qquad \text{V}$$

Substituting into equation II gives

$$E^2 \psi = \frac{d^2 f}{dr^2}\sin^2 \theta + \frac{\sin \theta}{r^2}\frac{\partial}{\partial \theta}\left(\frac{f}{\sin \theta}\frac{\partial \sin^2 \theta}{\partial \theta}\right)$$

$$= \frac{d^2 f}{dr^2}\sin^2 \theta - \frac{2f}{r^2}\sin^2 \theta$$

$$\therefore \quad E^2 \psi = \left(\frac{d^2 f}{dr^2} - \frac{2f}{r^2}\right)\sin^2 \theta \qquad\qquad \text{VI}$$

Denoting $\dfrac{d^2 f}{dr^2} - \dfrac{2f}{r^2}$ by $F(r)$, and applying the operator E^2 to equation VI, the steps between equations V and VI will be repeated identically with f replaced by F. Therefore

$$E^4 \psi = \left(\frac{d^2 F}{dr^2} - \frac{2F}{r^2}\right)\sin^2 \theta \qquad\qquad \text{VII}$$

Substituting for F in terms of f and equating to zero as given by equation I,

$$\frac{d^2}{dr^2}\left(\frac{d^2 f}{dr^2} - \frac{2f}{r^2}\right) - \frac{2}{r^2}\left(\frac{d^2 f}{dr^2} - \frac{2f}{r^2}\right) = 0$$

$$\therefore \quad \frac{d^4 f}{dr^4} - \frac{4}{r^2}\frac{d^2 f}{dr^2} + \frac{8}{r^3}\frac{df}{dr} - \frac{8}{r^4}f = 0 \qquad\qquad \text{VIII}$$

Equation VIII is linear and homogeneous and has the solution

$$f = Ar^4 + Br^2 + Cr + D/r \qquad\qquad\qquad \text{IX}$$

Substituting into equation V, therefore

$$\psi = (Ar^4 + Br^2 + Cr + D/r)\sin^2 \theta \qquad\qquad \text{X}$$

is a solution of equation I. To satisfy boundary condition III

$$A = 0$$

and $$B = \tfrac{1}{2}U_0$$

$$\therefore \quad \psi = (\tfrac{1}{2}U_0 r^2 + Cr + D/r)\sin^2 \theta \qquad\qquad \text{XI}$$

Using boundary conditions IV gives

$$\tfrac{1}{2}U_0 a^2 + Ca + D/a = 0 \qquad\qquad \text{XII}$$

and
$$U_0 a + C - D/a^2 = 0 \qquad\qquad \text{XIII}$$

Solving equations XII and XIII for C and D and substituting into equation XI gives the final solution

$$\psi = \tfrac{1}{2}U_0 r^2 \left(1 - \frac{3}{2}\frac{a}{r} + \frac{1}{2}\frac{a^3}{r^3}\right)\sin^2\theta \qquad\qquad \text{XIV}$$

the vorticity distribution can be obtained by substituting equation XIV into equation (7.136). Thus

$$\zeta = \frac{3U_0 a}{2r^2}\sin\theta \qquad\qquad \text{XV}$$

Comparing equation XIV in Example 3 with equation XIV in Example 4, it can be seen that the two solutions are quite different, and yet they are frequently confused because both are symmetrical about the equatorial plane of the sphere. In the ideal fluid solution the fluid slips over the surface of the sphere and the vorticity is zero everywhere, whereas in viscous flow, the fluid does not slip at the boundary, and a vorticity distribution is set up. It should be noted that a second order equation was solved in Example 3, but a fourth order equation arose in Example 4, hence more boundary conditions could be satisfied in the second case. This explains why there is good agreement between theory and experiment at very low Reynolds numbers where inertial effects are small; whereas there is only approximate agreement for $\theta < 90°$ between theory and experiment at high Reynolds numbers, because viscous effects can never be completely ignored.

8.6. Orthogonal Functions

Before the method of separation of variables can be used to solve partial differential equations, a fundamental relationship between the individual members of a set of functions must be investigated. The method of separation of variables normally gives the solution as the sum of an infinite set of related functions, and the method is most useful when this set of functions satisfies the following definition of orthogonality.

Two functions $\phi_n(x)$ and $\phi_m(x)$ are said to be orthogonal with respect to a weighting function $r(x)$ over the interval from a to b if

$$\int_a^b r(x)\,\phi_n(x)\,\phi_m(x)\,dx = 0 \quad (\text{for } m \neq n) \qquad\qquad (8.82)$$

Thus, if there is a set of functions $\phi_n(x)$ where n is a positive integer, and the integrated product of any pair of functions with a fixed weighting function is zero, then the set of functions is orthogonal. If $m = n$ (i.e. the same function is taken twice) then the integral in equation (8.82) will not normally vanish.

Example 1. Show that the functions $\sin nx$ and $\sin mx$ are orthogonal with respect to unity in the range $0 \leqslant x \leqslant \pi$, for integer values of m and n.

Starting from the trigonometrical identity

$$2 \sin nx \sin mx = \cos (n-m)x - \cos (n+m)x \qquad \text{I}$$

and integrating over the given range, therefore

$$2 \int_0^\pi \sin nx \sin mx\, dx = \int_0^\pi \cos (n-m)x\, dx - \int_0^\pi \cos (n+m)x\, dx \qquad \text{II}$$

$$= \frac{1}{n-m} [\sin (n-m)x]_0^\pi - \frac{1}{n+m} [\sin (n+m)x]_0^\pi$$

$$= 0$$

because the sine functions vanish at both limits of integration. If $m = n$, the first integral in equation III becomes

$$\int_0^\pi dx = \pi \qquad \text{III}$$

$$\therefore \int_0^\pi \sin nx \sin mx\, dx = \begin{cases} 0 & \text{if } n \neq m \\ \pi/2 & \text{if } n = m \end{cases} \qquad \text{IV}$$

which is the complete evaluation of the orthogonality integral.

8.6.1. *The Sturm-Liouville Equation*

This is the name which describes any second order linear ordinary differential equation which can be written in the form

$$\frac{d}{dx}\left[p(x)\frac{dy}{dx} \right] + [q(x)+\lambda r(x)]y = 0 \qquad (8.83)$$

where λ is a constant, and p, q, and r are functions of x. It should be noted that the first and second differential terms of a second order equation cannot always be combined into the form given in equation (8.83).

For any particular set of functions p, q, and r, the solution of equation (8.83) for y will depend upon λ. Hence, if λ can take a set of discrete values λ_n, a corresponding set of solutions $y = \phi_n(x)$ will be obtained. Taking any two values of λ (λ_n and λ_m) and the corresponding solutions ($y = \phi_n(x)$ and $y = \phi_m(x)$), then

$$\frac{d}{dx}\left[p(x)\frac{d\phi_n}{dx} \right] + [q(x)+\lambda_n r(x)]\phi_n = 0$$

and

$$\frac{d}{dx}\left[p(x)\frac{d\phi_m}{dx} \right] + [q(x)+\lambda_m r(x)]\phi_m = 0$$

Multiplying the first of these equations by ϕ_m, the second by ϕ_n, and subtracting the second from the first gives

$$\phi_m \frac{d}{dx}\left[p(x)\frac{d\phi_n}{dx} \right] - \phi_n \frac{d}{dx}\left[p(x)\frac{d\phi_m}{dx} \right] + (\lambda_n - \lambda_m)r(x)\phi_n\phi_m = 0 \qquad (8.84)$$

Integrating equation (8.84) with respect to x from a to b gives

$$(\lambda_n - \lambda_m) \int_a^b r(x)\phi_n \phi_m \, dx = \int_a^b \phi_n \frac{d}{dx}\left[p(x)\frac{d\phi_m}{dx} \right] dx - \int_a^b \phi_m \frac{d}{dx}\left[p(x)\frac{d\phi_n}{dx} \right] dx$$

Evaluating each of the integrals on the right-hand side by parts gives

$$(\lambda_n - \lambda_m) \int_a^b r(x)\phi_n \phi_m \, dx$$

$$= \left[\phi_n p(x)\frac{d\phi_m}{dx} \right]_a^b - \int_a^b p(x)\frac{d\phi_m}{dx}\frac{d\phi_n}{dx} \, dx - \left[\phi_m p(x)\frac{d\phi_n}{dx} \right]_a^b + \int_a^b p(x)\frac{d\phi_n}{dx}\frac{d\phi_m}{dx} \, dx$$

Simplifying by cancelling the two identical integrals and combining the boundary values gives

$$(\lambda_n - \lambda_m) \int_a^b r(x)\phi_n \phi_m \, dx = \left[p(x)\left\{ \phi_n \frac{d\phi_m}{dx} - \phi_m \frac{d\phi_n}{dx} \right\} \right]_a^b \qquad (8.85)$$

Hence the functions $\phi_n(x)$ and $\phi_m(x)$ which correspond to two different values (λ_n and λ_m) of the constant, will be orthogonal if the right-hand side of equation (8.85) is zero. It is possible for the function on the right-hand side of (8.85) to have the same value at both limits and thus cancel itself out, but it is more usual for the term in brackets to vanish independently at both limits. The term is zero when $p(x) = 0$ at the limit or when the boundary conditions are suitable. When the same boundary conditions apply to every equation of the set, independent of the value of λ, there are three types of boundary condition which are suitable.

(i) at $\qquad\qquad x = a, \qquad y = 0$

$$\therefore \quad \phi_n = \phi_m = 0$$

(ii) at $\qquad\qquad x = a, \qquad \frac{dy}{dx} = 0$

$$\therefore \quad \frac{d\phi_n}{dx} = \frac{d\phi_m}{dx} = 0$$

(iii) at $\qquad\qquad x = a, \qquad \frac{dy}{dx} = \beta y$

$$\therefore \quad \frac{d\phi_n}{dx} = \beta\phi_n, \qquad \frac{d\phi_m}{dx} = \beta\phi_m$$

Therefore, if both boundary conditions are of the above three types (with duplication allowed), then the set of functions $\phi_n(x)$ will be orthogonal with respect to the weighting function $r(x)$ which occurs in equation (8.83) in conjuction with λ.

It should be noted that the conditions given above for the solutions to be orthogonal are more restrictive than the three types of boundary conditions listed in Section 8.4. Condition (i) states that the boundary value of the dependent variable must be zero and cannot be a function of another independent variable. This condition can be relaxed a little to allow the dependent variable to have a constant finite value at the boundary by moving the origin so that the new dependent variable will be zero at the boundary. If condition (i) is used at both boundaries, the origin cannot be moved to two different places, but one method of overcoming this difficulty will be described in Example 2 of Section 8.7. Thus most type 1 boundary conditions will give rise to an orthogonal set of solutions to a Sturm-Liouville equation, provided that there is no dependence upon another independent variable.

There is no easy way of extending condition (ii) to include a constant gradient at the boundary, hence only a vanishing derivative of type 2 boundary conditions will give orthogonal solutions. The same remarks apply to condition (iii) as to condition (i). That is, any type 3 boundary condition is suitable provided that only one movement of the origin is required to bring the condition at both boundaries to one of the forms (i), (ii), or (iii). Condition (iii) does include conditions (i) and (ii) as the special cases $\beta = \infty$, and $\beta = 0$ respectively.

Finally, the integro-differential boundary condition given in Section 8.4.4 is not suitable for obtaining orthogonal solutions to a Sturm-Liouville equation.

8.7. Method of Separation of Variables

When a dependent variable, say T, is related to two independent variables x and t by means of a partial differential equation, the solution will be of the form

$$T = F(x, t) \tag{8.86}$$

The method of separation of variables looks for solutions of the form

$$T = f(x) \cdot g(t) \tag{8.87}$$

where the functional dependence upon x is separated from the dependence upon t. A glance at the particular solutions (8.74) or (8.78) of equation (8.47) is sufficient to show that they cannot be expressed in the form (8.87), and thus any solution which is obtained by the method of separation of variables will be a new one.

The procedure to follow in this method is to substitute equation (8.87) into the differential equation and separate the terms dependent upon x from those dependent upon t by the equality sign. The equation thus takes the form of a function of x only, being equal to a function of t only, which can only be satisfied by both sides of the equation having the same constant value. Thus, two ordinary differential equations, each involving an unknown parameter are derived from one partial differential equation. The procedure can be better understood in reference to particular examples, and special applications of the time dependent Laplace equation will be used in

Choosing the constants A_n to satisfy equation (8.108) is accomplished by using the properties of orthogonal functions. Comparing equation (8.94) with the general Sturm-Liouville equation (8.83) shows that $p(x) = r(x) = 1$, $q(x) = 0$, so that equation (8.94) is of Sturm-Liouville type. The boundary conditions (8.102) and (8.103) are of the suitable form (i) and thus the functions $\sin (n\pi x/L)$ are orthogonal with respect to unity in the range 0 to L. This property is utilized by multiplying both sides of equation (8.108) by any other function from the set $[\sin(m\pi x/L)]$ and integrating the result from 0 to L. Thus

$$\int_0^L f_0(x) \sin \frac{m\pi x}{L} \, dx = \sum_{n=1}^{\infty} \int_0^L A_n \sin \frac{n\pi x}{L} \sin \frac{m\pi x}{L} \, dx$$

$$= \int_0^L A_m \left[\sin \frac{m\pi x}{L} \right]^2 dx \qquad (8.109)$$

by using the orthogonality property (8.82). Evaluating the final integral in equation (8.109) gives

$$A_m = \frac{2}{L} \int_0^L f_0(x) \sin \frac{m\pi x}{L} \, dx \qquad (8.110)$$

which can be evaluated from the known initial distribution $f_0(x)$. Substitution of the value given by equation (8.110) into equation (8.106) gives the final solution

$$T = \sum_{n=1}^{\infty} \frac{2}{L} \sin \frac{n\pi x}{L} \int_0^L f_0(x) \sin \frac{n\pi x}{L} \, dx \, e^{-n^2\pi^2\alpha t/L^2} \qquad (8.111)$$

It is convenient to introduce the nomenclature of the method in relationship to the above calculation. The method relies upon the feasibility of separating the variable dependence as in equation (8.93) so that a "separation constant" $(-\lambda)$ can be introduced. This constant can be zero, positive, negative or even complex, and the choice is usually made on a physical basis. The λ used in the above calculation has to be real and positive to make the solution of equation (8.95) physically reasonable. Thus equation (8.97) gives the time dependence of the particular solution as a decaying exponential for positive values of λ. If λ were complex, its real part would have to be positive to control the temperature at large times, and its imaginary part would introduce hyperbolic functions into equation (8.101). The hyperbolic cosine term would be removed by condition (8.102) and the hyperbolic sine term by condition (8.103). Hence only real positive values of λ are permitted by the boundary conditions. It is not always possible to substitute the right form for the constant initially, but the right form is usually apparent at a later stage. In most of the illustrations of the method in this book, the most convenient form will be chosen at the start for ease of presentation, although in an actual problem this form would not be known.

Any other constant (such as α in the above problem) is normally transferred to the simpler side of the separated equation (8.93) for algebraic convenience. When the equivalent of equation (8.104) is reached, the separation constant is usually restricted to an infinite number of discrete values which can be labelled by an integer suffix. Thus

$$\lambda_n = (n\pi/L)^2 \tag{8.112}$$

and these are called the "eigen-values" of the problem because they are the only permitted values of the separation constant. The functions arising from the eigen-values are called the "eigen-functions".

By comparing the ordinary differential equation and its boundary conditions which determine the eigen-values with the conditions given in Section 8.6.1, the orthogonality of the eigen-functions can be proved without the necessity of performing the integrations. Hence, the last set of arbitrary constants is determined by the orthogonality property.

8.7.2. *Steady State Heat Transfer with Axial Symmetry*

Laplace's equation in spherical polar coordinates with axial symmetry was derived in Section 8.3.2 for the analogous process of mass transfer in the more general case in which fluid velocity was allowed. Putting $u = v = 0$, removing the time deriving from equation (8.52), and replacing c by T gives

$$\frac{\partial}{\partial r}\left(r^2 \frac{\partial T}{\partial r}\right) + \frac{1}{\sin\theta}\frac{\partial}{\partial\theta}\left(\sin\theta\frac{\partial T}{\partial\theta}\right) = 0$$

or
$$r^2\frac{\partial^2 T}{\partial r^2} + 2r\frac{\partial T}{\partial r} + \frac{\partial^2 T}{\partial\theta^2} + \cot\theta\frac{\partial T}{\partial\theta} = 0 \tag{8.113}$$

Looking for solutions of the form

$$T = f(r)\,g(\theta) \tag{8.114}$$

by substituting into equation (8.113) gives

$$r^2 f''g + 2rf'g + fg'' + \cot\theta fg' = 0 \tag{8.115}$$

Dividing by fg and separating the variables gives

$$\frac{r^2 f'' + 2rf'}{f} = -\frac{g'' + \cot\theta g'}{g} = l(l+1) \tag{8.116}$$

The conventional choice of separation constant in this case is $l(l+1)$ for convenience of presentation. λ can be chosen, but the algebra becomes formidable and the above form of separation constant is then derived in the argument leading to equation (8.132). The first part of equation (8.116) is

$$r^2\frac{d^2f}{dr^2} + 2r\frac{df}{dr} - l(l+1)f = 0 \tag{8.117}$$

which is linear and homogeneous with a solution of the form

$$f = Ar^n \tag{8.118}$$

$$\therefore \quad n(n-1)Ar^n + 2nAr^n - l(l+1)Ar^n = 0$$

$$\therefore \quad n^2 + n - l^2 - l = 0$$

$$\therefore \quad (n-l)(n+l+1) = 0$$

$$\therefore \quad f = Ar^l + Br^{-l-1} \tag{8.119}$$

which partially explains the choice of separation constant.

The second part of equation (8.116) can be written

$$\frac{d^2g}{d\theta^2} + \cot\theta \frac{dg}{d\theta} + l(l+1)g = 0 \tag{8.120}$$

Because of the product $\sin\theta \, d\theta$ in the denominator of the second term, it is convenient to change the dependent variable by putting

$$m = \cos\theta \quad \text{and} \quad dm = -\sin\theta \, d\theta \tag{8.121}$$

Hence,

$$(1-m^2)\frac{d^2g}{dm^2} - 2m\frac{dg}{dm} + l(l+1)g = 0 \tag{8.122}$$

which is known as "Legendre's equation of order l". This has to be solved by the method of Frobenius given in Chapter 3. Thus let

$$g = \sum_0^\infty a_n m^{n+c}$$

$$\therefore \quad (1-m^2)\sum_0^\infty (n+c)(n+c-1)a_n m^{n+c-2} -$$

$$- 2m\sum_0^\infty (n+c)a_n m^{n+c-1} + l(l+1)\sum_0^\infty a_n m^{n+c} = 0 \tag{8.123}$$

The indicial equation is found by equating coefficients of m^{c-2}, hence

$$c(c-1)a_0 = 0$$

$$\therefore \quad c = 0 \text{ or } 1 \tag{8.124}$$

Equating coefficients of m^{c-1} gives

$$(c+1)ca_1 = 0$$

$$\therefore \quad c = 0 \quad \text{or} \quad a_1 = 0 \tag{8.125}$$

The recurrence relation obtained by equating coefficients of m^{c+s} is

$$(s+c+2)(s+c+1)a_{s+2} = (s+c-l)(s+c+l+1)a_s \tag{8.162}$$

The roots of the indicial equation differ by an integer, but since a_1 is indeterminate when $c = 0$, the solution falls into case IIIb and the method yields two normal ascending power series solutions. As stated in Section 3.5.5, the complete solution can be obtained in this case by putting $c = 0$

K

and leaving a_0 and a_1 as the arbitrary constants. Thus, the recurrence relation (8.126) becomes

$$(s+2)(s+1)a_{s+2} = (s-l)(s+l+1)a_s \tag{8.127}$$

Putting $s = 2p$ will give the recurrence relation governing the series multiplied by a_0, and putting $s = 2p+1$ will give the other series multiplied by a_1. Thus

$$(2p+2)(2p+1)a_{2p+2} = (2p-l)(2p+l+1)a_{2p} \tag{8.128}$$

and

$$(2p+3)(2p+2)a_{2p+3} = (2p-l+1)(2p+l+2)a_{2p+1} \tag{8.129}$$

If the solutions are to be useful, they must be convergent at all points in space, and in particular the series must be convergent when $\theta = 0$, i.e. $m = 1$. The ratio of successive terms of the series defined by equation (8.128) when $m = 1$ is given by

$$\frac{u_n}{u_{n+1}} = \frac{(2n+2)(2n+1)}{(2n-l)(2n+l+1)} \tag{8.130}$$

where the symbolism of Chapter 3 has been introduced and the terms have been renumbered. After some algebra, equation (8.130) can be put in a form suitable for Gauss' test (Section 3.2.5) thus

$$\frac{u_n}{u_{n+1}} = \frac{4n^2+6n+2}{4n^2+2n-l^2-l}$$

$$= 1 + \frac{1}{n} + \frac{f(n)}{n^2}$$

where

$$f(n) = \frac{l^2n^2 + ln^2 + l^2n + ln}{4n^2+2n-l^2-l} \tag{8.131}$$

As $n \to \infty$, $f(n) \to \frac{1}{4}l(l+1)$ which is finite. Hence the series is divergent by Gauss' test. Similarly, it can be proved that the series defined by equation (8.129) is divergent and thus both solutions are physically unreasonable for general values of l. However, there are special values of l which are exceptions to the above analysis, and these provide the solutions.

Suppose $l = 1$. Then equation (8.129) with $p = 0$ gives

$$(3)(2)a_3 = (0)(3)a_1$$

i.e.

$$a_3 = 0$$

$$\therefore \quad a_5 = a_7 = a_9 = \ldots = 0$$

Hence, when $l = 1$, $g = a_1m$ is a solution of equation (8.122). This can easily be verified by substitution, and the solution is finite when $m = 1$. The solution is thus physically reasonable.

It can readily be seen that if l is an odd integer, there will be a value of p making the right-hand side of equation (8.129) zero and thus giving a polynomial of finite degree. Similarly, if l is any even integer, there will be a value of p making the right-hand side of equation (8.128) zero with similar effect. These solutions are called the "Legendre polynomials" and are given the symbol $P_l(m)$. The solution of equation (8.122) is thus

$$g = AP_l(m) + BQ_l(m) \tag{8.132}$$

where $Q_l(m)$ denotes the infinite series. It is as well to remember that this solution exists mathematically, but it is invariably unreasonable on physical grounds and it will be rejected at this stage.

Combining equations (8.119) and (8.132) according to equation (8.114) gives the particular solution

$$T = (A_l r^l + B_l r^{-l-1}) P_l(\cos \theta) \tag{8.133}$$

Again, any number of these solutions can be superposed for integer values of l giving

$$T = \sum_{l=0}^{\infty} (A_l r^l + B_l r^{-l-1}) P_l(\cos \theta) \tag{8.134}$$

Equation (8.122) can be written in the form

$$\frac{d}{dm}\left[(1-m^2)\frac{dg}{dm}\right] + l(l+1)g = 0 \tag{8.135}$$

which shows that it is of Sturm-Liouville type with unit weighting function. The function $p(m) = 1 - m^2$ is zero at both limits of integration (-1 and $+1$) and thus the solutions in this range will be orthogonal for any boundary conditions as shown by equation (8.85). Hence the Legendre polynomials are orthogonal with respect to unity in the range from -1 to $+1$.

A convenient way of deriving the polynomials is given by Rodrigue's formula

$$P_n(x) = \frac{1}{2^n n!}\frac{d^n}{dx^n}(x^2-1)^n \tag{8.136}$$

which gives

$$\left.\begin{array}{ll} P_0(x) = 1 & P_2(x) = \tfrac{1}{2}(3x^2-1) \\[2mm] P_1(x) = x & P_3(x) = \tfrac{1}{2}(5x^3-3x) \\[2mm] \text{etc.} \end{array}\right\} \tag{8.137}$$

for the first few polynomials.

Example 1. Two concentric spherical metallic shells of radii a and b (where $b > a$), are separated by a solid thermal insulator. The inner shell is kept at a constant uniform temperature T_1 by a steady distributed source of heat. The temperature on the outer shell is found experimentally to vary with angular distribution from a fixed point on the surface. The distribution can be specified as

$$T = T_2 + T_3 \cos \theta + T_4 \cos^2 \theta$$

How should T_1, T_2, T_3, and T_4 be plotted against heat input so that the thermal conductivity of the insulator can be found from a straight line plot of results for different rates of heat input?

The relevant differential equation is Laplace's equation with axial symmetry in spherical polar coordinates (8.113). This equation has just been solved in terms of Legendre polynomials to give the solution

$$T = \sum_{l=0}^{\infty} (A_l r^l + B_l r^{-l-1}) P_l(\cos \theta) \qquad (8.134)$$

The boundary conditions given in the problem are:

at $r = a$, $T = T_1 = T_1 P_0(\cos \theta)$ I

at $r = b$, $T = T_2 + T_3 \cos \theta + T_4 \cos^2 \theta$

$$= \tfrac{2}{3} T_4 P_2(\cos \theta) + T_3 P_1(\cos \theta) + (T_2 + \tfrac{1}{3} T_4) P_0(\cos \theta) \qquad \text{II}$$

by using equations (8.137). Putting these boundary conditions into equation (8.134) gives

$$\sum_{l=0}^{\infty} (A_l a^l + B_l a^{-l-1}) P_l(\cos \theta) = T_1 P_0(\cos \theta) \qquad \text{III}$$

$$\sum_{l=0}^{\infty} (A_l b^l + B_l b^{-l-1}) P_l(\cos \theta)$$

$$= (T_2 + \tfrac{1}{3} T_4) P_0(\cos \theta) + T_3 P_1(\cos \theta) + \tfrac{2}{3} T_4 P_2(\cos \theta) \qquad \text{IV}$$

Multiplying both sides of equations III and IV by $P_n(\cos \theta) d(\cos \theta)$, integrating over the range $0 \leqslant \theta \leqslant \pi$, and using the orthogonality property of the Legendre polynomials amounts to the same thing as equating coefficients of the same polynomials in equations III and IV. For example, multiplying by $P_1(\cos \theta) d(\cos \theta)$ and integrating would remove all terms from both sides except those which already contained $P_1(\cos \theta)$. Hence,

$$A_0 + B_0 a^{-1} = T_1 \qquad \text{V}$$

$$A_l a^l + B_l a^{-l-1} = 0 \quad (\text{for } l > 0) \qquad \text{VI}$$

$$A_0 + B_0 b^{-1} = T_2 + \tfrac{1}{3} T_4 \qquad \text{VII}$$

$$A_1 b + B_1 b^{-2} = T_3 \qquad \text{VIII}$$

$$A_2 b^2 + B_2 b^{-3} = \tfrac{2}{3} T_4 \qquad \text{IX}$$

$$A_l b^l + B_l b^{-l-1} = \qquad (\text{for } l > 2) \qquad \text{X}$$

Although there are an infinite number of equations and unknowns in the above set, they can be solved in pairs. Thus equations V and VII can be solved for A_0 and B_0, and equation VI with $l = 1$ and equation VIII can be solved for A_1 and B_1. Rather than complete the algebra at this stage, it is more efficient to find the required answer in terms of A_l and B_l, then solve sufficient of equations V to X for the constants required.

The rate at which the solid conducts heat away from the sphere of radius a is given by

$$Q = -k \int_0^{\pi} 2\pi a^2 \left(\frac{\partial T}{\partial r} \right)_{r=a} \sin \theta \, d\theta \qquad \text{XI}$$

Differentiating equation (8.134) with respect to r and substituting into equation XI gives

$$Q = -2\pi k a^2 \int_0^\pi \sum_{l=0}^\infty [lA_l a^{l-1} - (l+1)B_l a^{-l-2}]P_l(\cos\theta)\sin\theta\,d\theta$$

$$= -2\pi k a^2 \sum_{l=0}^\infty [lA_l a^{l-1} - (l+1)B_l a^{-l-2}] \int_{-1}^{+1} P_l(m)\,dm \qquad \text{XII}$$

But the integral occurring in equation XII is the orthogonality integral if $P_0(m) = 1$ is inserted into it. Therefore, all terms after the first are zero in the series in equation XII.

$$\therefore \quad Q = 4\pi k\, B_0 \qquad \text{XIII}$$

and hence only B_0 need be determined from the set of equations V to X. Thus

$$A_0 + B_0 a^{-1} = T_1$$

$$A_0 + B_0 b^{-1} = T_2 + \tfrac{1}{3}T_4$$

$$\therefore \quad B_0(a^{-1} - b^{-1}) = T_1 - T_2 - \tfrac{1}{3}T_4$$

$$\therefore \quad B_0 = \frac{ab}{b-a}(T_1 - T_2 - \tfrac{1}{3}T_4) \qquad \text{XIV}$$

Substituting into equation XIII gives

$$Q = \frac{4\pi k ab}{b-a}(T_1 - T_2 - \tfrac{1}{3}T_4) \qquad \text{XV}$$

Therefore, if Q is plotted as ordinate and $(T_1 - T_2 - \tfrac{1}{3}T_4)$ as abscissa, for a variety of heat supply rates, the gradient will be $4\pi k ab/(b-a)$ from which the thermal conductivity (k) can be evaluated.

8.7.3. Equations Involving Three Independent Variables

The steady state flow of heat in a cylinder is governed by Laplace's equation in cylindrical polar coordinates (7.125)

$$\frac{\partial^2 T}{\partial\omega^2} + \frac{1}{\omega}\frac{\partial T}{\partial\omega} + \frac{1}{\omega^2}\frac{\partial^2 T}{\partial\theta^2} + \frac{\partial^2 T}{\partial z^2} = 0 \qquad (8.138)$$

where there are three independent variables ω, θ, and z. This equation has to be solved in stages and solutions are first sought in the form

$$T = f(\omega, \theta)\cdot g(z) \qquad (8.139)$$

Substituting this form into equation (8.138) gives

$$\frac{\partial^2 f}{\partial\omega^2}g + \frac{1}{\omega}\frac{\partial f}{\partial\omega}g + \frac{1}{\omega^2}\frac{\partial^2 f}{\partial\theta^2}g + fg'' = 0$$

Dividing by fg and separating the terms dependent upon z,

$$\frac{1}{f}\left[\frac{\partial^2 f}{\partial\omega^2} + \frac{1}{\omega}\frac{\partial f}{\partial\omega} + \frac{1}{\omega^2}\frac{\partial^2 f}{\partial\theta^2}\right] = \frac{-g''}{g} = -v^2 \qquad (8.140)$$

where $-v^2$ is the chosen separation constant. Each side of equation (8.140) must still be constant because a function of ω and θ is equated to a function of z only.

The second half of equation (8.140) gives

$$\frac{d^2g}{dz^2} - v^2 g = 0 \tag{8.141}$$

which has the solution

$$g = A_v e^{vz} + B_v e^{-vz} \tag{8.142}$$

The other half of equation (8.140) gives the partial differential equation

$$\omega^2 \frac{\partial^2 f}{\partial \omega^2} + \omega \frac{\partial f}{\partial \omega} + \frac{\partial^2 f}{\partial \theta^2} + \omega^2 v^2 f = 0 \tag{8.143}$$

which has only two independent variables. Applying the method of separation of variables again, by looking for solutions of the type

$$f(\omega, \theta) = F(\omega) \cdot G(\theta) \tag{8.144}$$

$$\therefore \quad \omega^2 F''G + \omega F'G + FG'' + \omega^2 v^2 FG = 0 \tag{8.145}$$

Dividing by FG and separating the variables gives

$$\frac{\omega^2 F'' + \omega F'}{F} + \omega^2 v^2 = \frac{-G''}{G} = k^2 \tag{8.146}$$

Solving the second part as before gives

$$G = A_k \cos k\theta + B_k \sin k\theta \tag{8.147}$$

The first part of equation (8.146) gives

$$\omega^2 F'' + \omega F' + (\omega^2 v^2 - k^2)F = 0$$

Changing the variable by substituting

$$\omega v = x \tag{8.148}$$

$$\therefore \quad x^2 \frac{d^2 F}{dx^2} + x \frac{dF}{dx} + (x^2 - k^2)F = 0 \tag{8.149}$$

which is the standard form of Bessel's equation (3.48).

The most convenient form has been chosen for both separation constants, and k must be an integer for the trigonometrical functions in equation (8.147) to be cyclic with period 2π. The boundary conditions usually make v real as chosen. Equation (8.149) has the solution

$$F = AJ_k(x) + BY_k(x) \tag{8.150}$$

but at the axis of the cylinder, $Y_k(x) = Y_k(v\omega)$ is infinite and thus $B = 0$ on physical grounds. Combining equations (8.142, 147, 150) gives the particular solution

$$T = (A_v e^{vz} + B_v e^{-vz}) \cos(k\theta + \varepsilon)J_k(v\omega) \tag{8.151}$$

Solutions of this type can be superposed for integer values of k, and values of v permitted by the boundary conditions, which involves a double summation.

Bessel's equation (8.149) can be rewritten as

$$\frac{d}{dx}\left(x\frac{dF}{dx}\right) + (x - k^2 x^{-1})F = 0$$

which is of Sturm-Liouville type with a weighting function $(1/x)$. The range of integration is dependent upon v because of equation (8.148) and it is not useful to proceed further with the general case. However, for suitable boundary conditions, the eigen-functions will be orthogonal because equation (8.149) is of Sturm-Liouville type.

8.7.4. *General Use of the Orthogonality Property*

If the separated partial differential equation is of Sturm-Liouville type (8.83) and the boundary conditions are suitable, the solution of the complete partial differential equation takes the form

$$T = a_0 f_0(t)\phi_0(x) + a_1 f_1(t)\phi_1(x) + \ldots + a_n f_n(t)\phi_n(x) + \ldots \qquad (8.152)$$

where t is the other independent variable and $\phi_n(x)$ are orthogonal. The other boundary condition will be given at a fixed value of t (say $t = 0$, $T = f(x)$). Therefore

$$f(x) = A_0\phi_0(x) + A_1\phi_1(x) + \ldots + A_n\phi_n(x) + \ldots \qquad (8.153)$$

Multiplying equation (8.153) by $r(x)\phi_m(x)$ and integrating to generate the orthogonality integrals gives

$$\int_a^b r(x)f(x)\phi_m(x)\,dx = \int_a^b \sum_{n=0}^{\infty} A_n\phi_n(x)r(x)\phi_m(x)\,dx \qquad (8.154)$$

But all terms in the infinite sum are zero except the term when $n = m$. Hence

$$\int_a^b r(x)f(x)\phi_m(x)\,dx = \int_a^b A_m r(x)[\phi_m(x)]^2\,dx$$

or rearranging,

$$A_m = \frac{\displaystyle\int_a^b r(x)f(x)\,\phi_m(x)\,dx}{\displaystyle\int_a^b r(x)[\phi_m(x)]^2\,dx} \qquad (8.155)$$

8.7.5. *Eigen-functions not Orthogonal*

Sometimes the variables will separate in the partial differential equation to give an equation of Sturm-Liouville type, but the boundary conditions are such that the resulting eigen-functions are not orthogonal. If an attempt is made to use the orthogonality relationships, the general equation (8.154) is obtained, but the terms in the infinite sum are not zero. Instead of each equation (8.154) being solvable for A_m, each equation contains all of the A_ms and thus an infinite set of equations, each containing an infinite number of unknowns is obtained. Such a system of equations is normally insoluble and an approximate solution has to be found by assuming that A_7, A_8, ... etc. are all zero and solving the first six equations for the first six coefficients. The accuracy can be improved by taking an increasing number of equations and coefficients, but the effort is rarely worth while and six equations is the normal practical limit. There are however still two ways of finding an exact solution and these are illustrated below.

Example 2. A solid rectangular slab at a uniform temperature T_0 has its four edges thermally insulated. The temperature of one exposed face is raised to and maintained at T_1, whilst the temperature of the other exposed face is held constant at T_0. Find how the temperature distribution varies with time.

Because the edges are insulated, heat will only flow in one direction and equation (8.47) will describe the process. The solution follows the method given in Section 8.7.1 identically until the particular solutions (8.100) and (8.101) arise. The boundary conditions can be written:

at $\qquad\qquad x = 0, \qquad T = T_0 \qquad\qquad$ I

and at $\qquad\qquad x = L, \qquad T = T_1 \qquad\qquad$ II

These do not satisfy the conditons of orthogonality given in Section 8.6.

Substituting equations I and II into the particular solution (8.100) gives

$$T_0 = A_0 \qquad\qquad\qquad\qquad \text{III}$$

$$T_1 = A_0 + B_0 L \qquad\qquad\qquad \text{IV}$$

Hence, the particular solution is

$$T = T_0 + (T_1 - T_0)x/L \qquad\qquad \text{V}$$

and this should be recognized as the steady state solution.

Equation V is now used to define a new variable Z thus,

$$Z = T - T_0 - (T_1 - T_0)x/L \qquad\qquad \text{VI}$$

Substituting into the differential equation (8.47) gives the new equation

$$\alpha \frac{\partial^2 Z}{\partial x^2} = \frac{\partial Z}{\partial t} \qquad\qquad\qquad \text{VII}$$

which is the same as equation (8.47) with T replaced by Z. The boundary conditions I and II become:

at $\qquad\qquad x = 0, \qquad Z = 0 \qquad\qquad$ VIII

and at $\qquad\qquad x = L, \qquad Z = 0 \qquad\qquad$ IX

The equation and boundary conditions in terms of Z are now completely identical with the corresponding equations in Section 8.7.1. Hence, the solution is given by equation (8.111) with T replaced by Z. In the present problem, the final boundary condition that the temperature is T_0 at all points initially becomes

$$Z = -(T_1 - T_0)x/L \quad \text{when } t = 0 \qquad \qquad \text{X}$$

Comparing equation X with equation (8.107) shows that

$$f_0(x) = -(T_1 - T_0)x/L \qquad \qquad \text{XI}$$

$$\therefore \quad \int_0^L f_0(x) \sin \frac{n\pi x}{L} dx = \frac{T_1 - T_0}{n\pi} \left[x \cos \frac{n\pi x}{L} - \int \cos \frac{n\pi x}{L} dx \right]_0^L$$

$$= \frac{T_1 - T_0}{n\pi} [(-1)^n L] \qquad \qquad \text{XII}$$

by integrating by parts and simplifying. Substituting equation XII into the solution (8.111) gives

$$Z = \sum_{n=0}^{\infty} \frac{2}{n\pi} (-1)^n (T_1 - T_0) \sin \frac{n\pi x}{L} e^{-n^2\pi^2 \alpha t/L^2} \qquad \qquad \text{XIII}$$

Returning to the original variables by using equation VI,

$$\frac{T - T_0}{T_1 - T_0} = \frac{x}{L} + \sum_{n=0}^{\infty} \frac{2}{n\pi} (-1)^n \sin \frac{n\pi x}{L} e^{-n^2\pi^2 \alpha t/L^2} \qquad \qquad \text{XIV}$$

The above method, which should be adopted when the boundary conditions I and II will not give an orthogonal set of eigen-functions, involves finding any particular solution (such as V) which satisfies the conditions; and defining a new variable (Z) so that the new solution consists of an orthogonal set of eigen-functions. In this example, the first eigen-function is given by equation V and provided it is removed from the others an orthogonal set remains and the method can be pursued as if it were normal.

Example 3. In the study of flow distribution in a column packed with woven wire gauze,† it has been observed that the liquid tends to aggregate at the walls. If the column is a cylinder of radius b ft and the feed to the column is distributed within a central core of radius a ft with velocity U_0 ft/sec, determine the fractional amount of liquid on the walls as a function of distance from the inlet in terms of the parameters of the system.

The problem is illustrated in Fig. 8.8. where the vertical velocity U ft/sec is considered to be a function of the radial coordinate r and the vertical coordinate z measured from the inlet. It is assumed that a normal diffusion equation

$$V = -D \frac{\partial U}{\partial r} \qquad \qquad \text{I}$$

applies to the velocity distribution. V ft/sec is the horizontal component of fluid velocity and D ft is the coefficient governing the equalization of velocities. D will be a property of the packing and of the particular fluid used.

† Porter, K. E. and Jones, M. C. *Trans. Instn. Chem. Engrs.*, **41**, 240 (1963).

Taking a material balance over the element shown in Fig. 8.8 gives

$$\text{Input} = 2\pi r U \, \delta r - D \frac{\partial U}{\partial r} 2\pi r \, \delta z$$

$$\text{Output} = 2\pi r U \, \delta r + \frac{\partial}{\partial z}(2\pi r U \, \delta r)\delta z - D \frac{\partial U}{\partial r} 2\pi r \, \delta z - \frac{\partial}{\partial r}\left(D \frac{\partial U}{\partial r} 2\pi r \, \delta z\right) \delta r$$

$$\text{Accumulation} = 0$$

$$\therefore \quad \frac{\partial}{\partial z}(2\pi r U \, \delta r)\delta z - \frac{\partial}{\partial r}\left(D \frac{\partial U}{\partial r} 2\pi r \, \delta z\right) \delta r = 0 \qquad\qquad \text{II}$$

$$\therefore \quad r \frac{\partial U}{\partial z} = D \frac{\partial}{\partial r}\left(r \frac{\partial U}{\partial r}\right)$$

$$\therefore \quad \frac{\partial U}{\partial z} = D\left(\frac{\partial^2 U}{\partial r^2} + \frac{1}{r}\frac{\partial U}{\partial r}\right) \qquad\qquad \text{III}$$

FIG. 8.8.   Flow in a packed column

The boundary conditions are as follows.

At $\qquad\qquad\qquad z = 0,\;$ if $\; r < a,\qquad U = U_0$ $\left.\begin{array}{l}\\\\\end{array}\right\}$ IV

$\qquad\qquad\qquad\qquad$ if $\; r > a,\qquad U = 0$

and at $\qquad\qquad\qquad r = 0,\quad U$ must be finite $\qquad\qquad\qquad$ V

The final boundary condition at $r = b$ must allow fluid to accumulate on the walls and a reasonable assumption is that there is a capacity $2\pi bk$ ft^2/ unit length at $r = b$. It is further assumed that fluid which has diffused to the wall is equally distributed in this capacity, so that the same flow rate exists in this fictitious layer on the wall as in the packing in contact with the wall. This condition can be stated symbolically thus,

at $\qquad\qquad r = b, \qquad -D\dfrac{\partial U}{\partial r}\,2\pi b = 2\pi bk\dfrac{\partial U}{\partial z}$

i.e. $\qquad\qquad\qquad\qquad -D\dfrac{\partial U}{\partial r} = k\dfrac{\partial U}{\partial z} \qquad\qquad$ VI

The problem is thus to solve equation III, satisfy the initial condition IV, and satisfy the boundary conditions V and VI. Trying the method of separation of variables by putting

$$U = f(r)\,g(z) \qquad\qquad \text{VII}$$

$$\therefore \quad fg' = D(f''g + f'g/r)$$

Dividing by Dfg gives

$$\frac{g'}{Dg} = \frac{f'' + f'/r}{f} = -\alpha^2 \qquad\qquad \text{VIII}$$

where $-\alpha^2$ is the chosen separation constant. The first part of the equation gives

$$\frac{dg}{dz} + \alpha^2 Dg = 0$$

which has the solution

$$g = A'\,e^{-\alpha^2 Dz} \qquad\qquad \text{IX}$$

indicating that α is real and has been chosen correctly.

The second part of equation VIII gives

$$r^2\frac{d^2f}{dr^2} + r\frac{df}{dr} + \alpha^2 r^2 f = 0 \qquad\qquad \text{X}$$

Equation X can be transformed to the standard form of Bessel's equation (3.48) by putting $x = \alpha r$. The solution is thus

$$= AJ_0(\alpha r) + BY_0(\alpha r) \qquad\qquad \text{XI}$$

if $\alpha \neq 0$, or

$$f = A_0 + B_0 \ln r \qquad\qquad \text{XII}$$

if $\alpha = 0$.

Since $Y_0(0) = -\infty$ and $\ln 0 = -\infty$, boundary condition V asserts that $B_0 = B = 0$. The solutions of equation III are thus

if $\qquad\qquad \alpha = 0, \qquad U = A_0 \qquad\qquad$ XIII

if $\qquad\qquad \alpha \neq 0, \qquad U = A_\alpha J_0(\alpha r)\,e^{-\alpha^2 Dz} \qquad\qquad$ XIV

Boundary condition VI is satisfied by solution XIII, and putting equation XIV into equation VI gives

$$DA_\alpha \alpha J_1(\alpha b)\,e^{-\alpha^2 Dz} = -kA_\alpha \alpha^2 DJ_0(\alpha b)\,e^{-\alpha^2 Dz} \qquad\qquad \text{XV}$$

by using equations (3.88) and (3.97) to differentiate the Bessel function. Simplifying equation XV gives

$$J_1(\alpha_n b) + k\alpha_n J_0(\alpha_n b) = 0 \qquad\qquad \text{XVI}$$

which determines the eigen-values α_n. There are an infinite number of solutions of equation XVI, the first few of which have been tabulated.† The most general solution of equation III is therefore obtained by adding all permissible particular solutions together. Thus

$$U = A_0 + \sum_{n=1}^{\infty} A_n J_0(\alpha_n r) e^{-\alpha_n^2 Dz} \qquad \text{XVII}$$

where the eigen-functions are zero order Bessel functions of the first kind.

It can be shown by rearranging equation X that it is of Sturm-Liouville type with a weighting function r. Boundary condition VI is not one of the types listed in Section 8.6 and hence the eigen-functions will not be orthogonal. Nevertheless, the usual method can be followed by putting $z = 0$ and multiplying equation XVII by $r J_0(\alpha_m r)$ and integrating. This gives

$$\int_0^b U|_{z=0}\, rJ_0(\alpha_m r)\, dr = \int_0^b A_0 rJ_0(\alpha_m r)\, dr + \sum_{n=1}^{\infty} A_n \int_0^b J_0(\alpha_n r)J_0(\alpha_m r)r\, dr \qquad \text{XVIII}$$

It is simpler to evaluate the terms of equation XVIII separately. Thus the first term becomes

$$\int_0^b U|_{z=0}\, rJ_0(\alpha_m r)\, dr = \int_0^a U_0 rJ_0(\alpha_m r)\, dr$$

$$= U_0 aJ_1(\alpha_m a)/\alpha_m \qquad \text{XIX}$$

by using equation (3.88) with $k = 1$. Similarly, the next term gives

$$\int_0^b A_0 rJ_0(\alpha_m r)\, dr = A_0 b\, J_1(\alpha_m b)/\alpha_m$$

$$= A_0\, k\, b\, J_0(\alpha_m b) \qquad \text{XX}$$

Taking a general term with $n \neq m$ from the infinite sum and using equation (3.92) gives

$$A_n \int_0^b J_0(\alpha_n r)J_0(\alpha_m r)r\, dr = \frac{A_n b}{\alpha_n^2 - \alpha_m^2}[\alpha_n J_0(\alpha_m b)J_1(\alpha_n b) - \alpha_m J_0(\alpha_n b)J_1(\alpha_m b)]$$

$$= \frac{A_n b}{\alpha_n^2 - \alpha_m^2}[-k\alpha_n^2 J_0(\alpha_n b)J_0(\alpha_m b) + k\alpha_m^2 J_0(\alpha_n b)J_0(\alpha_m b)]$$

because α_n must satisfy equation XVI. Therefore

$$A_n \int_0^b J_0(\alpha_n r) J_0(\alpha_m r)r\, dr = -k A_n\, b\, J_0(\alpha_n b)J_0(\alpha_m b) \qquad \text{XXI}$$

For the special term in the series when $n = m$, equation (3.93) must be used. Hence

† Crank, J. "The Mathematics of Diffusion." Oxford University Press (1956). Carslaw, H. S. and Jaeger, J. C. "Conduction of Heat in Solids." Oxford University Press (1947).

$$A_m \int_0^b [J_0(\alpha_m r)]^2 r \, dr = \tfrac{1}{2}b^2 A_m[J_0^2(\alpha_m b)+J_1^2(\alpha_m b)]$$

$$= \tfrac{1}{2}b^2 A_m(1+k^2\alpha_m^2)J_0^2(\alpha_m b) \qquad \text{XXII}$$

by using equations (3.97) and XVI.

Combining equations XIX, XX, XXI and XXII into equation XVIII,

$$\frac{U_0 a}{\alpha_m} J_1(\alpha_m a) = -A_0 \, k \, b \, J_0(\alpha_m b)+\tfrac{1}{2}b^2 A_m(1+k^2\alpha_m^2)J_0^2(\alpha_m b)$$

$$- \sum_{n \neq m} k \, A_n \, b \, J_0(\alpha_n b) \, J_0(\alpha_m b) \qquad \text{XXIII}$$

Completing the infinite series by inserting the terms $k \, A_m \, b \, J_0^2(\alpha_m b)$ twice with opposite signs, therefore

$$\frac{U_0 a}{\alpha_m} J_1(\alpha_m a) = -A_0 b \, k \, J_0(\alpha_m b)+\tfrac{1}{2}A_m(b^2+2kb+b^2k^2\alpha_m^2)J_0^2(\alpha_m b)$$

$$- k \, b \, J_0(\alpha_m b) \sum_{n=1}^{\infty} A_n \, J_0(\alpha_n b) \qquad \text{XXIV}$$

But when $z = 0$ and $r = b$, equations IV and XVII give

$$0 = A_0 + \sum_{n=1}^{\infty} A_n J_0(\alpha_n b) \qquad \text{XXV}$$

Because all of the terms in equation XXV occur in equation XXIV with a factor $-kb \, J_0(\alpha_m b)$, then

$$\frac{U_0 a}{\alpha_m} J_1(\alpha_m a) = \tfrac{1}{2}A_m(b^2+2bk+b^2k^2\alpha_m^2)J_0^2(\alpha_m b) \qquad \text{XXVI}$$

which determines A_m. It is both fortunate and unusual that equation XXV eliminates all coefficients except A_m from equation XXIV. The solution by putting A_m from equation XXVI into equation XVII is thus

$$U = A_0 + \sum_{n=1}^{\infty} \frac{2U_0 a}{\alpha_n} \frac{J_1(\alpha_n a) \, J_0(\alpha_n r)}{(b^2+2bk+b^2k^2\alpha_n^2)J_0^2(\alpha_n b)} e^{-\alpha_n^2 Dz} \qquad \text{XXVII}$$

Taking an overall material balance at large values of z,

$$\pi a^2 U_0 = (\pi b^2 + 2\pi bk)A_0$$

$$\therefore \quad a^2 U_0 = b(b+2k)A_0 \qquad \text{XXVIII}$$

Which determines A_0, the equilibrium velocity in the packing.

The fraction of total fluid in the wall layer is given by

$$F = \frac{2\pi bkU}{\pi a^2 U_0}$$

$$= \frac{2k}{b+2k} + \sum_{n=1}^{\infty} \frac{4bk}{a\alpha_n} \frac{J_1(\alpha_n a) e^{-\alpha_n^2 Dz}}{(b^2+2bk+b^2k^2\alpha_n^2)J_0(\alpha_n b)} \qquad \text{XXIX}$$

8.8. The Laplace Transform Method

It was shown in Chapter 6 that a Laplace transformation would remove the derivatives from an ordinary differential equation. It is thus fairly obvious that the same technique can be used to remove all derivatives with respect to one independent variable from a partial differential equation. However, a particular independent variable can only be removed if it has an open range, because the Laplace transformation involves integrating with respect to the variable from zero to infinity. Since the boundary conditions can only be used at the extremities of the range of integration, they must all be imposed at zero. Hence the variable to be transformed must have an open range as described in Section 8.4.5.

If the partial differential equation has two independent variables the removal of one of them yields an ordinary differential equation which can be solved by the methods of Chapter 2. An added complication in the study of partial differential equations is the occurrence of arbitrary constants in the solution of the transformed equation. These constants must be evaluated before the solution is inverted because they are normally functions of the transform parameter as will be seen in the examples. Hence the boundary conditions which are not used to transform the equation must themselves be transformed.

These ideas are better illustrated by solving specific equations, and in the first three examples below, the one dimensional heat conduction equation will be solved again for the same selection of boundary conditions as used in the previous sections of this chapter. This duplicate derivation emphasizes the versatility of the Laplace transformation by determining all of the solutions by one technique instead of using a different method for each specific example. The later examples illustrate the solutions of different partial differential equations.

Example 1. Solutions of the linear heat conduction equation in a semi-infinite medium. Taking the now familiar form of the conduction equation (8.47),

$$\alpha \frac{\partial^2 T}{\partial x^2} = \frac{\partial T}{\partial t}$$

and using the initial condition that

at $\qquad\qquad t = 0, \qquad T = T_0$ $\qquad\qquad$ II

the Laplace transformation can be used to remove the variable t as follows.

Equation (6.11) from Chapter 6 gives

$$\mathscr{L}\left[\frac{\partial T}{\partial t}\right] = s\bar{T} - T_0$$

Because x and t are independent variables, then

$$\mathscr{L}\left[\frac{\partial^2 T}{\partial x^2}\right] = \frac{d^2 \bar{T}}{dx^2}$$

Hence the transform of equation I is

$$\alpha \frac{d^2 \overline{T}}{dx^2} = s\overline{T} - T_0 \qquad\qquad \text{III}$$

Equation III is a second order linear ordinary differential equation having the solution

$$\overline{T} = Ae^{-qx} + Be^{qx} + T_0/s \qquad\qquad \text{IV}$$

where $\qquad\qquad q^2 = s/\alpha \qquad\qquad$ V

has been introduced for simplicity of presentation.

(a) The first problem, solved in Section 8.5.1, involved maintaining the exposed face of the slab at a fixed temperature, i.e.

at $\qquad\qquad x = 0, \qquad T = T_1 \qquad\qquad$ VI

Transforming equation VI gives:

at $\qquad\qquad x = 0, \qquad \overline{T} = T_1/s \qquad\qquad$ VII

As x approaches infinity, T must remain finite, and hence $\overline{T}$ must remain finite. Therefore $B = 0$ and condition VII substituted into equation IV gives

$$\frac{T_1}{s} = A + \frac{T_0}{s}$$

Eliminating A from equation IV gives

$$\overline{T} = (T_1 - T_0)(e^{-\sqrt{s/\alpha} x}/s) + T_0/s \qquad\qquad \text{VIII}$$

Inverting by using transforms 83 and 1 in the table gives

$$T = (T_1 - T_0)\,\text{erfc}\,(x/2\sqrt{\alpha t}) + T_0 \qquad\qquad \text{IX}$$

which can be compared with equation (8.74).

(b) In Section 8.5.2 it was shown that equation (8.78) was the solution expressing the movement of a fixed quantity of heat within a solid body when the heat is initially concentrated at the surface. This solution will now be derived from equation IV.

If all of the heat is at the surface initially, then $T_0 = 0$; and since $B = 0$ to satisfy conditions at infinity, equation IV becomes

$$\overline{T} = Ae^{-qx} \qquad\qquad \text{X}$$

If the total heat content (H) of the body is constant,

$$H = \int_0^\infty \rho C_p T \, dx \qquad\qquad (8.79)$$

Transforming equation (8.79) gives

$$\frac{H}{\rho C_p s} = \int_0^\infty \overline{T} \, dx \qquad\qquad \text{XI}$$

Using equation X for $\bar{T}$ and integrating, therefore

$$\frac{H}{\rho C_p s} = \frac{A}{q} = A\sqrt{\frac{\alpha}{s}} \qquad \text{XII}$$

Eliminating A from equation X gives

$$\bar{T}_i = \frac{H}{\rho C_p \sqrt{\alpha}} \cdot \frac{e^{-\sqrt{s/\alpha}\,x}}{\sqrt{s}} \qquad \text{XIII}$$

This can be inverted by using transform 84 to give

$$T = \frac{H}{\rho C_p \sqrt{\alpha\pi}} t^{-\frac{1}{2}} e^{-x^2/4\alpha t} \qquad \text{XIV}$$

which is identical with equation (8.78) with H given by equation (8.81).

(c) In Example 1 from Section 8.5.2, heat was supplied at a fixed rate to the exposed face and this boundary condition can be expressed by the equation:

at $\qquad\qquad x = 0, \qquad Q = -k\dfrac{\partial T}{\partial x} \qquad\qquad$ XV

Taking the uniform initial temperature as the datum and applying the physical limitation on the temperature at infinite depth, equation IV simplifies to

$$\bar{T} = A e^{-qx} \qquad \text{XVI}$$

Transforming the boundary condition XV,

at $\qquad\qquad x = 0, \qquad \dfrac{-Q}{ks} = \dfrac{\partial \bar{T}}{\partial x} \qquad\qquad$ XVII

Substituting equation XVI into equation XVII gives

$$\frac{-Q}{ks} = -Aq\, e^{-qx} = -Aq$$

$$\therefore \quad A = Q/kqs \qquad \text{XVIII}$$

$$\therefore \quad \bar{T} = \frac{Q\sqrt{\alpha}}{k} s^{-3/2} e^{-\sqrt{s/\alpha}\,x} \qquad \text{XIX}$$

Because integrating a function with respect to t is equivalent to dividing its transform by s, as shown by equation (6.21), equation XIX can be inverted by integrating the function given in transform 84 in the tables. Thus

$$T = \frac{Q\sqrt{\alpha}}{k} \int_0^t \frac{1}{\sqrt{\pi\tau}} e^{-x^2/4\alpha\tau} \, d\tau \qquad \text{XX}$$

which is the same result as that given by equation III in the original example.

At the surface ($x = 0$), equation XX gives

$$T_s = \frac{2Q}{k}\sqrt{\frac{\alpha t}{\pi}} \qquad\qquad \text{XXI}$$

as in Example 1, Section 8.5.2, equation IV.

Example 2. Heat conduction between parallel planes. In Section 8.7.5, the second example considered the flow of heat between parallel planes maintained at different temperatures. The boundary conditions were:

at	$t = 0,$	$T = T_0$	I
at	$x = 0,$	$T = T_0$	II
at	$x = L,$	$T = T_1$	III

Because condition I is the same, the Laplace transformation of equation (8.47) is as above, and the general solution is

$$\overline{T} = A e^{-qx} + B e^{qx} + T_0/s \qquad\qquad \text{IV}$$

where
$$q^2 = s/\alpha \qquad\qquad \text{V}$$

Transforming the boundary conditions II and III gives

at	$x = 0,$	$\overline{T} = T_0/s$	VI
at	$x = L,$	$\overline{T} = T_1/s$	VII

Using these conditions, solving for A and B, and substituting into equation IV gives

$$\overline{T} = \frac{T_1 - T_0}{s} \cdot \frac{e^{qx} - e^{-qx}}{e^{qL} - e^{-qL}} + \frac{T_0}{s} \qquad\qquad \text{VIII}$$

The first term on the right-hand side of equation VIII must be inverted by the method of residues (see Section 6.8) as follows. The denominator is zero when either

$$s = 0 \qquad\qquad \text{IX}$$

or
$$q_n L = in\pi \quad \text{(i.e. } s_n = -\alpha n^2 \pi^2 / L^2) \qquad\qquad \text{X}$$

and all of the above poles are simple poles.
The residue at $s = 0$ is

$$(T_1 - T_0) \lim_{q \to 0} \left[\frac{e^{qx} - e^{-qx}}{e^{qL} - e^{-qL}} \right]$$

which can be evaluated by L'Hôpital's rule to give:

residue at $\qquad s = 0 \quad$ is $(T_1 - T_0)x/L \qquad\qquad$ XI

The simplest method of evaluating the other residues is to express equation VIII in terms of hyperbolic functions and use equation (4.113) from Section 4.16.1. Thus

$$\overline{T} = \frac{T_1 - T_0}{s} \frac{\sinh(\sqrt{s/\alpha}\,x)}{\sinh(\sqrt{s/\alpha}\,L)} + \frac{T_0}{s} \qquad\qquad \text{XII}$$

The residue at s_n is

$$\frac{T_1 - T_0}{s_n} \cdot \frac{\sinh(\sqrt{s_n/\alpha}\,x)}{\cosh(\sqrt{s_n/\alpha}\,L)} \cdot \frac{2\sqrt{s_n}\,\alpha}{L}\, e^{s_n t}$$

or using equation X,

$$\frac{2(T_1 - T_0)}{in\pi} \cdot \frac{\sinh(in\pi x/L)}{\cosh(in\pi)}\, e^{-\alpha n^2 \pi^2 t/L^2} = \frac{2}{n\pi}(T_1 - T_0)(-1)^n \sin\left(\frac{n\pi x}{L}\right) e^{-\alpha n^2 \pi^2 t/L^2}$$

Adding all of the residues together, and inverting the last term by transform 1 in the tables, gives

$$\frac{T - T_0}{T_1 - T_0} = \frac{x}{L} + \sum_{n=0}^{\infty} \frac{2}{n\pi}(-1)^n \sin\frac{n\pi x}{L}\, e^{-n^2 \pi^2 \alpha t/L^2} \qquad\qquad \text{XIII}$$

as in Example 2, Section 8.7.5, equation XIV.

    Example 3. *Symmetrical heat conduction between parallel planes.* The example in Section 8.5.3 again involved the linear heat conduction equation with the boundary conditions:

at $\qquad\qquad\qquad t = 0, \qquad T = 0$ I

at $\qquad\qquad\qquad x = 0, \qquad T = T_0$ II

at $\qquad\qquad\qquad x = L, \qquad \dfrac{\partial T}{\partial x} = 0$ III

Solving as in Example 1 above gives

$$\bar{T} = A e^{-qx} + B e^{qx} \qquad\qquad \text{IV}$$

where $\qquad\qquad\qquad q^2 = s/\alpha$ V

The transformed boundary conditions are

at $\qquad\qquad\qquad x = 0, \qquad \bar{T} = \dfrac{T_0}{s}$ VI

at $\qquad\qquad\qquad x = L, \qquad \dfrac{\partial \bar{T}}{\partial x} = 0$ VII

Using conditions VI and VII to determine A and B in equation IV gives the transformed solution

$$\bar{T} = \frac{T_0}{s} \cdot \frac{(e^{2qL} - 1)e^{-qx} + (1 - e^{-2qL})e^{qx}}{e^{2qL} - e^{-2qL}} \qquad\qquad \text{VIII}$$

This could be inverted by the method of residues as in the last example, but to obtain the error function form given in Section 8.5.3, it is necessary to expand equation VIII in terms of exponential functions. The method is similar to that used in Section 6.7.3 and proceeds thus.

$$\frac{(e^{2qL}-1)e^{-qx}}{e^{2qL}-e^{-2qL}} = e^{-qx}(1-e^{-2qL})(1-e^{-4qL})^{-1}$$

$$= e^{-qx}(1-e^{-2qL})(1+e^{-4qL}+e^{-8qL}+\ldots)$$

$$= e^{-qx}(1-e^{-2qL}+e^{-4qL}-e^{-6qL}+e^{-8qL}-\ldots)$$

$$= \sum_{n=0}^{\infty} (-1)^n e^{-(2nL+x)q} \qquad\qquad\qquad\text{IX}$$

Similarly, it can be shown that

$$\frac{(1-e^{-2qL})e^{qx}}{e^{2qL}-e^{-2qL}} = \sum_{n=0}^{\infty} (-1)^n e^{-(2nL+2L-x)q} \qquad\qquad\text{X}$$

Substituting equations IX and X into VIII, using V and inverting each term by using transform 83 in the tables, gives

$$T = T_0 \sum_{n=0}^{\infty} (-1)^n \{\operatorname{erfc}[(x+2nL)/2\sqrt{\alpha t}] + \operatorname{erfc}[(2nL+2L-x)/2\sqrt{\alpha t}]\} \qquad\text{XI}$$

which agrees with its counterpart in Example 2, Section 8.5.3.

The above solutions of the linear heat conduction equation and the analogous linear diffusion equation are all contained in Crank or Carslaw and Jaeger†, together with many other solutions for different combinations of the four types of boundary condition in the three common coordinate systems. As pointed out by those authors, the error function type of solution arising from the Laplace transform is useful for determining the behaviour of the system in the early stages, but the summation of eigen-functions is more useful for determining the approach to equilibrium in the later stages of the process.

Example 4. *Exploitation of an oilfield.* An extensive shallow oilfield is to be exploited by removing product at a constant rate from one well. How will the pressure distribution in the formation vary with time?

Taking a radial coordinate r measured from the base of the well system it is known that the pressure (p) obeys the normal diffusion equation

$$\frac{\partial^2 p}{\partial r^2} + \frac{1}{r}\frac{\partial p}{\partial r} = \frac{1}{\eta}\frac{\partial p}{\partial t} \qquad\qquad\qquad\text{I}$$

where η is the hydraulic diffusivity.

The initial pressure in the formation is assumed to be uniform at p_0. If oil is removed at a constant rate q, then

$$q = \lim_{r\to 0} \frac{2\pi r k h}{\mu}\frac{\partial p}{\partial r} \qquad\qquad\qquad\text{II}$$

where k is the permeability, h is the thickness of the formation, and μ is the coefficient of viscosity.

† Crank, J. "The Mathematics of Diffusion." Oxford University Press (1956). Carslaw, H. S. and Jaeger, J. C. "Conduction of Heat in Solids." Oxford University Press (1947).

Transforming equation I by the same procedure as given in Example 1

$$\frac{d^2\bar{p}}{dr^2} + \frac{1}{r}\frac{d\bar{p}}{dr} - \frac{s}{\eta}\bar{p} = -\frac{p_0}{\eta} \qquad \text{III}$$

Putting

$$x = r\sqrt{s/\eta} \qquad \text{IV}$$

$$\therefore \quad x^2\frac{d^2\bar{p}}{dx^2} + x\frac{d\bar{p}}{dx} - x^2\bar{p} = -\frac{x^2 p_0}{s} \qquad \text{V}$$

which is the modified form of Bessel's equation (3.64) having the solution

$$\bar{p} = AI_0(x) + BK_0(x) + p_0/s \qquad \text{VI}$$

Equation (3.82) shows that as $x \to \infty$, $I_0(x) \to \infty$ and hence $A = 0$ and

$$\bar{p} = BK_0(x) + p_0/s \qquad \text{VII}$$

Transforming boundary condition II gives

$$\frac{q}{s} = \lim_{r \to 0} \frac{2\pi rkh}{\mu}\frac{d\bar{p}}{dr} \qquad \text{VIII}$$

Using equation (3.71) that $I_0(0) = 1$, and taking the limit of equation (3.68) as $x \to 0$ gives

$$K_0(x) \to -\ln x \qquad \text{IX}$$

Therefore, near the base of the well, equation VII becomes

$$\bar{p} \simeq -B\ln x = -B\ln(r\sqrt{s/\eta}) \qquad \text{X}$$

Substituting into equation VIII, therefore

$$\frac{q}{s} = \lim_{r \to 0} -\frac{2\pi rkh}{\mu}\frac{B}{r} = -\frac{2\pi khB}{\mu} \qquad \text{XI}$$

$$\therefore \quad B = \frac{-\mu q}{2\pi khs} = -\frac{\alpha}{s} \qquad \text{XII}$$

Hence the transformed solution VII becomes

$$\bar{p} = -\alpha\frac{K_0(r\sqrt{s/\eta})}{s} + \frac{p_0}{s} \qquad \text{XIII}$$

Since integration of a function with respect to t is equivalent to dividing its transform by s, as shown by equation (6.21), transform number 117 in the tables enables equation XIII to be inverted, thus

$$p = -\int_0^t \frac{\alpha}{2t}e^{-r^2/4\eta t}\,dt + p_0 \qquad \text{XIV}$$

Putting

$$t = r^2/4\eta z \qquad \text{XV}$$

and hence

$$dt = -\frac{r^2\,dz}{4\eta z^2}$$

$$\therefore \quad p = \int_{\infty}^{z_0} \frac{\alpha}{2z} e^{-z} dz + p_0$$

$$= -\tfrac{1}{2}\alpha \int_{z_0}^{\infty} \frac{e^{-z}}{z} dz + p_0 \qquad \text{XVI}$$

where $z_0 = r^2/4\eta t$. Comparing the integral in equation XVI with equation (5.44), the solution can be written in terms of a tabulated function. Thus

$$p = \frac{\mu q}{4\pi k h} Ei(-r^2/4\eta t) + p_0 \qquad \text{XVII}$$

Example 5. Gas absorption accompanied by a first order reaction in a falling film. A wetted wall column is to be used for the absorption of a gas (A). The gas is consumed in the liquid phase by a pseudo first order reaction in terms of the gas concentration. Develop expressions giving the point absorption rate and effective penetration depth as a function of distance from the liquid inlet.

Figure 8.9 shows a section through the liquid film where z is the distance from the liquid inlet, and x is a coordinate measured inwards from the

Fig. 8.9. Velocity distribution in a falling film

surface of the film which is assumed to be of uniform thickness L. Although it is a poor assumption which depends upon inlet conditions, the parabolic velocity distribution $v(x)$ will be assumed to exist right at the inlet and remain unchanged throughout the length of the column.

The gas is assumed pure so that there will be no gas phase resistance and the surface concentration of A in the liquid will be constant at c_0. For any element of the liquid ($\delta x\,\delta z$) to be in equilibrium, the amount of A carried in the z direction by bulk flow, plus the amount diffusing in the x direction, must be sufficient to supply the chemical reaction proceeding within the element. Expressing this fact symbolically,

Input rate $\qquad = vc\,\delta x - D\dfrac{\partial c}{\partial x}\delta z$

Output rate $\qquad = vc\,\delta x + \dfrac{\partial}{\partial z}(vc\,\delta x)\delta z - D\dfrac{\partial c}{\partial x}\delta z + \dfrac{\partial}{\partial x}\left(-D\dfrac{\partial c}{\partial x}\delta z\right)\delta x$

Consumption rate $\quad = kc\,\delta x\,\delta z$

where c is the concentration of A in the liquid, D is its diffusivity, and k is the specific reaction rate constant. Completing the balance and cancelling appropriate terms gives

$$-v\frac{\partial c}{\partial z} + D\frac{\partial^2 c}{\partial x^2} = kc \qquad\qquad \text{I}$$

Transforming equation I by the method previously explained gives

$$-sv\bar{c} + D\frac{d^2\bar{c}}{dx^2} = k\bar{c}$$

$$\therefore\quad D\frac{d^2\bar{c}}{dx^2} - (k+sv)\bar{c} = 0 \qquad\qquad \text{II}$$

But $v = V(1-x^2/L^2)$ where V is the interfacial velocity, and equation II would have to be integrated using the method of Frobenius to obtain an accurate solution. However, the penetration of A into the liquid will be small for small values of z and as a first approximation it will be assumed that $x \ll L$ so that v can be replaced by V in equation II. Thus

$$D\frac{d^2\bar{c}}{dx^2} - (k+sV)\bar{c} = 0 \qquad\qquad \text{III}$$

which is a linear second order differential equation with constant coefficients having the solution

$$\bar{c} = A'\exp\left(x\sqrt{\frac{k+sV}{D}}\right) + B\exp\left(-x\sqrt{\frac{k+sV}{D}}\right) \qquad\qquad \text{IV}$$

As x increases, the concentration of A must decrease to zero, and hence $A' = 0$. At $x = 0$, the boundary condition gives $c = c_0$

$$\therefore\quad \bar{c} = c_0/s$$

$$\therefore\quad \bar{c} = \frac{c_0}{s}\exp\left[-x\sqrt{\frac{V}{D}\left(s + \frac{k}{V}\right)}\right] \qquad\qquad \text{V}$$

Using transform 82 and the shifting theorem (Section 6.2.2),

$$\mathscr{L}\left[\frac{x}{2}\sqrt{\frac{V}{D\pi z^3}}\exp\left(\frac{-x^2 V}{4Dz}\right)\exp\left(\frac{-kz}{V}\right)\right] = \exp\left[-x\sqrt{\frac{V}{D}\left(s + \frac{k}{V}\right)}\right] \qquad \text{VI}$$

Applying the property given in equation (6.21) to equation VI and inverting equation V gives

$$c = c_0 \int_0^z \frac{x}{2} \sqrt{\frac{V}{D\pi z^3}} \exp\left(-\frac{x^2 V}{4Dz} - \frac{kz}{V}\right) dz \qquad \text{VII}$$

Putting

$$\alpha^2 = x^2 V/4D$$

and

$$\beta^2 = k/V \qquad \text{VIII}$$

to simplify the algebra, gives

$$c = c_0 \int_0^z \frac{\alpha}{\sqrt{(\pi z^3)}} \exp\left(-\frac{\alpha^2}{z} - \beta^2 z\right) dz \qquad \text{IX}$$

It is difficult to evaluate this integral, but its form can be changed by putting

$$r = \frac{\alpha}{\sqrt{z}} - \beta\sqrt{z} \qquad \text{X}$$

and hence

$$r^2 = \frac{\alpha^2}{z} + \beta^2 z - 2\alpha\beta$$

and

$$dr = \left(-\frac{\alpha}{2z^{\frac{3}{2}}} - \frac{\beta}{2z^{\frac{1}{2}}}\right) dz$$

into equation IX to give

$$c = c_0 \int_0^z \frac{2}{\sqrt{\pi}}\left(\frac{\alpha}{2z^{\frac{3}{2}}} + \frac{\beta}{2z^{\frac{1}{2}}} - \frac{\beta}{2z^{\frac{1}{2}}}\right) \exp\left(-r^2 - 2\alpha\beta\right) dz$$

$$= \frac{-2c_0}{\sqrt{\pi}} \int_\infty^r e^{-2\alpha\beta} e^{-r^2} dr - c_0 \beta \int_0^z \frac{1}{\sqrt{\pi z}} \exp\left(-\frac{\alpha^2}{z} - \beta^2 z\right) dz$$

$$\therefore \quad c = c_0 e^{-2\alpha\beta} \operatorname{erfc}\left(\frac{\alpha}{\sqrt{z}} - \beta\sqrt{z}\right) - c_0 \beta \int_0^z \frac{1}{\sqrt{\pi z}} \exp\left(-\frac{\alpha^2}{z} - \beta^2 z\right) dz \quad \text{XI}$$

If the sign of β were reversed in equation IX, the integral would not be altered in any way. Hence the sign of β may be reversed in equation XI without altering the result. Thus

$$c = c_0 e^{2\alpha\beta} \operatorname{erfc}\left(\frac{\alpha}{\sqrt{z}} + \beta\sqrt{z}\right) + c_0 \beta \int_0^z \frac{1}{\sqrt{\pi z}} \exp\left(-\frac{\alpha^2}{z} - \beta^2 z\right) dz \qquad \text{XII}$$

Adding equations XI and XII together, dividing the result by 2 and returning to the original symbols through equation VIII yields the final result

$$\frac{c}{c_0} = \tfrac{1}{2}\exp\left(-x\sqrt{\frac{k}{D}}\right)\operatorname{erfc}\left(\frac{x}{2}\sqrt{\frac{V}{Dz}} - \sqrt{\frac{kz}{V}}\right) +$$

$$+ \tfrac{1}{2}\exp\left(x\sqrt{\frac{k}{D}}\right)\operatorname{erfc}\left(\frac{x}{2}\sqrt{\frac{V}{Dz}} + \sqrt{\frac{kz}{V}}\right) \qquad \text{XIII}$$

The point absorption rate per unit area is given by

$$R = -D\frac{\partial c}{\partial x}\bigg|_{x=0} \qquad \text{XIV}$$

Transforming equation XIV gives

$$\bar{R} = -D\frac{\partial \bar{c}}{\partial x}\bigg|_{x=0} \qquad \text{XV}$$

and substituting for $\bar{c}$ from equation V gives

$$\bar{R} = \frac{Dc_0}{s}\sqrt{\frac{V}{D}\left(s + \frac{k}{V}\right)}$$

$$\therefore \quad \bar{R} = c_0\sqrt{DV}\sqrt{\frac{s+k/V}{s}} \qquad \text{XVI}$$

Inverting equation XVI by using transform 38 and the shifting theorem (Section 6.2.2), therefore

$$R = c_0\sqrt{DV}\,e^{-kz/V}\left[\frac{1}{\sqrt{\pi z}} + \sqrt{\frac{k}{V}}\,e^{kz/V}\operatorname{erf}\sqrt{kz/V}\right]$$

$$\therefore \quad R = c_0\sqrt{kD}\left[\operatorname{erf}\sqrt{kz/V} + \sqrt{V/\pi kz}\exp(-kz/V)\right] \qquad \text{XVII}$$

In order to determine the depth of penetration of the solute, some arbitrary limit must be set for its concentration to be negligible. This limit

Fig. 8.10. Approximation for erfc y

is chosen as $c/c_0 = 0\cdot002$, and equation XIII gives an implicit expression for the penetration depth x as a function of film length z. The relationship is simple enough to solve by trial and error except for small values of z but an approximate solution can be found for this region as follows.

Figure 8.10 shows $(2/\sqrt{\pi})e^{-y^2}$ plotted against y so that erfc y is the shaded area. If y is large it is reasonable to suppose that erfc y is some constant multiple of the area of the triangle formed as shown by the tangent to the curve. Putting

$$h = \frac{2}{\sqrt{\pi}} e^{-y^2} \qquad\qquad \text{XVIII}$$

$$\therefore \quad \frac{dh}{dy} = \frac{-4y}{\sqrt{\pi}} e^{-y^2} = -2yh$$

but from the triangle,

$$\frac{dh}{dy} = \frac{-h}{a}$$

$$\therefore \quad a = \tfrac{1}{2}y \qquad\qquad \text{XIX}$$

The approximation can be written

$$\text{erfc } y = \tfrac{1}{2}Kha \qquad\qquad \text{XX}$$

where K is some proportionality constant greater than unity. Substituting for h and a from equations XVIII and XIX gives

$$\text{erfc } y = \frac{K}{2y\sqrt{\pi}} e^{-y^2} \qquad\qquad \text{XXI}$$

Evaluating K by putting $y = 1\cdot5$ on both sides of equation XXI gives $K = 1\cdot71$. Hence

$$\text{erfc } y \simeq (0\cdot484/y)e^{-y^2} \qquad\qquad \text{XXII}$$

If $y = 2\cdot5$, the error in equation XXII is less than $\tfrac{1}{2}\%$, and if $y = 1$, erfc $y = 0\cdot178$ whereas $(0\cdot484/y)e^{-y^2} = 0\cdot157$. Hence equation XXII should only be used for $y > 1$.

Introducing dimensionless coordinates into equation XIII by putting

$$X = x\sqrt{k/D} \quad \text{and} \quad Z^2 = kz/V \qquad\qquad \text{XXIII}$$

$$\therefore \quad \frac{c}{c_0} = \tfrac{1}{2}e^{-X}\,\text{erfc}\left(\frac{X}{2Z} - Z\right) + \tfrac{1}{2}e^{X}\,\text{erfc}\left(\frac{X}{2Z} + Z\right)$$

Using equation XXII gives

$$\frac{c}{c_0} \simeq \left[\frac{0\cdot242}{\dfrac{X}{2Z} - Z} + \frac{0\cdot242}{\dfrac{X}{2Z} + Z}\right] \exp\left(-\frac{X^2}{4Z^2} - Z^2\right)$$

$$\simeq \frac{0\cdot242X}{Z\left(\dfrac{X^2}{4Z^2} - Z^2\right)} \exp\left(-\frac{X^2}{4Z^2} - Z^2\right)$$

which is valid for

$$\frac{X}{2Z} > 1 + Z \qquad\qquad \text{XXIV}$$

The penetration depth is thus given by

$$0\cdot002\,Z\left(\frac{X^2}{4Z^2} - Z^2\right) = 0\cdot242X\exp\left(-\frac{X^2}{4Z^2} - Z^2\right) \qquad \text{XXV}$$

Solving by trial and error using equation XXV for $Z < 1$ and equation XIII for $Z \geqslant 1$ gives:

Z	0·1	0·5	1·0	1·5	2·0	3·0
X	0·435	2·130	4·00	5·33	6·00	6·215

which is plotted in Fig. 8.11.

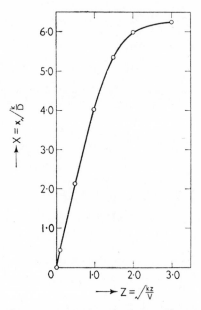

FIG. 8.11.   Relation between penetration of solute and length of wetted wall

8.9. OTHER TRANSFORMS

In the last section, the Laplace transform was shown to be quite versatile, and although the transform involved introducing an exponential function, this did not influence the type of solution obtained. The chief restriction on its use is that the problem must be of initial value type, but provided the dependent variable and its derivative remain finite† as the transformed variable tends to infinity, no analytical difficulties arise. The inversion process is often tedious if the method of residues has to be adopted, but in principle the inversion process can always be completed.

† The method is still applicable when the dependent variable or its derivative become infinite to a finite exponential order, but physical variables never actually take infinite values so there is no restriction.

No reason has been given for using the function e^{-st} as the "kernel" of the Laplace transform and attempts have been made to use other functions as kernels thus giving rise to other transforms. The purpose of the present section is to give the names and formulae for these other transforms and indicate their range of applicability.

8.9.1. *Finite Fourier Transforms*

The finite Fourier sine transform can be derived from the general formula developed in Section 8.7.1 for linear heat conduction. Replacing the boundary condition (8.107) into the general solution (8.111) and dropping the suffix from $f_0(x)$ gives the identity

$$f(x) = \sum_{n=1}^{\infty} \frac{2}{L} \sin \frac{n\pi x}{L} \int_0^L f(x) \sin \frac{n\pi x}{L} dx \qquad (8.156)$$

which is universally true and no longer related to the specific problem of Section 8.7.1. To obtain the conventional notation, put $z = \pi x/L$.

$$\therefore \quad f(z) = \frac{2}{\pi} \sum_{n=1}^{\infty} \sin nz \int_0^\pi f(z) \sin nz \, dz \qquad (8.157)$$

The finite Fourier sine transform is defined as

$$\bar{f}(n) = \int_0^\pi f(z) \sin nz \, dz \qquad (8.158)$$

Equation (8.157) provides the means of inverting the transform. Thus

$$f(z) = \frac{2}{\pi} \sum_{n=1}^{\infty} \bar{f}(n) \sin nz \qquad (8.159)$$

which is very much simpler than the inversion formula for the Laplace transform (6.31).

The most important properties of the finite Fourier sine transform can be determined by transforming a second derivative. Thus,

$$\int_0^\pi \frac{\partial^2 V}{\partial z^2} \sin nz \, dz = \left[\frac{\partial V}{\partial z} \sin nz - n \int \frac{\partial V}{\partial z} \cos nz \, dz \right]_0^\pi \qquad (8.160)$$

Provided the first derivative is finite at both ends of the range (as it will be in practical cases) and since $\sin nz$ vanishes at both ends of the range, then

$$\int_0^\pi \frac{\partial^2 V}{\partial z^2} \sin nz \, dz = -n \int_0^\pi \frac{\partial V}{\partial z} \cos nz \, dz$$

$$= -n \left[V \cos nz + n \int V \sin nz \, dz \right]_0^\pi$$

$$= -n^2 \bar{V} + n[V_0 - (-1)^n V_\pi] \qquad (8.161)$$

Thus the value of the dependent variable must be known at both ends of the range. Little further investigation is needed to show the following severe restrictions on the use of the finite Fourier sine transform.

S(a) The variable to be transformed must have a closed range.
S(b) Type 1 boundary conditions must be given at both ends of the range.
S(c) All derivatives to be transformed must be of even order.

Similarly, a finite Fourier cosine transform can be defined by

$$\bar{f}(n) = \int_0^\pi f(z) \cos nz\, dz \tag{8.162}$$

and inverted by

$$f(z) = \frac{1}{\pi}\bar{f}(0) + \frac{2}{\pi}\sum_{n=1}^\infty \bar{f}(n) \cos nz \tag{8.163}$$

but again the following restrictions apply.

C(a) The variable to be transformed must have a closed range.
C(b) Type 2 boundary conditions must be given at both ends of the range.
C(c) All derivatives to be transformed must be of even order.

8.9.2. *Fourier Transforms*

Equation (8.156) can be written

$$f(x) = \sum_{n=1}^\infty 2\sin\frac{n\pi x}{L} \int_0^L f(x) \sin\frac{n\pi x}{L}\, dx\, \delta\left(\frac{n}{L}\right) \tag{8.164}$$

where $\delta n = 1$. Putting $p = n\pi/L$ and taking the limit as $L \to \infty$, then $\delta(n\pi/L) \to dp$ and the sum becomes an integral in terms of the "continuous" variable p. Thus

$$f(x) = \frac{2}{\pi}\int_0^\infty \sin px \left(\int_0^\infty f(x) \sin px\, dx\right) dp \tag{8.165}$$

The Fourier sine transform is defined by

$$\bar{f}(p) = \int_0^\infty f(x) \sin px\, dx \tag{8.166}$$

and equation (8.165) gives the inversion formula

$$f(x) = \frac{2}{\pi}\int_0^\infty \bar{f}(p) \sin px\, dp \tag{8.167}$$

This transform is mathematically elegant because the same formula (except for a constant $2/\pi$) is used both for forming the transform and for inverting it. Although the Fourier sine transform is less restricted than the finite transform, it does not overcome all of the difficulties. If an attempt is made to remove a second derivative as in equation (8.160) with the upper limit changed, the term $(\partial V/\partial z) \sin pz$ oscillates boundedly as z increases indefinitely unless $(\partial V/\partial z) \to 0$ as $z \to \infty$. Hence the Fourier sine transform has the following limitations.

(i) The variable to be transformed must have an open range.
(ii) A type 1 boundary condition must be given at the lower limit.
(iii) The dependent variable and its derivative must vanish as $z \to \infty$.
(iv) All derivatives to be transformed must be of even order.

Similarly, a Fourier cosine transform can be defined by

$$\bar{f}(p) = \int_0^\infty f(x) \cos px \, dx \tag{8.168}$$

and inverted by

$$f(x) = \frac{2}{\pi} \int_0^\infty \bar{f}(p) \cos px \, dp \tag{8.169}$$

but the same restrictions as given above for the Fourier sine transform apply, except that the boundary condition at the lower limit must be type 2.

The more general complex Fourier transform is defined by

$$\bar{f}(p) = \int_{-\infty}^\infty f(x) e^{ipx} \, dx \tag{8.170}$$

and inverted by

$$f(x) = \frac{1}{2\pi} \int_{-\infty}^\infty \bar{f}(p) e^{ipx} \, dp \tag{8.171}$$

This transform is not so severely restricted in application because derivatives of any order can be removed by its use, but it does not allow boundary conditions to be used at all! It is thus useful for general problems, but for specific practical problems it is virtually useless.

8.9.3. *Hankel and Mellin Transforms*

When the next two transforms are used, it is usually to remove the radial coordinate from a system of cylindrical polar coordinates, and because the integrals range from zero to infinity, they can only be applied to axisymmetrical disturbances in infinite media.

The Hankel transform is defined by

$$\bar{f}(p) = \int_0^\infty f(x) \, x \, J_n(px) \, dx \tag{8.172}$$

and inverted by the symmetrical formula

$$f(x) = \int_0^\infty \bar{f}(p) \, p \, J_n(px) \, dp \qquad (8.173)$$

where $J_n(px)$ is the Bessel function of the first kind of order n.

The Mellin transform is defined by

$$\bar{f}(p) = \int_0^\infty f(x) \, x^{p-1} \, dx \qquad (8.174)$$

and inverted by

$$f(x) = \frac{1}{2\pi i} \int_{\gamma - i\infty}^{\gamma + i\infty} \bar{f}(p) \, x^{-p} \, dp \qquad (8.175)$$

which has certain similarities with the inversion formula for the Laplace transform.

8.10. CONCLUSIONS

The methods given in Section 8.5 are useful for finding isolated particular solutions of partial differential equations, but these solutions are unlikely to satisfy the desired boundary conditions. If the boundary conditions are of type 1, or vanishing derivative type 2, then the method of images can be very useful for generating a more general solution. The most powerful methods for finding solutions are undoubtedly the separation of variables (Section 8.7) and the Laplace transform (Section 8.8). Due to its versatility, the Laplace transform should be tried whenever a variable has an open range, and the method of separation of variables should be used in all other cases, including those in which the Laplace transform has been tried and found to be inconvenient. There are many partial differential equations which cannot be solved by either method, and the numerical methods described in Chapter 11 are recommended for these.

The other transform methods of Section 8.9 are specialized in that the four real Fourier transforms are only capable of removing derivatives of even order, and cannot solve any problem in which there is either a mixture of type 1 and type 2 boundary conditions, or a type 3 condition. The complex Fourier transform can be taken without reference to boundary conditions and is thus only suitable for problems in which a variable can alter throughout its entire range from $-\infty$ to $+\infty$ without crossing a boundary. The use of other transforms such as the Hankel or Mellin transform is only advantageous when cylindrical polar coordinates would normally be used for stating the problem. It is not efficient for an engineer to try and learn the characteristics of all of these transforms when most problems requiring their use can be solved conveniently by using the Laplace transform. The reader is therefore recommended to familiarize himself with the Laplace transform, and turn to the other transforms later if he so desires.

Chapter 9

FINITE DIFFERENCES

9.1. INTRODUCTION

CHEMICAL processes involving separation, purification and chemical reactions are frequently carried out in a series of stages, and these processes are often analysed by stage to stage calculations or in the simpler examples by graphical methods. Thus distillation, gas absorption and extraction operations performed in plate columns involve stepwise changes in the concentration of each phase as it passes from plate to plate. In particular, in a distillation column, the vapours leaving any plate differ in composition from the vapours entering the same plate by a finite amount, thus an abrupt change in the vapour composition occurs on the plate. Therefore, in contrast with a packed distillation column where the vapour composition changes continuously throughout the packed height and where the height of the packing is estimated from the solution of a differential equation, a plate column should be analysed in such a way that these abrupt finite changes enter into the analysis. This is possible by finite difference calculus and in particular by the solution of finite difference equations; as will be shown in this chapter.

9.2. THE DIFFERENCE OPERATOR, Δ

Considering an independent variable x which can take a number of discrete values x_0; $(x_0 + h)$; $(x_0 + 2h)$; etc., then any function $y = f(x)$ will take a corresponding set of values

$$y_0; y_1; y_2; \cdots y_n$$

From this series of values of the dependent variable y, a series of differences can be constructed as follows.

$$y_1 - y_0; y_2 - y_1; y_3 - y_2; \cdots y_n - y_{n-1}$$

This series can be written in the form

$$\Delta y_0; \Delta y_1; \Delta y_2; \cdots \Delta y_{n-1}$$

where $$\Delta y_0 = y_1 - y_0 = f(x_0 + h) - f(x_0) = \Delta f(x_0) \quad (9.1)$$

Δy is called the "first difference" of y with respect to h. The symbol "Δ" is called the difference operator, and has meaning only when applied to a function of a given independent variable with reference to a specific increment h. In fact writing Δ before a variable or function takes a lot on trust. A more precise representation would be $\Delta^1_{x,h}$ implying that the differencing

307

operation has been applied once to a function of an independent variable x through an increment h. However, it is seldom necessary to make these additions to Δ as both x and h would be clearly understood in a particular problem. Since it is possible to repeat the differencing operation, the number just above and on the right of Δ should be inserted for all differences greater than the first. Thus Δ^2 would be the second difference of a variable or function, and Δ^n would be the nth difference. These will be discussed more fully below.

9.2.1. *Properties of the Difference Operator* Δ

Let there be another function of the independent variable x that has discrete values at x_0; (x_0+h); etc., and let this function be expressed as

$$z = \phi(x) \tag{9.2}$$

Then the series of first differences of z can be written

$$z_1-z_0; \, z_2-z_1; \, z_3-z_2; \, \ldots; \, z_n-z_{n-1}$$

or in difference form

$$\Delta z_0; \, \Delta z_1; \, \Delta z_2; \, \Delta z_3 \ldots \, ; \, \Delta z_{n-1}$$

where

$$\Delta z_0 = z_1-z_0 = \phi(x_0+h)-\phi(x_0) \tag{9.3}$$

Adding equations (9.1) and (9.3) gives

$$\Delta y_0 + \Delta z_0 = (y_1-y_0)+(z_1-z_0) = (y_1+z_1)-(y_0+z_0) = \Delta(y_0+z_0) \tag{9.4}$$

or more generally

$$\Delta(y_n+z_n) = \Delta y_n+\Delta z_n \tag{9.5}$$

That is, Δ obeys the "distributive law of algebra".

If k is a finite constant

$$\Delta(ky_n) = ky_{n+1} - ky_n = k\Delta y_n \tag{9.6}$$

so that k and Δ can be interchanged without altering the result. That is, Δ obeys the "commutative law of algebra" with regard to constants.

Finally, Δ obeys the "index law of algebra". That is

$$\Delta^{p+q} = \Delta^p\Delta^q = \Delta^q\Delta^p \tag{9.7}$$

This will be further explained below.

9.2.2. *Differences of Second and Higher Orders*

In Section 9.2 a sequence of first differences of the function $y = f(x)$ was constructed thus

$$(y_1-y_0); (y_2-y_1); \ldots; (y_n-y_{n-1}) = \Delta y_0; \Delta y_1; \ldots; \Delta y_{n-1} \tag{9.8}$$

The differencing process described by equation (9.8) can be repeated to give

$$\Delta y_1 - \Delta y_0 = \Delta^2 y_0 \tag{9.9}$$

But from the relationship of Δy to y it can be seen that

$$\Delta^2 y_0 = \Delta y_1 - \Delta y_0 = (y_2-y_1)-(y_1-y_0) = y_2-2y_1+y_0 \tag{9.10}$$

Second difference relationships of the type given in equation (9.10) are employed to replace second derivatives in differential equations by finite differences prior to using a numerical method of solution. This will be illustrated later in Section 11.4.1 *et seq.*

The procedure developed in the above paragraph to obtain an expression for the second difference of a variable y can be extended to differences of higher order. For example the third difference of y_0 is

$$\Delta^3 y_0 = y_3 - 3y_2 + 3y_1 - y_0 \qquad (9.11)$$

and the fourth difference is

$$\Delta^4 y_0 = y_4 - 4y_3 + 6y_2 - 4y_1 + y_0 \qquad (9.12)$$

In general terms for any variable y_n in a sequence, the mth difference is

$$\Delta^m y_n = y_{m+n} - \binom{m}{1} y_{m+n-1} + \binom{m}{2} y_{m+n-2} - \ldots (-1)^m y_n \qquad (9.13)$$

In equation (9.13) the coefficients of the expansion on the right of the equation are the same as those obtainable from a binomial expansion of $(1-x)^m$.

9.2.3. *Difference Tables*

The most convenient way of expressing the first, second and higher order differences of a function is by means of difference tables. Such a table is illustrated below for a function $y = f(x)$.

TABLE 9.1. *The Difference Table*

Variable	Function	Δ	Δ^2	Δ^3	Δ^4
x_0	y_0				
		Δy_0			
x_1	y_1		$\Delta^2 y_0$		
		Δy_1		$\Delta^3 y_0$	
x_2	y_2		$\Delta^2 y_1$		$\Delta^4 y_0$
		Δy_2		$\Delta^3 y_1$	
x_3	y_3		$\Delta^2 y_2$		
		Δy_3			
x_4	y_4				

In the above table, the second column gives the value of the function at specified values of the variable x. The third column having the heading Δ is constructed from the values of y in the second column by subtracting y_0 from y_1, y_1 from y_2, and so on to give the column of first differences. The fourth column of second differences is obtained from the first differences in the third column by subtracting the entry above from the one below. The difference table is completed by repeating the procedure outlined above. This will be illustrated by the following example.

L

Example. Construct a difference table of $y = f(x)$ from the following data and state what conclusions can be drawn from the result.

x	1·0	1·1	1·2	1·3	1·4	1·5	1·6
y	7·567	12·159	17·399	23·339	30·031	37·527	45·879

The difference table of these data is

x	y	Δ^1	Δ^2	Δ^3	Δ^4
1·0	7·567				
		4·592			
1·1	12·159		0·648		
		5·240		0·052	
1·2	17·399		0·700		0
		5·940		0·052	
1·3	23·339		0·752		0
		6·692		0·052	
1·4	30·031		0·804		0
		7·496		0·052	
1·5	37·527		0·856		
		8·352			
1·6	45·879				

Inspection of this difference table shows that all the 3rd differences have the same value which from the elementary properties of a polynomial suggests that the data represents a function of the third degree.

Difference tables are very useful for assessing scientific data whether it be interpolation, extrapolation or fitting an equation to a curve of experimetal data. These applications will be illustrated in Section 9.4 after more of the background has been established. However, certain properties of difference tables will be stated at this point. These are:

(i) If the value of a function is known at equally spaced values of the independent variable of the function, or if the difference between successive values of the function is known, all the columns of higher differences can be constructed.

(ii) If one complete column of differences of any order, and one item of each column on the left of the complete column is known, all the columns of the lower differences and the values of the function itself can be determined within the range of the independent variable.

(iii) If the members of the column of nth differences have the same constant value, the data from which the difference table was constructed is derived from a polynomial of degree n.

These rules can be tested by considering the example given above. Thus $\Delta^3 y = 0\cdot052$ and the last member of the Δ^2 column is 0·856. Therefore the last but one member will be $(0\cdot856 - 0\cdot052) = 0\cdot804$. In a similar manner each item in the Δ^2 column can be inserted and thereafter the Δ^1 column can be completed if one of its members is given.

9.2.4. *Finite Difference of a Product or Quotient*

On occasion it is necessary to find the difference of a product of two functions. Thus, if two functions of an independent variable n, which can have integer values only, are written as $f(n)$ and $\phi(n)$, then the first difference of the product of these two functions is

$$
\begin{aligned}
\Delta[f(n)\phi(n)] &= f(n+1)\phi(n+1) - f(n)\phi(n) \\
&= f(n+1)[\phi(n+1) - \phi(n)] + \phi(n)[f(n+1) - f(n)] \\
&= f(n+1)\Delta\phi(n) + \phi(n)\Delta f(n)
\end{aligned}
\tag{9.14}
$$

or grouping the terms differently,

$$
\Delta[f(n)\phi(n)] = \phi(n+1)\Delta f(n) + f(n)\Delta\phi(n)
\tag{9.15}
$$

which demonstrates the similarities between finite difference calculus and infinitesimal calculus in respect of the differential coefficient of a product of two functions.

If the first difference of the quotient of $f(n)$ and $\phi(n)$ is desired, a similar procedure gives,

$$
\begin{aligned}
\Delta\left[\frac{f(n)}{\phi(n)}\right] &= \frac{f(n+1)}{\phi(n+1)} - \frac{f(n)}{\phi(n)} \\
&= \frac{f(n+1)\phi(n) - \phi(n+1)f(n)}{\phi(n+1)\phi(n)} \\
&= \frac{\phi(n)[f(n+1) - f(n)] - f(n)[\phi(n+1) - \phi(n)]}{\phi(n+1)\phi(n)} \\
&= \frac{\phi(n)\Delta f(n) - f(n)\Delta\phi(n)}{\phi(n+1)\phi(n)}
\end{aligned}
\tag{9.16}
$$

which again demonstrates the similarity between finite difference calculus and infinitesimal calculus. However, it should be observed that the denominator of equation (9.16) does not contain a squared term and in this respect differs slightly from the differential coefficient of a quotient.

9.3. OTHER DIFFERENCE OPERATORS

The differences presented in the above sections are, to be precise, called "forward differences" and are the ones most generally used for the solution of engineering problems. Consequently they are simply referred to as the first, second or nth differences and the prefix "forward" is omitted when it is clearly understood which type of difference is meant. However, in certain interpolation formulae the terms "backward difference" and "central difference" are employed and therefore their meanings must be understood. In actual fact there is no basic difference between a forward difference and a backward difference since both express the difference between the higher and next lower value of the function, and the significance between these terms is best understood by reference to Table 9.1. In that table it will be seen that the first entry in each column refers to y_0 and the various differences are obtained from successive members of the series starting from y_0. These are the forward differences and they are shown by the solid arrow. On the other hand, the last entry in each column is the first, second and third forward difference of each successively lower member of the series as shown by the dotted arrow. These entries in the table can be relabelled as backward differences by using the following definition.

$$\nabla y_n = y_n - y_{n-1} = \Delta y_{n-1} \qquad (9.17)$$

The second backward difference is written similarly thus,

$$\nabla^2 y_n = y_n - 2y_{n-1} + y_{n-2} = \Delta^2 y_{n-2} \qquad (9.18)$$

It is now clear that all of the backward differences shown by the dotted arrow in Table 9.1 refer to y_4.

A third type of difference known as the "central difference" is symbolized by prefixing δ to the function.
Thus

$$\delta y_n = y_{n+\frac{1}{2}} - y_{n-\frac{1}{2}} \qquad (9.19)$$

Central differences would be represented by a horizontal line in Table 9.1.

To sum up, forward differences should be used when data from the initial parts of a table are to be assessed and backward differences used when data from the end of a table are to be considered. This is particularly true for interpolation and extrapolation purposes. Finally, for interpolation near the centre of a collection of data central differences should be employed.

There are two further important difference operators which will be described in the following sub-sections.

9.3.1. *The operator E*

The operation of changing the value of a function to correspond with a change of one increment in the independent variable is denoted by E.
That is
$$E y_0 = y_1 \qquad (9.20)$$
In a similar manner

$$y_n = E y_{n-1} = E(E y_{n-2}) = E^2 y_{n-2} = \dots = E^n y_0 \qquad (9.21)$$

Equation (9.21) shows that E^n operates on y_0 n times to increase the value of the function corresponding to an increase of n increments in the independent variable.

The exponent n in E^n can take any positive or negative integer value.
Thus

$$E^{-1} f(x_0) = f(x_0 - h) \qquad (9.22)$$

where the exponent (-1) signifies that the function is reduced to the next lower value of the independent variable.

The operator E has significance only when it is placed before a function or variable, and in this respect it is similar to other operators. Also, E can be treated like an algebraic symbol in that it obeys the distributive, commutative, and index laws of algebra. The reader is asked to verify these for himself.

Since E and Δ are both finite difference operators that obey the same laws of algebra, it would be expected that they must be inter-related. The relationship between them can be shown as follows.

$$y_{n+1} = Ey_n \tag{9.23}$$

$$y_{n+1} - y_n = \Delta y_n \tag{9.24}$$

Substituting equation (9.23) into (9.24) gives

$$(E-1)y_n = \Delta y_n \tag{9.25}$$

which can be written as an identity between operators thus,

$$E = 1 + \Delta \tag{9.26}$$

This simple relationship is most important because it often allows algebraic expressions in terms of the one operator to be simplified in terms of the other by using ordinary algebraic manipulations. Thus, if x is the independent variable that is capable of taking the values x_0; (x_0+h); (x_0+2h); etc., then

$$f(x_0+h) = Ef(x_0) \tag{9.27}$$

By Taylor's theorem (see Section 3.3.7)

$$Ef(x_0) = f(x_0+h) = f(x_0) + hDf(x_0) + \frac{h^2}{2!}D^2f(x_0) + \frac{h^3}{3!}D^3f(x_0) + \dots \tag{9.28}$$

where D is the differential operator d/dx. From equation (9.28) it can be seen that

$$\left[1 + hD + \frac{(hD)^2}{2!} + \frac{(hD)^3}{3!} + \dots\right]f(x_0) = Ef(x_0) = (1+\Delta)f(x_0) \tag{9.29}$$

The terms in the square bracket form the expansion of the exponential function e^{hD}, and therefore equation (9.29), provides a relationship between the differential operator and the finite difference operators. That is

$$E = 1 + \Delta = e^{hD} \tag{9.30}$$

The three symbols in equation (9.30) are all operators and they can be treated like algebraic quantities. In the mathematical relations developed to show the relationship between them, the analysis has been confined to the first order of the operator. This was done for convenience only, and for any value of m

$$E^m = (1+\Delta)^m = e^{mhD} \tag{9.31}$$

In addition, any polynomial of these symbols having constant coefficients represents an operation on a function. Thus

$$E^mf(x_0) = (1+\Delta)^mf(x_0)$$

$$= f(x_0) + \binom{m}{1}\Delta f(x_0) + \binom{m}{2}\Delta^2f(x_0) + \binom{m}{3}\Delta^3f(x_0) + \dots$$

$$= \left[1 + \binom{m}{1}\Delta + \binom{m}{2}\Delta^2 + \binom{m}{3}\Delta^3 + \dots\right]f(x_0) \tag{9.32}$$

Equation (9.32) is known as "Newton's forward difference formula". The polynomial within the square bracket is a polynomial operator and m is any number, integer or otherwise. This polynomial operator only has significance when it operates on a function such as $f(x)$ in equation (9.32). This result finds extensive use in interpolation (Section 9.4).

In a similar manner it is possible to produce an expansion of E^m in terms of the operator ∇. Thus by equation (9.26)

$$E^m = \left(\frac{E}{E-\Delta}\right)^m = (1-\Delta E^{-1})^{-m} \qquad (9.33)$$

and if the last expression in equation (9.33) is expanded and made to operate on $f(x_0)$ the result is

$$E^m f(x_0) = (1-\Delta E^{-1})^{-m} f(x_0)$$

$$= f(x_0) + \binom{m}{1}\Delta f(x_0-h) + \binom{m+1}{2}\Delta^2 f(x_0-2h) +$$

$$+ \ldots \binom{m+r-1}{r}\Delta^r f(x_0-rh) + \ldots \qquad (9.34)$$

Using equations (9.17, 18) to introduce backward differences,

$$E^m f(x_0) = f(x_0) + \binom{m}{1}\nabla f(x_0) + \binom{m+1}{2}\nabla^2 f(x_0) + \ldots \binom{m+r-1}{r}\nabla^r f(x_0) + \ldots$$

$$= \left[1 + \binom{m}{1}\nabla + \binom{m+1}{2}\nabla^2 + \binom{m+2}{3}\nabla^3 + \ldots\right] f(x_0) \qquad (9.35)$$

Equation (9.35) is known as "Newton's backward difference formula" and like equation (9.32) is used for interpolation. Again m can be any number, integer or otherwise.

9.3.2. *The Difference Quotient*

The difference quotient was introduced by Norlund (1920) in order to show the similarity between finite difference calculus and infinitesimal calculus. The difference quotient is defined by the equation

$$\underset{h}{\Delta} f(x_0) = \frac{f(x_0+h)-f(x_0)}{h} \qquad (9.36)$$

On occasion it is referred to as "Norlund's Operator".

Similarly $\underset{h}{\overset{2}{\Delta}}$ would be the second difference quotient and is written

$$\underset{h}{\overset{2}{\Delta}} f(x_0) = \underset{h}{\Delta}\left[\frac{f(x_0+h)-f(x_0)}{h}\right] = \frac{f(x_0+2h)-2f(x_0+h)+f(x_0)}{h^2} \qquad (9.37)$$

These concepts can be extended to the mth difference quotient, thus

$$\underset{h}{\overset{m}{\Delta}} f(x_0) = \frac{1}{h^m}\left[f(x_0+mh) + \binom{m}{1}f(x_0+\overline{m-1}h) + \right.$$

$$\left. + \binom{m}{2}f(x_0+\overline{m-2}h) + \ldots + f(x_0)\right] \qquad (9.38)$$

Equation (9.38) shows the relationship between the difference operator and difference quotient which may be summarized as

$$\Delta^m f(x_0) = h^m \underset{h}{\Delta} f(x_0) \qquad (9.39)$$

Thereafter the relationship of the difference quotient with the other finite difference operators follows from the above sections which may be summarized thus:

$$\Delta^m = (E-1)^m = (e^{hD}-1)^m = h^m \underset{h}{\overset{m}{\Delta}} \qquad (9.40)$$

Finally, it can be shown that the difference quotient obeys the distributive law for addition, the index law for positive integers and the commutative law for constants. It is left for the reader to verify this statement.

9.4. INTERPOLATION

It frequently happens that the engineer is confronted with a collection of data relating two variables, such as the pressure inside a vessel corresponding to the temperature of its contents. The pressure is thus some unknown function of the temperature, and he is required to predict the pressure at some temperature in between or outside the limits of the data he possesses. If the pressure is required within the limits of the data, the mathematical procedure is called "interpolation"; whereas if the point lies outside the range of the data, the mathematical process is called "extrapolation".

Interpolation or extrapolation depends on the assumption that the functional relationship between the two variables is continuous over the range of the independent variable being considered. Therefore in order to be able to interpolate or extrapolate, the engineer must obtain this functional relationship or some other functional relationship that approximates to it. For this purpose the trends in the data must be considered from the point of view of the experimental results and the mathematical analysis. For example, the chemical engineer would be familiar with the general shape of a vapour pressure–temperature curve and its position on a graph from the experimental data. The mathematician is able to assign an approximate equation to this curve and thereafter interpolation is straightforward.

Usually the experimental data is approximated by a polynomial and the degree of the polynomial can often be estimated by preparing a difference table from the collected data. The difference column that gives an approximately constant value, gives the degree of the polynomial which can be fitted to the data by selection of the constants.

9.4.1. Newton's Formulae

When the data points are available at equal intervals of the independent variable, Newton's difference formulae can be employed and the procedure is best illustrated by the following examples.

Example 1. Estimate the value of $J_0(z)$ at $z = 3\cdot479$ from the values of $J_0(z)$ given in the following table.

z	$3\cdot2$	$3\cdot4$	$3\cdot6$	$3\cdot8$	$4\cdot0$
$J_0(z)$	$-0\cdot3202$	$-0\cdot3643$	$-0\cdot3918$	$-0\cdot4026$	$-0\cdot3971$

The following difference table is constructed from the data supplied.

n	z	$J_0(z)$	$\Delta J_0(z)$	$\Delta^2 J_0(z)$	$\Delta^3 J_0(z)$
0	$3\cdot2$	$-0\cdot3202$			
			$-0\cdot0441$		
1	$3\cdot4$	$-0\cdot3643$		$+0\cdot0166$	
			$-0\cdot0275$		$0\cdot0001$
2	$3\cdot6$	$-0\cdot3918$		$+0\cdot0167$	
			$-0\cdot0108$		$-0\cdot0004$
3	$3\cdot8$	$-0\cdot4026$		$+0\cdot0163$	
			$+0\cdot0055$		
4	$4\cdot0$	$-0\cdot3971$			

From the above table it can be seen that $J_0(z)$ can be approximated by a polynomial of second degree within the range of data supplied.

(a) Using forward differences

$$z = z_0 + mh$$

and

$$z_0 = 3\cdot2 \text{ and } h = 0\cdot2$$

$$\therefore \quad m = 1\cdot395$$

Then by Newton's forward difference equation (9.32)

$$J_0(z_0 + mh) = J_0(z_0) + \binom{m}{1} \Delta J_0(z_0) + \binom{m}{2} \Delta^2 J_0(z_0)$$

Substituting from the difference table gives

$$J_0(z) = -0\cdot3202 + (1\cdot395 \times -0\cdot0441) + \frac{1\cdot395 \times 0\cdot395}{2} \times 0\cdot0166$$

$$= -0\cdot3771$$

(b) Using backward differences.

For this interpolation, z_0 will be selected at $3\cdot8$ because $\Delta^2 J_0(z)$ will give a value derived from $J_0(3\cdot4)$. Consequently the interpolation formula will include differences obtained from the neighbourhood of $J_0(3\cdot479)$ as shown by the lines in the difference table.

Thus let $\qquad z_0 = 3\cdot8 \quad$ and $h = 0\cdot2$

Then $\qquad 3\cdot479 = 3\cdot8 + m \times 0\cdot2$

$$\therefore \quad m = -1\cdot605$$

Inserting these figures into Newton's backward difference formula (9.35)

$$_0(z_0+mh) = J_0(z_0) + \binom{m}{1}\nabla J_0(z_0) + \binom{m+1}{2}\nabla^2 J_0(z_0)$$

$$= -0.4026 + \left[\frac{-1.605 \times -0.0108}{1}\right] +$$

$$+ \left[\frac{-1.605 \times -0.605 \times 0.0167}{2}\right]$$

$$= -0.3772$$

The value of $J_0(3.479)$ predicted by the forward difference formula agrees very well with the result obtained using the backward difference formula. The result estimated from Chistova† for $J_0(3.479)$ is -0.3772 which agrees with both results.

Either of the difference formulae can be used for interpolation, but for extrapolation the forward difference formula must be used.

Example 2. Using the data given in the table below, estimate the vapour pressure and density of ammonia vapour at 167°F. Latent heat of ammonia = 544 Btu/lb.

Temperature °	70	80	90	100	110	120	130	140
Pressure lb/in²	128·8	153·0	180·6	211·9	247·0	286·4	330·3	379·1

From the above data the following difference table is prepared

t	p	Δp	$\Delta^2 p$	$\Delta^3 p$
70	128·8			
		24·2		
80	153·0		3·4	
		27·6		0·3
90	180·6		3·7	
		31·3		0·1
100	211·9		3·8	
		35·1		0·5
110	247·0		4·3	
		39·4		0·2
120	286·4		4·5	
		43·9		0·4
130	330·3		4·9	
		48·8		
140	379·1			

The fourth differences $\Delta^4 p$ have not been calculated because $\Delta^3 p$ are very small and will make very little contribution to the estimated pressure. Inspection of the difference table shows that the last entry in the $\Delta^3 p$ column (i.e. 0·4) is derived from $p = 247.0$ lb/in² corresponding to 110°F. Therefore 110°F will be taken as the base temperature.

Then $$p = f(t) = f(t_0+mh)$$

† Chistova E. A. "Tables of Bessel Functions." Pergamon Press, London (1959).

where $\qquad$ $t = 167°,\quad t_0 = 110°\quad$ and $h = 10°$

$$\therefore\quad 167 = 110 + 10m\quad \text{or}\quad m = 5\cdot7$$

Newton's forward difference formula (9.32) gives

$$p = p_0 + \binom{m}{1}\Delta p_0 + \binom{m}{2}\Delta^2 p_0 + \binom{m}{3}\Delta^3 p_0 \qquad\qquad \text{I}$$

$$= 247\cdot0 + \frac{5\cdot7}{1}\times 39\cdot4 + \frac{5\cdot7\times4\cdot7}{1\times2}\times 4\cdot5 + \frac{5\cdot7\times4\cdot7\times3\cdot7}{1\times2\times3}\times 0\cdot4$$

$$= 247\cdot0 + 224\cdot58 + 60\cdot28 + 6\cdot61$$

$$= 538\cdot5\,\text{lb/in}^2$$

The value extrapolated from Perry† is $538.0\,\text{lb/in}^2$.

In order to find the density of the ammonia vapour it is convenient to use the Clausius Clapeyron equation‡

$$\frac{dp}{dT} = \frac{\delta H}{T(V_v - V_L)} \qquad\qquad \text{II}$$

where T is the temperature in degrees Rankine. Assuming that the volume of the liquid is negligible compared with the volume of the vapour gives

$$\rho = \frac{1}{V_v} = \frac{T}{\delta H}\frac{dp}{dT} \qquad\qquad \text{III}$$

dp/dT can be evaluated from the difference table by taking the logarithm of equation (9.30). Thus

$$hD = \ln(1+\Delta) = \Delta - \tfrac{1}{2}\Delta^2 + \tfrac{1}{3}\Delta^3 - \dots \qquad\qquad \text{IV}$$

Interpreting D as d/dT and substituting equation IV into III gives

$$\rho = \frac{T}{h\delta H}(\Delta p - \tfrac{1}{2}\Delta^2 p + \tfrac{1}{3}\Delta^3 p - \dots) \qquad\qquad \text{V}$$

The values of the differences in the bracket of equation V must be determined at the required temperature of 167°F. This can be done by extrapolating each column of differences in the table using the same method as the extrapolation for p at 167°F. The results are

at $\qquad$ $t = 167°\text{F},\ p = 538\cdot5,\ \Delta p = 70\cdot4,\ \Delta^2 p = 6\cdot8,\ \Delta^3 p = 0\cdot4$

Substituting into equation V gives

$$\rho = \frac{627}{10\times544\times778}\left(70\cdot4 - \frac{6\cdot8}{2} + \frac{0\cdot4}{3}\right)$$

$$\therefore\quad \rho = 0\cdot0099\,\text{lb/ft}^3$$

This value is more reliable than that obtained from the ideal gas laws.

† Perry, J. H. (Ed.). "Chemical Engineers Handbook," 3rd edition. McGraw Hill (1950).

‡ Bransom, S. H. "Applied Thermodynamics." Van Nostrand (1960).

9.4.2. *Bessel's Interpolation Formula*

This formula is for use with central differences along a horizontal line in the difference table. It can be seen in Table 9.1 that values are only available in alternate columns. The gaps are filled by taking an arithmetical average of the two values adjacent to the one required in the same column and denoting the value by $\mu\delta$, $\mu\delta^2$, ... etc., depending upon the order of the difference. It is customary to choose a fractional value of m which is less than unity and use the formula

$$E^m f(x_0) = f(x_0) + m\delta f(x_0 + \tfrac{1}{2}h)$$

$$+ \frac{m(m-1)}{2!} \left[\mu\delta^2 f(x_0 + \tfrac{1}{2}h) + \frac{m-\tfrac{1}{2}}{3} \delta^3 f(x_0 + \tfrac{1}{2}h) \right]$$

$$+ \frac{(m+1)m(m-1)(m-2)}{4!} \left[\mu\delta^4 f(x_0 + \tfrac{1}{2}h) + \frac{m-\tfrac{1}{2}}{5} \delta^5 f(x_0 + \tfrac{1}{2}h) \right]$$

$$+ \dots \text{etc.} \tag{9.41}$$

9.4.3. *Lagrange's Interpolation Formula*

Quite often, the data are available at unequal intervals of the independent variable and this precludes the use of a normal difference table.† Lagrange's method fits a polynomial to the data but otherwise has no connection with finite difference calculus: it is included in this chapter merely for completeness within this section concerning interpolation.

The fourth degree polynomial which passes through the four points (x_0, y_0), (x_1, y_1), (x_2, y_2), (x_3, y_3) can be written

$$y = y_0 \frac{(x-x_1)(x-x_2)(x-x_3)}{(x_0-x_1)(x_0-x_2)(x_0-x_3)}$$

$$+ y_1 \frac{(x-x_0)(x-x_2)(x-x_3)}{(x_1-x_0)(x_1-x_2)(x_1-x_3)}$$

$$+ y_2 \frac{(x-x_0)(x-x_1)(x-x_3)}{(x_2-x_0)(x_2-x_1)(x_2-x_3)}$$

$$+ y_3 \frac{(x-x_0)(x-x_1)(x-x_2)}{(x_3-x_0)(x_3-x_1)(x_3-x_2)} \tag{9.42}$$

and this form is known as "Lagrange's interpolation formula". The extension to more than four points is fairly obvious: the numerator and denominator of each fraction is extended to include the further values of x_n and the complete equation is extended by adding further terms to include all values of y_n. It is to be noted that the term corresponding to the appropriate y_n is

† It is possible to calculate in terms of " divided differences " where the first difference is found from the ratio of δy to δx, but the method used herein is considered to be more satisfactory.

omitted from each numerator and its counterpart from the denominator. The use of many more than four points is not recommended due to the computational effort.

Example 3. Find the thermal conductivity of propane at 100 atm. and 210°F from the following data given by Leng and Comings.†

$T(°F)$	P(atm)	k(Btu/h ft².°F ft⁻¹)
154	96·7	0·0490
	131·5	0·0518
189	88·9	0·0440
	131·8	0·0466
222	96·7	0·0402
	140·9	0·0435
284	95·3	0·0353
	123·0	0·0376

From the graph given in the paper, other results show that in this region the conductivity varies approximately linearly with pressure so that a linear interpolation is adequate in this direction.

A set of values for conductivity and temperature at a pressure of 100 atm. can be found from the above values as follows. At 154°F and 100 atm.,

$$k = 0.0490 + \frac{100.0 - 96.7}{131.5 - 96.7}(0.0518 - 0.0490)$$

$$= 0.0493$$

Hence the following table can be compiled.

T	154	189	222	284
k	0·0493	0·0447	0·0404	0·0357

Substituting these values into equation (9.42) gives the thermal conductivity of propane at 100 atm. and 210°F. Thus

$$k = 0.0493 \frac{(210-189)(210-222)(210-284)}{(154-189)(154-222)(154-284)}$$

$$+ 0.0447 \frac{(210-154)(210-222)(210-284)}{(189-154)(189-222)(189-284)}$$

† Leng, D. E. and Comings, E. W. *I.E.C.* **49** (ii), 2042, 1957.

$$+ 0{\cdot}0404 \frac{(210-154)(210-189)(210-284)}{(222-154)(222-189)(222-284)}$$

$$+ 0{\cdot}0357 \frac{(210-154)(210-189)(210-222)}{(284-154)(284-189)(284-222)}$$

$$\therefore \quad k = 0{\cdot}0419 \text{ Btu/hft}^2.{}^\circ\text{F ft}^{-1}$$

9.5. FINITE DIFFERENCE EQUATIONS

A finite difference equation is a relationship between an independent variable that can take discrete values only, a dependent variable, and successive differences of the dependent variable. Thus an equation of the type

$$a_0 y_0 + a_1 y_1 + a_2 y_2 + \ldots + a_n y_n = \phi(x) \qquad (9.43)$$

is a finite difference equation if $y = f(x)$ and x can take the values x_0, $x_0 + h$, ... $x_0 + nh$ only. In equation (9.43), a_0, a_1, a_2, ... a_n can be constants or functions of the independent variable. $\phi(x)$ could be a constant or a function of x. Equation (9.43) can therefore be written

$$a_0 f(x_0) + a_1 f(x_0 + h) + \ldots + a_n f(x_0 + nh) = \phi(x)$$

or

$$(a_n E^n + a_{n-1} E^{n-1} + \ldots + a_0) f(x_0) = \phi(x) \qquad (9.44)$$

because

$$f(x_0 + rh) = E^r f(x_0). \quad \text{But } E = 1 + \Delta,$$

$$\therefore \quad (p_n \Delta^n + p_{n-1} \Delta^{n-1} + \ldots + p_0) f(x_0) = \phi(x) \qquad (9.45)$$

where the coefficients p_r are obtained from a_r. Equations (9.43) to (9.45) are different forms of the same finite difference equation.

Finite difference equations are similar to differential equations in that they can be classified by "order" and "degree". Thus the order of a finite difference equation is determined by the order of the highest difference. For example, the equation

$$y_{n+1} - a y_n = 0 \qquad (9.46)$$

is of order 1 because it involves only the first difference, i.e.

$$(E - a) y_n = [\Delta - (a-1)] y_n = 0 \qquad (9.47)$$

On the other hand the equation

$$y_n - a y_{n-1} + b y_{n-2} = 0 \qquad (9.48)$$

is of order 2 because the highest difference is of order 2, thus

$$[\Delta^2 + (2-a)\Delta + (1-a+b)] y_{n-2} = 0 \qquad (9.49)$$

It should be noted from equations (9.47) and (9.49) that it is the difference between the highest and lowest members of the dependent variable that determines the order of the equation, and not the highest member as indicated by the suffix to the dependent variable.

where A' and B' are two arbitrary constants that would be evaluated by the boundary conditions of the problem.

It will be noticed that equation (9.56) is the complementary solution of the original second order equation and that it contains two arbitrary constants. In a similar manner it can be shown that an nth order equation will provide a complementary solution containing n arbitrary constants; which again shows the similarity to the complementary function of a linear differential equation.

Equation (9.52) is known as the "characteristic equation" of the finite difference equation (9.50). Its roots may be different or equal, real or complex. The case of different roots is given above, and if ρ_1 and ρ_2 are real, equation (9.56) is the final complementary solution. If the roots are complex, they will occur in conjugate pairs thus,

$$\rho_1 = \alpha + i\beta = re^{i\phi}; \qquad \rho_2 = \alpha - i\beta = re^{-i\phi} \tag{9.57}$$

In this case, the solution (9.56) can be written in the form

$$y_n = r^n(A' \cos n\phi + B' \sin n\phi) \tag{9.58}$$

by using De Moivre's theorem (Section 4.7). This is the complementary solution when the roots of the characteristic equation are complex and is similar to the solution of the corresponding differential equation.

Finally, when the roots of the characteristic equation are equal, the complementary solution takes the form

$$y_n = (A' + B'n)\rho^n \tag{9.59}$$

again like the comparable form of the differential equation (Section 2.5.2b).

9.6.2. The Particular Solution

This can invariably be found either by the method of undetermined coefficients or the method of inverse operators; both of which are very similar to the corresponding method for linear differential equations. Since these methods were described in Section 2.5, they will only be repeated briefly here with reference to the second order finite difference equation

$$(E^2 - AE + B)y_n = \phi(n) \tag{9.50}$$

A particular solution of this equation is

$$y_n = \left(\frac{1}{E^2 - AE + B}\right)\phi(n) \tag{9.60}$$

by the method of inverse operators. The operator can be factorized as in the above sub-section, and separated into partial fractions. Thus

$$\frac{1}{E^2 - AE + B} = \frac{1}{(E - \rho_1)(E - \rho_2)} = \frac{\alpha}{(E - \rho_1)} - \frac{\alpha}{(E - \rho_2)} \tag{9.61}$$

where $\alpha = 1/(\rho_1 - \rho_2)$. Each partial fraction on the right-hand side of equation (9.61) can be expanded as follows

$$\frac{\alpha}{E-\rho_1} = \frac{\alpha}{(1-\rho_1)}\left[1+\left(\frac{\Delta}{1-\rho_1}\right)\right]^{-1}$$

$$= \frac{\alpha}{(1-\rho_1)}\left[1-\frac{\Delta}{1-\rho_1}+\frac{\Delta^2}{(1-\rho_1)^2}-\cdots\right] \qquad (9.62)$$

and
$$\frac{\alpha}{E-\rho_2} = \frac{\alpha}{(1-\rho_2)}\left[1-\frac{\Delta}{1-\rho_2}+\frac{\Delta^2}{(1-\rho_2)^2}-\cdots\right] \qquad (9.63)$$

The forms (9.62, 63) of the operators are most convenient for finding the particular solution if $\phi(n)$ is a polynomial in n, because only a finite number of terms will be needed in the expansions.

When $\phi(n) = ka^n$, an alternative procedure is advantageous. Thus,

$$Ea^n = a^{n+1} = a \cdot a^n$$

and
$$E^m a^n = a^{m+n} = a^m \cdot a^n$$

In general,

$$f(E)a^n = f(a)a^n \qquad (9.64)$$

provided $f(E)$ can be expanded as a polynomial in E. Equation (9.64) is the key to a particular solution when $\phi(n) = ka^n$. The usual difficulties can arise when $f(a)$ is infinite, but these can be overcome by techniques similar to those given in Section 2.5.5. It should be noted, however, that the equation analogous to equation (2.79) takes the form

$$f(E)(a^n y_n) = a^n f(aE)y_n \qquad (9.65)$$

where a and E appear as a product instead of a sum on the right-hand side. Equation (9.65) is of little practical value since it does not lead to any simplification in the form of the operator.

Hence, rewriting equation (9.50) with $\phi(n) = ka^n$,

$$(E^2 - AE + B)y_n = ka^n \qquad (9.66)$$

and using equation (9.64), the particular solution is

$$y_n = \frac{ka^n}{a^2 - Aa + B} \qquad (9.67)$$

provided $a^2 - Aa + B \neq 0$. This exceptional case can be treated in a similar manner to the corresponding differential equation by using equation (9.65) and introducing the difference operator Δ using equation (9.26).

In concluding this sub-section on the determination of particular solutions of finite difference equations, it should be pointed out that a particular solution can be obtained in most cases when $\phi(n)$ takes the form of a polynomial or power by the method of undetermined coefficients. Here there is no difference in technique between finite difference equations and differential equations; the trial solutions take exactly the same form in the corresponding cases.

Finally the complete solution is the sum of the complementary solution and a particular solution in a manner similar to differential equations. If possible the operational method should be used to evaluate both parts of the solution, but on occasion the method of undetermined coefficients may be more suitable.

Example 1. G_{N+1} lb moles/h of a wet gas containing Y_{N+1} lb moles/mole of solute are fed into the base of a plate absorption column where the solute is to be stripped from the gas by absorption in L_0 lb moles/h of lean oil which is fed into the top of the column. If the solute in the entering oil is X_0 lb moles/mole of lean oil and the solute in the exit gas is Y_1 lb moles of solute per mole of wet gas, show that the performance of the absorber can be expressed in terms of the absorption factor $A = (L_0/KG_{N+1})$ and the number of ideal stages by the Kremser-Brown equation

$$\frac{Y_{N+1} - Y_1}{Y_{N+1} - Y_0} = \frac{A^{N+1} - A}{A^{N+1} - 1}$$

where K_m is the equilibrium constant. That is

$$y_m = K_m x_m$$

where y_m and x_m are the mole fractions of the solute in the gas and liquid phases respectively.

Fɪɢ. 9.1

Considering Fig. 9.1 and taking a material balance over plate m gives

$$L_0(X_m - X_{m-1}) = G_{N+1}(Y_{m+1} - Y_m) \qquad\qquad \text{I}$$

But
$$y_m G_m = Y_m G_{N+1} \quad \text{and} \quad x_m L_m = X_m L_0 \qquad \text{II}$$

$$\therefore \quad Y_m \frac{G_{N+1}}{G_m} = K_m \frac{X_m L_0}{L_m}$$

or
$$X_m = \left(\frac{G_{N+1}}{L_0}\right)\left(\frac{L_m}{K_m G_m}\right) Y_m \qquad \text{III}$$

Substituting equation III into equation I to eliminate X_m and X_{m-1} gives

$$Y_m = \frac{Y_{m+1} + (L_{m-1}/K_{m-1} G_{m-1}) Y_{m-1}}{1 + (L_m/K_m G_m)} \qquad \text{IV}$$

But $(L_{m-1}/K_{m-1} G_{m-1}) = A_{m-1}$, the absorption factor for plate $m-1$; and $(L_m/K_m G_m) = A_m$, the absorption factor for plate m. Therefore equation IV can be written as

$$Y_m = \frac{Y_{m+1} + A_{m-1} Y_{m-1}}{1 + A_m} \qquad \text{V}$$

Taking a mean value of the absorption factor as suggested by Edmister† or Horton and Franklin‡ equation V becomes

$$Y_{m+1} - (1+A)Y_m + A Y_{m-1} = 0 \qquad \text{VI}$$

where A is the mean value of the absorption factor between the bottom and top of the column.

Putting equation VI into operational form and factorizing gives

$$[E^2 - (1+A)E + A] Y_m = (E-1)(E-A) Y_m = 0 \qquad \text{VII}$$

which has the solution

$$Y_m = C_1 + C_2 A^m \qquad \text{VIII}$$

where C_1 and C_2 are arbitrary constants.

Now
$$Y_0 = K X_0 \qquad \text{IX}$$

since A is assumed constant; and equation VIII gives

$$Y_0 = C_1 + C_2 \qquad \text{X}$$

Similarly,
$$Y_{N+1} = C_1 + C_2 A^{N+1} \qquad \text{XI}$$

$$\therefore \quad Y_{N+1} - Y_0 = C_2(A^{N+1} - 1) \qquad \text{XII}$$

and also
$$Y_{N+1} - Y_1 = C_2(A^{N+1} - A) \qquad \text{XIII}$$

Dividing equation XIII by equation XII gives

$$\frac{Y_{N+1} - Y_1}{Y_{N+1} - Y_0} = \frac{A^{N+1} - A}{A^{N+1} - 1} \qquad \text{XIV}$$

which is the well known Kremser equation.

† Edmister, W. C. *I.E.C.* **35**, 837 (1943).
‡ Horton, G. and Franklin, W. B. *I.E.C.* **32**, 1384 (1940).

9.6.3. *Simultaneous Linear Difference Equations*

The analysis presented in the sections above has been confined to one dependent variable. However, when two or more dependent variables are present in a system of difference equations it is usually possible to eliminate all of these variables except one by the normal rules of algebra. Thus consider the following examples.

Example 2. In a proposed chemical process 10 000 lb/h of a pure liquid A is to be fed continuously to the first of a battery of two equal sized stirred tank reactors operating in series. If both vessels are to be maintained at the same constant temperature so that the chemical reaction

$$A \xrightarrow{k_1} B \xrightarrow{k_2} C \qquad\qquad I$$

will take place, estimate the size of the vessels that will give the maximum yield of the product B. The specific reaction rate constant $k_1 = 0\cdot1$ min^{-1} and $k_2 = 0\cdot05$ min^{-1} at the temperature of the reactors, and the fluid density is constant at 60 lb/ft^3.

Let the concentration of A leaving any vessel n be $C_{A,n}$, the concentration of B be $C_{B,n}$, and of C be $C_{C,n}$. Then a material balance over stage n gives for:

component A,

$$C_{A,n-1} - C_{A,n} = k_1 C_{A,n}\theta \qquad\qquad II$$

where θ is the nominal holding time in the reactor;

component B,

$$C_{B,n-1} - C_{B,n} = k_2 C_{B,n}\theta - k_1 C_{A,n}\theta \qquad\qquad III$$

Solution of equation II is obtained in the usual way. Thus let $k_1\theta = \alpha$ and $k_2\theta = \beta$. Then

$$(1+\alpha)C_{A,n} - C_{A,n-1} = 0 \qquad\qquad IV$$

$$[E(1+\alpha)-1]C_{A,n} = 0 \qquad\qquad V$$

or

$$C_{A,n} = K_1 \rho_1^n \qquad\qquad VI$$

where K_1 is an arbitrary constant and $\rho_1 = 1/(1+\alpha)$. Substituting for $C_{A,n}$ from equation VI into equation III and rearranging gives

$$[(1+\beta)E-1]C_{B,n-1} = \alpha K_1 \rho_1^n \qquad\qquad VII$$

The complementary solution of equation VII is

$$C_{B,n} = K_2 \rho_2^n \qquad\qquad VIII$$

where K_2 is the arbitrary constant and $\rho_2 = 1/(1+\beta)$.

The particular solution of equation VII can be written

$$\begin{aligned}
C_{B,n-1} &= \left[\frac{1}{(1+\beta)E-1}\right]\alpha K_1 \rho_1^n \\
&= \frac{\alpha K_1 \rho_1^n}{(1+\beta)\rho_1 - 1} \\
&= \frac{\alpha K_1 \rho_1^{n-1}}{\beta-\alpha} \qquad\qquad IX
\end{aligned}$$

by using equation (9.64). The complete solution of equation VII is thus

$$C_{B,n} = K_2 \rho_2^n + \frac{\alpha K_1}{\beta - \alpha} \rho_1^n \qquad \text{X}$$

Since the initial feed to the reactors is pure A, at $n = 0$, $C_A = C_{A,0}$ and $C_B = 0$.

$$\therefore \quad K_1 = C_{A,0} \qquad \text{XI}$$

and

$$K_2 = \frac{\alpha}{\alpha - \beta} C_{A,0} \qquad \text{XII}$$

Substituting these values into equation X gives

$$C_{B,n} = \frac{\alpha C_{A,0}}{\beta - \alpha} (\rho_1^n - \rho_2^n) \qquad \text{XIII}$$

The condition required is that $C_{B,n}$ must be a maximum for $n = 2$ and some value of θ. It is easier to find the maximum by varying n at fixed θ, than by varying θ at fixed n. Hence, by differentiating equation XIII,

$$\frac{dC_{B,n}}{dn} = \frac{\alpha C_{A,0}}{\beta - \alpha} (\rho_1^n \ln \rho_1 - \rho_2^n \ln \rho_2) = 0 \qquad \text{XIV}$$

$$\therefore \quad \frac{\rho_1^n}{\rho_2^n} = \frac{\ln \rho_1}{\ln \rho_2} \qquad \text{XV}$$

Since

$$\rho_1 = \frac{1}{1 + \alpha} = \frac{1}{1 + 0.10\theta}$$

and

$$\rho_2 = \frac{1}{1 + \beta} = \frac{1}{1 + 0.050\theta}$$

then

$$\left(\frac{1 + 0.050\theta}{1 + 0.10\theta} \right)^2 = \frac{\ln(1 + 0.050\theta)}{\ln(1 + 0.10\theta)} \qquad \text{XVI}$$

Following the methods of Section 11.5 to solve this by successive approximation gives the result

$$\theta = 0.456 \qquad \text{XVII}$$

$$\therefore \quad \frac{\text{Reactor volume}}{\text{Volumetric feed rate}} = \frac{60 \times 60v}{10,000} = 0.456$$

$$\therefore \quad \text{Optimum volume of each reactor is } 1.27 \text{ ft}^3.$$

Example 3. 8540 lb/h of an animal fat are to be hydrolyzed and extracted in a spray column using 3760 lb/h of water.† If the column is to operate under counter current flow conditions, the percentage hydrolyzable glycerine in the fat is 8·53% by weight, and the glycerine in the fatty acid leaving the tower is 0·24% by weight, calculate the number of theoretical stages in the column.

† Jefferys, G. V., Jenson, V. G. and Miles, F. R. *Trans. Instn. Chem. Eng.* **39**, 389 (1961).

A mass balance will give a glycerine concentration in the sweetwater of 18·8%, and the total weight of fat phase held up in the column is 12 200 lb. The distribution ratio of glycerine between water and fat is 10·32, and the reaction rate constant is $10·2\ \mathrm{h}^{-1}$.

Solution. In order to determine N, the number of theoretical stages, the plate column illustrated in Fig. 9.2 is considered and the following symbols are used.

L lb/h fat phase rising through the column.
G lb/h water phase descending through the column.
H lb fat phase held up per stage.
x weight fraction of glycerine in raffinate.
y weight fraction of glycerine in extract.
z weight fraction of unreacted fat in raffinate.
w lb fat required to produce 1·0 lb of glycerine.
k pseudo first order reaction rate constant expressed in terms of fat concentration (h^{-1}).

FIG. 9.2

A glycerine balance over stage n gives

$$Gy_{n-1}+Lx_{n+1}+\frac{kH}{w}z_n = Gy_n+Lx_n \qquad\qquad \text{I}$$

and an equivalent glycerine balance between plate n and the base of the column gives

$$\frac{L}{w}z_{N+1}+Gy_{n-1} = Gy_N+L\left(x_n+\frac{z_n}{w}\right) \qquad\qquad \text{II}$$

The equilibrium relation is

$$y_n = mx_n \qquad\qquad\text{III}$$

where m is the equilibrium ratio.

Substitution of (z_n/w) from equation I into equation II, and elimination of x by the use of equation III gives

$$\frac{mG}{L}(y_{n-1}-y_n)+y_{n+1}-y_n+\frac{kH}{L}\left(\frac{m}{w}z_{N+1}+\frac{mG}{L}y_{n-1}-\frac{mG}{L}y_N-y_n\right)=0 \quad \text{IV}$$

Letting $mG/L = \alpha$, $kH/L = \beta$, and rearranging IV gives

$$y_{n+1}-(\alpha+\beta+1)y_n+(\alpha+\alpha\beta)y_{n-1}=\beta\left(\alpha y_N-\frac{m}{w}z_{N+1}\right) \qquad \text{V}$$

Equation V is a linear finite difference equation. The subsidiary equation is

$$[E^2-(\alpha+\beta+1)E+\alpha(1+\beta)]y_n=0 \qquad\qquad \text{VI}$$

and the complementary solution is

$$y_n = A\alpha^n+B(1+\beta)^n \qquad\qquad \text{VII}$$

The particular solution is

$$y_n = \frac{1}{(E-\alpha)(E-1-\beta)}C \qquad\qquad \text{VIII}$$

where

$$C = \beta\left(\alpha y_N-\frac{m}{w}z_{N+1}\right)$$

Because C is independent of n and $E = 1+\Delta$, E can be replaced by unity. Hence equation VIII becomes

$$y_n = \frac{-C}{\beta(1-\alpha)}$$

$$= \frac{\alpha y_N-mz_{N+1}/w}{\alpha-1} \qquad\qquad \text{IX}$$

The complete solution of equation V is then

$$y_n = A\alpha^n+B(1+\beta)^n+\frac{\alpha y_N-mz_{N+1}/w}{\alpha-1} \qquad\qquad \text{X}$$

with the boundary conditions that at $n = 0$, $y = 0$; and at $n = N+1$, $x = 0$. Substituting these boundary conditions into equation X gives

$$A = \left(\frac{\alpha y_N-mz_{N+1}/w}{\alpha-1}\right)\left[\frac{(1+\beta)^{N+1}-1}{\alpha^{N+1}-(1+\beta)^{N+1}}\right]$$

and

$$B = -\left(\frac{\alpha y_N-mz_{N+1}/w}{\alpha-1}\right)\left[\frac{\alpha^{N+1}-1}{\alpha^{N+1}-(1+\beta)^{N+1}}\right]$$

The final solution after simplifying is

$$y_N = \frac{mz_{N+1}}{w(\alpha-1)}\left[\alpha^N+\frac{(\alpha-1)\alpha^N-\beta(1+\beta)^N}{(1-\alpha+\beta)(1+\beta)^N}\right] \qquad\qquad \text{XI}$$

Substituting the data supplied into equation XI gives

$$\alpha = \frac{mG}{L} = \frac{10 \cdot 32 \times 3760}{8540} = 4 \cdot 54$$

$$\beta = \frac{kH}{L} = \frac{10 \cdot 2 \times 12\,200}{8540 \times N} = \frac{14 \cdot 6}{N}$$

where $12\,200/N = H$, the hold-up per stage.
Then from equation XI

$$0 \cdot 188 = \left(\frac{10 \cdot 32 \times 0 \cdot 0853}{4 \cdot 54^{N+1} - 1}\right) \left[4 \cdot 54^N + \frac{3 \cdot 54 \times 4 \cdot 54^N - (14 \cdot 6/N)(1 + 14 \cdot 6/N)^N}{\left(\dfrac{14 \cdot 6}{N} - 3 \cdot 54\right)\left(1 + \dfrac{14 \cdot 6}{N}\right)^N}\right] \quad \text{XII}$$

gives

$$N = 2 \cdot 8 \text{ (by trial and error)}$$

9.7. Non-Linear Finite Difference Equations

These types of equation occasionally arise in the solution of engineering problems and they are difficult and sometimes impossible to solve. However, first order non-linear equations can be solved graphically, and some second order equations can be solved by special substitutions. These methods will be discussed separately below.

9.7.1. *Graphical Solution*

Consider the first order non-linear difference equation

$$y_{n+1} - y_n^2 + Ay_n + B = 0 \tag{9.68}$$

where A and B are constants, and rearrange it to separate the terms according to their subscripts. Thus

$$y_{n+1} = y_n^2 - Ay_n - B \tag{9.69}$$

By selecting arbitrarily a suitable set of values for y_n, a corresponding set of values of y_{n+1} can be calculated from equation (9.69). Hence a table of values of y_n and y_{n+1} can be compiled and the results plotted on rectangular coordinates in the form y_n vs y_{n+1}. The curve AB in Fig. 9.3 illustrates equation (9.69). In order to find the solution, the diagonal $y_n = y_{n+1}$ shown by the line PQ is constructed. Starting at the boundary condition y_0 at A (of coordinates y_0, y_1) and drawing the ordinate, the point C is located on the diagonal where $y_0 = y_1$. From C, a horizontal line is drawn back to meet the curve AB at the point D. The coordinates of D are (y_1, y_2) by equation (9.66) and hence y_2 is evaluated. By continuing this stepwise procedure to N steps, the value of y_{N+1} can be obtained. Thus the value of y corresponding to any value of n can be obtained.

This method will work for all first order equations provided that they can be separated into a simple form such as equation (9.69). It is usually easier to choose values for the variable on the more complicated side of the

FIG. 9.3. Graphical solution of a finite difference equation

equation and solve for the other variable. Thus it is simpler to choose a set of values for y_n and solve equation (9.69) for y_{n+1}, than assume values for y_{n+1} and solve the quadratic for y_n.

Example 1. 1000 lb/h of ethyl alcohol is to be esterified by reacting with 850 lb/h of acetic acid in a battery of continuous stirred tank reactors, each of 30 ft³ capacity and maintained at 100°C. If the equilibrium relation is such that 75·2% of the acid will be esterified, estimate the number of reactors required for 60% conversion.

At 100°C the specific reaction rate for esterification is $4·76 \times 10^{-4}$ l/g mole min and that for the hydrolysis of the ester is $1·63 \times 10^{-4}$ l/g mole min. The density of the reaction mixture can be assumed constant at 54 lb/ft³.

Solution. In a battery of N stirred tank reactors, consider a material balance on reactor m. That is,

$$qC_{A,m-1} - qC_{A,m} = rV \qquad\qquad \text{I}$$

where $C_{A,m}$ is the concentration of reactant A leaving vessel m, r is the rate of reaction, q is the volumetric flow rate, and V is the volume of one reactor.

For a second order reaction

$$A + B \rightleftharpoons C + D \qquad\qquad \text{II}$$

the rate of chemical reaction is

$$r = k_1 C_A C_B - k_2 C_C C_D \qquad\qquad \text{III}$$

and if the agitation is assumed to be perfect, the concentration of the components in the effluent from the vessel will be the same as the contents of the vessel. Therefore equation I becomes

$$C_{A,m-1} - C_{A,m} = (k_1 C_A C_B - k_2 C_C C_D)_m \theta \qquad\qquad \text{IV}$$

where θ is the nominal holding time in the vessel.

If the concentration of reactant B exceeds that of reactant A by an amount c initially, this difference will be maintained throughout the system.

That is, in any reactor m the concentration of reactant B is $(C_{A,m}+c)$. By the stoichiometry of the reaction the concentration of each product is $(C_{A,0}-C_{A,m})$.

Substituting these concentrations of components B, C, and D into equation IV and rearranging gives

$$C_{A,m-1} = C_{A,m}+[k_1 C_{A,m}(C_{A,m}+c)-k_2(C_{A,0}-C_{A,m})^2]\theta \qquad \text{V}$$

Equation V is a first order non-linear finite difference equation which will be solved graphically for the total number of reactors required to convert 60% of the acetic acid. Thus assuming the feed is uniformly mixed, the initial concentration of acetic acid is

$$C_{A,0} = \frac{850 \times 54}{1850} = 24\cdot8\,\frac{\text{lb}}{ft^3} \equiv \frac{24\cdot8 \times 454}{60 \times 28\cdot3} = 6\cdot63\,\frac{\text{g moles}}{1}$$

Similarly, $\qquad\qquad C_{B,0} = 10\cdot18$ g moles/l.

$$\therefore \quad c = 10\cdot18-6\cdot63 = 3\cdot55 \text{ g moles/l.}$$

$$\theta = \frac{30\cdot0 \times 54 \times 60}{1850} = 52\cdot6 \text{ min.}$$

Substituting these values into equation V gives

$$C_{A,m-1} = C_{A,m}+[4\cdot76 \times 10^{-4}C_{A,m}(C_{A,m}+3\cdot55)-1\cdot63 \times$$
$$\times 10^{-4}(6\cdot63-C_{A,m})^2]\,52\cdot6$$
$$= 0\cdot0164\,C_{A,m}^2+1\cdot202\,C_{A,m}-0\cdot376 \qquad \text{VI}$$

Arbitrary values of $C_{A,m}$ given in the table were selected and substituted into equation VI to give the corresponding values of $C_{A,m-1}$.

$C_{A,m}$	$C_{A,m-1}$
6·6	8·27
6·0	7·43
5·0	6·05
4·0	4·70
3·0	3·38
2·0	2·09

$C_{A,m-1}$ is plotted against $C_{A,m}$ in Fig. 9.4; and starting with the feed composition of 6.63 g moles/l, the number of reactors is "stepped off" as shown.

The required conversion is 60%,

$$\therefore \text{ acid in final effluent} = 0\cdot40 \times 6\cdot63 = 2\cdot65 \text{ g moles/l;}$$
$$\therefore \text{ number of reactors to produce this effluent is 7.}$$

Tiller[†] extended the graphical procedure presented above to second order

† Tiller, F. M. *Chem. Eng. Prog.* **44**, 299 (1948).

equations. Thus consider the second order non-linear finite difference equation

$$y_{n+2} + Py_{n+1} + Qy_n = R \qquad (9.70)$$

where R and Q are functions of y_n and P can be a function of y_{n+1}.

FIG. 9.4. Graphical reactor analysis

The graphical procedure is as follows. On rectangular coordinates plot $(R - Qy_n)$ vs y_n as represented by the curve AB in Fig. 9.5. Similarly plot $[R - (Q+P)y_{n+1}]$ vs y_{n+1} on the same scales and let this curve be represented by AC. Finally, plot the diagonal y_n vs y_n, represented by OD. Two

FIG. 9.5. Graphical solution of a nonlinear second order difference equation

boundary conditions will be known for a second order equation; y_0 will be one, and y_1 can be evaluated by using an overall material or energy balance for the problem. Mark off y_0 and y_1 on the abscissa and draw ordinates from each to the curve AC. The vertical difference between the curves at y_1 corresponds to $-Py_1$ and if this is added to $(R-Qy_0)$ at L to give the point M, the vertical distance from the abscissa to M corresponds to y_{n+2} by equation (9.70). Drawing a horizontal line to the diagonal at T and a vertical line to the axis locates y_2 in its correct position. It cuts the curves AB and AC to give $-Py_2$ which on adding to the AB curve at y_1 gives the value of y_3 which is located in its correct position relative to y_2 by drawing a horizontal line from V to the diagonal. This establishes the stepwise procedure and can be continued to locate y_n. In Fig. 9.5 the stepwise procedure is indicated by the arrows.

The graphical procedure given above for second order non-linear difference equations is of limited application. Thus it cannot be applied to the solution of equations in which product terms appear from more than one level of y. For instance, in Example 3, Section 3.3.9, equation I could not be solved by this graphical method because on rearrangement to the form

$$y_{n+1}-(A-Cy_{n-1}+Ey_n)y_n+(B-Dy_{n-1})y_{n-1} = 0 \qquad (9.71)$$

the function

$$P = A-Cy_{n-1}+Ey_n \qquad (9.72)$$

It will be noticed that P contains terms involving y_n and y_{n-1}. The term Cy_ny_{n-1} cannot be transferred to the other term without upsetting the condition to be satisfied by Q in equation (9.70). Hence equation (9.71) cannot be solved by the graphical method proposed by Tiller; the numerical method to be presented in Section 11.4.1 must be used.

9.7.2. *Analytical Solution*

At the present time only a limited number of non-linear finite difference equations can be solved analytically and these are solvable because they can be transformed into linear equations. Thus consider the following example.

Example 2. Solve the equation

$$y_{n+2}y_n = y_{n+1}^2 \qquad \text{I}$$

Converting equation I to logarithmic form,

$$\log y_{n+2} + \log y_n = 2\log y_{n+1} \qquad \text{II}$$

Letting

$$u_n = \log y_n$$

equation II becomes the second order linear equation

$$u_{n+2}-2u_{n+1}+u_n = 0 \qquad \text{III}$$

Solution of equation III by the methods already explained is

$$u_n = C_1+C_2 n \qquad \text{IV}$$

or

$$\log y_n = C_1+C_2 n \qquad \text{V}$$

Now let $\qquad\qquad C_1 = \log A \quad \text{and} \quad C_2 = \log B$

then $\qquad\qquad\qquad\qquad y_n = AB^n$ $\qquad\qquad\qquad$ VI

The solution of the above equation depended on the linearization of equation I and unless such a transformation can be found it is not possible to solve the equation.

A non-linear finite difference equation of second order that frequently appears in engineering problems is the Riccati finite difference equation.

$$y_{n+1}y_n + Ay_{n+1} + By_n + C = 0 \qquad (9.73)$$

where A, B and C are constants. It is converted to a linear difference equation by the following method.

Let $\qquad\qquad\qquad\qquad y_n = u_n + \delta$ $\qquad\qquad\qquad$ (9.74)

and substitute equation (9.74) into (9.73) and rearrange thus

$$(u_{n+1}+\delta)(u_n+\delta) + A(u_{n+1}+\delta) + B(u_n+\delta) + C = 0$$

$$u_{n+1}u_n + (A+\delta)u_{n+1} + (B+\delta)u_n + [\delta^2 + (A+B)\delta + C] = 0 \qquad (9.75)$$

If δ is chosen so that

$$\delta^2 + (A+B)\delta + C = 0 \qquad (9.76)$$

and equation (9.75) is divided by $(u_{n+1}u_n)$, then

$$(B+\delta)\frac{1}{u_{n+1}} + (A+\delta)\frac{1}{u_n} + 1 = 0 \qquad (9.77)$$

Putting $\qquad\qquad\qquad x_n = 1/u_n = 1/(y_n - \delta)$ $\qquad\qquad$ (9.78)

then equation (9.77) becomes

$$x_{n+1} + Px_n + Q = 0 \qquad (9.79)$$

which is a first order linear finite difference equation with

$$P = \frac{A+\delta}{B+\delta} \quad \text{and} \quad Q = \frac{1}{B+\delta}$$

Equation (9.79) can be solved by the methods already given, to yield the final solution

$$\frac{1}{y_n - \delta} = K\left[-\frac{A+\delta}{B+\delta}\right]^n - \frac{1}{A+B+2\delta} \qquad (9.80)$$

where the constant K is to be evaluated from the boundary conditions of the problem. This is illustrated in the example below.

Example 3. A benzene-toluene feed containing 60 mole per cent of benzene is fed continuously to a distillation column. If there are 9 plates between the reboiler and the feed plate, and the top product contains 98 mole per cent benzene whilst the liquid leaving the base of the column contains 2 mole per cent benzene, estimate the overall plate efficiency of the column. The feed enters the column at its boiling point and the relative volatility of benzene to toluene can be considered to be constant at 2·3. The reflux ratio is 3·0.

Consider 100 lb moles feed and let D = moles distillate;

$$W = \text{moles residue.}$$

$$\therefore \quad 100 = D + W \qquad\qquad \text{I}$$

and
$$60 = 0{\cdot}98D + 0{\cdot}02(100 - D) \qquad\qquad \text{II}$$

from which $D = 60{\cdot}4$ lb moles and $W = 39{\cdot}6$ lb moles.
A mass balance between the bottom of the column and some plate n in the stripping section is

$$Lx_{n+1} = Gy_n + Wx_w \qquad\qquad \text{III}$$

where L is the molar reflux down the column and
$\quad\;\; G$ is the molar vapour rate up the column.

Since the relative volatility is constant, the equilibrium relationship between x and y on any plate is

$$y_n = \frac{\alpha x_n}{1 + (\alpha - 1)x_n} \qquad\qquad \text{IV}$$

Substituting equation IV into equation III gives

$$Lx_{n+1} = \frac{\alpha G x_n}{1 + (\alpha - 1)x_n} + Wx_w \qquad\qquad \text{V}$$

or
$$x_{n+1}x_n + \frac{x_{n+1}}{\alpha - 1} - \left[\frac{\alpha G + (\alpha - 1)Wx_w}{L(\alpha - 1)}\right]x_n - \frac{Wx_w}{L(\alpha - 1)} = 0 \qquad\qquad \text{VI}$$

Now
$$L = F + RD = (100 + 3 \times 60{\cdot}4) = 281{\cdot}2 \text{ lb moles/h}$$

and letting

$$A = \frac{1}{\alpha - 1} = \frac{1}{1{\cdot}3} = 0{\cdot}769$$

$$B = \frac{\alpha G + (\alpha - 1)Wx_w}{L(\alpha - 1)} = \frac{(2{\cdot}3 \times 4 \times 60{\cdot}4) + (1{\cdot}3 \times 39{\cdot}6 \times 0{\cdot}02)}{281{\cdot}2 \times 1{\cdot}3}$$

$$= 1{\cdot}523$$

$$C = \frac{Wx_w}{L(\alpha - 1)} = \frac{39{\cdot}6 \times 0{\cdot}02}{281{\cdot}2 \times 1{\cdot}3} = 0{\cdot}0022$$

equation VI becomes the Riccati equation

$$x_{n+1}x_n + Ax_{n+1} - Bx_n - C = 0 \qquad\qquad \text{VII}$$

The solution of equation VII is obtained by following the procedure set out in the above text. Thus let

$$z_n = \frac{1}{x_n - \delta} \qquad\qquad \text{VIII}$$

where δ is obtained from the equation

$$\delta^2 + (A - B)\delta - C = 0$$

or
$$\delta^2 - 0{\cdot}754\delta = 0{\cdot}0022$$

The roots of this equation are

$$\delta = 0.757 \quad \text{or} \quad -0.003$$

The complete solution of equation VII is

$$z_n = \frac{1}{x_n - \delta} = K\left[\frac{A+\delta}{B-\delta}\right]^n - \frac{1}{A-B+2\delta} \qquad \text{XI}$$

Selecting the root $\delta = -0.003$ and inserting the boundary condition that when $n = 0$, $x_n = 0.02$ gives

$$K = 42.2$$

The value of n corresponding to $x_n = 0.60$ is given by

$$1.66 = 42.2\left[\frac{0.766}{1.526}\right]^n + 1.32 \qquad \text{XII}$$

as $n = 7.0$ ideal stages. Subtracting the reboiler from this number gives the overall plate efficiency as $6.0/9 \equiv 67\%$.

9.8. Differential-Difference Equations

It has been shown in the above sections that chemical engineering equipment consisting of a number of stages can be analysed by means of finite difference equations when the operating conditions are steady. However, when this type of equipment is subjected to a step change in operating conditions, or is started up, or is being shut down, the compositions of the streams passing through these stages change with time. This results in the presence of differential terms in addition to the finite difference terms in what is known as a "differential-difference" equation. This type of equation will be treated in this section, but it should be pointed out that on many occasions the final equation describing the process is too complex for analytical solution, and it is necessary to make a "stage-to-stage" analysis with the aid of a computer. The solution of such problems will be treated in Chapter 11.

The analytical solution of differential-difference equations is accomplished by converting this type of equation into a finite difference form by means of the Laplace transformation. The transformed equation is solved and inverted to show how the conditions of the process streams passing through the equipment vary with time during the transient period. The technique to apply, where possible, is illustrated by the following examples.

Example 1. A system consists of N stirred tanks each of volume v ft^3 arranged in cascade. If each tank initially contains pure water and a salt stream of concentration x_0 lb/ft^3 is fed to the first tank at a rate R ft^3/h, calculate what the output concentration from the last tank should be as a function of time if the stirring is 100% efficient.

Use the result to compare the transient behaviour of all systems of total volume $Nv = V$ (constant).

Solution. With the normal convention regarding subscripts, a salt balance over the nth stage gives

$$Rx_{n-1} - Rx_n = v\frac{dx_n}{dt} \qquad \text{I}$$

Taking the Laplace transformation of equation I by using equation (6.11) to remove the derivative, and remembering that the system initially contains no salt,

$$\therefore \quad R\bar{x}_{n-1} - R\bar{x}_n = vs\bar{x}_n \qquad \text{II}$$

Solving this linear finite difference equation by the method of Section 9.6 gives

$$\bar{x}_n = A\left(\frac{R}{R+vs}\right)^n \qquad \text{III}$$

Because the feed composition is constant,

$$\bar{x}_0 = x_0/s \qquad \text{IV}$$

$$\therefore \quad \bar{x}_n = \frac{x_0}{s}\left(\frac{R}{R+vs}\right)^n \qquad \text{V}$$

$$\therefore \quad \bar{x}_N = \frac{x_0}{s}\left(\frac{R}{R+vs}\right)^N \qquad \text{VI}$$

From transform number 10 in the table at the end of the book,

$$\mathscr{L}\left[\frac{t^{N-1}e^{-at}}{(n-1)!}\right] = \frac{1}{(s+a)^N}$$

Hence, using equation (6.21),

$$\mathscr{L}^{-1}\left[\frac{1}{s(s+a)^N}\right] = \int_0^t \frac{t^{N-1}e^{-at}}{(N-1)!}\,dt \qquad \text{VII}$$

Integrating the right-hand side of equation VII by parts $(N-1)$ times gives

$$\mathscr{L}^{-1}\left[\frac{1}{s(s+a)^N}\right] = \frac{1}{(N-1)!}\left[\frac{-t^{N-1}}{a}e^{-at} + \frac{N-1}{a}\int t^{N-2}e^{-at}\,dt\right]_0^t$$

$$= \frac{-t^{N-1}e^{-at}}{a(N-1)!} + \frac{1}{a(N-2)!}\int_0^t t^{N-2}e^{-at}\,dt$$

$$= \ldots\ldots$$

$$= \frac{-t^{N-1}e^{-at}}{a(N-1)!} - \frac{t^{N-2}e^{-at}}{a^2(N-2)!} - \ldots - \frac{e^{-at}}{a^N} + \frac{1}{a^N} \qquad \text{VIII}$$

Inverting equation VI by using equation VIII,

$$x_N = x_0\left[1 - e^{-Rt/v} - \frac{Rt}{v}e^{-Rt/v} - \ldots - \frac{(Rt/v)^{N-1}}{(N-1)!}e^{-Rt/v}\right]$$

$$\therefore \quad x_N = x_0 - x_0\, e^{-Rt/v}\left[1 + \frac{Rt}{v} + \frac{(Rt/v)^2}{2!} + \dots + \frac{(Rt/v)^{N-1}}{(N-1)!}\right] \qquad \text{IX}$$

which is the solution to the first part of the problem.

For the second part, if $V = Nv$, equation IX becomes

$$x_N = x_0 - x_0\, e^{-NRt/V}\left[1 + \frac{NRt}{V} + \frac{(NRt/V)^2}{2!} + \dots + \frac{(NRt/V)^{N-1}}{(N-1)!}\right] \qquad \text{X}$$

In particular, if $N = 1$,

$$x_N = x_0 - x_0\, e^{-Rt/V} \qquad \text{XI}$$

and if $N = 4$,

$$x_N = x_0 - x_0\, e^{-4Rt/V}\left[1 + \frac{4Rt}{V} + 8\left(\frac{Rt}{V}\right)^2 + \frac{32}{3}\left(\frac{Rt}{V}\right)^3\right] \qquad \text{XII}$$

FIG. 9.6. Output from an N tank system of total volume V

It is difficult to evaluate equation X in the limit as $N \to \infty$, but putting $V = Nv$ into equation VI gives

$$\bar{x}_N = \frac{x_0}{s}\left(1 + \frac{Vs}{RN}\right)^{-N} \qquad \text{XIII}$$

which can be expanded by the binomial theorem thus,

$$\bar{x}_N = \frac{x_0}{s}\left[1 - \frac{Vs}{R} + \frac{N+1}{2N}\left(\frac{Vs}{R}\right)^2 - \frac{(N+1)(N+2)}{3!\,N^2}\left(\frac{Vs}{R}\right)^3 + \dots\right]$$

If N is large, the expression in the square brackets can be approximated to give

$$\bar{x}_N = \frac{x_0}{s}\left[1 - \frac{Vs}{R} + \frac{1}{2}\left(\frac{Vs}{R}\right)^2 - \frac{1}{3!}\left(\frac{Vs}{R}\right)^3 + \ldots\right]$$

$$= \frac{x_0}{s}e^{-Vs/R} \qquad\qquad \text{XIV}$$

The inversion of equation XIV is given by number 61 in the table at the end of the book. Hence as $N \to \infty$

$$x_N \to x_0 S_k(t) \qquad\qquad \text{XV}$$

where
$$k = V/R$$

Equations X, XI, XII, and XIV have been plotted in Fig. 9.6 to show how the system responds for different values of N. The important result emerges that a large number of small stirred tanks in series has approximately the same response to a step change as a single tube of the same volume with plug flow. The converse is also true, that flow in a tube with a small amount of back-mixing can be represented by a chain of stirred tanks of the same total volume.

Example 2. Acetic anhydride is to be hydrolyzed in a laboratory stirred tank reactor battery consisting of three vessels of equal size. 1800 ml of anhydride solution of concentration 0·21 g moles/l is charged into each vessel at 40°C, and 600 ml/min of a solution containing 0·137 g moles/l is continuously fed to the first reactor. Estimate the time required for the reactor system to settle down to steady state operation.

The specific reaction rate constant for the hydrolysis at 40°C is 0·38 min^{-1}.

Solution. Initially let there be a battery of n reactors in series and consider a material balance over reactor m.

Let q be the volumetric flow rate.

V be the volume of each reaction vessel.

C be the concentration of anhydride.

If the density of the liquid and the temperature of each reaction vessel is considered to be constant, then

$$qC_{m-1} - qC_m = r_m V + V\frac{dC_m}{dt} \qquad\qquad \text{I}$$

Now $V/q = \theta$ the holding time, and $r_m = kC_m$.

$$\therefore \quad \frac{dC_m}{dt} = \frac{C_{m-1}}{\theta} - C_m\left(\frac{1+k\theta}{\theta}\right) \qquad\qquad \text{II}$$

Since all the vessels are to be of the same size and the battery is to be operated isothermally,

$$\frac{1+k\theta}{\theta} = Q \text{ (constant)} \qquad\qquad \text{III}$$

M

Thus carrying out the Laplace transformation on equation II, by making use of

$$\mathscr{L}\left[\frac{dC_m}{dt}\right] = s\bar{C}_m(s) - C_m(0)$$

from Section 6.2.1, gives

$$s\bar{C}_m(s) - C_m(0) + Q\bar{C}_m(s) - \frac{1}{\theta}\bar{C}_{m-1}(s) = 0 \qquad\qquad \text{IV}$$

But the vessels all start with the same composition in them, hence $C_m(0) = 0.21$. Equation IV can be put into the standard form for a first order difference equation thus,

$$\theta(s+Q)\bar{C}_m(s) - \bar{C}_{m-1}(s) = 0.21\theta \qquad\qquad \text{V}$$

Solving equation V by the methods of Section 9.6 gives the general solution

$$\bar{C}_m(s) = A[\theta(s+Q)]^{-m} + \frac{0.21\theta}{\theta(s+Q)-1} \qquad\qquad \text{VI}$$

where A is an arbitrary constant.
When

$$m = 0$$
$$C_0 = 0.137$$
$$\therefore \quad \bar{C}_0(s) = \frac{0.317}{s}$$
$$\therefore \quad \frac{0.137}{s} = A + \frac{0.21\theta}{\theta(s+Q)-1} \qquad\qquad \text{VII}$$

which determines A. Substituting into equation VI and rearranging gives

$$\bar{C}_m(s) = \frac{0.137}{s\theta^m(s+Q)^m} + \frac{0.21\theta}{\theta(s+Q)-1}\left[1 - \frac{1}{\theta^m(s+Q)^m}\right]$$

$$= \frac{0.137}{s\theta^m(s+Q)^m} + 0.21\theta\left[\frac{1}{\theta(s+Q)} + \frac{1}{\theta^2(s+Q)^2} + \dots + \frac{1}{\theta^m(s+Q)^m}\right] \qquad \text{VIII}$$

by algebraic division.

Each term in the square brackets can be inverted directly by using the tables at the end of the book (transform number 10), and the first term can be inverted by using the property of the transform given by equation (6.21). Hence the solution is

$$C_m = \frac{0.137}{(\theta Q)^m} - \frac{0.137}{(\theta Q)^m}\left[1 + Qt + \frac{(Qt)^2}{2!} + \dots + \frac{(Qt)^{n-1}}{(n-1)!}\right]e^{-Qt}$$

$$+ 0.21\left[1 + \frac{t}{\theta} + \frac{1}{2!}\left(\frac{t}{\theta}\right)^2 + \dots + \frac{(t/\theta)^{n-1}}{(n-1)!}\right]e^{-Qt} \qquad \text{IX}$$

Equation IX is a general expression giving the concentration of the effluent from a stirred tank reactor battery containing n vessels of equal size, each starting from the same initial concentration. Expressions of this type have been derived for different kinds of reaction by Mason and Piret[†] and the reader is advised to consult these authors for a more extensive analysis.

In the special example considered here, the last vessel to reach steady state will be the third, and since

$$\theta = \frac{V}{q} = \frac{1800}{600} = 3 \cdot 0$$

$$Q = \frac{1 + k\theta}{\theta} = \tfrac{1}{3} + 0 \cdot 38 = 0 \cdot 713$$

$$\theta Q = 2 \cdot 14$$

$$\therefore \quad C_3 = 0 \cdot 014 - 0 \cdot 014(1 + 0 \cdot 713t + 0 \cdot 254t^2)\, e^{-0 \cdot 713t}$$
$$+ 0 \cdot 21(1 + 0 \cdot 333t + 0 \cdot 056t^2)\, e^{-0 \cdot 713t}$$

$$\therefore \quad C_3 = 0 \cdot 014 + (0 \cdot 196 + 0 \cdot 060t + 0 \cdot 0082t^2)\, e^{-0 \cdot 713t} \qquad \text{X}$$

Equation X which gives C_3, the composition of the effluent from the final reactor as a function of time, has been plotted in Fig. 9.7. This shows that the laboratory reactor battery has reached steady state conditions within the limits of experimental detection in about 15 minutes.

FIG. 9.7.   Time to reach steady state

Example 3. 1000 lb/h of a solution containing 0·01 lb nicotine per lb of water is being extracted by 1200 lb/h of kerosine in a counter current extractor containing 8 stages. If the concentration of the feed liquor is suddenly changed to 0·02 lb nicotine per lb of water, how long will it take for the extractor to settle down to steady state operation under the new conditions?

The equilibrium relation is

$$Y = 0 \cdot 86\,X$$

where Y is lb nicotine per lb of kerosine;

and X is lb nicotine per lb of water.

The hold up per stage can be taken to be constant at

400 lb water and 200 lb kerosine.

† Mason, D. R. and Piret, E. L. *I.E.C.* **42**, 817 (1950).

FIG. 9.8.   Stagewise counterflow system

Solution

The system is illustrated in Fig. 9.8 and the symbols have the following meanings.

R   Flow rate of water phase (1000 lb/h)
S   Flow rate of kerosine phase (1200 lb/h)
N   Total number of stages (8)
X_n Nicotine concentration in water phase in nth stage
Y_n Nicotine concentration in kerosine phase in nth stage
m   Distribution ratio (0·86)
h   Hold up of kerosine per stage (200 lb)
H   Hold up of water per stage (400 lb)
X_0' Original feed concentration (0·01 lb/lb)
X_F New feed concentration (0·02 lb/lb)

A nicotine balance over the nth stage gives

$$RX_{n-1}+SY_{n+1}-RX_n-SY_n = h\frac{dX_n}{dt}+H\frac{dY_n}{dt} \qquad \text{I}$$

The equilibrium relationship gives

$$Y_n = mX_n \qquad \text{II}$$

Eliminating Y_n, Y_{n+1} between equations I and II and rearranging,

$$\therefore \quad \alpha X_{n+1}-(\alpha+1)X_n+X_{n-1} = \beta\frac{dX_n}{dt} \qquad \text{III}$$

where 	$$\alpha = mS/R, \qquad \beta = (h+mH)/R \qquad \text{IV}$$

The plant is initially operating at steady state, and the concentration in each stage must be determined for these conditions first. Thus, putting $dX_n/dt = 0$, equation III becomes

$$\alpha X_{n+1}-(\alpha+1)X_n+X_{n-1} = 0 \qquad \text{V}$$

The method of Section 9·6 gives the general solution

$$X_n = A+B\alpha^{-n} \qquad \text{VI}$$

The boundary conditions for this part of the problem are:—

at 	$n = 0,$ 	$X_0 = X_0'$

at 	$n = N+1,$ 	$Y_{N+1} = mX_{N+1} = 0$ 	VII

Hence, $$A = \frac{-X_0'}{\alpha^{N+1}-1} \qquad B = \frac{\alpha^{N+1}X_0'}{\alpha^{N+1}-1} \qquad \text{VIII}$$

Therefore, equation VI gives the initial state of the system where A and B are determined by equations VIII.

For the unsteady state part of the problem, it is necessary to take the Laplace transformation of equation III. Thus

$$\alpha\overline{X}_{n+1}-(\alpha+1)\overline{X}_n+\overline{X}_{n-1} = \beta(s\overline{X}_n-A-B\alpha^{-n}) \qquad \text{IX}$$

where equation VI has been used for the initial conditions. Rearranging,

$$\alpha\overline{X}_{n+1}-(\alpha+1+s\beta)\overline{X}_n+\overline{X}_{n-1} = -A\beta-B\beta\alpha^{-n}$$

or in operator form,

$$[\alpha E^2-(\alpha+1+s\beta)E+1]\overline{X}_{n-1} = -A\beta-B\beta\alpha^{-n} \qquad \text{X}$$

Equation X is linear so that its solution can be expressed as the sum of a complementary function and a particular solution. The complementary function is given by

$$\overline{X}_{n-1} = C\rho_1^{n-1}+D\rho_2^{n-1} \qquad \text{XI}$$

where $$\rho_1+\rho_2 = (\alpha+1+s\beta)/\alpha \qquad \text{XII}$$

and $$\rho_1\rho_2 = 1/\alpha \qquad \text{XIII}$$

The particular solutions for the separate terms on the right hand side of X can be found by the inverse operator method described in Section 9.6.2. Thus for the first term

$$\overline{X}_{n-1} = \frac{-A\beta}{\alpha-\alpha-1-s\beta+1} = \frac{A}{s} \qquad \text{XIV}$$

and for the second term,

$$\overline{X}_{n-1} = \frac{-B\beta\alpha^{-n}}{\alpha^{-1}-1-\alpha^{-1}-s\beta\alpha^{-1}+1} = \frac{B}{s}\alpha^{-n+1} \qquad \text{XV}$$

Combining equations XI, XIV, and XV gives the complete solution of equation X; which is

$$\overline{X}_{n-1} = C\rho_1^{n-1}+D\rho_2^{n-1} + \frac{A+B\alpha^{-n+1}}{s}$$

or $$\overline{X}_n = C\rho_1^n+D\rho_2^n + \frac{A+B\alpha^{-n}}{s} \qquad \text{XVI}$$

The boundary conditions can also be transformed thus,

at $\quad n = 0, \qquad X_0 = X_F, \quad \therefore \quad \overline{X}_0 = X_F/s$

at $\quad n = N+1, \quad X_{N+1} = 0, \quad \therefore \quad \overline{X}_{N+1} = 0$ $\qquad$ XVII

Substituting these boundary values into equation XVI and using equations VIII to eliminate A and B, gives

$$\frac{X_F}{s} = C+D+\frac{A+B}{s} = C+D+\frac{X_0'}{s} \qquad \text{XVIII}$$

and
$$0 = C\rho_1^{N+1} + D\rho_2^{N+1} + \frac{A + B\alpha^{-N-1}}{s}$$

$$= C\rho_1^{N+1} + D\rho_2^{N+1} \qquad \text{XIX}$$

Solving equations XVIII and XIX for C and D, and substituting into equation XVI gives the solution

$$\bar{X}_n = \frac{A + B\alpha^{-n}}{s} + \frac{X_F - X_0'}{s}\left[\frac{\rho_2^{N+1}\rho_1^n - \rho_1^{N+1}\rho_2^n}{\rho_2^{N+1} - \rho_1^{N+1}}\right] \qquad \text{XX}$$

In order to invert equation XX it must be remembered that ρ_1 and ρ_2 are determined by equations XII and XIII as functions of s. Therefore, the method of residues must be used to invert the last term in equation XX.

To simplify the nomenclature, put

$$\bar{f}(s) = \frac{\rho_2^{N+1}\rho_1^n - \rho_1^{N+1}\rho_2^n}{s(\rho_2^{N+1} - \rho_1^{N+1})} \qquad \text{XXI}$$

The numerator on the right-hand side of equation XXI could become infinite if $|\rho_2|$ became infinite. But if $|\rho_2|$ is large, equation XIII ensures that $|\rho_1|$ is small. Hence it can be shown that as $|\rho_2| \to \infty$, $\bar{f}(s) \to 0$; and the only singularities of $\bar{f}(s)$ arise from the zeros of the denominator. These zeros occur at $s = 0$ and when $\rho_1^{N+1} = \rho_2^{N+1}$. The second solution shows that $|\rho_1| = |\rho_2|$, and since ρ_1 and ρ_2 are the roots of a quadratic equation with real coefficients, they must be equal, or mutual complex conjugates. Therefore, putting

$$\rho_1 = r\,e^{-i\theta}, \qquad \rho_2 = r\,e^{i\theta} \qquad \text{XXII}$$

$$\therefore \quad \rho_2^{N+1} - \rho_1^{N+1} = r^{N+1}\left[e^{(N+1)i\theta} - e^{-(N+1)i\theta}\right]$$

$$= 2ir^{N+1}\sin(N+1)\theta \qquad \text{XXIII}$$

Hence $\bar{f}(s)$ has singularities when $s = 0$, and when

$$(N+1)\theta = k\pi \qquad \text{XXIV}$$

where k is an integer.

Putting equations XXII into equations XIII and XII gives

$$r^2 = 1/\alpha \qquad \text{XXV}$$

$$2\alpha r \cos\theta = \alpha + 1 + s\beta \qquad \text{XXVI}$$

$$\therefore \quad s = -\frac{\alpha + 1 - 2\sqrt{\alpha}\cos[k\pi/(N+1)]}{\beta} \qquad \text{XXVII}$$

Equation XXVII gives a distinct set of values of s for $k = 0, 1, \ldots (N+1)$, but repeated values for integer values of k exceeding $(N+1)$. When $k = 0$, or $(N+1)$, equations XXII show that $\rho_1 = \rho_2$, and an application of L'Hôpital's rule to equation XXI shows that $\bar{f}(s)$ remains finite as $\rho_2 \to \rho_1$. Therefore $\bar{f}(s)$ has $(N+1)$ simple poles:

one at $s = 0$,
and N given by equation XXVII with $k = 1, 2, \ldots N$.

Using equation (4.113) to find the residue of $\bar{f}(s)$ at $s = 0$, gives at

$$s = 0, \qquad \rho_1 = 1, \qquad \rho_2 = \alpha^{-1}$$

$$\therefore \quad B_0 = \frac{\alpha^{-N-1}-\alpha^{-n}}{\alpha^{-N-1}-1} = \frac{\alpha^{N+1-n}-1}{\alpha^{N+1}-1} \qquad \text{XXVIII}$$

Substituting equations XXII into equation XXI gives

$$\bar{f}(s) = \frac{r^n}{s} \frac{\sin(N+1-n)\theta}{\sin(N+1)\theta} \qquad \text{XXIX}$$

$$\therefore \quad e^{st}\bar{f}(s) = \frac{r^n}{s} \frac{\sin(N+1-n)\theta}{\sin(N+1)\theta} e^{st} \qquad \text{XXX}$$

Remembering that θ is a function of s given by equation XXVI, and using equation (4.113) to find the residue of $e^{st}\bar{f}(s)$ gives

$$B_k = \frac{r^n}{s} \frac{\sin(N+1-n)\theta}{(N+1)\cos(N+1)\theta} \frac{e^{st}}{(d\theta/ds)}$$

$$= \frac{-r^n}{s(N+1)} \frac{\sin(N+1-n)\theta}{\cos(N+1)\theta} \frac{2\alpha r \sin\theta\, e^{st}}{\beta} \qquad \text{XXXI}$$

Using equations XXIV, XXV, and XXVII to simplify XXXI,

$$B_k = \frac{2(-1)^k \alpha^{-(n-1)/2}\sin\theta \sin(N+1-n)\theta}{(N+1)(\alpha+1-2\sqrt{\alpha}\cos\theta)} \exp\left[\frac{-(\alpha+1-2\sqrt{\alpha}\cos\theta)t}{\beta}\right]$$

Combining the residues as given by equation (6.43) and inverting the remainder of equation XX,

$$X_n = X_0'\left[\frac{\alpha^{N+1-n}-1}{\alpha^{N+1}-1}\right] + (X_F-X_0')\left[\frac{\alpha^{N+1-n}-1}{\alpha^{N+1}-1}\right]$$

$$+ (X_F-X_0')\sum_{k=1}^{N} \frac{2(-1)^k\alpha^{-(n-1)/2}\sin\theta\sin(N+1-n)\theta}{(N+1)(\alpha+1-2\sqrt{\alpha}\cos\theta)} e^{st}$$

$$\therefore \quad X_n = X_F\left[\frac{\alpha^{N+1-n}-1}{\alpha^{N+1}-1}\right]$$

$$+ (X_F-X_0')\sum_{k=1}^{N} \frac{2(-1)^k\alpha^{-(n-1)/2}\sin\theta\sin(N+1-n)\theta}{(N+1)(\alpha+1-2\sqrt{\alpha}\cos\theta)} e^{st} \qquad \text{XXXII}$$

Equation XXXII is the complete solution to the problem where θ is given by equation XXIV, and s by equation XXVII.

Since the final stage will be the last to reach the new steady state conditions, a graph should be plotted showing X_8 as a function of time. From equation XXXII,

$$X_8 = X_F\left[\frac{\alpha-1}{\alpha^9-1}\right] + (X_F-X_0')\sum_{k=1}^{8} \frac{2(-1)^k\alpha^{-7/2}\sin^2\theta}{9(\alpha+1-2\sqrt{\alpha}\cos\theta)} e^{st} \qquad \text{XXXIII}$$

Using the numerical values given in the problem,

$$\theta = k\pi/9 = 20k°$$

$$\alpha = mS/R = 1.032$$

$$\beta = \frac{h+mH}{R} = 0.544$$

$$\therefore \quad \alpha^9 = 1.3278, \qquad \alpha^{-7/2} = 0.8956$$

k	θ	$2\sqrt{\alpha}\cos\theta$	$-s$	$\sin^2\theta$	$\dfrac{2\alpha^{-7/2}\sin^2\theta}{9(\alpha+1-2\sqrt{\alpha}\cos\theta)}$
1	20	1.9092	0.2257	0.1170	0.1896
2	40	1.5564	0.8743	0.4132	0.1729
3	60	1.0159	1.868	0.7500	0.1469
4	80	0.3528	3.087	0.9699	0.1149
5	100	−0.3528	4.384	0.9699	0.0809
6	120	−1.0159	5.603	0.7500	0.0489
7	140	−1.5564	6.596	0.4132	0.0230
8	160	−1.9092	7.245	0.1170	0.0059

$$\therefore \quad 100X_8 = 0.195 - 0.1896\,e^{s_1 t} + 0.1729\,e^{s_2 t} - 0.1469\,e^{s_3 t} +$$

$$+ 0.1149\,e^{s_4 t} - 0.0809\,e^{s_5 t} + 0.0489\,e^{s_6 t} - 0.0230\,e^{s_7 t} + 0.0059\,e^{s_8 t} \qquad \text{XXXIV}$$

Equation XXXIV has been plotted in Fig. 9.9 from the following calculated values.

t	X_8	t	X_8
0	0.0972	10	0.1752
1	0.0975	12	0.1824
2	0.1012	14	0.1870
3	0.1107	16	0.1899
4	0.1232	18	0.1917
6	0.1470	20	0.1929
8	0.1640	24	0.1942

FIG. 9.9. Nicotine concentration in extract

It can be seen that it takes about 24 hours for the system to settle down to the new conditions.

Chapter 10

TREATMENT OF EXPERIMENTAL RESULTS

10.1. Introduction

THE analysis of many chemical engineering problems is concerned with using experimental results to verify theories or develop empirical formulae. Some of the data points are often inaccurate and methods must be found for eliciting reliable information with reasonable certainty. This subject falls into the realm of statistics, but the mathematical approach given in this chapter yields valid conclusions.

A great deal can be learnt by presenting the results graphically with suitably chosen coordinates and inspecting them visually; and the use of various kinds of available graph paper is described in the first part of the chapter. With the exception of Section 10.4, where a contour representation of three variables is described, all discussion is confined to systems of two variables; it being assumed that all other variables can be kept constant and treated as parameters.

Experimental results can also be used to determine an average value of a variable, or a set of data can be integrated to find some total value. For example, the determination of an average velocity across the cross-section of a pipe or piece of equipment involves averaging data points; and the prediction of an accumulated composition from a set of values of point composition necessitates numerical or graphical integration. Methods for performing these calculations are given in the final part of this chapter.

10.2. Graph Paper

Results can be presented in the form of a table or as a graph. Although the tabular form is capable of showing greater accuracy, the graphical presentation is more readily assimilated, because it gives a clearer picture of the behaviour of the variables. The graphical method is usually sufficiently accurate for the presentation of experimental points, but for theoretical points calculated from a numerical method (see Chapter 11) a tabular form is preferred.

For a particular piece of equipment where the number of variable parameters is small, a direct plot of the variables is the most useful, but if comparison with other work on similar equipment is envisaged, the appropriate dimensionless groups should be used along the axes. If the dimensionless groups are chosen correctly, each group should only contain one principal variable and the rest of its constituent parts should be parameters.

No purpose would be served by plotting a dimensionless group against a dimensional variable and this form of presentation should be avoided. Any mathematical equation must be dimensionally consistent and hence if one term is dimensionless, so must all other terms be dimensionless. Disregard of this important fact can lead to apparent anomalies, particularly when a logarithmic plot is used.

There are many types of graph paper which are described below and the correct type should be chosen for each problem. " The most desirable shape for a curve is a straight line," and the scales should be chosen in such a way that the major part of the curve is inclined at 45° to each axis. This ensures equal accuracy in all regions of the graph both in plotting the curve and reading results from it.

10.2.1. *Linear Graph Paper*

The most common and generally used graph paper has its axes divided into equal intervals so that any range of numerical values of a variable can be accommodated by choosing a suitable scale. Most normal types of graph paper are subdivided into ten divisions, and it is customary to count in a decimal system; hence factors of three should be avoided when choosing the scales, so that each subdivision will represent an easily written number.

The equation of a straight line is usually written

$$y = mx + c \tag{10.1}$$

where m is the gradient, and c (the intercept) is the value of y corresponding to $x = 0$. Because c is defined in this manner, the origin should not be suppressed.

For a general curve on linear scales, the equation

$$y = f(x) \tag{10.2}$$

is satisfied. By differentiating equation (10.2) the gradient of the tangent at a point can be found. Conversely, if a tangent is drawn to the curve then a numerical value can be found for the derivative at that point. The most accurate way to differentiate a curve graphically is to choose a gradient and construct a set of parallel lines with that gradient which intersect the curve

FIG. 10.1. Graphical differentiation

as shown in Fig. 10.1. If each chord so constructed is bisected, and the midpoints are joined with a smooth curve, this curve must intersect the original curve orthogonally at the point where the tangent has the chosen slope.

Integration of equation (10.2) with respect to x between the fixed limits $x = a$ and $x = b$ is represented graphically by the area bounded by the curve $y = f(x)$, the ordinates $x = a$ and $x = b$, and the x axis. This can readily be visualized by dividing the area into vertical strips of equal width and considering the integral as the limit of the sum of the areas of these strips as their width approaches zero. This area can be evaluated by counting the squares on the graph paper which form the desired area, or by using a numerical method from Section 10.7.

10.2.2. *Semi-Logarithmic Graph Paper*

In many practical cases, particularly those involving the approach to steady state conditions of a process, the dependent variable is a decaying exponential function of the independent variable. For example, in Section 1.6, equation (1.29) is of the form

$$y = A e^{-bx} \tag{10.3}$$

after a change of origin. If an experiment is designed to determine the coefficients A and b from a series of measurements of x and y, it is more convenient to use the logarithmic form of equation (10.3) which is

$$\ln y = \ln A - bx \tag{10.4}$$

Defining a new dependent variable by

$$Y = \ln y \tag{10.5}$$

equation (10.4) becomes

$$Y = -bx + \ln A \tag{10.6}$$

By comparison of equations (10.1) and (10.6) it can be seen that $-b$ is the gradient of the curve of Y against x, and $\ln A$ is the intercept. Because such plots are frequently needed, semi-logarithmic graph paper is available which has one scale divided logarithmically, as on a slide rule. Hence, the values of y can be used directly instead of consulting log tables to evaluate Y, the logarithms being intrinsically taken on the graph paper itself. It must be remembered however, that the gradient $(-b)$ must be determined from the linear measurement of Y and not from reading the scales which give values of y. The intercept can be measured as a linear value of $\ln A$ when $x = 0$, or read directly from the scale of y as A, which is simpler and more usual.

It should be noted that the logarithms are all taken to the base e and the gradient must be corrected for the scales of the axes. To do this, the measured gradient must be multiplied by the length of the unit on the linear scale and divided by the length of the unit on the logarithmic scale. The logarithmic unit is the distance between 1 and 2·718 on the scale of y. Graph paper is usually printed with these two units approximately equal, but a 5% discrepancy is quite common and should be corrected.

10.2.3. *Logarithmic Graph Paper*

Dimensional analysis frequently indicates an empirical equation of the form

$$y = Cx^n \qquad (10.7)$$

where x and y are dimensionless groups and C and n are constants to be determined experimentally. Because the groups are usually made dimensionless by using the physical properties of the materials used, the values of x and y are likely to vary over very wide ranges. To combine many results into a single correlation applicable to such a wide range, a logarithmic scale is superior to a linear scale. Also, the logarithmic form of equation (10.7) is

$$Y = nX + c \qquad (10.8)$$

where $Y = \ln y$, $X = \ln x$, and $c = \ln C$; and this is the equation of a straight line. Therefore, for plotting such equations as (10.8), graph paper with both axes subdivided logarithmically is available. It is normal for the logarithmic unit to be the same along each axis so that the gradient n can be found by direct linear measurement. The intercept c is the value of Y when $X = 0$. This can be found more easily as the value $y = C$ when $x = 1$.

The origin of linear scales can never be plotted on logarithmic graph paper. If any point is referred to as the origin, the point $x = 1$, $y = 1$, corresponding to $X = 0$, $Y = 0$, is usually meant. The intercept as described above is determined relative to axes through this origin.

Inspection of equation (10.7) shows that if n is positive, then the curve will pass through the origin of linear scales. If n is negative, the curve will

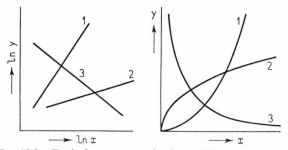

FIG. 10.2. Equivalent curves on log-log and linear graph paper

be asymptotic to both axes. It is therefore useless trying to fit an equation of the form (10.7) to any set of points which obviously intersect either axis, unless the point of intersection can be transferred to the origin. The three types of curve which give rise to straight line plots on log-log paper are illustrated in Fig. 10.2.

10.2.4. *Triangular Graph Paper*

In the study of liquid-liquid extraction systems where three components are present in two phases, a convenient graphical representation of the composition of a phase is needed. The data can be presented on a triangular diagram by using the geometrical property of a triangle which is proved below.

Figure 10.3 shows any triangle ABC and any interior point P. The lines AP, BP, CP are produced to meet BC, AC, AB at D, E, F respectively.

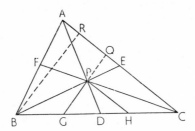

FIG. 10.3. The triangular diagram

PG is drawn parallel to AB, and PH is drawn parallel to AC so that G and H lie on BC.

Triangles BPH, BEC are similar.

$$\therefore \quad PE : BE :: HC : BC \tag{10.9}$$

Similarly, triangles CPG, CFB are similar.

$$\therefore \quad PF : CF :: BG : BC \tag{10.10}$$

Also, triangles PGH, ABC are similar

$$\therefore \quad PD : AD :: GH : BC \tag{10.11}$$

Adding equations (10.9, 10, 11) together gives

$$\frac{PE}{BE} + \frac{PF}{CF} + \frac{PD}{AD} = 1 \tag{10.12}$$

Dropping perpendiculars from P and B on to AC at Q and R shows that

$$\frac{PE}{BE} = \frac{PQ}{BR} \tag{10.13}$$

Hence, if lines are constructed parallel to AC and subdividing BR into equal intervals, the concentration of one component of the ternary mixture can be read against the scale as the ratio PQ/BR which is the same as PE/BE. Similarly, the other two components can be represented by the ratios PD/AD and PF/CF. Equation (10.12) then shows that the three separate concentrations add up to the whole mixture, for any point P inside any triangle ABC.

Although the above proof is valid for any triangle, it is normal practice to use an equilateral triangle for a symmetrical representation of the three components. If printed triangular paper is not available, however, it is more convenient to use rectangular graph paper and construct diagonals so that an isosceles right-angle triangle can be used.

10.2.5. *Special Graph Papers*

There are many other types of graph paper available for special applications. For example, the axes can be subdivided to a quadratic scale or a square root scale for orifice calibrations. Alternatively, a reciprocal scale can be used to automatically change a flow rate into a residence time. Other special graph papers are provided for thermometer calibrations, and then the borderline between special graph papers and charts for chart recorders is rather ill-defined. Any of the above graph papers can aid the understanding of a phenomenon by providing a pictorial representation, and anything which does this can be loosely described as a graph.

10.3. THEORETICAL PROPERTIES

Whenever a set of experimental data is plotted against linear scales, a decision has to be taken regarding the type of curve which best summarizes the results. Experimental data are always subject to error and the assessment of these errors will be discussed in Section 10.5. Hence any fundamental properties which the curve must possess on theoretical grounds are invaluable aids to the correct choice of representative curve. There are three points which are always worth considering and these will be discussed separately.

10.3.1. *The Origin*

It is often possible to state with certainty the value of the dependent variable when the independent variable is zero. For example, if the pressure drop across a length of pipe is being determined for various flow rates, it is certainly true that the pressure drop is zero for a zero flow rate. Although all other points on the graph are subject to experimental error and the curve need only pass close to them, the origin is one point which the curve must pass through. Hence the origin is more important than any single experimental point.

When time is the independent variable, the intercept at zero time is frequently set as a boundary condition instead of being a measured value, and this point is thus more accurately determined than any other. If a chemical reaction is being studied by plotting the concentration of one of the products as a function of time, the origin must be a point on the curve.

There are many other examples, and a few moments' thought should always indicate whether or not a curve should pass through the origin.

10.3.2. *Starting Gradient*

In most problems involving axial symmetry, the gradient of the curve tends to zero as the axis is approached. Examples of this are the velocity profiles for flow inside a cylindrical pipe, temperature profiles within a cylindrical conductor, or the variation of local mass transfer coefficient near the front pole of a dissolving sphere. Not all dependent variables have a vanishing derivative on the axis of a symmetrical system as may be seen from equation XV, example 4, Section 8.5.4, which gives the vorticity distribution for slow flow past a sphere. When $\theta = 0$, $\zeta = 0$, but $\partial\zeta/\partial\theta \neq 0$.

If the concentration of the final product of two or more consecutive chemical reactions is being plotted against time from mixing the reactants, the curve must pass through the origin, and have a vanishing derivative when it does so. This is because the rate of formation of the product is proportional to the concentration of the intermediate product which is initially zero.

10.3.3. *Efficiencies*

A lot depends upon the context, but most efficiency curves either approach a limit asymptotically, or pass through a maximum value before decaying to zero. One thing is certain, however; an efficiency curve cannot be a straight line over an appreciable range. Any straight line, except a horizontal one, must exceed 100% and fall below zero for some values of the independent variable, and both types of behaviour are inconsistent with a properly defined efficiency.

10.4. CONTOUR PLOTS

It is often difficult to isolate the independent variables in a system so that one variable can be altered through a range of values whilst all other independent variables are held constant. When only two independent variables are involved, it is possible to establish a family of curves by presenting the results in a manner analogous to a contour map which shows height as a function of two independent coordinates. This method has been

FIG. 10.4.   Contour plot of three variables

used to illustrate the dependence of start-up time on boil-up rate and feed composition for a distillation column.† The results are shown in Fig. 10.4 in the form of start-up time varying with feed composition, using the boil-up rate as a parameter. It will be seen that very few experiments were performed

† Barker, P. E., Jenson, V. G. and Rustin, A. *Inst. Pet. J.* (To be published).

at the exact boil-up rate, the actual rates being indicated adjacent to the points. However, the three curves shown are almost as accurately determined as they would have been from the same number of experiments performed at the three exact boil-up rates. There is no reason why the positions of the three variables should not be interchanged, but it is customary to plot one of the independent variables as abscissa.

10.5. Propagation of Errors

Any experimentally determined quantity is subject to error, and hence any calculated result which is based on experimental evidence is also limited in accuracy. The determination of the derived error from the observed error is a calculation of some importance since it indicates the position where experimental technique should be improved. The way in which errors accumulate is governed by different rules depending upon the type of calculation performed (i.e. addition, subtraction, multiplication, etc.), and these will be considered separately.

10.5.1. *Propagation through Addition*

If a quantity z is calculated from

$$z = x + y \qquad (10.14)$$

where x and y are two measured variables, then any error in determining x or y will result in an error in z. Equation (10.14) is assumed to be exactly true and satisfied identically by the exact values of x, y, and z. But any experimental reading (x') for the variable (x) will only approximate to the true value and this is usually stated in the form

$$x - \delta x < x' < x + \delta x \qquad (10.15)$$

i.e. the error in the determination of x is given by

$$|x' - x| < \delta x \qquad (10.16)$$

δx is called the " absolute error " in x, has the same dimensions as x, and is usually assigned by the observer with due regard to the manner in which the measurement was made.

A similar argument leads to the definition of δy, the absolute error in y. Thus

$$y - \delta y < y' < y + \delta y \qquad (10.17)$$

The inequalities (10.15) and (10.17) can be written in the alternative forms

$$x' - \delta x < x < x' + \delta x \qquad (10.18)$$
$$y' - \delta y < y < y' + \delta y \qquad (10.19)$$

Adding y to each term in inequality (10.18) and using (10.19) gives

$$x' + y' - \delta x - \delta y < x' - \delta x + y < x + y < x' + \delta x + y < x' + y' + \delta x + \delta y \qquad (10.20)$$

Remembering that x and y cannot be determined except by means of x', y', δx and δy, inequality (10.20) can be combined with equation (10.14) to give

$$x'+y'-\delta x-\delta y < z < x'+y'+\delta x+\delta y \qquad (10.21)$$

But z' is the result obtained by putting the experimental values (x' and y') into equation (10.14), and hence

$$z'-(\delta x+\delta y) < z < z'+(\delta x+\delta y) \qquad (10.22)$$

Comparing the inequalities (10.18) and (10.22) it can be seen that

$$\delta z = \delta x+\delta y \qquad (10.23)$$

where δz is the absolute error in z. Hence, the absolute error in the result is the sum of the absolute errors in the constituent parts.

10.5.2. *Propagation through Subtraction*

Assuming that

$$z = x-y \qquad (10.24)$$

and using the same terminology as above, the following set of inequalities can be obtained from (10.18) and (10.19).

$$x'-\delta x-(y'+\delta y) < x'-\delta x-y < x-y < x'+\delta x-y < x'+\delta x-(y'-\delta y) \qquad (10.25)$$

But
$$z' = x'-y'$$

$$\therefore \quad z'-(\delta x+\delta y) < z < z'+(\delta x+\delta y) \qquad (10.26)$$

$$\therefore \quad \delta z = \delta x+\delta y \qquad (10.27)$$

Hence, the absolute error in the difference of two quantities is the sum of the absolute errors in those quantities.

The above two results can be generalized to any number of operations involving addition and subtraction only. Thus, the absolute error in the result of any calculation involving only addition and subtraction is the sum of the absolute errors in the constituent parts.

It should be noted that each operation increases the absolute error, but any subtraction reduces the result. Hence the " relative error", which is the ratio of the absolute error to the result, will always increase during subtraction. The relative error is usually expressed as a percentage and is dimensionless.

10.5.3. *Propagation through Multiplication and Division*

Using the same terminology as before but letting z be determined from

$$z = xy \qquad (10.28)$$

the inequality

$$(x'-\delta x)(y'-\delta y) < z < (x'+\delta x)(y'+\delta y) \qquad (10.29$$

is valid provided that x' and y' are both positive.

Defining the relative errors by

$$x_r = \delta x/x' \qquad \text{and } y_r = \delta y/y'$$

inequality (10.29) can be rewritten

$$x'y'(1-x_r)(1-y_r) < z < x'y'(1+x_r)(1+y_r) \tag{10.30}$$

Provided the errors are small, products of two errors can be neglected by comparison with the error itself. Since z' is the value calculated by substituting x' and y' into equation (10.28), (10.30) can be written in the form

$$z'(1-x_r-y_r) < z < z'(1+x_r+y_r)$$

which shows that

$$z_r = x_r + y_r \tag{10.31}$$

Thus, the relative error in a product is the sum of the relative errors in the constituent parts.

Starting with the inequality

$$\frac{x'-\delta x}{y'+\delta y} < \frac{x}{y} < \frac{x'+\delta x}{y'-\delta y} \tag{10.32}$$

it can be shown that the relative error in a quotient is also the sum of the relative errors in the constituent parts.

10.5.4. *Propagation through a General Functional Relationship*

It can be seen from the above calculations that the error in the calculated result is greatest when the individual readings are at the ends of the error ranges. The terminology can be simplified by writing

$$x' = x + \delta x \tag{10.33}$$

with the interpretation that x' is the poorest acceptable reading obtained for the unknown true value x; and δx can be either positive or negative. If z is to be determined from the general expression

$$z = f(x, y) \tag{10.34}$$

by using the values x' and y' for x and y, then the value obtained (z') will be in error as follows. Applying equation (8.9) to equation (10.34) gives

$$dz = \frac{\partial f}{\partial x} dx + \frac{\partial f}{\partial y} dy \tag{10.35}$$

Provided the errors δx and δy are small, dx and dy can be replaced by them in equation (10.35). Thus

$$\delta z = \frac{\partial f}{\partial x} \delta x + \frac{\partial f}{\partial y} \delta y \tag{10.36}$$

Equation (10.36) can also be obtained from the generalized form of Taylor's theorem by neglecting products of errors in comparison with the errors themselves. The equation can be applied to functions of any number of variables and is the general law for propagation of errors.

Example 1. If $z = xy^n$ with n known and x and y determined experimentally, determine the relative error in z in terms of the relative errors in x and y.

$$(x, y) = xy^n \qquad\qquad\qquad \text{I}$$

$$\therefore \quad \frac{\partial f}{\partial x} = y^n \qquad \frac{\partial f}{\partial y} = nxy^{n-1} \qquad\qquad \text{II}$$

Substituting into equation (10.36),

$$\delta z = y^n\,\delta x + nxy^{n-1}\,\delta y$$

$$= z\left(\frac{\delta x}{x} + \frac{n\,\delta y}{y}\right)$$

$$\therefore \quad z_r = x_r + ny_r \qquad\qquad\qquad \text{III}$$

The special case $n = 1$ reduces to equation (10.31) for the product. Because δx and δy can have either sign, if n is negative equation III should be written

$$z_r = x_r - ny_r \qquad\qquad\qquad \text{IV}$$

Hence, if $n = -1$ the relative error in a quotient is the sum of the relative errors in the constituent parts.

Example 2. It was shown in the first problem in Section 2.5.7 that if a chemical reaction

$$A \rightarrow B$$

has a first order reaction rate constant k hr^{-1}, the concentration of A leaving a tubular reactor of length L ft with velocity u ft/h is given by

$$c = c_0\, e^{-kL/u}$$

where c_0 is the initial concentration of A, diffusion has been neglected and plug flow has been assumed. How accurately must k be known and the flow rate be steady for it to be possible to design a reactor to give $94\frac{1}{2}$–$95\frac{1}{2}\%$ completion?

When the reactor is designed, L will be known very accurately; and (c/c_0) can be considered as a single variable (f) since the limit is on completion.

$$f = e^{-kL/u} \qquad\qquad\qquad \text{I}$$

Applying equation (10.36),

$$\therefore \quad \delta f = -\frac{L}{u}f\delta k + \frac{kL}{u^2}f\delta u$$

which can be rearranged using equation I to give

$$\frac{-\delta f}{f\ln f} = \frac{\delta u}{u} - \frac{\delta k}{k} \qquad\qquad\qquad \text{II}$$

Since $f < 1$ the left hand side will be positive. Th errors can be of either sign and the worst case must be considered, therefore

$$\frac{-\delta f}{f \ln f} = \frac{\delta u}{u} + \frac{\delta k}{k} = u_r + k_r \qquad\qquad \text{III}$$

Using the numerical values given,

$$u_r + k_r = \frac{0 \cdot 005}{0 \cdot 95 \times 0 \cdot 0513} = 0 \cdot 10 \qquad\qquad \text{IV}$$

Equation IV shows that if the relative error in k exceeds 10% it will be impossible to design the reactor to contain the completion within the given limits. If the flow rate is likely to surge by 5%, then k must be known to an accuracy of 5% otherwise the design is impossible.

10.5.5. *Sources of Error*

There are many sources of error which should be assessed before quoting the accuracy of any determination. They can be classified as follows.

(i) Errors of measurement.
(ii) Precision errors.
(iii) Errors of method.

The first type of error is due to physical limitations of reading a scale. Without a vernier attachment a length of 2 cm could easily be in error by $\frac{1}{2}$ mm which is $2\frac{1}{2}$%. Precision errors are the " built-in " errors of the apparatus. For example, the scales on a mercury-in-glass thermometer assume that the bore is uniform, so that a reading of 28°C could easily be 1°C in error due to an uncalibrated scale. Errors of method include such faults as neglecting heat losses, assuming constant molal overflow, or neglecting back-mixing in a tubular reactor.

All of the above errors can only be estimated and rarely measured, consequently an error is usually given to only one or two significant figures. A " significant figure " is any digit, except zero when it is positioning the decimal point. It is usual to imply the accuracy of a reading by the number of significant figures quoted. That is, if a reading is known to be in error by about 2%, three significant figures are barely justified; whilst an error of 10% will only justify two significant figures. To quote too many significant figures is misleading since it implies a false sense of accuracy; whilst quoting too few squanders the accuracy which has been dearly bought. One extra significant figure should always be carried through a calculation to smother the calculation errors due to rounding-off.

10.6. CURVE FITTING

If a set of experimental data is to be represented by an empirical equation, the equation must possess the correct theoretical properties as discussed in Section 10.3. Assuming that an equation of the form

$$y = a + bx^n \qquad\qquad (10.37)$$

is known to fit a set of results for x and y, values are required for a, b, and n. The best way of finding them graphically is to estimate a value for a and plot $(y-a)$ against x on log-log paper. If the value of a is correct, the result will be a straight line of slope n and intercept $\ln b$ as described in Section 10.2.3, but this is unlikely. Too large a value for a will give a curve on log-log paper which is convex upwards, and too small a value for a gives a curve which is concave upwards as illustrated in Fig. 10.5.

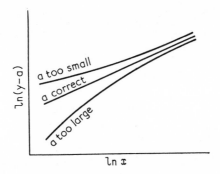

Fig. 10.5.   Log-log plot of $y = a + bx^n$

The approach to curve fitting in the earlier sections of this chapter has been of a visual or graphical nature, but there are two analytical methods available. However, it is still necessary to choose the appropriate type of curve, but instead of determining the parameters graphically, they can be found analytically by the method of averages, or the method of least squares.

10.6.1. *Method of Averages*

Having chosen the type of curve which it is desired to fit to the experimental data, the problem becomes one of determining the values of certain parameters in the equation so that the " best fit " is obtained. In graphical methods, the best fit is a matter of opinion, but in the present method a set of average points is defined and the best curve is the one passing through the average points.

Suppose that eight experimental values of a variable y are available at eight different known values of x, and the best curve of the type

$$y = A + B \sin x + C \cos x \qquad (10.38)$$

is to be chosen to represent them. Because the values of y are experimental, it is unlikely that any pair of values (x_n, y_n) will satisfy the best fit curve (10.38) exactly. Therefore, the experimental results are substituted into equation (10.38) and an extra term is included for the unknown error. Thus

$$y_1 - A - B \sin x_1 - C \cos x_1 = R_1$$
$$y_2 - A - B \sin x_2 - C \cos x_2 = R_2$$
$$y_3 - A - B \sin x_3 - C \cos x_3 = R_3$$
$$\cdots\cdots$$
$$\cdots\cdots$$
$$y_8 - A - B \sin x_8 - C \cos x_8 = R_8$$

$$(10.39)$$

where R_n are the error terms.

In order to determine A, B, and C analytically, three equations are required, and these can be obtained from the set of eight equations (10.39) by assuming relationships between the error terms. Assuming that

$$R_1 + R_2 + R_3 = 0 \qquad (10.40)$$

and adding together the first three of equations (10.39) gives

$$\sum_{n=1}^{3} y_n - 3A - B \sum_{n=1}^{3} \sin x_n - C \sum_{n=1}^{3} \cos x_n = 0 \qquad (10.41)$$

Dividing by the number of points used (3) gives

$$\frac{y_1 + y_2 + y_3}{3} - A - B \frac{\sin x_1 + \sin x_2 + \sin x_3}{3} - C \frac{\cos x_1 + \cos x_2 + \cos x_3}{3} = 0$$

$$(10.42)$$

Equation (10.42) can be obtained directly from equation (10.38) by using an " average point " to represent the three actual points. It should be noted that the average point is determined in a special manner which depends upon the functions arising in the type of equation (10.38) chosen.

Two further equations, similar to (10.42) can be obtained by arranging the remaining points in two groups.
Thus

$$\frac{y_4 + y_5}{2} - A - B \frac{\sin x_4 + \sin x_5}{2} - C \frac{\cos x_4 + \cos x_5}{2} = 0 \qquad (10.43)$$

$$\frac{y_6 + y_7 + y_8}{3} - A - B \frac{\sin x_6 + \sin x_7 + \sin x_8}{3} - C \frac{\cos x_6 + \cos x_7 + \cos x_8}{3} = 0$$

$$(10.44)$$

Because every symbol with a suffix is a known experimental result, only A, B, and C are unknown in the three equations (10.42, 43, 44) and hence they can be determined.

In applications of the method of averages, the following points must be observed.

(i) Points must be arranged in ascending values of x.
(ii) The number of groups must equal the number of unknown parameters.
(iii) Groups should contain approximately equal numbers of points.
(iv) Each experimental point should be used once only.
(v) The appropriate average must be taken.

Example 1. The thermal conductivity of graphite varies with temperature according to the equation

$$k = k_0 - \alpha T \qquad \text{I}$$

Experimentally, it is only possible to obtain a mean conductivity over a temperature range. It is required to find the point conductivity from the mean conductivity given below.†

$T(°C)$	390	500	1000	1500
k_m	1·41	1·38	1·19	1·15

k_m is determined between T and 25°C in kilo-erg/cm^2 sec°C cm^{-1}.

Solution

It is first necessary to determine the relationship between k_m and the point values of k. Considering unit cross-sectional area of a conductor of length L and end temperatures T_1 and T_2, an elementary heat balance yields the equation

$$-k\frac{dT}{dx} = k_m \frac{T_1 - T_2}{L} = K \qquad \text{II}$$

which defines the constant K. Substituting equation I into equation II gives

$$-(k_0 - \alpha T)\, dT = K\, dx$$
$$\therefore \quad -k_0 T + \tfrac{1}{2}\alpha T^2 = Kx + \beta \qquad \text{III}$$

Using the boundary conditions that

at $\qquad\qquad\qquad\qquad x = 0, \qquad T = T_1 \qquad\qquad\qquad\qquad$ IV

at $\qquad\qquad\qquad\qquad x = L, \qquad T = T_2 \qquad\qquad\qquad\qquad$ V

$$\therefore \quad -k_0 T_1 + \tfrac{1}{2}\alpha T_1^2 = \beta \qquad\qquad\qquad\qquad \text{VI}$$

and $\qquad\qquad\qquad -k_0 T_2 + \tfrac{1}{2}\alpha T_2^2 = \beta + KL \qquad\qquad\qquad$ VII

Subtracting equation VII from VI gives

$$k_0(T_2 - T_1) - \tfrac{1}{2}\alpha(T_2 - T_1)(T_2 + T_1) = -KL = k_m(T_2 - T_1) \qquad \text{VIII}$$
$$\therefore \quad k_m = k_0 - \alpha T_m \qquad\qquad\qquad\qquad \text{IX}$$

where T_m is the arithmetic mean temperature between the end points.

There are four experimental points and two parameters k_0 and α. Therefore, the points must be split into two groups of two, thus

$$\begin{array}{r} k_0 - 207{\cdot}5\alpha - 1{\cdot}41 = R_1 \\ k_0 - 262{\cdot}5\alpha - 1{\cdot}38 = R_2 \\ \hline 2k_0 - 470\alpha\ -2{\cdot}79 = 0 \end{array} \qquad \cdot\ \text{X}$$

† *I.C.T.* **5**, 86. McGraw-Hill, New York (1937).

and
$$k_0 - 512 \cdot 5\alpha - 1 \cdot 19 = R_3$$
$$k_0 - 762 \cdot 5\alpha - 1 \cdot 15 = R_4$$
$$\overline{2k_0 - 1275\alpha - 2 \cdot 34 =} \qquad \text{XI}$$

Solving equations X and XI for k_0 and α gives

$$\alpha = 0 \cdot 00056$$
$$k_0 = 1 \cdot 526$$

hence,
$$k = 1 \cdot 526 - 0 \cdot 00056T \qquad \text{XII}$$

Substituting the experimental temperatures into equation IX gives the following comparison.

$T (^\circ C)$	390	500	1000	1500
k_m (experimental)	1·41	1·38	1·19	1·15
k_m (equation IX)	1·41	1·38	1·24	1·10

Equation XII can be expressed in terms of engineering units by multiplying the right hand side by 57·8, multiplying α by 5/9, and moving the origin from 32°F to 0°F. The result is

$$k = 88 \cdot 9 - 0 \cdot 0180T \qquad \text{XIII}$$

where T is measured in °F, and k in Btu/h ft^2 °F ft^{-1}. This result was used in example 4, Section 2.4.3.

10.6.2. *Method of Least Squares*

More often than not, this method is used to fit the best straight line to a set of data. Hence the formulae will be derived determining the values of m and c which give the best least mean squares fit of the equation

$$y = mx + c \qquad (10.1)$$

to N pairs of results for x and y.

Following the method of the previous section, each pair of results is substituted into equation (10.1) and an extra term is introduced to allow for the unknown error.

$$y_n - mx_n - c = R_n \qquad (10.45)$$

R_n may be either positive or negative, therefore, to obtain a positive representation for the errors, equation (10.45) is squared thus,

$$y_n^2 + m^2 x_n^2 + c^2 - 2mx_n y_n - 2cy_n + 2cmx_n = R_n^2 \qquad (10.46)$$

Equations (10.46) for the individual experimental points are now added together to give

$$\sum_{n=1}^{N} y_n^2 + m^2 \sum_{n=1}^{N} x_n^2 + Nc^2 - 2m \sum_{n=1}^{N} x_n y_n - 2c \sum_{n=1}^{N} y_n + 2cm \sum_{n=1}^{N} x_n = \sum_{n=1}^{N} R_n^2$$

(10.47)

Equation (10.47) gives an expression for the sum of the squares of the error terms. The " method of least squares " defines the best straight line as the one for which the sum of the squares of the error terms is a minimum.

It will be shown in Section 13.3 that the left-hand side of equation (10.47) will have a turning value when its partial derivatives with respect to both m and c are zero. Thus

$$2m \sum_{n=1}^{N} x_n^2 - 2 \sum_{n=1}^{N} x_n y_n + 2c \sum_{n=1}^{N} x_n = 0$$

(10.48)

$$2cN - 2 \sum_{n=1}^{N} y_n + 2m \sum_{n=1}^{N} x_n = 0$$

(10.49)

Solving equations (10.48) and (10.49) gives the result

$$\left. \begin{aligned} m &= \frac{N \sum x_n y_n - \sum x_n \sum y_n}{N \sum x_n^2 - (\sum x_n)^2} \\ c &= \frac{\sum x_n^2 \sum y_n - \sum x_n y_n \sum x_n}{N \sum x_n^2 - (\sum x_n)^2} \end{aligned} \right\}$$

(10.50)

where all sums must be taken over all experimental points.

The best way to use the above formula is to construct a table with four columns headed x_n, y_n, x_n^2, $x_n y_n$ and complete the table for the experimental results. The sums of the columns will then give all of the values required by equations (10.50). If a desk calculating machine is available, the four sums can be obtained from two cumulative calculations without constructing the table.

The following example shows how the method can be extended to a third variable by fitting the best plane to the three dimensional plot.

Example 2. It has been proposed† that the second order chemical reaction

$$CO + Cl_2 \rightarrow COCl_2$$

proceeds on the surface of an activated carbon catalyst after adsorption of the two reactants. Each of the three substances are adsorbed to a different extent, but the number of sites occupied by carbon monoxide is small compared with sites otherwise occupied. Assuming that the process is controlled by the surface reaction, which is irreversible, find the best values of the adsorption coefficients from the following experimental results.

† Potter, C. and Barron, S. *Chem. Eng. Prog.* **47**, 473 (1951).

Partial Pressures			Reaction Rate gm mols/h gm catalyst
CO	Cl_2	$COCl_2$	
0·406	0·352	0·226	0·00414
0·396	0·363	0·231	0·00440
0·310	0·320	0·356	0·00241
0·287	0·333	0·367	0·00245
0·253	0·218	0·522	0·00157
0·610	0·118	0·231	0·00390
0·179	0·608	0·206	0·00200

Solution

The following nomenclature is used.

C number of sites in the state specified
K adsorption coefficient
k specific reaction rate constant
p partial pressure
r rate of reaction

Subscripts denote the following:

a carbon monoxide
b chlorine
c phosgene
v vacant site
t total number of sites

The equilibrium of the three components between the catalyst and the vapour phase can be expressed thus,

$$C_a = K_a p_a C_v \qquad\qquad \text{I}$$
$$C_b = K_b p_b C_v \qquad\qquad \text{II}$$
$$C_c = K_c p_c C_v \qquad\qquad \text{III}$$

The reaction rate is given by

$$r = k C_a C_b \qquad\qquad \text{IV}$$

The total number of active sites must be equal to the sum of the number of sites in each state. Therefore

$$C_t = C_v + C_a + C_b + C_c \qquad\qquad \text{V}$$

But C_a is known to be small compared with C_b and C_c, hence it can be ignored in equation V. Using equations II and III to eliminate C_b and C_c from equation V,

$$C_t = C_v(1 + K_b p_b + K_c p_c) \qquad\qquad \text{VI}$$

Eliminating C_a and C_b from equation IV by using equations I and II,

$$r = k K_a K_b C_v^2 p_a p_b \qquad\qquad \text{VII}$$

Eliminating C_v between equations VI and VII and rearranging gives

$$1 + K_b p_b + K_c p_c = C_t \sqrt{kK_a K_b}\, \sqrt{p_a p_b/r} \qquad \text{VIII}$$

Equation VIII is of the form

$$1 + \alpha x_n + \beta y_n - \gamma z_n = R_n \qquad \text{IX}$$

where x_n, y_n, and z_n are the experimental quantities p_b, p_c, and $\sqrt{p_a p_b/r}$. α, β, and γ are the constants to be determined, and R_n is the experimental error.

Squaring equation IX and summing over the N experimental points gives

$$N + \alpha^2 \sum x_n^2 + \beta^2 \sum y_n^2 + \gamma^2 \sum z_n^2 + 2\alpha \sum x_n + 2\beta \sum y_n - 2\gamma \sum z_n +$$
$$+ 2\alpha\beta \sum x_n y_n - 2\alpha\gamma \sum x_n z_n - 2\beta\gamma \sum y_n z_n = \sum R_n^2 \qquad \text{X}$$

Differentiating equation X partially with respect to α, β, and γ in turn, and equating to zero gives the three equations:

$$\alpha \sum x_n^2 + \sum x_n + \beta \sum x_n y_n - \gamma \sum x_n z_n = 0 \qquad \text{XI}$$

$$\beta \sum y_n^2 + \sum y_n + \alpha \sum x_n y_n - \gamma \sum y_n z_n = 0 \qquad \text{XII}$$

$$-\gamma \sum z_n^2 + \sum z_n + \alpha \sum x_n z_n + \beta \sum y_n z_n = 0 \qquad \text{XIII}$$

In order to solve equations XI, XII and XIII for α, β, and γ it is necessary to evaluate the nine sums over the given experimental results. Inspection of the given data indicates that there is a much higher level of inert gas in the sixth result. This is considered unlikely, and the result should be rejected. However, the data is sparse and it has been assumed that an error has been made which did not affect the proportions of the components present. This result has therefore been scaled to the same order of inerts as the other readings.

The preliminary calculations are shown in Table 10.1. Equations XI, XII and XIII now become

$$0 \cdot 9008\alpha + 0 \cdot 6673\beta - 14 \cdot 595\gamma + 2 \cdot 315 = 0$$

$$0 \cdot 6673\alpha + 0 \cdot 7370\beta - 12 \cdot 890\gamma + 2 \cdot 145 = 0$$

$$14 \cdot 595\alpha + 12 \cdot 890\beta - 256 \cdot 3\gamma + 41 \cdot 99 = 0$$

Solving for α, β, and γ by successive elimination, or by matrix inversion (see Section 12.10) gives

$$\alpha = 2 \cdot 61, \qquad \beta = 1 \cdot 60, \qquad \gamma = 0 \cdot 393$$

Returning to the original symbols, this means that

$$K_b = 2 \cdot 61, \qquad K_c = 1 \cdot 60, \qquad C_t \sqrt{kK_a} = 0 \cdot 243$$

Putting these values into equation VIII, the final column in Table 10.1 can be calculated to show the agreement between the experimental results and the empirical equation.

It can be seen that the greatest error in z is 5% which corresponds to a 10% error in predicting the rate of reaction.

TABLE 10.1. *Least Squares Fit of Reaction Data*

$r(\times 10^3)$	p_a	$x=p_b$	$y=p_c$	$z=\sqrt{\dfrac{p_a p_b}{r}}$	x^2	y^2	z^2	xy	yz	zx	z (calculated)
4·14	0·406	0·352	0·226	5·88	0·1239	0·0511	34·52	0·0796	1·329	2·070	5·80
4·40	0·396	0·363	0·231	5·72	0·1318	0·0534	32·67	0·0838	1·321	2·076	5·89
2·41	0·310	0·320	0·356	6·42	0·1024	0·1267	41·16	0·1139	2·285	2·054	6·12
2·45	0·287	0·333	0·367	6·25	0·1109	0·1347	39·01	0·1222	2·294	2·081	6·25
1·57	0·253	0·218	0·522	5·93	0·0475	0·2725	35·13	0·1138	3·096	1·293	6·11
3·90	0·626	0·121	0·237	4·41	0·0146	0·0562	19·42	0·0287	1·045	0·534	4·31
2·0	0·179	0·608	0·206	7·38	0·3697	0·0424	54·42	0·1253	1·520	4·487	7·42
—	—	2·315	2·145	41·99	0·9008	0·7370	256·3	0·6673	12·890	14·595	—

The methods of averages and least squares are based on different definitions of the best curve which fits the data. If a desk calculating machine is available, the method of least squares should always be used since it is more soundly based. Without the aid of a machine, however, the calculation is rather tedious and liable to arithmetical error and the method of averages, which is shorter, should be used to give an adequate result.

10.7. NUMERICAL INTEGRATION

It is sometimes necessary to perform a calculation which involves integration. For example, the volumetric flow rate of a gas through a duct can be determined from the linear velocity distribution by evaluating a suitable integral. If an average value is required for a particular quantity, it is frequently obtained by integration. For instance, an average surface temperature can be determined by integrating the measured temperature distribution over the surface and dividing by the area. Also, if a representative sample of a process stream is required during a steady state investigation, it is much more reliable to use a composite sample than a single sample. The intervals at which the parts of the composite sample are taken, and the proportions in which they should be mixed, will be determined theoretically in the following work. Occasionally, a difficult integral arises in a theoretical prediction, and this has to be evaluated numerically for each individual case.

Many of the problems mentioned above are treated graphically, by plotting the variables against one another and evaluating the area enclosed by two ordinates and the parts of the abscissa and curve which join the ordinates. In this section, numerical methods for calculating this area will be presented as an alternative to the graphical method.

One way of integrating a set of data is by fitting an empirical equation to the points, using one of the methods from the previous section, and then integrating the equation analytically. Unless the empirical equation is needed for some other purpose, this procedure is not usually worth the effort. All of the methods to be described involve fitting a polynomial to a set of points so that the polynomial passes through the points. Since the points may be subject to experimental error, the curve obtained in this way will not be a

FIG. 10.6.   Polynomial fit for integration

good representation of the data, and would certainly give false results for a derivative; but for purposes of integration the method is quite satisfactory. The above statement is illustrated in Fig. 10.6 where a cubic has been fitted to four points. For general purposes, the straight line is as good a fit to the four points as is justified by their accuracy; and if the slope of the curve is required, the cubic fit would give misleading results. It is quite clear, however, that the area beneath both curves is approximately the same. Although the cubic is the more complex curve, it is the easier to fit because it passes through the points. Thus, polynomials are used to fit data for integration purposes.

10.7.1. *The Trapezium Rule*

The simplest polynomial, consisting of two terms, is the linear equation

$$y = a_0 + a_1 x \tag{10.51}$$

Since it only contains two parameters (a_0 and a_1) it gives the equation of the straight line joining two points. Taking two points (x_1, y_1) and (x_2, y_2), a_0 and a_1 can be evaluated as

$$a_0 = \frac{x_2 y_1 - x_1 y_2}{x_2 - x_1} \qquad a_1 = \frac{y_2 - y_1}{x_2 - x_1} \tag{10.52}$$

Integrating equation (10.51) with respect to x between $x = x_1$ and $x = x_2$ gives

$$I = \int_{x_1}^{x_2} y\, dx = [a_0 x + \tfrac{1}{2} a_1 x^2]_{x_1}^{x_2}$$
$$= a_0(x_2 - x_1) + \tfrac{1}{2} a_1 (x_2 - x_1)(x_2 + x_1) \tag{10.53}$$

Using the values for a_0 and a_1 given in equations (10.52) gives

$$I = x_2 y_1 - x_1 y_2 + \tfrac{1}{2}(x_2 y_2 - x_2 y_1 + x_1 y_2 - x_1 y_1)$$
$$= \tfrac{1}{2}(x_2 y_2 + x_2 y_1 - x_1 y_2 - x_1 y_1)$$
$$= \tfrac{1}{2}(y_2 + y_1) \times (x_2 - x_1) \tag{10.54}$$
$$= \text{average height} \times \text{width}$$

The value of the integral is thus proved to be the arithmetic average of the two ordinates multiplied by the distance between them. Figure 10.7 illustrates a repeated use of equation (10.54). It can be seen that if the curve

FIG. 10.7. The trapezium rule

is convex upwards, the trapezium rule under-estimates the area by neglecting the segments shown. Conversely, if the curve is convex downwards, the trapezium rule over-estimates the area. The error can be reduced by sub-dividing the intervals still further.

If the intervals Δx are all equal, and there are four of them, the integral can be written

$$I = \int_{x_1}^{x_5} y\,dx = 2\Delta x(y_1+2y_2+2y_3+2y_4+y_5)$$

$$= \tfrac{1}{8}(y_1+2y_2+2y_3+2y_4+y_5)\times(x_5-x_1) \qquad (10.55)$$

$$= \text{average height} \times \text{width}$$

In this combined formula, the average height is no longer a plain arithmetic average, but twice as much weight is given to the interior points as to the end points.

10.7.2. *Simpson's Rule*

The next polynomial which contains three terms is the quadratic

$$y = a_0+a_1 x+a_2 x^2 \qquad (10.56)$$

and this can be fitted to three points. However, it will now be shown that all cubic equations of the type

$$y = a_0+a_1 x+a_2 x^2+a_3 x^3 \qquad (10.57)$$

which pass through any three chosen points at equally spaced values of x, all have the same area beneath them between the end ordinates. The three ordinates and the area required are illustrated in Fig. 10.8, where h is the increment of x.

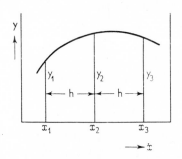

FIG. 10.8. Simpson's rule

The algebra in the following derivation is simpler if the variable x is changed to a new variable z according to the formula

$$z = (x-x_2)/h \qquad (10.58)$$

which transforms the required integral as follows

$$I = \int_{x_1}^{x_3} y\, dx = h \int_{-1}^{1} y\, dz \tag{10.59}$$

and the three ordinates y_1, y_2, and y_3 are now at $z = -1, 0$, and 1.

The polynomial (10.57) can be transformed using (10.58) to a polynomial of the same order in z, thus

$$y = b_0 + b_1 z + b_2 z^2 + b_3 z^3 \tag{10.60}$$

where the b_ns are functions of the a_ns. Following the same method as for the trapezium rule, the three values of z are substituted into equation (10.60) with the corresponding ordinates. Thus

$$y_1 = b_0 - b_1 + b_2 - b_3 \tag{10.61}$$

$$y_2 = b_0 \tag{10.62}$$

$$y_3 = b_0 + b_1 + b_2 + b_3 \tag{10.63}$$

Substituting equation (10.60) into equation (10.59) and evaluating the integral gives

$$I = h \int_{-1}^{1} (b_0 + b_1 z + b_2 z^2 + b_3 z^3)\, dz$$
$$= h[b_0 z + \tfrac{1}{2}b_1 z^2 + \tfrac{1}{3}b_2 z^3 + \tfrac{1}{4}b_3 z^4]_{-1}^{1}$$
$$= h(2b_0 + \tfrac{2}{3}b_2) \tag{10.64}$$

Adding equations (10.61) and (10.63) together gives

$$y_1 + y_3 = 2b_0 + 2b_2 \tag{10.65}$$

and using equation (10.62) shows that

$$y_1 - 2y_2 + y_3 = 2b_2 \tag{10.66}$$

Substituting equations (10.62) and (10.66) into (10.64) gives

$$I = h[2y_2 + \tfrac{1}{3}(y_1 - 2y_2 + y_3)]$$
$$= \tfrac{1}{6}(y_1 + 4y_2 + y_3) \times 2h \tag{10.67}$$
$$= \text{average height} \times \text{width}$$

The average height in this case is found by adding the end values to four times the central value, and dividing the result by six.

The same result is obtained for all cubics through the three points because the step from equations (10.61) and (10.63) to equation (10.65) eliminates two parameters (b_1 and b_3) instead of one, which is normally the case.

If the range of integration is subdivided into equal intervals by using any odd number of ordinates (say 7), Simpson's rule can be applied to each group of three points and the result of all integrations added together.

Thus

$$I = \int_{x_1}^{x_7} y\,dx = \tfrac{1}{18}(y_1+4y_2+2y_3+4y_4+2y_5+4y_6+y_7)\times(x_7-x_1) \quad (10.68)$$

$$= \text{average height} \times \text{width}$$

The average height in equation (10.68) is found by adding four times the even ordinates, and twice the interior odd ordinates, to the end ordinates; the sum being divided by the total number of times an ordinate has been used.

Formula (10.68) gives twice as much weight to some of the interior points than to others, and is not really satisfactory for this reason. It implies that some of the interior points should be measured more accurately than others. Nevertheless, the results obtained from the use of the formula are quite accurate if sufficient sub-intervals are used.

The methods used above can be extended by fitting polynomials of higher degree to a greater number of points, but this is inconvenient. The increased complexity arising from the greater number of points is not justified by a significant improvement in accuracy. A slightly different approach, due to Gauss, enables a polynomial of degree $(2n-1)$ to be fitted to n points, resulting in a much more efficient process.

10.7.3. *Gauss' Method*

The derivation of the formula for fitting a quintic equation to three points will be described below in order to illustrate the method.

It is always possible to transform an integral over a finite range to an integral between the limits -1 and 1, as shown in the derivation of Simpson's rule. In this derivation, it will be assumed that this change of variable has been made by considering the integral

$$I = \int_{-1}^{1} y\,dx = 2y_m \quad (10.69)$$

which defines y_m, the average height.

Assuming that the quintic

$$y = a_0+a_1 x+a_2 x^2+a_3 x^3+a_4 x^4+a_5 x^5 \quad (10.70)$$

adequately represents the shape of the curve y vs x between $x = -1$ and $x = 1$, an expression for y_m can be obtained by substituting equation (10.70) into equation (10.69) and integrating. Thus

$$2y_m = [a_0 x+\tfrac{1}{2}a_1 x^2+\tfrac{1}{3}a_2 x^3+\tfrac{1}{4}a_3 x^4+\tfrac{1}{5}a_4 x^5+\tfrac{1}{6}a_5 x^6]_{-1}^{1}$$

$$= 2a_0+\tfrac{2}{3}a_2+\tfrac{2}{5}a_4$$

or $\quad y_m = a_0+\tfrac{1}{3}a_2+\tfrac{1}{5}a_4 \quad (10.71)$

Referring back to the derivation of Simpson's rule, equations (10.61, 62, 63) contained four unknowns and could not be solved completely. However, the coefficients b_0 and b_2 could be evaluated due to b_1 and b_3

N

being eliminated together. It will now be shown that in Gauss' method, the three coefficients a_0, a_2, a_4 occurring in equation (10.71) can be evaluated from only three ordinates, if three special values of the abscissa are chosen. Denoting these three values by x_1, x_2, x_3, and the corresponding ordinates by y_1, y_2, y_3, each pair of values must satisfy equation (10.70). Hence

$$y_1 = a_0 + a_1 x_1 + a_2 x_1^2 + a_3 x_1^3 + a_4 x_1^4 + a_5 x_1^5 \qquad (10.72)$$

$$y_2 = a_0 + a_1 x_2 + a_2 x_2^2 + a_3 x_2^3 + a_4 x_2^4 + a_5 x_2^5 \qquad (10.73)$$

$$y_3 = a_0 + a_1 x_3 + a_2 x_3^2 + a_3 x_3^3 + a_4 x_3^4 + a_5 x_3^5 \qquad (10.74)$$

It is now assumed that the above three equations can be added together in the proportions $K_1 : K_2 : K_3$ so that a_1, a_3, a_5, are simultaneously eliminated, and the coefficients of a_0, a_2, a_4 correspond with equation (10.71).
Thus,

$$K_1 y_1 + K_2 y_2 + K_3 y_3 = (K_1 + K_2 + K_3)a_0 +$$
$$+ (K_1 x_1 + K_2 x_2 + K_3 x_3)a_1$$
$$+ (K_1 x_1^2 + K_2 x_2^2 + K_3 x_3^2)a_2$$
$$+ (K_1 x_1^3 + K_2 x_2^3 + K_3 x_3^3)a_3$$
$$+ (K_1 x_1^4 + K_2 x_2^4 + K_3 x_3^4)a_4$$
$$+ (K_1 x_1^5 + K_2 x_2^5 + K_3 x_3^5)a_5 \qquad (10.75)$$

and hence

$$\left. \begin{aligned} K_1 + K_2 + K_3 &= 1 \\ K_1 x_1 + K_2 x_2 + K_3 x_3 &= 0 \\ K_1 x_1^2 + K_2 x_2^2 + K_3 x_3^2 &= \tfrac{1}{3} \\ K_1 x_1^3 + K_2 x_2^3 + K_3 x_3^3 &= 0 \\ K_1 x_1^4 + K_2 x_2^4 + K_3 x_3^4 &= \tfrac{1}{5} \\ K_1 x_1^5 + K_2 x_2^5 + K_3 x_3^5 &= 0 \end{aligned} \right\} \qquad (10.76)$$

(10.76) is a set of six equations in the six unknowns x_1, x_2, x_3, K_1, K_2, K_3 and can thus be solved. The solution is tedious and proceeds according to the following pattern.

(i) Eliminate K_1 by multiplying each equation by x_1 and subtracting it from the following equation.

(ii) Eliminate K_2 from the new set of five equations by multiplying each by x_2 and subtracting from the following equation.

(iii) Eliminate K_3 in a similar manner.

(iv) The three remaining equations show that x_1, x_2, x_3 can be interpreted as the roots of the cubic equation

$$5x^3 - 3x = 0 \qquad (10.77$$

(v) Therefore $x_3 = -x_1 = \sqrt{}\,/5$, and $x_2 = 0$.
(vi) Substituting these values back into various parts of the calculation it can be shown that $K_2 = 4/9$, and $K_1 = K_3 = 5/18$.

Equations (10.71) and (10.75) are identical, and hence

$$\tfrac{1}{2}\int_{-1}^{1} y\,dx = \frac{5y_1 + 8y_2 + 5y_3}{18} \tag{10.78}$$

where y_1, y_2, y_3 are evaluated at $x = -0.7746$, 0, and 0.7746 respectively.

Gauss' two-point method is seldom used since it shows little advantage over Simpson's rule, but Gauss' four-point method should be used for improved accuracy. The formulae are:

$$\tfrac{1}{2}\int_{-1}^{1} y\,dx = \tfrac{1}{2}(y_1 + y_2) \tag{10.79}$$

where y_1 and y_2 are evaluated at $x = \pm 0.5773$; and

$$\tfrac{1}{2}\int_{-1}^{1} y\,dx = 0.1739(y_1 + y_4) + 0.3261(y_2 + y_3) \tag{10.80}$$

where y_1, y_2, y_3, y_4 are evaluated at $x = -0.8611$, -0.3400, 0.3400 and 0.8611 respectively.

Example. Evaluate $\int_0^4 (1+x^2)^{-\frac{1}{2}}\,dx$ by using the following methods.

(a) Analytical
(b) Trapezium rule (3 points)
(c) Trapezium rule (9 points)
(d) Simpson's rule (3 points)
(e) Simpson's rule (9 points)
(f) Gauss 3 point.
(g) Gauss 4 point.

Compare all other results with the analytical solution to determine their accuracy in representing the above function.

Solution

(a) Put $x = \sinh z$, and hence $dx = \cosh z\,dz$.

$$\therefore\quad I = \int_0^4 (1+x^2)^{-\frac{1}{2}}\,dx = \int_0^\alpha \frac{\cosh z\,dz}{\sqrt{(1+\sinh^2 z)}}$$
$$= [z]_0^\alpha$$
$$= \sinh^{-1} 4$$
$$= 2.0947$$

x	$1+x^2$	$y = (1+x^2)^{-\frac{1}{2}}$
0·0	1·00	1·00000
0·5	1·25	0·89445
1·0	2·00	0·70711
1·5	3·25	0·55475
2·0	5·00	0·44722
2·5	7·25	0·37138
3·0	10·00	0·31623
3·5	13·25	0·27473
4·0	17·00	0·24254

(b) From the trapezium rule for three points,

$$I = y_1 + 2y_2 + y_3$$
$$= 1·00000 + 2(0·44722) + 0·24254$$
$$= 2·1369$$

(c) From the trapezium rule for nine points,

$$I = \tfrac{1}{4}(y_1 + 2y_2 + 2y_3 + 2y_4 + 2y_5 + 2y_6 + 2y_7 + 2y_8 + y_9)$$
$$= \tfrac{1}{4}(1·00000 + 0·24254) + \tfrac{1}{2}(0·89445 + 0·70711 + 0·55475 +$$
$$+ 0·44722 + 0·37138 + 0·31623 + 0·27473)$$
$$= 2·0936$$

(d) Simpson's rule for three points (10.67) gives

$$I = \tfrac{1}{6}(y_1 + 4y_2 + y_3) \times 4$$
$$= \tfrac{2}{3}(1·00000 + 1·78888 + 0·24254)$$
$$= 2·0209$$

(e) Simpson's rule for nine points gives

$$I = \tfrac{1}{24}(y_1 + 4y_2 + 2y_3 + 4y_4 + 2y_5 + 4y_6 + 2y_7 + 4y_8 + y_9) \times 4$$
$$= \tfrac{1}{6}(1·00000 + 0·24254) + \tfrac{1}{3}(0·70711 + 0·44722 + 0·31623) +$$
$$+ \tfrac{2}{3}(0·89445 + 0·55475 + 0·37138 + 0·27473)$$
$$= 2·0941$$

(f) In Gauss' three point method (10.78), if the range of integration is -1 to 1, then the ordinates are required at 0 and $\pm$ 0·7746. Therefore, if the range of integration is 0 to 4, then ordinates are required at $x = 2$ and $x = 2 \pm 2$ (0·7746) = 3·5492 and 0·4508.

$$I = \tfrac{4}{18}[5(0·91165 + 0·27118) + 8(0·44722)]$$
$$= 2·1093$$

(g) In Gauss' four point method, the ordinates will be required at $x = $ 0·2778, 1·3200, 2·6800, and 3·7222. Equation (10.80) then gives the average height within the range of integration.

$$I = 4[0·1739(0·96351 + 0·25945) + 0·3261(0·60386 + 0·34959)]$$
$$= 2·0944$$

The above results can be compared in Table 10.2.

TABLE 10.2. *Comparison of Integration Formulae*

Method	Result	Absolute error	Relative error (%)
Trapezium rule (3 pts)	2·1369	0·0422	2·1
,, ,, (9 pts)	2·0936	−0·0011	0·05
Simpson's ,, (3 pts)	2·0209	0·0738	3·5
,, ,, (9 pts)	2·0941	−0·0006	0·03
Gauss 3 point	2·1093	0·0146	0·7
Gauss 4 point	2·0944	−0·0003	0·01

It can be seen that Gauss' method is the superior one for three points, and that Gauss' four point method is better than either of the other nine point methods. The reason why Simpson's rule is so poor for three points is illustrated in Fig. 10.9, where the true curve and the parabolic fit can be compared.

FIG. 10.9. Parabolic approximation for Simpson's rule

The cause of the bad fit is the point of inflection at $x = 0·7071$ which cannot be represented by a quadratic equation.

10.7.4. *Comparison of Methods*

In most cases, the four-point method of Gauss gives an accuracy equivalent to the use of Simpson's rule with nine points equally spaced across the same range. Gauss' method is thus more economical in the use of data, but the calculations are a little more complicated because of the more difficult weighting factors.

Gauss' method should have many applications to the investigation of the behaviour of full scale production equipment, where it is necessary to compress all readings into as short a time as possible due to plant fluctuations. A reduction in the number of readings required without loss of accuracy is an obvious advantage. Another example is obtaining a representative sample of a steady state process stream. It is much more efficient to take a set of samples at the Gauss intervals, mix them in the Gauss proportions and analyze the composite sample; than to take twice as many samples at equal intervals and analyze each one separately or mix them all together in equal proportions.

An interesting point has been noted by McDermott† concerning the integration of experimental results. Figure 10.10 illustrates the true relationship between two variables x and y as the straight line AB. The two groups

FIG. 10.10.   Comparison of the trapezium rule and Simpson's rule

of three equally spaced experimental points (a), (b) have been chosen so that the total error in each group is zero, and these are the only two possible groups which satisfy this condition (except for their mirror images in the line AB). It is obvious from the group (a) that the parabolic fit seriously under-estimates the area, whilst the two straight lines joining the points give a closer approximation. For the group (b), the difference between the straight line area and the parabolic area is small, but does show a marginal advantage in favour of the trapezium rule. It is thus apparent that the trapezium rule is more satisfactory than Simpson's rule. This conclusion is in direct contrast to the result demonstrated in Table 10.2, where the higher polynomials gave the better results.

These two conflicting conclusions can be reconciled as follows. For evaluating analytical integrals or integrating accurate experimental data, the methods of Gauss and Simpson's rule should be used; but if the data are

† McDermott, C.   M.Sc. Thesis, Chemical Engineering Department, University of Birmingham (1962).

inherently inaccurate, the trapezium rule should be used. The question of how accurate the data must be to justify the use of Gauss' method or Simpson's rule is a very difficult one, and the answer must depend upon the type of curve being fitted. For linear relationships the trapezium rule appears to be the best for all experimental data, and the simplicity of the method is a further recommendation. However, this statement does not detract from the value of Gauss' method or Simpson's rule for integrating accurate experimental or theoretical data; nor does it invalidate a planned experiment to sample a process at the Gauss intervals.

Chapter 11

NUMERICAL METHODS

11.1. Introduction

THERE are many problems in mathematics for which no analytical solution is known. There are also others, for which the analytical solution is tedious and the answer may be in the form of an infinite series that can only be interpreted after much computational effort. A numerical method may be the only one which will yield a solution to the first kind of problem, and may be the most efficient method of solving the second kind of problem. Mistakes are difficult to locate in some analytical solutions and the self-checking features of numerical methods based on successive approximation eliminate this difficulty.

Simpson's rule and Gauss' method, which were described in Chapter 10, can be interpreted as numerical solutions of the first order differential equation

$$\frac{dy}{dx} = f(x) \tag{11.1}$$

These solutions are valuable if $f(x)$ is not a simple function.

The purpose of this present chapter is to present numerical solutions for more complicated types of ordinary differential equations, to locate roots of algebraic and transcendental equations, and solve partial differential equations numerically.

11.2. First Order Ordinary Differential Equations

In Section 2.3 many first order differential equations were solved, but if the equation is not linear and the variables will not separate, none of the methods given can be applied. The problem is thus to solve

$$\frac{dy}{dx} = f(x, y) \tag{11.2}$$

There are two methods available, one due to Picard which is algebraic, and the other due to Runge and Kutta which is numerical.

11.2.1. *Picard's Method*

It is first assumed that a boundary condition of the type

at $\qquad\qquad x = a, \qquad y = b \tag{11.3}$

is available to particularize the solution of equation (11.2).   As a first approximation, in the neighbourhood of the starting point, y can be replaced by b on the right-hand side of equation (11.2). Thus

$$\frac{dy^{(1)}}{dx} = f(x, b) \qquad (11.4)$$

Equation (11.4) can now be integrated with respect to x giving

$$y^{(1)} = \int f(x, b)\, dx \qquad (11.5)$$

which determines $y^{(1)}$ as a function of x. If $y^{(1)}$ is now substituted into the right-hand side of equation (11.2), a further solution $y^{(2)}$ can be obtained. Thus

$$y^{(2)} = \int f(x, y^{(1)})\, dx \qquad (11.6)$$

This process can be continued indefinitely, by putting the latest version of $y^{(n)}$ in the right-hand side of equation (11.2) to determine $y^{(n+1)}$. Thus

$$y^{(n+1)} = \int f(x, y^{(n)})\, dx \qquad (11.7)$$

After each integration (11.7), equation (11.3) must be used to evaluate the constant of integration.

Example 1. If $y = 1$ when $x = 1$, and the equation

$$\frac{dy}{dx} = \frac{x^2 - y}{x} \qquad \text{I}$$

is satisfied, find the value of y when $x = 2$.

Putting $y = 1$ in the right-hand side of equation I gives

$$\frac{dy^{(1)}}{dx} = \frac{x^2 - 1}{x}$$

Integrating, $\qquad y^{(1)} = \int \left(x - \frac{1}{x} \right) dx$

$$= \tfrac{1}{2}x^2 - \ln x + C_1 \qquad \text{II}$$

But $y^{(1)} = 1$ when $x = 1$,

$$\therefore \quad C_1 = \tfrac{1}{2}$$

$$\therefore \quad y^{(1)} = \tfrac{1}{2} + \tfrac{1}{2}x^2 - \ln x \qquad \text{III}$$

Substituting $y^{(1)}$ into the right-hand side of equation I gives

$$\frac{dy^{(2)}}{dx} = x - \frac{1}{2x} - \frac{x}{2} + \frac{\ln x}{x}$$

$$= \frac{x}{2} - \frac{1}{2x} + \frac{\ln x}{x}$$

Integrating,

$$y^{(2)} = \tfrac{1}{4}x^2 - \tfrac{1}{2}\ln x + \tfrac{1}{2}(\ln x)^2 + C_2 \qquad \text{IV}$$

But $y^{(2)} = 1$ when $x = 1$,

$$\therefore \quad C_2 = 1 - \tfrac{1}{4} = \tfrac{3}{4}$$

$$\therefore \quad y^{(2)} = \tfrac{3}{4} + \tfrac{1}{4}x^2 - \tfrac{1}{2}\ln x + \tfrac{1}{2}(\ln x)^2 \qquad\qquad \text{V}$$

A further cycle of calculation gives

$$y^{(3)} = \tfrac{5}{8} + \tfrac{3}{8}x^2 - \tfrac{3}{4}\ln x + \tfrac{1}{4}(\ln x)^2 - \tfrac{1}{6}(\ln x)^3 \qquad \text{VI}$$

Putting $x = 2$ in each approximation gives

$$y^{(1)} = 1\cdot807$$

$$y^{(2)} = 1\cdot644$$

$$y^{(3)} = 1\cdot670$$

It is apparent from these figures that a few further cycles of calculation are necessary, but that the true answer lies within the range $1\cdot644 \rightarrow 1\cdot670$; nearer to the latter figure.

An analytical solution is available for this problem because equation I is linear. Solving by the method of Section 2.3.4 gives

$$y = \tfrac{1}{3}x^2 + \tfrac{2}{3}x^{-1} \qquad\qquad\qquad \text{VII}$$

so that at $x = 2$,

$$y = 1\cdot667 \qquad\qquad\qquad\qquad \text{VIII}$$

It can be demonstrated that Picard's method is converging towards the analytical solution in this particular case by expanding equation VII into a logarithmic series. If $x = e^t$,

$$x^{-1} = e^{-t}$$

$$= 1 - t + \frac{t^2}{2!} - \frac{t^3}{3!} + \dots$$

$$= 1 - \ln x + \frac{(\ln x)^2}{2!} - \frac{(\ln x)^3}{3!} + \dots$$

Using equation VII, therefore

$$y = \tfrac{1}{3}x^2 + \tfrac{2}{3} - \tfrac{2}{3}\ln x + \tfrac{1}{3}(\ln x)^2 - \tfrac{1}{9}(\ln x)^3 + \dots \qquad \text{IX}$$

Comparing coefficients in equations III, V, and VI with the corresponding coefficients in equation IX, it can be seen that the set of approximate solutions $y^{(n)}$ approaches the true solution as n increases.

Picard's method has two disadvantages. Firstly, as successive substitutions are made the amount of work is increased and the integrations become more complex; and secondly, integrals frequently arise which cannot be evaluated analytically and these have to be solved by a numerical method. It is reasonable therefore to use a numerical method from the very beginning.

11.2.2. The Runge–Kutta Method

The method to be described is a composite one, using the principles discovered separately by Runge and by Kutta. The analytical details of the modern method differ from the original development and the algebra is rather tedious; however, the general principles can be outlined by reference to Fig. 11.1. Assuming that equation (11.2) is satisfied, and an initial condition ($y = y_0$ at $x = x_0$) is given, it is desired to find the value of y when $x = x_0 + h$ where h is some given constant.

FIG. 11.1.   Third order Runge-Kutta process

The general solution of equation (11.2) will consist of a family of curves, each curve having a particular value of the constant of integration. Three specially chosen curves of this family (a, b, c) are illustrated in Fig. 11.1; the curve b passing through the point (x_0, y_0). The gradient of the tangent to the curve at (x_0, y_0) can be calculated from equation (11.2) thus determining the length k_1 by

$$k_1 = hf(x_0, y_0) \qquad (11.8)$$

$y_0 + k_1$ is obviously a poor approximation to the desired answer unless the curve happens to be a straight line, and a better approximation can be obtained from the following reasoning. The gradient of the chord to the curve between x_0 and $x_0 + h$ should be approximately equal to the gradient of the tangent to the curve at $x_0 + \frac{1}{2}h$. Unfortunately, at this stage of the calculation, the position of the curve at $x_0 + \frac{1}{2}h$ is not known; however, an approximate value for y at $x = x_0 + \frac{1}{2}h$ is given by $y = y_0 + \frac{1}{2}k_1$. This point ($x_0 + \frac{1}{2}h$, $y_0 + \frac{1}{2}k_1$) lies on a different curve of the family as illustrated by c in Fig. 11.1. The gradient of the tangent to curve c at ($x_0 + \frac{1}{2}h$, $y_0 + \frac{1}{2}k_1$) can be calculated from equation (11.2) and the length k_2 constructed by drawing a line parallel to this tangent through (x_0, y_0). Thus

$$k_2 = hf(x_0 + \tfrac{1}{2}h, y_0 + \tfrac{1}{2}k_1) \qquad (11.9)$$

For the type of curve illustrated, k_2 is also an underestimate. The method of obtaining an even closer estimate for the end ordinate is to find some average gradient of three tangents, one at the start of the interval, one in the centre, and one at the end. All three tangents should be taken to the correct curve b but this is not possible. The tangents so far, are to the correct curve b, and to the curve c which lies below b. To compensate for the effect of the latter tangent, the final tangent must be taken to a curve lying above b. On the ordinate at $x = x_0+h$, $y = y_0+k_2$ is approximately on curve b, $y = y_0+k_1$ is definitely below b, hence

$$y = y_0+k_2+(k_2-k_1)$$

should be above b. Finding the gradient of the tangent to the curve a which passes through this point from equation (11.2) gives

$$k_3 = hf(x_0+h, y_0+2k_2-k_1) \tag{11.10}$$

It can be shown analytically that the ordinate at $x = x_0+h$ to the curve through (x_0, y_0) is given by

$$y = y_0+\tfrac{1}{6}(k_1+4k_2+k_3) \tag{11.11}$$

where k_1, k_2, k_3 are given by the equations:

$$k_1 = hf(x_0, y_0) \tag{11.8}$$

$$k_2 = hf(x_0+\tfrac{1}{2}h, y_0+\tfrac{1}{2}k_1) \tag{11.9}$$

$$k_3 = hf(x_0+h, y_0+2k_2-k_1) \tag{11.10}$$

This formula (11.11) is known as the " third order Runge–Kutta formula " because the term corresponding to the third derivative term in the Taylor series for y expanded about (x_0, y_0) is correct.

To illustrate the use of this method, it will be applied to the problem given in example 1.

Example 2. If $y = 1$ when $x = 1$, and the equation

$$\frac{dy}{dx} = \frac{x^2-y}{x}$$

is satisfied, find the value of y when $x = 2$.

Using the above symbols, $h = 1$; hence equation (11.8) gives

$$k_1 = f(1,1) = 0 \qquad\qquad \text{II}$$

Equation (11.9) now gives

$$k_2 = f(1\tfrac{1}{2}, 1) = \frac{(9/4)-1}{3/2}$$

$$= \tfrac{5}{6} \qquad\qquad \text{III}$$

Putting equations II and III into (11.10) gives

$$k_3 = f(2, 2\tfrac{2}{3}) = \frac{4-2\tfrac{2}{3}}{2}$$

$$= \tfrac{2}{3} \qquad\qquad \text{IV}$$

Substituting equations II, III and IV into (11.11) gives the answer

$$y = 1 + \tfrac{1}{6}(0 + 3\tfrac{1}{3} + \tfrac{2}{3})$$
$$= 1\tfrac{2}{3} \qquad\qquad\qquad \text{V}$$

which is identical with the analytical solution given by equation VIII in example 1.

If the range of integration is large, it can be subdivided just as for Simpson's rule, with consequent increase of accuracy. This will be illustrated by an example in the next sub-section.

The method of Picard, and the original formulae of Runge and Kutta are given by Piaggio,† together with the theoretical justification of each method.

11.3. HIGHER ORDER DIFFERENTIAL EQUATIONS (INITIAL VALUE TYPE)

It is a simple matter to convert an nth order differential equation to n simultaneous first order equations. It is only necessary to define $(n-1)$ new variables by

$$\left.\begin{array}{c} w_1 = \dfrac{dy}{dx} \\[2mm] w_2 = \dfrac{d^2 y}{dx^2} \\[1mm] \text{etc.} \\[2mm] w_{n-1} = \dfrac{d^{n-1} y}{dx^{n-1}} \end{array}\right\} \qquad (11.12)$$

and remove all derivatives from the original differential equation except $(d^n y/dx^n)$ which is replaced by (dw_{n-1}/dx).

The solution of the set of equations (11.12) with the original differential equation is now very similar to the solution of a single first order equation, provided that the boundary conditions are of initial value type (Section 8.4.5). In this case, at some value $x = x_0$, values for $y, w_1, w_2 \ldots , w_{n-1}$, will be available and an extension of the Runge–Kutta process can be used. The formulae for the second order differential equation

$$\frac{d^2 y}{dx^2} = F\left(x, y, \frac{dy}{dx}\right) \qquad (11.13)$$

are as follows. Putting

$$\frac{dy}{dx} = w \qquad (11.14)$$

equation (11.13) becomes

$$\frac{dw}{dx} = F(x, y, w) \qquad (11.15)$$

† Piaggio, H. T. H. " Differential Equations ". G. Bell & Sons Ltd., London (1928).

From the initial values (x_0, y_0, w_0) and the interval (h) in x, k_1 and K_1 can be defined as before. Thus

$$k_1 = hw_0 \tag{11.16}$$

$$K_1 = hF(x_0, y_0, w_0) \tag{11.17}$$

where k_1 is the first approximation to the change in y and K_1 is the corresponding change in w. Proceeding in a similar manner to the first order case,

$$k_2 = h(w_0 + \tfrac{1}{2}K_1) \tag{11.18}$$

$$K_2 = hF(x_0 + \tfrac{1}{2}h, y_0 + \tfrac{1}{2}k_1, w_0 + \tfrac{1}{2}K_1) \tag{11.19}$$

$$k_3 = h(w_0 + 2K_2 - K_1) \tag{11.20}$$

$$K_3 = hF(x_0 + h, y_0 + 2k_2 - k_1, w_0 + 2K_2 - K_1) \tag{11.21}$$

The values of y and w at the end of the interval are given by

$$y = y_0 + \tfrac{1}{6}(k_1 + 4k_2 + k_3) \tag{11.22}$$

$$w = w_0 + \tfrac{1}{6}(K_1 + 4K_2 + K_3) \tag{11.23}$$

Example 1. Given the differential equation

$$8\frac{d^2y}{dx^2} - x^2\frac{dy}{dx} + 2y^2 = 0$$

and the initial conditions that at $x = 0$, $y = 1$ and $dy/dx = 0$, find the value of y when $x = 1$.

Solution. Putting

$$\frac{dy}{dx} = w \qquad\qquad\qquad \text{I}$$

$$\therefore \quad \frac{dw}{dx} = \frac{x^2w - 2y^2}{8} \qquad\qquad \text{II}$$

Since $h = 1$, $x_0 = 0$, $y_0 = 1$, $w_0 = 0$, equations (11.16) to (11.21) can be used in succession. Thus

$$k_1 = 0 \qquad\qquad\qquad\qquad \text{III}$$

$$K_1 = 1\left(\frac{0-2}{8}\right) = -0.2500 \qquad\qquad \text{IV}$$

$$k_2 = 1(0 - 0.1250) = -0.1250 \qquad\qquad \text{V}$$

$$K_2 = 1\left[\frac{(0.5)^2(-0.125) - 2(1)^2}{8}\right]$$

$$= -0.25391 \qquad\qquad\qquad \text{VI}$$

$$2k_2 - k_1 = -0.2500 \qquad\qquad\qquad \text{VII}$$

$$2K_2 - K_1 = -0.25782 \qquad\qquad\qquad \text{VIII}$$

$$k_3 = -0.25782 \qquad\qquad\qquad \text{IX}$$

$$K_3 = 1 \left[\frac{(1)^2(-0.25782) - 2(0.7500)^2}{8} \right]$$

$$= -0.17285 \hspace{3cm} \text{X}$$

Equation (11.22) now gives the solution

$$y = 1 - \tfrac{1}{6}(0 + 0.50000 + 0.25782)$$

$$\therefore \quad y = 0.8737 \hspace{3cm} \text{XI}$$

There is a large relative variation between k_1, k_2, and k_3 in this example and the above solution may not be very accurate. To check this, the integration can be performed in two stages by choosing $h = \tfrac{1}{2}$ and applying the formulae (11.16) to (11.23) twice. The intermediate and final results are

at $\hspace{2cm} x = 0.5, \hspace{1cm} y = 0.9687, \hspace{1cm} w = -0.1230$

and at $\hspace{1.8cm} x = 1.0, \hspace{1cm} y = 0.8779 \hspace{3cm}$ XII

The answers given by equations XI and XII agree to better than 1%, and the solution can be written

$$y = 0.878$$

with reasonable certainty that the third significant figure is within two units of the correct solution.

11.3.1. *Direct Use of Taylor's Theorem*

The following method has been rendered almost obsolete by the increased availability of digital computers, but for manual calculations with a desk machine it can still give accurate answers quite efficiently.

Taylor's theorem (Section 3.3.7) states that

$$f(x_0 + h) = f(x_0) + hf'(x_0) + \tfrac{1}{2}h^2 f''(x_0) + \ldots + \frac{h^n}{n!}f^{(n)}(x_0) + \ldots \quad (11.24)$$

if $f(x)$ can be differentiated indefinitely. For a second order differential equation of the form (11.13), with the initial values of y and dy/dx given at $x = x_0$, all terms in equation (11.24) can be found as follows.

The boundary conditions specify $f(x_0)$ and $f'(x_0)$, and the differential equation (11.13) can be used to calculate $f''(x_0)$. By differentiating equation (11.13) with respect to x, an equation can be developed giving $f^{(3)}(x_0)$ in terms of x_0, $f(x_0)$, $f'(x_0)$, and $f''(x_0)$. Hence $f^{(n)}(x_0)$ can be found by differentiating equation (11.13) n–2 times. Equation (11.24) thus gives a series solution to the non-linear differential equation (11.13). The method will be illustrated by repeating example 1.

Example 2. Given the differential equation

$$8\frac{d^2y}{dx^2} - x^2\frac{dy}{dx} + 2y^2 = 0$$

and the initial conditions that at $x = 0$, $y = 1$ and $dy/dx = 0$, find the value of y when $x = 1$.

Solution

At $x = 0$, it is given that

$$y = 1 \qquad\qquad\qquad\text{I}$$

$$y' = 0 \qquad\qquad\qquad\text{II}$$

The differential equation can be rewritten in the form

$$8y'' = x^2 y' - 2y^2 \qquad\qquad\qquad\text{III}$$

Using equations I and II, therefore

at $\qquad\qquad x = 0, \qquad y'' = -0{\cdot}2500 \qquad\qquad\qquad\text{IV}$

Differentiating equation III gives

$$8y^{(3)} = x^2 y'' + 2xy' - 4yy' \qquad\qquad\qquad\text{V}$$

$$\therefore \quad \text{at } x = 0, \qquad y^{(3)} = 0 \qquad\qquad\qquad\text{VI}$$

Differentiating equation V gives

$$8y^{(4)} = x^2 y^{(3)} + 4xy'' + 2y' - 4yy'' - 4(y')^2 \qquad\qquad\qquad\text{VII}$$

$$\therefore \quad \text{at } x = 0, \qquad y^{(4)} = 0{\cdot}1250 \qquad\qquad\qquad\text{VIII}$$

Continuing in this manner,

$$8y^{(5)} = x^2 y^{(4)} + 6xy^{(3)} + 6y'' - 4yy^{(3)} - 12y'y'' \qquad\qquad\qquad\text{IX}$$

$$\therefore \quad \text{at } x = 0, \qquad y^{(5)} = -0{\cdot}1875 \qquad\qquad\qquad\text{X}$$

$$8y^{(6)} = x^2 y^{(5)} + 8xy^{(4)} + 12y^{(3)} - 4yy^{(4)} - 16y'y^{(3)} - 12(y'')^2 \qquad\qquad\text{XI}$$

$$\therefore \quad \text{at } x = 0, \qquad y^{(6)} = -0{\cdot}1562 \qquad\qquad\qquad\text{XII}$$

Substituting into equation (11.24) with $h = 1$ gives

$$y = 1{\cdot}0000 - 0{\cdot}1250 + 0{\cdot}0052 - 0{\cdot}0016 - 0{\cdot}0002$$

$$\therefore \quad y = 0{\cdot}8784 \qquad\qquad\qquad\text{XIII}$$

The direct use of Taylor's theorem is apparently simpler than the Runge–Kutta method in this application, because both calculations have been done manually. However, the successive differentiations performed above cannot be done by a digital computer and a more complicated problem would favour the use of a computer programmed for the Runge–Kutta method using many sub-intervals of integration.

11.4. HIGHER ORDER DIFFERENTIAL EQUATIONS (BOUNDARY VALUE TYPE)

With second and higher order differential equations, the boundary conditions may be specified at two different values of the independent variable. In such cases, there is insufficient data available at $x = x_0$, for either of the above methods to be used directly. However, a trial and error method based on either of the above methods is practicable for second order equations. Thus, consider the equation

$$\frac{d^2y}{dx^2} = F\left(x, y, \frac{dy}{dx}\right) \tag{11.13}$$

again, with the boundary conditions:

at $\qquad\qquad\qquad x = x_0, \qquad y = y_0 \tag{11.25}$

and at $\qquad\qquad\quad x = x_N, \qquad y = y_N \tag{11.26}$

where it has been assumed that N integration steps are necessary to cover the distance between the boundaries. If a value is assumed for $y'(x_0)$, equation (11.13) can be solved as an initial value problem, thus generating a value for y at $x = x_N$. This value is unlikely to equal y_N, therefore a second choice is made for $y'(x_0)$, resulting in a second value for y at $x = x_N$. The value of y at $x = x_N$ can thus be evaluated as a function of $y'(x_0)$, and the correct value of $y'(x_0)$ can be found by using an interpolation formula from Chapter 10. The value of $y'(x_0)$ obtained in this way can then be checked by a final solution of an initial value problem.

If this method is adopted, the early trials are usually made with a small value of N and widely spaced values of $y'(x_0)$. As the solution is refined, the value of N is increased and the assumed values of $y'(x_0)$ are contained within a narrower band. The calculated internal point values then give the shape of the solution curve (y vs x).

Example 1. In example 4, Section 2.4.3, the problem of cooling a graphite electrode was considered, and the problem was stated in mathematical terms as follows. Find the rate of flow of heat into the water cooler at $x = 1$ ft when the temperature distribution satisfies

$$(k_0 - \alpha T)\frac{d^2T}{dx^2} - \alpha\left(\frac{dT}{dx}\right)^2 - \beta(T - T_0) = 0 \qquad\qquad \text{I}$$

where $T_0 = 70$, $k_0 = 88 \cdot 9$, $\alpha = 0 \cdot 0180$, and $\beta = 2 \cdot 40$.
The boundary conditions are

at $\qquad\qquad\qquad x = 0, \qquad T = 2700 \qquad\qquad \text{II}$

at $\qquad\qquad\qquad x = 1, \qquad T = 300 \qquad\qquad \text{III}$

and the rate of flow of heat into the cooler is given by

$$H = -16 \cdot 4 \frac{dT}{dx}\bigg|_{x=1} \qquad\qquad \text{IV}$$

Solution

Since dT/dx is required at $x = 1$, it is convenient to change the independent variable by putting

$$z = 1 - x \qquad\qquad \text{V}$$

$$\therefore \quad (k_0 - \alpha T)\frac{d^2T}{dz^2} - \alpha\left(\frac{dT}{dz}\right)^2 - \beta(T - T_0) = 0 \qquad\qquad \text{VI}$$

and the boundary conditions become,

at $\qquad\qquad\qquad\qquad z = 0, \qquad T = \ 300$ $\qquad\qquad$ VII

and at $\qquad\qquad\qquad\quad z = 1, \qquad T = 2700$ $\qquad\qquad$ VIII

From equations VII and VIII the average temperature gradient is 2400, but the gradient at $x = 0$ should be smaller than this because less heat reaches the water cooler than leaves the furnace, and the conductivity is higher at the lower temperature. Therefore, as a first approximation, put

$$T' = 2000 \quad \text{at } z = 0 \qquad\qquad\qquad\text{IX}$$

Putting $\qquad\qquad\qquad\qquad \dfrac{dT}{dz} = w$ $\qquad\qquad\qquad$ X

equation VI becomes

$$\frac{dw}{dz} = \frac{\alpha w^2 + \beta(T - T_0)}{k_0 - \alpha T} \qquad\qquad\qquad \text{XI}$$

Taking one interval and using the method of Section 11.3, the following values can be calculated.

$$
\begin{aligned}
k_1 &= 2000 & K_1 &= \ \ \ 868\cdot9 \\
k_2 &= 2434 & K_2 &= \ \ \ 1673 \\
2k_2 - k_1 &= 2868 & 2K_2 - K_1 &= \ \ \ 2477 \\
k_3 &= 4477 & K_3 &= 11\,543
\end{aligned}
$$

$\therefore \quad T = \ 300 + \tfrac{1}{6}(2000 + 9736 + \ 4477) = 3002 \qquad$ XII

$\therefore \quad w = 2000 + \tfrac{1}{6}(869 + 6692 + 11\,543) = 5184 \qquad$ XIII

The answer given by equation XIII is suspect because K_3 is so different from K_1 and K_2. It appears that $T'(0)$ has been chosen 10% too large by comparing equations VIII and XII. Therefore $T'(0)$ is reduced to 1800 for the second trial, and the interval is halved to reduce the discrepancy between K_3 and K_2.

The calculation for the first interval gives

$$
\begin{aligned}
k_1 &= \ 900 & K_1 &= 352\cdot5 \\
k_2 &= \ 988 & K_2 &= 476\cdot9 \\
k_3 &= 1201 & K_3 &= 834\cdot1
\end{aligned}
$$

$\therefore \quad T(\tfrac{1}{2}) = \ 300 + \tfrac{1}{6}(900 + 3952 + 1201) \qquad\quad = 1309 \qquad$ XIV

$\therefore \quad w(\tfrac{1}{2}) = 1800 + \tfrac{1}{6}(352\cdot5 + 1907\cdot6 + \ 834\cdot1) = 2316 \qquad$ XV

For the second interval,

$$
\begin{aligned}
k_1 &= 1158 & K_1 &= 761\cdot5 \\
k_2 &= 1348 & K_2 &= 1232 \\
k_3 &= 2009 & K_3 &= 3948
\end{aligned}
$$

$\therefore \quad T(1) = 1309 + \tfrac{1}{6}(1158 + 5392 + 2009) = 2735 \qquad$ XVI

$\therefore \quad w(1) = 2316 + \tfrac{1}{6}(762 + 4928 + 3948) \ = 3922 \qquad$ XVII

Equation XVI shows that the temperature drop across the electrode is now 2435° compared with the true value 2400°. Hence, the assumed value $T'(0) = 1800$ is probably $1\frac{1}{2}\%$ too high. Therefore, putting $dT/dx = -1770$ at $x = 1$ into equation IV gives the result

$$H = 29\,000 \text{ Btu/h} \qquad \text{XVIII}$$

This answer is considered to be sufficiently accurate for the purpose of the problem. It could be improved further by taking more intervals and choosing $T'(0)$ more accurately, but this is not justified by the accuracy of the original data.

11.4.1 *Finite Difference Methods*

An alternative method of solving higher order ordinary differential equations of boundary value type, is to replace the differential equation with an equivalent finite difference equation. This technique is most useful for second order equations, or higher order equations replaced by simultaneous second order equations.

There are many bases for the method, but the derivation from Taylor's theorem is probably the easiest to follow. The closed range of the independent variable $a \leqslant x \leqslant b$ is divided into equal intervals and the points are labelled x_n, where $x_0 = a$, and $x_N = b$. The dependent variable (y) can be expressed in the neighbourhood of any point (x_n) in terms of x and its derivatives at x_n by means of Taylor's theorem (Section 3.3.7), and if h denotes the increment of x between neighbouring points,

$$y_{n+1} = f(x_{n+1}) = f(x_n) + hf'(x_n) + \tfrac{1}{2}h^2 f''(x_n) + \dots \qquad (11.27)$$

$$y_n = f(x_n) \qquad (11.28)$$

$$y_{n-1} = f(x_{n-1}) = f(x_n) - hf'(x_n) + \tfrac{1}{2}h^2 f''(x_n) - \dots \qquad (11.29)$$

If h is chosen sufficiently small, terms in h^3 and higher degree can be neglected in equations (11.27, 29). These three equations relate neighbouring point values to the derivatives at the central point (x_n); and they can be solved to determine the derivatives in terms of the point values. Thus

$$f(x_n) = y_n \qquad (11.30)$$

$$f'(x_n) = \frac{y_{n+1} - y_{n-1}}{2h} \qquad (11.31)$$

$$f''(x_n) = \frac{y_{n+1} - 2y_n + y_{n-1}}{h^2} = \frac{\Delta^2 y_{n-1}}{h^2} \qquad (11.32)$$

These equations illustrate the use of Norlund's operator, as may be seen by comparing equations (11.32) and (9.37), and they allow any second order differential equation to be replaced by an equivalent second order difference equation.

The calculation details and treatment of boundary conditions is more easily explained with reference to a particular example.

Example 2. The cylindrical combustion chamber of a rocket motor has coolant ducts of lenticular cross-section at frequent evenly spaced intervals within the cylindrical wall. The dimensions of a typical duct are illustrated in Fig. 11.2. Radiant heat is received uniformly by the internal surface of

FIG. 11.2.   Rocket motor cooling duct

the combustion chamber at a rate $Q = 57$ cals/sec cm^2 and this heat is conducted into the liquid coolant at a bulk temperature $T_B = 130°$C according to a variable heat transfer coefficient h cals/sec cm^2°C. h can be determined from the Dittus-Boelter equation expressed for gases as $h = \alpha u^{0·8}$, where u is the local centre line velocity and $\alpha = 0·00626$ for the coolant used. Spikins† has determined the velocity distribution as

$$u = U_0 \left[1 - \left(\frac{z}{1·27} \right)^3 \right]$$

where z is the coordinate measured as shown in Fig. 11.2, and U_0, the axial velocity, has a value 100 cm/sec. If the metal conductivity $k = 0·107$ cals/sec cm^2°C cm^{-1}, find the temperature distribution within the chamber wall.

Solution

The shape of the duct is rather complicated, so it was idealized as shown in Fig. 11.3. There are lines of symmetry at AE, DG, and JK, and a typical section has been straightened out by distorting the junction CKJBF. In the idealized situation, radiant heat enters through AB and BC which is chosen to equal BJ, negligible heat passes through the external surface CD, and the coolant flows over EF and F′G. All areas and heat paths are correct in this model, except for the curved path from BF to CF which is only approximately correct. Neglecting the temperature drop through the metal wall with respect to the temperature drop within the coolant film, reduces the problem to the determination of the metal temperature (T) as a function of a single coordinate (x).

† Spikins, D. J., Ph.D. Thesis, Chemical Engineering Department, University of Birmingham, 1958.

FIG. 11.3. Idealized metal section

Taking a heat balance over an element of metal in the section ABFE gives

$$\frac{d^2T}{dx^2} - \frac{h}{ks}(T - T_B) + \frac{Q}{ks} = 0 \qquad \text{I}$$

or inserting the data

$$\frac{d^2T}{dx^2} - \frac{0.00626 \times 100^{0.8}}{0.107 \times 0.1219}\left[1 - \left(\frac{x}{1.27}\right)^3\right]^{0.8}(T - T_B) + \frac{57}{0.107 \times 0.1219} = 0 \qquad \text{II}$$

To simplify the arithmetic, it is convenient to put

$$x = 1.27X \qquad \text{III}$$

and

$$\theta = T - T_B \qquad \text{IV}$$

$$\therefore \quad \frac{d^2\theta}{dX^2} - 30.8(1 - X^3)^{0.8}\theta + 7048 = 0 \qquad \text{V}$$

Similarly, in the section BCF'F, where no coolant flows but heat is still absorbed in a thicker section,

$$\frac{d^2\theta}{dX^2} + 4228 = 0 \qquad \text{VI}$$

Finally, in the section $1.1 \leqslant X \leqslant 2.1$,

$$\frac{d^2\theta}{dX^2} - 18.5[1 - (2.1 - X)^3]^{0.8}\theta = 0 \qquad \text{VII}$$

In the finite difference representation, AB and CD are each divided into ten equal intervals, BC is one interval, and the point temperatures are labelled θ_n where $n = 10X$. The finite difference form of equation V can be found from equations (11.30, 31, 32) as

$$\theta_{n+1} - [2 + 0.308(1 - X_n^3)^{0.8}]\theta_n + \theta_{n-1} + 70.5 = 0 \qquad \text{VIII}$$

which is valid for $1 \leqslant n \leqslant 9$. The finite difference form of equation VII is

$$\theta_{n+1} - [2 + 0.185\{1 - (2.1 - X_n)^3\}^{0.8}]\theta_n + \theta_{n-1} = 0 \qquad \text{IX}$$

which is valid for $12 \leqslant n \leqslant 20$.

The four points 0, 10, 11, 21 are influenced by the boundary conditions in the following manner. Point 0 is in a plane of symmetry, and it can be assumed that a point $n = -1$ exists where $\theta_{-1} = \theta_1$. This ensures that the gradient is zero at the boundary and the point $n = 0$ becomes an ordinary point of equation VIII. Similarly, $\theta_{22} = \theta_{20}$ and equation IX is valid for $n = 21$.

The conditions at points 10 and 11 are rather more difficult, but returning to first principles, and using equation (11.31),

$$\frac{\theta_{10} - \theta_9}{1 \cdot 27 \, \delta X} \text{ is the temperature gradient at } n = 9\tfrac{1}{2}$$

$$\frac{\theta_{11} - \theta_{10}}{1 \cdot 27 \, \delta X} \text{ is the temperature gradient at } n = 10\tfrac{1}{2}$$

Fig. 11.4. Heat balance at BF

Taking a heat balance over an element of width $\delta X = 0 \cdot 1$ astride point 10 as illustrated in Fig. 11.4 gives

$$\frac{-0 \cdot 1219k}{1 \cdot 27 \, \delta X}(\theta_{10} - \theta_9) + 1 \cdot 27 Q \, \delta X = \frac{-0 \cdot 2032k}{1 \cdot 27 \, \delta X}(\theta_{11} - \theta_{10}) +$$

$$+ \tfrac{1}{4}(\theta_{10} + \theta_9) \, 1 \cdot 27 \, \delta X \, h \big|_{x = 0 \cdot 95} \qquad \text{X}$$

which simplifies to

$$0 \cdot 3666\theta_9 - \theta_{10} + 0 \cdot 6213\theta_{11} + 26 \cdot 3 = 0 \qquad \text{XI}$$

A similar balance at point 11 gives

$$0 \cdot 4976\theta_{10} - \theta_{11} + 0 \cdot 4927\theta_{12} + 10 \cdot 5 = 0 \qquad \text{XII}$$

There are thus ten equations of type VIII, ten of type IX, plus equations XI and XII which are to be solved for θ_n where $0 \leqslant n \leqslant 21$. The simplest method of solution is to estimate values of θ_n for odd values of n and solve the equations directly for θ_n at even values of n. From the calculated even values, improved odd values can be calculated. By repetition, the solution can be obtained as accurately as required.

Equations VIII and IX are first solved for θ_n and the coefficients of θ_{n+1}, θ_{n-1} evaluated at each point as shown in Table 11.1.

TABLE 11.1. *Coefficients in the Difference Equations*

n	coefficient of θ_{n-1}	coefficient of θ_{n+1}	plus	n	coefficient of θ_{n-1}	coefficient of θ_{n+1}	plus
0	—	0·8665	30·5	1	0·4333	0·4333	30·5
2	0·4336	0·4336	30·6	3	0·4345	0·4345	30·6
4	0·4363	0·4363	30·8	5	0·4392	0·4392	31·0
6	0·4438	0·4438	31·3	7	0·4504	0·4504	31·8
8	0·4601	0·4601	32·4	9	0·4743	0·4743	33·4
10	0·3666	0·6213	26·3	11	0·4976	0·4927	10·5
12	0·4842	0·4842	—	13	0·4752	0·4752	—
14	0·4690	0·4690	—	15	0·4646	0·4646	—
16	0·4616	0·4616	—	17	0·4597	0·4597	—
18	0·4585	0·4585	—	19	0·4579	0·4579	—
20	0·4577	0·4577	—	21	0·9154	—	—

To start the calculation shown in Table 11.2, values must be estimated for θ_n with n odd. Neglecting the change of heat transfer coefficient with velocity, and assuming that θ_n is constant for $n \leqslant 10$ gives $\theta_n = 227$ by equation VIII; hence $\theta_n = 250$ will be a fair approximation for odd values of n between 0 and 10. An approximate solution of equation VII by the methods of Chapter 2 after neglecting the term $(2\cdot1 - X)^3$ gives

$$\theta = 250\,e^{-4\cdot25(X-1\cdot1)} \qquad\qquad \text{XIII}$$

Evaluating equation XIII at the chosen points completes the estimate of the temperature distribution.

The equations given in the left-hand half of Table 11.1 can be used to calculate the values in the second row of Table 11.2. The calculation is thus started and alternate use of the left- and right-hand halves of Table 11.1 gives the solution. A quicker way to the solution is by making a fresh estimate at any stage, and this has been done on two rows of Table 11.2. The solution given in the last row was obtained from eight further rows of calculation.

This solution will be fairly accurate in the metal immediately surrounding the duct, but not very good in the weld section CKJBF. Taking a heat balance over an element within this section gives

$$\frac{d^2T}{dz^2} + \frac{Q}{ks} = 0 \qquad\qquad \text{XIV}$$

or

$$\frac{d^2T}{dz^2} + 1640 = 0 \qquad\qquad \text{XV}$$

Solving equation XV and remembering that $z = 1\cdot397$ is a plane of symmetry gives

$$T = A - 820(1\cdot397 - z)^2 \qquad\qquad \text{XVI}$$

TABLE 11.2. *Temperature Distribution Around a Cooling Duct*

0	1	2	3	4	5	6	7	8	9	10	11	12	13	14	15	16	17	18	19	20	21
247	250	247	250	249	250	253	250	262	250	273	250	173	107	72	46	30	20	13	8	5	4
243	245	243	246	248	251	260	264	286	287	276	232	169	116	76	47	31	20	13	8	5	5
239	241	241	244	248	254	267	278	298	300	280	231	168	116	78	50	32	20	13	9	6	5
237	238	239	243	249	257	272	286	306	308	284	233	169	117	79	51	33	21	14	9	6	5
236	237	239	243	250	260	276	292	311	313	287	235	171	118	80	52	34	22	14	9	6	5
235	236	238	243	251	262	279	296	314	317	290	238	173	119	81	53	35	22	14	9	6	5
	235		243		264		299		320		240		121		54		23		9		5
232	233	237	244	254	268	286	305	323	326	297	244	179	125	85	56	37	24	15	9	7	5
	234		244		268		306		327		246		125		57		24		10		5
233	235	238	244	254	268	286	307	324	329	299	248	180	126	85	57	37	24	16	11	7	6
	236		245		269		309		332		251		127		57		24		11		6
235	235	239	245	255	269	288	309	327	333	304	252	183	128	86	57	37	24	16	11	8	7
234	235	239	245	255	269	288	310	330	337	309	256	187	131	89	59	39	26	17	11	8	7

But the temperature at point F ($z = 1 \cdot 270$) is

$$T = T_B + \theta = 130 + \tfrac{1}{2}(309 + 256) = 412\tfrac{1}{2}$$

$$\therefore \quad A = 426 \qquad\qquad\qquad\qquad\qquad \text{XVII}$$

These results have been plotted in Fig. 11.5, which shows that the hottest part of the duct is about $1 \cdot 5$ mm from the corner of the coolant channel along the heated wall, and not at the centre of the uncooled weld. Because the temperature drop across the metal wall has been neglected, the results

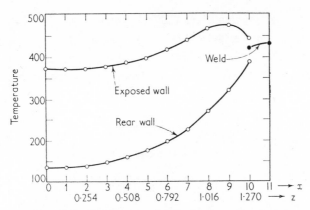

Fig. 11.5.   Temperature distribution in cooling duct

presented should approximate to the average temperature within the metal at the point in question, but the exposed surface temperature could be about 35°C higher than the figure given.

It is possible to modify the calculation procedure with advantage in more complicated problems, by working in terms of temperature changes instead of temperatures. To do this, the first row of estimated temperatures is subtracted from the first row of calculated temperatures at the same points. All subsequent calculations are then performed to give correction terms, and the final temperature at each point becomes the sum of the values in that column. The result obtained in this way should then be checked by one cycle of the basic calculation in terms of the temperatures.

11.5.   Algebraic Equations

In many problems it is necessary to solve a quadratic equation, and this is readily accomplished by means of the formula:

Roots of $\qquad\qquad\qquad ax^2 + bx + c = 0 \qquad\qquad\qquad\qquad (11.33)$

are $\qquad\qquad\qquad x = \dfrac{-b \pm \sqrt{(b^2 - 4ac)}}{2a} \qquad\qquad\qquad (11.34)$

Less frequently, a cubic equation needs to be solved, and this can also be done analytically without too much difficulty. An analytical solution of a quartic equation is also feasible but not very profitable in most practical cases; but polynomial equations of higher degree are insoluble analytically, hence numerical or graphical methods must be used. Transcendental equations such as

$$\tan x = kx \qquad (11.35)$$

are also insoluble analytically and methods must be established for solving such equations in particular numerical cases.

11.5.1. *Analytical Solution of the Cubic Equation*

A method due to Tartaglia (1545) is the following. The cubic equation

$$ax^3 + 3bx^2 + 3cx + d = 0 \qquad (11.36)$$

will have three roots, the sum of which will be $(-3b/a)$. Changing the variable by putting

$$z = x + \frac{b}{a} \qquad (11.37)$$

gives the equation

$$z^3 + 3Hz + G = 0 \qquad (11.38)$$

which has zero for the sum of its roots, where

$$a^2 H = ac - b^2$$

and

$$a^3 G = a^2 d - 3abc + 2b^3$$

To solve equation (11.38), a further substitution is made. That is,

$$z = u + v \qquad (11.39)$$

where v is a function of u which is still to be determined. Hence

$$u^3 + v^3 + 3(uv + H)(u + v) + G = 0 \qquad (11.40$$

Choosing $v = -H/u$ will simplify equation (11.40) to

$$u^6 - H^3 + Gu^3 = 0 \qquad (11.41)$$

Equation (11.41) is a quadratic in u^3 which has the solution

$$u^3 = -\tfrac{1}{2}G \pm \tfrac{1}{2}\sqrt{(G^2 + 4H^3)} \qquad (11.42)$$

Equation (11.42) determines six values for u and since $uv = -H$, six values of v are determined. Hence equation (11.39) appears to give six roots to the cubic (11.38). However, there are only three distinct values for z because each pair of values for u and v occurs twice, once as $u + v$ and again as $v + u$. Equation (11.37) transforms the values of z into the corresponding values of x which satisfy equation (11.36).

Example 1. Solve the equation

$$x^3 - 4x^2 + 7x - 5 = 0 \qquad \text{I}$$

Removing the second term by putting

$$z = x - 1\tfrac{1}{3} \qquad \text{II}$$

gives $\qquad\qquad 27z^3 + 45z - 11 = 0 \qquad\qquad$ III

Putting $\qquad\qquad z = u + v \qquad\qquad$ IV

$$\therefore \quad 27u^3 + 27v^3 + (81uv + 45)(u + v) - 11 = 0$$

Assuming that

$$81uv + 45 = 0$$

$$\therefore \quad v = \frac{-5}{9u} \qquad\qquad \text{V}$$

$$\therefore \quad 729u^6 - 297u^3 - 125 = 0 \qquad\qquad \text{VI}$$

The solution of equation VI is obtained from (11.34) as

$$u^3 = \frac{297 \pm \sqrt{(88\,209 + 364\,500)}}{1458}$$

$$= 0{\cdot}6652$$

$$\therefore \quad u = 0{\cdot}8729 \qquad\qquad \text{VII}$$

From equation V

$$v = -0{\cdot}6364 \qquad\qquad \text{VIII}$$

Hence, from equations IV and II,

$$x = 1{\cdot}5698 \qquad\qquad \text{IX}$$

is one root of the cubic equation I.

The simplest way of finding the other roots is to divide equation I by $(x - 1{\cdot}5698)$ algebraically to obtain

$$x^2 - 2{\cdot}4302x + 3{\cdot}1851 = 0 \qquad\qquad \text{X}$$

which has the roots

$$x = 1{\cdot}2151 \pm 2{\cdot}6143i \qquad\qquad \text{XI}$$

In general, if the cubic equation (11.36) has three real roots, $G^2 + 4H^3 < 0$ and equation (11.41) has complex roots. The cube root of equation (11.42) is best evaluated in the Argand diagram in this case. When the cubic has only one real root, as in example 1, the quadratic (11.41) will always have real roots. Hence the method is most useful for finding a single real root of a cubic equation.

11.5.2. *Graphical Location of Roots*

In all numerical methods it is useful to know an approximate answer to the problem; this can then be successively improved. This was the basic technique in example 2 of Section 11.4.1, where a very approximate temperature distribution was assumed. It can be seen that a very good first approximation will yield an accurate solution quickly, but even a poor first approximation will not extend the subsequent calculation unduly. Graphical methods are very useful for determining a first approximation. If the graph is drawn accurately, the graphical solution may be acceptable as the final solution; but even a rough sketch will give the approximate location of the root of an equation. Thus consider the following example.

Example 2. Find the approximate location of the roots of the equation

$$\tan x = kx \qquad \text{I}$$

where k is a constant.

Equation I can be resolved into two equations

$$y = \tan x \qquad \text{II}$$

and

$$y = kx \qquad \text{III}$$

which must be satisfied simultaneously. Taking a set of values for x, y can be evaluated from each of equations II and III, and both equations can be plotted graphically as shown in Fig. 11.6.

FIG. 11.6.   Graphical solution of $\tan x = kx$

The principal branch of $y = \tan x$ has asymptotes at $x = \pm\tfrac{1}{2}\pi$ and passes through the origin. This shape is then repeated indefinitely at intervals of π along the x axis. Equation III is just the equation of a straight line and the solutions of equation I are the points of intersection of the two curves. The gradient of equation II at the origin is unity and therefore two possibilities arise. If $k = k_1 < 1$, there is only one root on the principal branch; but if $k = k_2 > 1$, there are three roots on the principal branch. Altogether there are an infinite number of roots which occur approximately at odd multiples of $\tfrac{1}{2}\pi$. As already mentioned, the first few roots near the origin are a fair distance from the asymptotes and there may be one or three roots near the origin, depending upon the value of k.

11.5.3. *Improvement of Roots by Successive Approximation*

The equation to be solved can always be rearranged, as in the above example, to give a simple function on at least one side of the equation. After a graphical investigation to find an approximate root, the value obtained can be substituted into one side of the equation, and a second value obtained from the other side of the equation. This process of substituting into one side and estimating a new value from the other, can be repeated until two consecutive results agree. Only one side of the equation can be used for the evaluation step because the one side will give a convergent solution whereas the other side gives a divergent solution. The method is illustrated by reference to the problem arising in Section 6.9.3., equation VII.

Example 3. Find the root of equation

$$15\alpha^3 - 68\alpha^2 + 95\alpha - 47 = 0 \qquad\qquad \text{I}$$

which is close to $\alpha = 2.5$.

It is always useful when solving cubic equations to eliminate the second term by using the substitution (11.37). Thus putting

$$z = \alpha - \tfrac{68}{45} = \alpha - 1.5111 \qquad\qquad \text{II}$$

into equation I and rearranging,

$$z^3 = 0.5170z + 0.4641 \qquad\qquad \text{III}$$

Each side of equation III has been plotted in Fig. 11.7 to show the location of the root. The mechanism of the numerical method is also illustrated by

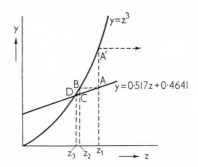

FIG. 11.7.   Solution of a cubic equation

the stepped path ABCD. Starting from the approximate value $z = z_1$, the right-hand side of equation III is evaluated to give the ordinate of A. The point where the curve $y = z^3$ has the same ordinate value at B, determines a new approximation for the root ($z = z_2$). Repeating the process gives the points C and D and a closer approximation to the root. It is obvious from the diagram that substituting into the left-hand side of equation III would give the point A′, and the subsequent evaluation of z from the right-hand side of III would be further from the root than the original estimate.

The determination of which side of an equation to substitute into, depends upon the nature of the two functions in the vicinity of the root. Thus, the left-hand side of equation III is very sensitive to small changes in z whereas the right-hand side is relatively insensitive. Hence, the approximate value is always put into the insensitive side, and the new root evaluated from the sensitive side.

The approximate root $\alpha = 2 \cdot 5$ corresponds to $z = 1 \cdot 0$ from equation II. Hence the calculation proceeds,

$$0 \cdot 5170 z_1 + 0 \cdot 4641 = 0 \cdot 9811 \ = z_2^3$$

$$\therefore \ z_2 = 0 \cdot 9937$$

$$0 \cdot 5170 z_2 + 0 \cdot 4641 = 0 \cdot 9778 \ = z_3^3$$

$$\therefore \ z_3 = 0 \cdot 9926$$

$$0 \cdot 5170 z_3 + 0 \cdot 4641 = 0 \cdot 9773 \ = z_4^3$$

$$\therefore \ z_4 = 0 \cdot 9924$$

$$0 \cdot 5170 z_4 + 0 \cdot 4641 = 0 \cdot 97717 = z_5^3$$

$$\therefore \ z_5 = 0 \cdot 99233$$

$$0 \cdot 5170 z_5 + 0 \cdot 4641 = 0 \cdot 97713 = z_6^3$$

$$\therefore \ z_6 = 0 \cdot 99232$$

Since z_5 and z_6 are approximately equal, z_6 is close enough to the true root. Hence, by equation II,

$$\alpha = 2 \cdot 5034$$

The idea in the above method is to divide the equation into two parts, one very sensitive, and the other insensitive. This is why the second term was removed from the original equation; otherwise it would have increased the sensitivity of the right-hand side of equation III.

11.5.4. Newton's Method

In this method, Taylor's theorem is used to improve an approximate root. If a root of the equation

$$f(x) = 0 \tag{11.43}$$

is required, and $x = x_1$ is an approximate root, the function in equation 11.43) can be expanded in the neighbourhood of x_1 thus,

$$f(x_1 + \delta x) = f(x_1) + \delta x f'(x_1) \tag{11.44}$$

where the higher order terms have been neglected. If $x_2 = x_1 + \delta x$ is to be a better approximation to the solution of equation (11.43), then (11.44) gives

$$f(x_1) + (x_2 - x_1) f'(x_1) = 0$$

or $$x_2 = x_1 - f(x_1)/f'(x_1) \tag{11.45}$$

Further approximations can be found by repeated application of equation (11.45). Thus

$$x_3 = x_2 - f(x_2)/f'(x_2), \quad \text{etc.}$$

This method can be employed to solve non-linear simultaneous equations and the following is an example of such use.

Example 4. In a study of the settling of suspensions of spherical particles, Oliver† has suggested the correlation

$$V_s = V_0(1-kc)(1-Kc^{1/3}) \qquad \text{I}$$

where V_s is the settling velocity of the suspension,

$\quad V_0$ is the Stokes' velocity of a single particle,

$\quad c$ is the volume concentration of the solids,

$\quad k, K$ are empirical constants.

From the following data given in the paper, find the best values for k, K, and V_0 by the method of least squares.

c	V_s(cm/sec)	c	V_s(cm/sec)
0	0·0943	0·10	0·0492
0·00333	0·0815	0·15	0·0397
0·00666	0·0761	0·20	0·0316
0·010	0·0740	0·25	0·0234
0·020	0·0688	0·30	0·0169
0·050	0·0612	0·35	0·0125

Solution

Rearranging equation I and introducing an error term to accommodate the experimental error,

$$V_s - V_0 + V_0\alpha c^{1/3} + \beta c - \alpha\beta c^{4/3} = R \qquad \text{II}$$

where
$$\alpha = K, \quad \text{and} \quad \beta = V_0 k \qquad \text{III}$$

Following the method described in Section 10.6.2 by squaring equation II and equating to zero the partial derivatives of R^2 with respect to V_0, α, and β gives

$$V_0(N + \alpha^2 \sum c^{2/3} - 2\alpha \sum c^{1/3})$$
$$= \sum V_s - \alpha \sum V_s c^{1/3} + \beta \sum c - 2\alpha\beta \sum c^{4/3} + \alpha^2\beta \sum c^{5/3} \qquad \text{IV}$$

$$\alpha(2\beta V_0 \sum c^{5/3} - \beta^2 \sum c^{8/3} - V_0^2 \sum c^{2/3})$$
$$= V_0 \sum V_s c^{1/3} - \beta \sum V_s c^{4/3} - V_0^2 \sum c^{1/3} + 2\beta V_0 \sum c^{4/3} - \beta^2 \sum c^{7/3} \qquad \text{V}$$

$$\beta(\sum c^2 + \alpha^2 \sum c^{8/3} - 2\alpha \sum c^{7/3})$$
$$= \alpha \sum V_s c^{4/3} + V_0 \sum c - 2\alpha V_0 \sum c^{4/3} + \alpha^2 V_0 \sum c^{5/3} - \sum V_s c \qquad \text{VI}$$

where $N = 12$ is the number of experimental points, and each sum is taken over all points. These sums, which are evaluated in Table 11.3, can be substituted into equations IV, V, and VI to give:

$$V_0(12 + 2\cdot4949\alpha^2 - 9\cdot5544\alpha)$$
$$= 62\cdot92 - 18\cdot093\alpha + 1\cdot440\beta - 1\cdot7516\alpha\beta + 0\cdot5488\alpha^2\beta \qquad \text{II}$$

† Oliver, D. R. *Chem. Eng. Sci.* **15**, 230, 1961.

TABLE 11.3. *Least Mean Squares Fit of Settling Data*

V_s^*	$c^{1/3}$	$c^{2/3}$	c	$c^{4/3}$	$c^{5/3}$	c^2	$c^{7/3}$	$c^{8/3}$	$V_s c^{1/3}$	$V_s c^{4/3}$	$V_s c$
9·43	0	0	0	0	0	0	0	0	0	0	0
8·15	0·1494	0·0223	0·0033	0·0005	0·0001	0·00001	0	0	1·218	0·0041	0·0272
7·61	0·1882	0·0354	0·0067	0·0013	0·0002	0·00004	0	0	1·432	0·0096	0·0507
7·40	0·2154	0·0464	0·0100	0·0022	0·0005	0·00010	0·00001	0	1·594	0·0159	0·0740
6·88	0·2714	0·0737	0·0200	0·0054	0·0015	0·00040	0·00002	0·00001	1·867	0·0373	0·1376
6·12	0·3684	0·1357	0·0500	0·0184	0·0068	0·00250	0·00011	0·00003	2·255	0·1127	0·3060
4·92	0·4642	0·2154	0·1000	0·0464	0·0215	0·01000	0·00092	0·00034	2·284	0·2284	0·4920
3·97	0·5313	0·2823	0·1500	0·0797	0·0423	0·02250	0·00464	0·00215	2·109	0·3164	0·5955
3·16	0·5848	0·3420	0·2000	0·1170	0·0684	0·04000	0·01195	0·00635	1·848	0·3696	0·6320
2·34	0·6300	0·3968	0·2500	0·1575	0·0992	0·06250	0·02339	0·01368	1·474	0·3686	0·5850
1·69	0·6694	0·4482	0·3000	0·2008	0·1345	0·09000	0·03938	0·02480	1·131	0·3394	0·5070
1·25	0·7047	0·4967	0·3500	0·2466	0·1738	0·12250	0·06025	0·04034	0·881	0·3083	0·4375
								0·06084			
62·92	4·7772	2·4949	1·4400	0·8758	0·5488	0·35055	0·22700	0·14854	18·092	2·1103	3·8445

* The values of V_s have been multiplied by 100 to simplify the arithmetic.

$$\alpha(1{\cdot}0976V_0\beta - 0{\cdot}14854\beta^2 - 2{\cdot}4949V_0^2)$$
$$= 18{\cdot}093V_0 - 2{\cdot}1103\beta - 4{\cdot}7772V_0^2 + 1{\cdot}7516V_0\beta - 0{\cdot}2270\beta^2 \qquad \text{VIII}$$

$$\beta(0{\cdot}35055 + 0{\cdot}14854\alpha^2 - 0{\cdot}4540\alpha)$$
$$= 2{\cdot}1103\alpha - 3{\cdot}8445 + 1{\cdot}440V_0 - 1{\cdot}7516\alpha V_0 + 0{\cdot}5488\alpha^2 V_0 \qquad \text{IX}$$

which are to be solved for α, β, and V_0.

The results given in the paper were obtained graphically, and they are

$$\alpha = 0{\cdot}75, \qquad \beta = 18{\cdot}98, \qquad V_0 = 9{\cdot}35 \qquad \text{X}$$

Using the method of Section 11.5.3 to improve these values by substituting α and β from equations X into equation VII to evaluate V_0, then using this value of V_0 with β from equation X in equation VIII to evaluate α etc., the following results were obtained.

$$\alpha = 0{\cdot}747, \qquad \beta = 18{\cdot}67, \qquad V_0 = 9{\cdot}21 \qquad \text{XI}$$

Unfortunately, there is no guarantee that the correct equation is being used for each determination and the results tended to oscillate in successive stages of calculation. Hence the values in equations XI can be checked by Newton's method as follows.

Each value is assumed to be in error by a small amount (x, y, or z). That is,

$$\alpha = 0{\cdot}747 + x, \qquad \beta = 18{\cdot}67 + y, \qquad V_0 = 9{\cdot}21 + z \qquad \text{XII}$$

The higher order functions can be linearized by neglecting products of the small quantities x, y, and z. Thus

$$\alpha^2 = 0{\cdot}55801 + 1{\cdot}494x$$
$$\beta^2 = 348{\cdot}57 + 37{\cdot}37y$$
$$V_0^2 = 84{\cdot}824 + 18{\cdot}42z$$
$$\alpha\beta = 13{\cdot}946 + 18{\cdot}67x + 0{\cdot}747y$$
$$\alpha V_0 = 6{\cdot}880 + 9{\cdot}21x + 0{\cdot}747z$$
$$\beta V_0 = 171{\cdot}95 + 9{\cdot}21y + 18{\cdot}67z$$
$$\alpha^2\beta = 10{\cdot}418 + 27{\cdot}89x + 0{\cdot}558y$$
$$\alpha^2 V_0 = 5{\cdot}1393 + 13{\cdot}76x + 0{\cdot}558z$$
$$\alpha\beta V_0 = 128{\cdot}45 + 172{\cdot}0x + 6{\cdot}880y + 13{\cdot}95z$$
$$\alpha\beta^2 = 260{\cdot}4 + 348{\cdot}6x + 27{\cdot}92y$$
$$\alpha V_0^2 = 63{\cdot}36 + 84{\cdot}82x + 13{\cdot}76z$$

Putting the above linearized expressions into equations VII, VIII, and IX and simplifying, therefore

$$18{\cdot}19x + 0{\cdot}438y - 6{\cdot}255z = 0{\cdot}029 \qquad \text{XIII}$$
$$74{\cdot}61x - 65{\cdot}82y - 18{\cdot}19z = 0{\cdot}15 \qquad \text{XIV}$$
$$2{\cdot}138x + 0{\cdot}0944y - 0{\cdot}438z = 0{\cdot}0029 \qquad \text{XV}$$

o

406   MATHEMATICAL METHODS IN CHEMICAL ENGINEERING

Solving these equations by successive elimination or by matrices gives the solutions

$$x = 0.0014, \qquad y = -0.0006, \qquad z = -0.0006 \qquad \text{XVI}$$

Hence, the values of α, β, and V_0 are

$$\alpha = 0.748, \qquad \beta = 18.67, \qquad V_0 = 9.21 \qquad \text{XVII}$$

from equations XII

Returning to the original constants by equations III, and remembering the factor (100) introduced in Table 11.3, gives the final result

$$V_0 = 0.0921 \text{ cm/sec}$$
$$k = 2.027$$
$$K = 0.748$$

which confirms the graphical values given in the original paper.

11.5.5. *Comparison of Methods*

The method of successive approximation consists of a simple operation repeated many times, and if the process is convergent, this is probably the easiest method to use because any calculation errors show up in the following cycle. Newton's method is more efficient but involves a fair amount of algebraic manipulation. An accurate solution is usually obtained after only two cycles of calculation, but if a second cycle were needed in the above example, a new set of equations XII would have to be substituted into equations VII, VIII, and IX and the complete calculation repeated.

Thus Newton's method is more efficient and reliable, but the self-checking feature and simplicity of the method of successive approximation, restore the balance of advantage and disadvantage between the two methods.

11.6. DIFFERENCE–DIFFERENTIAL EQUATIONS

The numerical solution of this type of equation follows directly from the method given in Section 11.3. Considering the general form of equation which arises in chemical engineering,

$$\frac{dy_n}{dt} = f(y_{n-1}, y_n, y_{n+1}) \tag{11.46}$$

where the values of y_n are given at some value of t (say $t = 0$) and taking an interval (h) in t, then the modified Runge–Kutta process can be performed on equation (11.46) for each value of n. Thus, evaluating

$$k_{n,1} = hf(y_{n-1}, y_n, y_{n+1}) \tag{11.47}$$

for each value of n, and then evaluating

$$k_{n,2} = hf(y_{n-1} + \tfrac{1}{2}k_{n-1,1}, y_n + \tfrac{1}{2}k_{n,1}, y_{n+1} + \tfrac{1}{2}k_{n+1,1}) \tag{11.48}$$

and finally

$$k_{n,3} = hf(y_{n-1} + 2k_{n-1,2} - k_{n-1,1}, y_n + 2k_{n,2} - k_{n,1}, y_{n+1} + 2k_{n+1,2} - k_{n+1,1}) \tag{11.49}$$

the value for y_n at the end of the increment is given by

$$y_n(h) = y_n + \tfrac{1}{6}(k_{n,1} + 4k_{n,2} + k_{n,3}) \tag{11.50}$$

The whole process is similar to that used from equation (11.15) to equation (11.23) except that many more dependent variables are involved.

Equations (11.47, 48, 49) can be used to evaluate the three approximations to k_n, which is the change in y_n during the time interval, at all values of n except the boundary values at $n = 0$, N. These boundary conditions take precedence over equations (11.47, 48, 49) and usually effect a simplification of the calculation in the region of the boundary.

The method just described is undoubtedly the most accurate way of solving an equation of the type (11.46) numerically, but the arithemetical details are rather complicated and confusing, leading to many errors by manual computation. It is usually used in digital computer programs and the following method is normally used for manual computation.

11.6.1. *Step-by-step Method*

The increment in y_n corresponding to an increment in t in equation (11.46), is given in equation (11.50) as a weighted average of $k_{n,1}$, $k_{n,2}$, and $k_{n,3}$. Provided the increment in t is small enough, the three approximations to k_n will not differ greatly from one another and $k_{n,1}$ can be accepted as a first approximation. This dispenses with the need to calculate $k_{n,2}$ and $k_{n,3}$ thus simplifying the arithmetic considerably, at the expense of accuracy. The loss of accuracy can be reduced in most cases by taking a larger number of smaller increments and hence the size of increment can usually be chosen to give an adequate solution. The following simplified example is chosen to illustrate the procedure.

Example 1. A gas absorption column contains six theoretical plates each having a liquid hold-up of 10 lb. An inert gas passes through the absorber between periods of continuous operation and the pure solvent is fed at a reduced rate of 200 lb/h. When the main process is restarted, gas containing 5% by weight of the soluble component enters the base of the absorber at 1000 lb/h. If the absorption coefficient is given by

$$y = 0 \cdot 40x \qquad\qquad \text{I}$$

what time interval can elapse before the liquor rate must be increased to keep the exit gas concentration below $0 \cdot 2\%$?

Solution

Taking a material balance over the nth plate as illustrated in Fig. 11.8,

$$Gy_{n-1} + Lx_{n+1} - Gy_n - Lx_n = H\frac{dx_n}{dt} \qquad\qquad \text{II}$$

Because the boundary conditions and concentration limit are expressed in terms of gas composition, it is convenient to use equation I in the form

$$y_n = kx_n \qquad\qquad \text{III}$$

FIG. 11.8.   Flow through nth plate of a gas absorber

to eliminate x_n and x_{n+1} from equation II. Thus

$$\alpha y_{n-1} + y_{n+1} - \alpha y_n - y_n = \frac{H}{L}\frac{dy_n}{dt} \qquad \text{IV}$$

where $$\alpha = kG/L \qquad \text{V}$$

Taking a time interval Δt and denoting the new gas composition above the nth plate by $y_n{}^*$, the derivative in equation IV can be replaced by a finite difference form. Thus

$$\alpha y_{n-1} + y_{n+1} - (\alpha+1)y_n = \frac{H}{L\Delta t}(y_n^* - y_n) \qquad \text{VI}$$

Solving equation VI for the unknown:

$$y_n^* = \frac{L\Delta t\,\alpha}{H} y_{n-1} + \left[1 - \frac{L\Delta t}{H}(\alpha+1)\right] y_n + \frac{L\Delta t}{H} y_{n+1} \qquad \text{VII}$$

On physical considerations, the new value $y_n{}^*$ is expected to depend upon the old value y_n on the same plate. Also, a hypothetical increase in the value of y_n at fixed values of y_{n-1} and y_{n+1} should result in an increase in the value of $y_n{}^*$. Hence to keep the problem physically reasonable, Δt must be chosen to satisfy

$$1 - \frac{L\Delta t}{H}(\alpha+1) > 0 \qquad \text{VIII}$$

or $$\Delta t < H/L(\alpha+1) \qquad \text{IX}$$

Inserting the numerical data given in the problem,

$$\alpha = \frac{0\cdot40 \times 1000}{200} = 2\cdot0$$

$$\frac{H}{L(\alpha+1)} = \frac{10}{200 \times 3\cdot0} = \frac{1}{60}$$

Hence, Δt is chosen to be $1/120$ to satisfy IX. Equation VII now takes the form

$$y_n^* = \tfrac{1}{6}(2y_{n-1} + 3y_n + y_{n+1}) \qquad \text{X}$$

The boundary conditions are:

at $\qquad$ $t = 0,$ $\qquad$ $y_n = 0$ $\qquad\qquad$ XI

at $\qquad$ $n = 0,$ $\qquad$ $y_0 = 0.05$ $\qquad\qquad$ XII

at $\qquad$ $n = 7,$ $\qquad$ $y_7 = 0$ $\qquad\qquad$ XIII

The third condition results from the pure solvent feed to the top of the absorber (i.e. $x_7 = 0$).

Table 11.4 can now be constructed to receive the results, and the boundary conditions can be inserted in the first row and the end columns (y_0 and y_7). The index (m) has been used to count the time increments. There is a contradiction between conditions XI and XII regarding the composition y_0 at $t = 0$, because of the step change in feed composition. Experience has shown that the best solution usually results from taking a value for y_0 equal to the arithmetic average of the two conflicting requirements.

TABLE 11.4. *Gas Compositions in Absorption Column* (%)

m	y_0	y_1	y_2	y_3	y_4	y_5	y_6	y_7
0	2·500	0	0	0	0	0	0	0
1	5·000	0·833	0	0	0	0	0	0
2	5·000	2·083	0·278	0	0	0	0	0
3	5·000	2·755	0·833	0·093	0	0	0	0
4	5·000	3·183	1·350	0·324	0·031	0	0	0
5	5·000	3·483	1·790	0·617	0·123	0·010	0	0
6	5·000	3·707	2·159	0·926	0·269	0·046	0·003	0
7	5·000	3·880	2·470	1·227	0·451	0·113	0·017	0
8	5·000	4·018	2·733	1·512	0·653	0·210	0·046	0
9	5·000	4·131	2·958	1·776	0·865	0·330	0·093	0
10	5·000	4·225	3·152	2·018	1·080	0·469	0·156	0
11	5·000	4·304	3·321	2·240	1·291	0·620	0·234	0

The table of results can now be built up, one row at a time, by successive use of equation X. This shows that the exit gas concentration (y_6) exceeds the limit of 0·2% after 11 time increments. Since $\Delta t = 1/120$ h $= \frac{1}{2}$min, the liquor rate must be increased 5 min after the rich gas has entered the absorber.

11.7. PARTIAL DIFFERENTIAL EQUATIONS

In Sections 11.3 and 11.4, it was shown that some methods of solving ordinary differential equations were unsuitable for boundary value problems, and others were unsuitable for initial value problems. It is again necessary to present independent methods of solution for the same classification of problems. Initial value problems were defined in Section 8.4.5 as those problems in which at least one independent variable has an open range; whereas boundary value problems have closed ranges for all independent variables. Time is the open range variable of most frequent occurrence in chemical engineering, and coordinates describing a finite space are the most usual closed range variables. Occasionally, time is disguised as the ratio of a coordinate to a velocity, as in the falling film of example 5 in Section 8.8.

Two methods will be presented for solving initial value problems, followed by two methods for boundary value problems. Whereas the latter two methods are equally useful and accurate, the iteration method is to be preferred for most initial value problems.

The discussion will be confined to equations containing only two independent variables; the extension to three variables presents no new ideas but leads to difficulties in organizing the calculation on a two dimensional piece of paper.

11.7.1. *Step-by-step Method for Initial Value Problems*

The simplest initial value partial differential equation is the time dependent linear heat conduction equation

$$\frac{\partial T}{\partial t} = \alpha \frac{\partial^2 T}{\partial x^2} \tag{11.51}$$

A few analytical solutions of equation (11.51) have already been presented in Chapter 8, but if the boundary conditions are functions of time, a numerical solution is often more easily obtained. The basis of the numerical method is to replace the space derivative in equation (11.51) by a finite difference representation, using equation (11.32). Thus

$$\frac{\partial T_m}{\partial t} = \frac{\alpha}{(\Delta x)^2}(T_{m+1} - 2T_m + T_{m-1}) \tag{11.52}$$

Comparisons of equations (11.46, 52) shows that the methods suggested for difference-differential equations can now be used to solve equation (11.52). In particular, the step-by-step method can be used by replacing the time derivative by an equivalent finite difference expression. To simplify the symbolism, it is convenient to introduce a second suffix (n) to count the time increments. Hence by using equation (11.31), equation (11.52) becomes

$$\frac{T_{m,n+1} - T_{m,n-1}}{2\Delta t} = \frac{\alpha}{(\Delta x)^2}(T_{m+1,n} - 2T_{m,n} + T_{m-1,n})$$

or

$$T_{m,n+1} = T_{m,n-1} + \frac{2\alpha\Delta t}{(\Delta x)^2}(T_{m+1,n} - 2T_{m,n} + T_{m-1,n}) \tag{11.53}$$

By using equations (11.31, 32) to replace the derivatives in equation (11.51), equation (11.53) is accurate to second order differences. Unfortunately, equation (11.53) is unstable, giving a solution showing an unbounded oscillation of temperature as time progresses. The reason for this is that the new point temperature ($T_{m,n+1}$) is calculated from four known temperatures, one of which ($T_{m,n}$) has a negative coefficient. This means that a small positive error in $T_{m,n}$ will lead to a negative error in $T_{m,n+1}$. On the next step in the calculation, this negative error in $T_{m,n+1}$ will augment the positive error in $T_{m,n}$ and generate an increased positive error in $T_{m,n+2}$. Equation (11.53) shows this quite clearly if the subscript n is increased by unity. As a general result, if all known point values are put on to the same side of an equation and any coefficient is negative, then the solution will be unstable.

Since equation (11.53) is unstable, an alternative finite difference expression must be used for the time derivative in equation (11.52). An expression which is only correct to first differences is

$$\frac{\partial T_{m,n}}{\partial t} = \frac{T_{m,n+1} - T_{m,n}}{\Delta t} \qquad (11.54)$$

which leads to the equation

$$T_{m,n+1} = MT_{m+1,n} + (1 - 2M)T_{m,n} + MT_{m-1,n} \qquad (11.55)$$

as a finite difference representation of equation (11.51).

$$M = \alpha(\Delta t)/(\Delta x)^2 \qquad (11.56)$$

is termed the "modulus" of the equation, and its value determines the "stability" and "convergence" of the method. Formulae do exist to determine which methods are stable and convergent, but the statement above that all coefficients in equation (11.55) should be positive for a stable solution is both simple and effective. Hence

$$M \leqslant \tfrac{1}{2} \qquad (11.57)$$

If the temperature is known at all values of x (or m) for a value of t (or n), then repeated application of equation (11.55) will determine the complete temperature distribution at time $t + \Delta t$ (or $n + 1$). Before the method can be started, values must be selected for Δx and Δt such that the condition (11.57) is satisfied. The most convenient procedure is to choose Δx to be a suitable fraction of the total range of x, and then choose M to satisfy (11.57) and give the simplest coefficients in equation (11.55).

The simplest choice of value for M is $\tfrac{1}{2}$ so that equation (11.55) becomes

$$T_{m,n+1} = \tfrac{1}{2}(T_{m+1,n} + T_{m-1,n}) \qquad (11.58)$$

This value of M is on the limit of stability and equation (11.58) cannot be expected to give answers of great accuracy, it does however have the merit of simplicity and will give a good approximation to the answer if Δx is chosen sufficiently small. The first known use of equation (11.58) was by Schmidt† who used it as the basis of a graphical construction.

Boundary conditions were classified in Section 8.4. The first type will simply fix the value of $T_{m,n}$ at some value of m for all values of n. The other two types both involve a derivative which must be replaced by a finite difference expression. Equation (11.31) is the best one for this purpose, but an equation analogous to (11.54) must frequently be used for speed of calculation. Thus accuracy is sacrificed by using an expression correct to

† Schmidt, E. "Foeppls Festschrift", Springer-Verlag OHG, Berlin (1924).

first differences only. Because this type of approximation has already been made to avoid the unstable form of the general equation (11.53), it is permissible to make a similar approximation in the representation of boundary conditions.

These remarks, and a few others are best illustrated by reference to an example. The following type of problem is of frequent occurrence in reactor design, and involves the simultaneous solution of two inter-connected initial value problems. No new difficulties arise as a result of the inclusion of a second dependent variable, but the calculation is of course about twice as long as a similar calculation with one dependent variable.

Example 1. The dehydrogenation of ethyl benzene has been studied by Wenner and Dybdal[†] by passing a gaseous mixture of ethyl benzene and steam through a tubular catalytic reactor. They have shown that the rate of reaction can be adequately expressed by

$$r_c = k\left(p_E - \frac{p_S p_H}{K}\right) \text{lb moles/h lb catalys} \qquad \text{I}$$

where p_E is the partial pressure of ethyl benzene (atm)
p_S is the partial pressure of styrene (atm)
p_H is the partial pressure of hydrogen (atm)

The reaction rate constant is given by

$$k = 12\,600\exp(-11\,000/T) \qquad \text{II}$$

and the equilibrium constant by

$$K = 0\!\cdot\!027\exp[0\!\cdot\!021(T-773)] \qquad \text{III}$$

where T is the temperature in °K.

If each reaction tube has an internal diameter ($2a = 4''$) and is to be supplied with 0·152 lb moles/h ethyl benzene and 1·52 lb moles/h steam at 600°C, the total mass velocity will be 500 lb/h ft^2. The tube is heated by flue gas which flows countercurrent to the reaction mixture at a rate ($R = 287$ lb/h) and leaves at a temperature of 620°C. The following data are also supplied.

Bulk density of catalyst (ρ)   = 90 lb/ft^3
Operating pressure (P)   = 1·2 atm
Heat of reaction of ethyl benzene (ΔH)   = 60 000 Btu/lb mole
Effective thermal conductivity of bed (k_E)   = 0·26 Btu/h ft^2 °F ft^{-1}
Ratio of effective diffusivity to linear velocity (D_E/u)
                                                 = 0·0014 ft
Specific heat of reaction mixture (C_p)   = 0·52 Btu/lb °F
Specific heat of flue gas (C_p')   = 0·24 Btu/lb °F

Estimate what length of reactor tube is required to achieve 45% conversion of ethyl benzene.

† Wenner, R. R. and Dybdal, E. C. *Chem. Eng. Prog.* **44,** 275, 1948.

Solution

In the element of volume shown in Fig. 11.9, ethyl benzene is consumed at a rate

$$2\pi r\, \delta r\, \delta z\, \rho r_c \text{ lb moles/h}$$

and heat is absorbed at a rate

$$2\pi r\, \delta r\, \delta z\, \rho r_c \Delta H \text{ Btu/h}$$

FIG. 11.9.   Element of reactor tube

Taking a balance of the mass flow rates of ethyl benzene through the element, accounting for bulk flow in the axial direction, mass diffusion in the radial direction, and losses by reaction, gives

$$2\pi r\, \delta r\, uc - 2\pi r\, \delta z\, \frac{D_E}{u} \frac{\partial(uc)}{\partial r} - \left[2\pi r\, \delta r\, uc + \frac{\partial}{\partial z}(2\pi r\, \delta r\, uc)\, \delta z \right] +$$

$$+ \left[2\pi r\, \delta z\, \frac{D_E}{u} \frac{\partial(uc)}{\partial r} + \frac{\partial}{\partial r}\left(2\pi r\, \delta z\, \frac{D_E}{u} \frac{\partial(uc)}{\partial r} \right) \delta r \right] = 2\pi r\, \delta r\, \delta z\, \rho r_c$$

where c is the concentration of ethyl benzene (lb moles/ft³) and u is the linear gas velocity (ft/h). After cancellation of terms, this equation simplifies to

$$\frac{\partial(uc)}{\partial z} - \frac{D_E}{u}\left(\frac{\partial^2(uc)}{\partial r^2} + \frac{1}{r}\frac{\partial(uc)}{\partial r} \right) + \rho r_c = 0 \qquad \text{IV}$$

Similarly, a heat balance for the volume element gives

$$\frac{\partial T}{\partial z} - \frac{k_E}{GC_p}\left(\frac{\partial^2 T}{\partial r^2} + \frac{1}{r}\frac{\partial T}{\partial r} \right) + \frac{\Delta H \rho r_c}{GC_p} = 0 \qquad \text{V}$$

It is more convenient to work in terms of the fraction of ethyl benzene converted which is denoted by

$$x = \frac{u_0 c_0 - uc}{u_0 c_0} \qquad \text{VI}$$

where the subscript $(_0)$ denotes entry conditions. Differentiating,

$$\therefore \quad d(uc) = -u_0 c_0 \, dx$$

Hence equation IV becomes

$$\frac{\partial x}{\partial z} - \frac{D_E}{u}\left(\frac{\partial^2 x}{\partial r^2} + \frac{1}{r}\frac{\partial x}{\partial r}\right) - \frac{\rho r_c}{u_0 c_0} = 0 \qquad \text{VII}$$

The coefficients in equations V and VII can be evaluated by using the given data. At this stage in the problem it is also convenient to check that the units used are consistent. Here for instance, two temperature scales are being used and a correction must be made. Thus

$$\frac{k_E}{GC_p} = \frac{0 \cdot 26}{500 \times 0 \cdot 52} = 0 \cdot 0010 \text{ ft}$$

$$\frac{\Delta H \rho r_c}{GC_p} = \frac{60\,000 \times 90 r_c}{500 \times 0 \cdot 52} = 20\,800 r_c \; ^\circ F/\text{ft}$$

$$= 11\,600 r_c \; ^\circ K/\text{ft}$$

$$\frac{D_E}{u} = 0 \cdot 0014 \text{ ft}$$

$$\frac{\rho r_c}{u_0 c_0} = \frac{90 r_c \times \pi}{0 \cdot 152 \times 36} = 51 \cdot 7 r_c \; \text{ft}^{-1}$$

Hence equations V and VII become

$$\frac{\partial T}{\partial z} - 0 \cdot 0010 \left(\frac{\partial^2 T}{\partial r^2} + \frac{1}{r}\frac{\partial T}{\partial r}\right) + 11\,600 r_c = 0 \qquad \text{VIII}$$

$$\frac{\partial x}{\partial z} - 0 \cdot 0014 \left(\frac{\partial^2 x}{\partial r^2} + \frac{1}{r}\frac{\partial x}{\partial r}\right) - 51 \cdot 7 r_c = 0 \qquad \text{IX}$$

After the reaction mixture has passed a distance z through the bed, a fraction (x) of the ethyl benzene will have been converted. Thus the reaction mixture will consist of:

10	moles steam
$1-x$	moles ethyl benzene
x	moles styrene
x	moles hydrogen
$11+x$	total

Since the total pressure is 1·2 atmospheres, the partial pressures of the reactants are:

$$p_E = \frac{1 \cdot 2(1-x)}{11+x}, \qquad p_S = p_H = \frac{1 \cdot 2 x}{11+x} \qquad \text{X}$$

Substituting equations II and X into equation I gives

$$r_c = 15\,100 \exp\left(-11\,000/T\right)\left[\frac{1-x}{11+x} - \frac{1 \cdot 2x^2}{K(11+x)^2}\right] \qquad \text{XI}$$

where K is given by equation III.

Two of the boundary conditions for this problem are,

when $\qquad\qquad\qquad z = 0, \qquad T = 873 \qquad\qquad\qquad$ XII

and when $\qquad\qquad r = 0, \qquad \dfrac{\partial T}{\partial r} = 0 \qquad\qquad\qquad$ XIII

The third condition expresses the fact that the flue gas loses heat to the reaction mixture through the wall of the tube. Taking a heat balance over an element of the tube of length δz,

$$\delta z\, RC_p' \frac{\partial T}{\partial z} = 2\pi a\, \delta z\, k_E \left.\frac{\partial T}{\partial r}\right|_{r=a}$$

or

$$\frac{\partial T}{\partial z} = \frac{2\pi a k_E}{RC_p'} \left.\frac{\partial T}{\partial r}\right|_{r=a} \qquad \text{XIV}$$

Inserting the numerical values, equation XIV becomes

$$\frac{\partial T}{\partial z} = 0 \cdot 0040 \left.\frac{\partial T}{\partial r}\right|_{r=a} \qquad \text{XV}$$

The corresponding boundary conditions for the mass transfer equation IX are,

when $\qquad\qquad\qquad z = 0, \qquad x = 0 \qquad\qquad\qquad$ XVI

when $\qquad\qquad\qquad r = 0, \qquad \dfrac{\partial x}{\partial r} = 0 \qquad\qquad\qquad$ XVII

and when $\qquad\qquad r = a, \qquad \dfrac{\partial x}{\partial r} = 0 \qquad\qquad\qquad$ XVIII

This completes the mathematical description of the problem and to start its solution, equations (11.31) and (11.32) are used to replace all derivatives with respect to r in equations VIII and IX whilst an equation of the type (11.54) is used to replace the derivatives with respect to z. Thus

$$\frac{T_{m,n+1} - T_{m,n}}{\Delta z} - 0 \cdot 0010 \left[\frac{T_{m+1,n} - 2T_{m,n} + T_{m-1,n}}{(\Delta r)^2} + \frac{T_{m+1,n} - T_{m-1,n}}{2m(\Delta r)^2}\right] + \\ +11\,600 r_c = 0 \qquad \text{XIX}$$

and

$$\frac{x_{m,n+1} - x_{m,n}}{\Delta z} - 0 \cdot 0014 \left[\frac{x_{m+1,n} - 2x_{m,n} + x_{m-1,n}}{(\Delta r)^2} + \frac{x_{m+1,n} - x_{m-1,n}}{2m(\Delta r)^2}\right] - \\ -51 \cdot 7 r_c = 0 \qquad \text{XX}$$

Equations XIX and XX can be rearranged to the forms

$$T_{m,n+1} = M\left(1 + \frac{1}{2m}\right)T_{m+1,n} + (1-2M)T_{m,n} +$$

$$+ M\left(1 - \frac{1}{2m}\right)T_{m-1,n} - 11\,600\Delta z\,r_c \qquad \text{XXI}$$

and

$$x_{m,n+1} = M'\left(1 + \frac{1}{2m}\right)x_{m+1,n} + (1-2M')x_{m,n} +$$

$$+ M'\left(1 - \frac{1}{2m}\right)x_{m-1,n} + 51\cdot7\,\Delta z\,r_c \qquad \text{XXII}$$

where
$$M = 0\cdot0010\,\Delta z/(\Delta r)^2 \qquad \text{XXIII}$$
$$M' = 0\cdot0014\,\Delta z/(\Delta r)^2 \qquad \text{XXIV}$$

Before values are chosen for M and M', it is necessary to inspect equations XXI and XXII. Thus it is seen that when $m = 0$, four of the coefficients become infinite, and different equations must be found to represent VIII and IX along the axis of the tube. Boundary conditions XIII and XVII show that an indeterminate fraction arises in each of VIII and IX and L'Hôpital's rule must be used to resolve these terms. Thus

$$\lim_{r\to 0} \frac{\partial T/\partial r}{r} = \frac{\partial^2 T}{\partial r^2} \qquad \text{XXV}$$

The finite difference equations for use on the axis are thus

$$T_{0,n+1} = 2MT_{1,n} + (1-4M)T_{0,n} + 2MT_{-1,n} - 11\,600\,\Delta z\,r_c \qquad \text{XXVI}$$
$$X_{0,n+1} = 2M'x_{1,n} + (1-4M')x_{0,n} + 2M'x_{-1,n} + 51\cdot7\,\Delta z\,r_c \qquad \text{XXVII}$$

Equations XIII and XVII expressed in finite difference form by using equation (11.31) become

$$T_{1,n} = T_{-1,n} \quad \text{and} \quad x_{1,n} = x_{-1,n} \qquad \text{XXVIII}$$

For a stable calculation process, M and M' must be chosen such that no negative coefficients arise in any of equations XXI, XXII, XVI, or XXVII; and the largest permissible consistent values are

$$M = 0\cdot179, \qquad M' = 0\cdot250 \qquad \text{XXIX}$$

In order to obtain an approximate answer quickly, four radial increments are chosen. Hence $\Delta r = 1/24$, and equation XXIV gives

$$\Delta z = 0\cdot310 \text{ ft} \qquad \text{XXX}$$

Equations XXI, XXII, XXVI, and XXVII now take the form

$$T_{m,n+1} = 0\cdot179\left(1 + \frac{1}{2m}\right)T_{m+1,n} + 0\cdot642T_{m,n} +$$

$$+ 0\cdot179\left(1 - \frac{1}{2m}\right)T_{m-1,n} - 3600r_c \qquad \text{XXXI}$$

$$x_{m,n+1} = 0.25\left(1 + \frac{1}{2m}\right)x_{m+1,n} + 0.50x_{m,n} +$$

$$+ 0.25\left(1 - \frac{1}{2m}\right)x_{m-1,n} + 16.0r_c \qquad \text{XXXII}$$

$$T_{0,n+1} = 0.716T_{1,n} + 0.284T_{0,n} - 3600r_c \qquad \text{XXXIII}$$

$$x_{0,n+1} = x_{1,n} + 16.0r_c \qquad \text{XXXIV}$$

Boundary conditions XII and XVI state quite simply that $T_{m,0} = 873$, and $x_{m,0} = 0$; but the other two conditions XV and XVIII involve derivatives. The simplest yet accurate way of representing equation XVIII is to use a row of " fictitious points " at $r = a + \Delta r$ by imagining that the tube is one increment larger in radius than it actually is. In this example, the tube wall is at $n = 4$, but with a fictitious row of points at $n = 5$, equation XVIII gives

$$x_{5,n} = x_{3,n} \qquad \text{XXXV}$$

and $x_{4,n+1}$ can be calculated from the standard formula XXXII.

If the same idea of fictitious points is used in equation XV, difficulties arise due to a first order representation (11.54) being used for the z derivative, and the second order representation (11.31) being used for the r derivative. This inconsistency cannot be resolved at present by taking a second order representation for the z derivative without generating an oscillation: a first order representation must therefore be used for the r derivative. Thus

$$\frac{T_{4,n+1} - T_{4,n}}{\Delta z} = 0.004\frac{T_{4,n} - T_{3,n}}{\Delta r}$$

or

$$T_{4,n+1} = T_{4,n} + 0.030(T_{4,n} - T_{3,n}) \qquad \text{XXXVI}$$

(This is the least accurate equation in the present example, and the reader is referred to the next sub-section 11.7.2 for an improved method.)

The equations are now in a suitable form for calculation, and the next step is to evaluate the coefficients in equations XXXI and XXXII so that they can be presented as shown in Table 11.5.

TABLE 11.5. *Coefficients in Reactor Design Equations*

m	coefficient of			coefficient of		
	$T_{m-1,n}$	$T_{m,n}$	$T_{m+1,n}$	$x_{m-1,n}$	$x_{m,n}$	$x_{m+1,n}$
0	—	0·284	0·716	—	—	1·000
1	0·089	0·642	0·269	0·125	0·500	0·375
2	0·134	0·642	0·224	0·187	0·500	0·313
3	0·149	0·642	0·209	0·208	0·500	0·292
4	—	—	—	0·500	0·500	—

Next, the sheets on which the calculations are to be performed must be prepared. A double fold of foolscap is suitable in the present case, and this is ruled into two adjacent tables as shown in Table 11.6. The initial conditions of 873°K for the temperature and zero for the conversion are filled in on the first row, except at $T_{0,4}$ where the average of the reactant temperature and flue gas temperature is used, as in the example of Section 11.6.1. Equation III is then used to calculate K at each point in the temperature table. The function of x and K enclosed in square brackets in equation XI can now be evaluated in the conversion table. Since equation XXXII involves $16 \cdot 0 r_c$ it is convenient to tabulate $16 \cdot 0 \times 15\ 100 \exp\left(-11\ 000/T\right)$

FIG. 11.10. Conversion profiles at different reactor depths

for use in equation XI. The product of corresponding items as given by equation XI results in the evaluation of $16 \cdot 0 r_c$. The evaluation of the term $3600 r_c$ in equation XXXI is now simple. Equations XXXI, XXXII, XXXIII, XXXIV, and XXXVI can now be used to find $T_{1,m}$ and $x_{1,m}$, with the modification of adding the other $10°K$ to $T_{1,4}$ to complete the initial step change.

The remainder of the results are summarized in Table 11.6 until the last step from $n = 10$ to $n = 11$, which is presented in full detail. The conversion profiles are illustrated in Fig. 11.10.

TABLE 11.6. *Temperature and Conversion Calculations*

m	0	1	2	3	4
$T_{m,0}$	873	873	873	873	883
K	0·220	0·220	0·220	0·220	0·336
$242\,000\exp(-11\,000/T)$	0·814	0·814	0·814	0·814	0·938
$3600\,r_c$	16·6	16·6	16·6	16·6	—
$T_{m,1}$	856	856	856	858	893·3
$T_{m,2}$	844	844	844½	853	894·3
$T_{m,3}$	835	835	837	850	895·5
$T_{m,4}$	828	828	832	848	896·9
$T_{m,5}$	822	823	828½	848	898·4
$T_{m,6}$	817½	819	826½	848	899·9
$T_{m,7}$	814	816	825	849	901·5
$T_{m,8}$	812	814	825	850	903·1
$T_{m,9}$	810	813	825	852	904·7
$T_{m,10}$	809	813	826	854	906·3
K	0·0575	0·0625	0·0822	0·148	0·444
$242\,000\exp(-11\,000/T)$	0·300	0·322	0·398	0·616	1·293
$3600\,r_c$	2·5	2·7	3·2	5·0	11·2
$T_{m,11}$	809	813	827	856	907·9

m	0	1	2	3	4
$x_{m,0}$	0·0909	0·0909	0·0909	0·0909	0·0909
$\dfrac{1-x}{11+x} - \dfrac{1\cdot2x^2}{K(11+x)^2}$	0·0740	0·0740	0·0740	0·0740	0·0853
$16\,r_c$	0·0740	0·0740	0·0740	0·0740	0·0853
$x_{m,1}$	0·1269	0·1269	0·1269	0·1318	0·1690
$x_{m,2}$	0·1679	0·1679	0·1695	0·1881	0·2315
$x_{m,3}$	0·2010	0·2016	0·2091	0·2376	0·2850
$x_{m,4}$	0·2291	0·2317	0·2456	0·2814	0·3312
$x_{m,5}$	0·2549	0·2600	0·2792	0·3212	0·3718
$x_{m,6}$	0·2798	0·2868	0·3109	0·3568	0·4081
$x_{m,7}$	0·3039	0·3124	0·3402	0·3894	0·4408
$x_{m,8}$	0·3274	0·3370	0·3679	0·4193	0·4704
$x_{m,9}$	0·3499	0·3608	0·3938	0·4475	0·4974
$\dfrac{1-x}{11+x} - \dfrac{1\cdot2x^2}{K(11+x)^2}$	0·0375	0·0369	0·0358	0·0359	0·0387
$16\,r_c$	0·0113	0·0119	0·0142	0·0221	0·0500
$x_{m,11}$	0·3721	0·3837	0·4186	0·4730	0·5224

The average conversion of the material leaving the reactor is given by

$$\bar{x} = \frac{\int_0^a rx\,dr}{\int_0^a r\,dr} \qquad\qquad \text{XXXVII}$$

the numerator of which can be evaluated by Simpson's rule (Section 10.7.2). Thus

$$\bar{x} = \frac{2}{a^2}\frac{a}{12}(ax_{1,n} + ax_{2,n} + 3ax_{3,n} + ax_{4,n})$$

$$\therefore \quad \bar{x} = \tfrac{1}{6}(x_{1,n} + x_{2,n} + 3x_{3,n} + x_{4,n}) \qquad\qquad \text{XXXVIII}$$

Inserting the values of $x_{m,n}$ when $n = 11$ gives

$$\bar{x} = 0.4573 \qquad\qquad \text{XXXIX}$$

which is above 45% conversion. When $n = 10$, $\bar{x} = 0.4324$. Hence the length of the reactor tube required is

$$L = 10.7\,\Delta z = 3\text{ft 4 in.} \qquad\qquad \text{XL}$$

The above method of designing a tubular reactor is superior to the simpler method ignoring radial temperature and conversion variations, and the numerical work required about six hours with an electric desk calculating machine. In order to improve the accuracy of the solution, attention must be paid to the following points.

(i) The conversion profiles near the tube walls exhibit a point of inflexion which cannot be represented adequately by a formula which is only correct to second differences. This error can be reduced by choosing a smaller value for Δr.

(ii) The partial derivatives with respect to z have been represented by a difference equation correct to first order terms whereas the derivatives with respect to r are represented correctly to second order differences.

(iii) As noted previously, boundary condition XV is only represented correctly to first order differences.

In view of the approximations inherent in the expression for the reaction rate and distribution coefficient, and the low accuracy to which the effective thermal conductivity and mass diffusivity can be determined, the foregoing method is considered sufficiently accurate. However, an improved representation of this problem will be derived to illustrate the " iteration " technique.

11.7.2. *Iteration*

This is the correct name for an organized method of trial and error which leads to the solution by obtaining successively improved values.

To improve the ordinary step-by-step method, all derivatives need to be replaced by finite differences correct to second order terms. That is, equations

(11.31, 32) must be used. Referring to equation (11.51) and its stable finite difference equation (11.55), Fig. 11.11 shows diagrammatically, the layout of the points used in the calculation. Equation (11.55) represents equation

FIG. 11.11.   Point values used in iteration method

(11.51) at the point A and involves the temperatures at the points B, C, D. Viz.

$$T_{m,n+1} = MT_{m+1,n} + (1-2M)T_{m,n} + MT_{m-1,n} \qquad (11.55)$$

where
$$M = \alpha(\Delta t)/(\Delta x)^2 \qquad (11.56)$$

Equation (11.54) which was used to replace the time derivative is only correct to first order differences at point A, but is an adjusted form of equation (11.31) correct to second differences at point E, mid-way between A and D. Thus, if the differential equation is replaced by a difference equation valid at point E instead of point A, then an improvement should be apparent. Using equation (11.32) at point D gives

$$\frac{\partial^2 T_{m,n+1}}{\partial x^2} = \frac{1}{(\Delta x)^2}(T_{m+1,n+1} - 2T_{m,n+1} + T_{m-1,n+1}) \qquad (11.59)$$

Taking an arithmetic mean of the finite difference expressions for the second space derivative at points A and D gives the following expression correct to second differences for the space derivative at E.   Thus

$$\frac{\partial^2 T}{\partial x^2}\bigg|_E = \frac{1}{2(\Delta x)^2}(T_{m+1,n} + T_{m-1,n} + T_{m+1,n+1} + T_{m-1,n+1} - 2T_{m,n} - 2T_{m,n+1})$$
$$(11.60)$$

By substituting equations (11.54, 60) into (11.51) and rearranging, a finite difference equation correct to second differences is obtained.

$$(1+M)T_{m,n+1} = \tfrac{1}{2}M(T_{m+1,n+1} + T_{m-1,n+1}) +$$
$$+ (1-M)T_{m,n} + \tfrac{1}{2}M(T_{m+1,n} + T_{m-1,n}) \qquad (11.61$$

This is the form in which the equation is used, but there are two unknown terms on the right-hand side within the first bracket.   The use of equation (11.61) is very similar to the method described in Section 11.5.3 for improving a root of an algebraic equation, except that here, there is a set of simultaneous equations to be solved.   Therefore, a first approximation is guessed for $T_{m,n+1}$ for all values of m.   The right-hand side of equation (11.61) is next evaluated to provide a better approximation for $T_{m,n+1}$. These new quantities are then used on the right-hand side of equation (11.61) to determine a further approximation. Repetition of this process will give successively improved values. The above technique applied to equations of the type (11.51) is known as the " Crank-Nicolson " method.

A further advantage of equation (11.61) over (11.55) is its greater stability. Equation (11.61) is actually stable for all positive values of M, but the use of too large a value leads to inaccurate results, and very slow convergence. The effect can be described in relationship to Fig. 11.7. The speed of approach to the true solution depends upon the relative gradients of the two curves enclosing the stepwise construction; and as M is increased, the two gradients approach one another and more steps are needed to find the solution. Because a large value of M implies a large value of Δt, the finite difference representation correct to second order may not be good enough. Hence, a large value of M will squander the inherent accuracy of the method without accelerating the solution. The authors' recommended choice for M is the same value as would be used to make the ordinary step-by-step method stable.

The treatment of boundary conditions is little altered in this new method, but equation (11.31) should always be used to replace any derivatives in the boundary conditions, so that the whole process is correct to second order differences. The details are best illustrated by an example, and the reactor of the previous section will now be redesigned.

Example 2 (continuation of example 1). The problem and its treatment are identical until equation XVIII is reached, and replacing the finite difference representations XIX and XX by the more accurate second difference formulae gives

$$\frac{T_{m,n+1}-T_{m,n}}{\Delta z} - \frac{0\cdot0010}{2}\left[\frac{T_{m+1,n}-2T_{m,n}+T_{m-1,n}}{(\Delta r)^2} + \frac{T_{m+1,n}-T_{m-1,n}}{2m(\Delta r)^2} + \right.$$
$$\left. + \frac{T_{m+1,n+1}-2T_{m,n+1}+T_{m-1,n+1}}{(\Delta r)^2} + \frac{T_{m+1,n+1}-T_{m-1,n+1}}{2m(\Delta r)^2}\right] +$$
$$+ 5800[r_c(n+1)+r_c(n)] = 0 \qquad\qquad \text{XLI}$$

and

$$\frac{x_{m,n+1}-x_{m,n}}{\Delta z} - \frac{0\cdot0014}{2}\left[\frac{x_{m+1,n}-2x_{m,n}+x_{m-1,n}}{(\Delta r)^2} + \frac{x_{m+1,n}-x_{m-1,n}}{2m(\Delta r)^2} + \right.$$
$$\left. + \frac{x_{m+1,n+1}-2x_{m,n+1}+x_{m-1,n+1}}{(\Delta r)^2} + \frac{x_{m+1,n+1}-x_{m-1,n+1}}{2m(\Delta r)^2}\right] -$$
$$- 25\cdot85[r_c(n+1)+r_c(n)] = 0 \qquad\qquad \text{XLII}$$

Introducing M and M' as defined by equations XXIII and XXIV, and treating the axis points as before gives the set of equations,

$$(1+M)T_{m,n+1} = \tfrac{1}{2}M\left[\left(1+\frac{1}{2m}\right)(T_{m+1,n}+T_{m+1,n+1})+\right.$$
$$\left.+\left(1-\frac{1}{2m}\right)(T_{m-1,n}+T_{m-1,n+1})\right]+$$
$$+(1-M)T_{m,n}-5800[r_c(n+1)+r_c(n)]\,\Delta z \qquad \text{XLIII}$$

$$(1+M')x_{m,n+1} = \tfrac{1}{2}M'\left[\left(1+\frac{1}{2m}\right)(x_{m+1,n}+x_{m+1,n+1})+\right.$$
$$\left.+\left(1-\frac{1}{2m}\right)(x_{m-1,n}+x_{m-1,n+1})\right]+$$
$$+(1-M')x_{m,n}+25\cdot85[r_c(n+1)+r_c(n)]\,\Delta z \qquad \text{XLIV}$$

$$(1+2M)T_{0,n+1} = 2M(T_{1,n}+T_{1,n+1})+(1-2M)T_{0,n}-$$
$$-5800[r_c(n+1)+r_c(n)]\,\Delta z \qquad \text{XLV}$$

$$(1+2M')x_{0,n+1} = 2M'(x_{1,n}+x_{1,n+1})+(1-2M')x_{0,n}+$$
$$+25\cdot85[r_c(n+1)+r_c(n)]\,\Delta z \qquad \text{XLVI}$$

Choosing M and M' to have the same values as given by equations XXIX following the recommendation above, and selecting six radial increments to improve the accuracy gives

$$\Delta r = 1/36$$

and hence $\qquad\qquad\qquad \Delta z = 0\cdot138 \qquad\qquad\qquad$ XLVII

Equations XLIII to XLVI thus become

$$T_{m,n+1} = 0\cdot0758\left[\left(1+\frac{1}{2m}\right)(T_{m+1,n}+T_{m+1,n+1})+\right.$$
$$\left.+\left(1-\frac{1}{2m}\right)(T_{m-1,n}+T_{m-1,n+1})\right]+$$
$$+0\cdot697T_{m,n}-678[r_c(n+1)+r_c(n)] \qquad \text{XLVIII}$$

$$x_{m,n+1} = 0\cdot100\left[\left(1+\frac{1}{2m}\right)(x_{m+1,n}+x_{m+1,n+1})+\right.$$
$$\left.+\left(1-\frac{1}{2m}\right)(x_{m-1,n}+x_{m-1,n+1})\right]+$$
$$+0\cdot600x_{m,n}+2\cdot85[r_c(n+1)+r_c(n)] \qquad \text{XLIX}$$

$$T_{0,n+1} = 0\cdot263(T_{1,n}+T_{1,n+1})+0\cdot474T_{0,n}-589[r_c(n+1)+r_c(n)] \qquad \text{L}$$

$$x_{0,n+1} = 0\cdot333(x_{1,n}+x_{1,n+1})+0\cdot334x_{0,n}+2\cdot37[r_c(n+1)+r_c(n)] \qquad \text{LI}$$

Boundary conditions XII, XVI, and XVIII are treated as before; the last by means of fictitious points. However, an equation correct to second differences can now be used for equation XV as follows. The tube wall is given by $m = 6$, hence, using equation (11.54),

$$\frac{\partial T}{\partial z} = \frac{T_{6,n+1}-T_{6,n}}{\Delta z} \qquad\qquad \text{LII}$$

Averaging the radial derivatives, as given by equation (11.31), gives

$$\frac{\partial T}{\partial r} = \frac{1}{4\Delta r}(T_{7,n} + T_{7,n+1} - T_{5,n} - T_{5,n+1}) \qquad \text{LIII}$$

Substituting equations LII and LIII into equation XV and rearranging gives

$$T_{7,n+1} = T_{5,n} + T_{5,n+1} - T_{7,n} + \frac{10^3 \Delta r}{\Delta z}(T_{6,n+1} - T_{6,n}) \qquad \text{LIV}$$

The high coefficient of the last term would necessitate calculating $T_{6,n}$ and $T_{6,n+1}$ to two decimal places to determine $T_{7,n+1}$ to the nearest unit. Since this is inconvenient, $T_{7,n+1}$ must be eliminated algebraically from equations LIV and XLIII. This simplifies to

$$\left(\frac{10^3 \Delta r M}{2\Delta z} - 1 - M\right)T_{6,n+1} = \left(\frac{10^3 \Delta r M}{2\Delta z} - 1 + M\right)T_{6,n} - M(T_{5,n} + T_{5,n+1}) +$$
$$+ 5800\Delta z[r_c(n+1) + r_c(n)] \qquad \text{LV}$$

or $T_{6,n+1} = 1 \cdot 0212 T_{6,n} - 0 \cdot 0106(T_{5,n} + T_{5,n+1}) + 47 \cdot 5[r_c(n+1) + r_c(n)]$ LVI

Table 11.7 can now be constructed to present the coefficients of equations XLVIII, XLIX, L, LI, and LVI. The actual calculation is performed on a double fold of foolscap again, ruled out in the same form as Table 11.6 except that there are more columns to accommodate $0 \leqslant m \leqslant 6$. The headings in the left-hand column are exactly the same and the figures are compounded according to the appropriate difference equation.

TABLE 11.7. *Coefficients in the Iteration Method*

m	coefficient of				coefficient of			
	$T_{m-1,n}$ $T_{m-1,n+1}$	$T_{m,n}$	$T_{m+1,n}$ $T_{m+1,n+1}$	r_c	$x_{m-1,n}$ $x_{m-1,n+1}$	$x_{m,n}$	$x_{m+1,n}$ $x_{m+1,n+1}$	r_c
0	—	0·4740	0·2630	−589	—	0·334	0·333	2·37
1	0·0379	0·6968	0·1137	−678	0·050	0·600	0·150	2·85
2	0·0569	0·6968	0·0947	−678	0·075	0·600	0·125	2·85
3	0·0632	0·6968	0·0884	−678	0·0833	0·600	0·1167	2·85
4	0·0663	0·6968	0·0853	−678	0·0875	0·600	0·1125	2·85
5	0·0682	0·6968	0·0834	−678	0·0900	0·600	0·1100	2·85
6	−0·0106	1·0212	—	47·5	0·2000	0·600	—	2·85

The calculation is commenced by inserting $T_{m,0} = 873$ for $m \leqslant 5$, $T_{6,0} = 893$, and $x_{m,0} = 0$. It should be noted that in the iteration process, the full value of the step change is used at $T_{6,0}$ because this figure is used in a difference equation valid at $n = \frac{1}{2}$ which is above the step change. In the ordinary step-by-step method, only half of the step change is included initially because the difference equation applies to $n = 0$ which coincides with the step.

Following the method of constructing Table 11.6, the functions K;
$15\ 100\ \exp\ (-11\ 000/T)$; $\dfrac{1-x}{11+x} - \dfrac{1 \cdot 2x^2}{K(11+x)^2}$; $100r_c$; $678r_c$; and $2 \cdot 85r_c$ are
calculated in turn. (The last two terms are modified at the boundaries according to the table of coefficients 11.7.) A first approximation must now be estimated for $T_{m,1}$ and $x_{m,1}$ for all values of m. The above functions are again calculated at $n = 1$ so that all terms needed in the equations are available for calculating $T_{m,1}$ and $x_{m,1}$ more accurately. These values are then used in a repeat calculation of the above coefficients, and hence further values are obtained for $T_{m,1}$ and $x_{m,1}$.

The results are presented in Table 11.8. A shortened version of the iterations leading to the first step are given in the first nine lines and the solution only is given thereafter. It can be seen that $T_{m,1}$ and $x_{m,1}$ were each calculated three times due to a poor initial estimate, but in all other cases only two iterations were ever necessary because the correct answer could frequently be predicted by using an extrapolation formula from Section 9.4. The numerical work on this calculation took considerably longer, but the increased accuracy and reliability is well worth the extra effort. The amount of desk calculation required in the solution of this type of problem is sometimes prohibitive, but the increased availability of digital computers has eliminated this physical restriction. This subject will be considered further in Chapter 14.

The required reactor length is predicted to be

$$L = 23 \cdot 8 \Delta z = 3\ \text{ft}\ 4\ \text{in} \qquad\qquad \text{LVII}$$

Although the agreement between this figure and that obtained previously by the step-by-step method is perfect, it is considered to be fortuitous. A more detailed comparison of the two solutions reveals a $4°$ discrepancy in the centre line exit temperature and more seriously a factor of two discrepancy between the two quantities of heat taken up from the flue gas.

Nine increments in the z direction in the iterative solution are equivalent to four increments in the step-by-step method, and Fig. 11.12 gives a pictorial comparison of the two versions of the situation at directly comparable stages along the length of the reactor. The iterative solution gives smaller conversions initially, but due to higher temperatures being maintained, the rate of conversion does not fall away so rapidly. Hence, at 45% conversion, the two effects have cancelled to predict the same reactor length.

There is a further calculation procedure of an iterative nature which is often used to solve problems of the above type. The method will be described by reference to equation (11.51) and Fig. 11.11.

Replacing the space derivative by its finite difference expression as in Section 11.7.1 gives

$$\frac{\partial T_{m,n}}{\partial t} = \frac{\alpha}{(\Delta x)^2}(T_{m+1,n} - 2T_{m,n} + T_{m-1,n}) \qquad\qquad (11.62)$$

Using the known temperatures at A, B, and C in Fig. 11.11 to evaluate the

TABLE 11.8. *Iteration Solution of Reactor Problem*

m	0	1	2	3	4	5	6	m	0	1	2	3	4	5	6
$T_{m,0}$	873·0	873·0	873·0	873·0	873·0	873·0	893·0	$x_{m,0}$	—	—	—	—	—	—	—
$678r_c$	2·7	3·1	3·1	3·1	3·1	3·1	0·3	$2.85r_c$	0·0110	0·0132	0·0132	0·0132	0·0132	0·0132	0·0175
$T_{m,1}$	867·0	867·0	867·0	867·0	867·3	871·0	894·1	$x_{m,1}$	0·0250	0·0250	0·0250	0·0250	0·0250	0·0280	0·0350
$678r_c$	2·4	2·8	2·8	2·8	2·8	2·9	0·3	$2.85r_c$	0·0098	0·0117	0·0117	0·0117	0·0118	0·0124	0·0171
$T_{m,1}$	866·4	866·4	866·4	866·4	866·7	870·2	894·0	$x_{m,1}$	0·0299	0·0299	0·0299	0·0299	0·0303	0·0317	0·0402
$678r_c$	2·4	2·8	2·8	2·8	2·8	2·9	0·3	$2.85r_c$	0·0096	0·0116	0·0116	0·0116	0·0116	0·0122	0·0169
$T_{m,1}$	866·2	866·2	866·2	866·2	866·4	870·0	894·1	$x_{m,1}$	0·0307	0·0308	0·0308	0·0308	0·0310	0·0325	0·0407
$678r_c$	2·4	2·7	2·7	2·7	2·8	2·9	0·3	$2.85r_c$	0·0096	0·0115	0·0115	0·0115	0·0116	0·0121	0·0170
$T_{m,1}$	866·2	866·2	866·2	866·3	866·4	870·0	894·1	$x_{m,1}$	0·0309	0·0309	0·0309	0·0309	0·0312	0·0326	0·0410
$T_{m,2}$	860·2	860·2	860·2	860·3	861·1	867·7	895·2	$x_{m,2}$	0·0580	0·0580	0·0580	0·0582	0·0593	0·0641	0·0774
$T_{m,3}$	854·8	854·8	854·8	855·1	856·9	866·0	896·4	$x_{m,3}$	0·0822	0·0822	0·0823	0·0829	0·0854	0·0942	0·1106
$T_{m,4}$	849·9	849·9	850·0	850·6	853·5	864·8	897·6	$x_{m,4}$	0·1038	0·1039	0·1042	0·1056	0·1101	0·1225	0·1413
$T_{m,5}$	845·5	845·5	845·7	846·7	850·7	863·9	898·9	$x_{m,5}$	0·1235	0·1237	0·1243	0·1267	0·1335	0·1492	0·1700
$T_{m,6}$	841·6	841·6	841·9	843·4	848·5	863·4	900·2	$x_{m,6}$	0·1416	0·1419	0·1430	0·1466	0·1558	0·1745	0·1970
$T_{m,7}$	838·0	838·1	838·6	840·6	846·8	863·3	901·5	$x_{m,7}$	0·1583	0·1588	0·1605	0·1656	0·1772	0·1986	0·2226
$T_{m,8}$	834·7	834·8	835·6	838·1	845·4	863·3	902·8	$x_{m,8}$	0·1739	0·1746	0·1771	0·1837	0·1978	0·2216	0·2468
$T_{m,9}$	831·7	831·9	832·9	836·0	844·3	863·6	904·1	$x_{m,9}$	0·1885	0·1895	0·1929	0·2011	0·2175	0·2436	0·2696
$T_{m,10}$	829·0	829·2	830·6	834·3	843·5	864·0	905·4	$x_{m,10}$	0·2024	0·2037	0·2080	0·2179	0·2364	0·2646	0·2914
$T_{m,11}$	826·5	826·9	828·6	832·8	843·0	864·5	906·8	$x_{m,11}$	0·2157	0·2173	0·2226	0·2342	0·2547	0·2848	0·3123
$T_{m,12}$	824·3	824·9	826·8	831·6	842·7	865·2	908·2	$x_{m,12}$	0·2285	0·2304	0·2368	0·2500	0·2725	0·3042	0·3323
$T_{m,13}$	822·4	823·1	825·2	830·0	842·5	866·0	909·5	$x_{m,13}$	0·2409	0·2431	0·2505	0·2653	0·2897	0·3229	0·3514
$T_{m,14}$	820·7	821·4	823·9	829·5	842·6	866·8	910·8	$x_{m,14}$	0·2529	0·2555	0·2639	0·2802	0·3064	0·3409	0·3697
$T_{m,15}$	819·2	819·9	822·8	829·1	842·8	867·7	912·1	$x_{m,15}$	0·2648	0·2677	0·2771	0·2948	0·3226	0·3582	0·3872
$T_{m,16}$	817·8	818·7	821·9	828·9	843·1	868·6	913·4	$x_{m,16}$	0·2765	0·2797	0·2900	0·3090	0·3383	0·3748	0·4041
$T_{m,17}$	816·7	817·7	821·2	828·9	843·5	869·6	914·7	$x_{m,17}$	0·2879	0·2914	0·3026	0·3229	0·3534	0·3909	0·4204
$T_{m,18}$	815·8	816·9	820·7	829·0	844·0	870·7	916·0	$x_{m,18}$	0·2992	0·3030	0·3150	0·3364	0·3681	0·4065	0·4361
$T_{m,19}$	815·0	816·2	820·4	829·2	844·7	871·8	917·3	$x_{m,19}$	0·3103	0·3144	0·3272	0·3496	0·3824	0·4214	0·4511
$T_{m,20}$	814·4	815·7	820·2	829·5	845·4	873·0	918·7	$x_{m,20}$	0·3213	0·3257	0·3391	0·3625	0·3963	0·4359	0·4656
$T_{m,21}$	813·9	815·3	820·1	829·9	846·2	874·2	920·0	$x_{m,21}$	0·3322	0·3368	0·3508	0·3751	0·4098	0·4500	0·4797
$T_{m,22}$	813·6	815·1	820·1	830·4	847·1	875·4	921·4	$x_{m,22}$	0·3429	0·3477	0·3623	0·3875	0·4229	0·4637	0·4934
$T_{m,23}$	813·4	815·0	820·2	831·0	848·1	876·7	922·7	$x_{m,23}$	0·3534	0·3585	0·3736	0·3996	0·4357	0·4769	0·5067
$T_{m,24}$	813·3	815·0	820·4	831·7	849·1	878·0	924·1	$x_{m,24}$	0·3638	0·3691	0·3847	0·4114	0·4481	0·4897	0·5195

right-hand side of equation (11.62) gives a value for $\partial T_{m,n}/\partial t$ at the point A. If equation (11.54) is now used to estimate $T_{m,n+1}$ at point D, the value obtained will be identical with that from the ordinary step-by-step method. This value is now treated as a first approximation to $T_{m,n+1}$ which can be improved as follows. A set of first approximations for the temperatures at

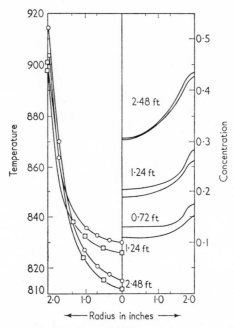

FIG. 11.12. Comparison of step by step and iteration solution

points D, F, and G are now available for calculating $\partial T_{m,n+1}/\partial t$ from a formula analogous to (11.62). By taking the average of this rate of change of temperature at D with the previously calculated rate at A gives a good value for the rate at E. I.e.

$$\left.\frac{\partial T_m}{\partial t}\right|_E = \frac{1}{2}\left(\left.\frac{\partial T_m}{\partial t}\right|_A + \left.\frac{\partial T_m}{\partial t}\right|_D\right) \qquad (11.63)$$

Using this value of the rate at E and the known temperature at A, an improved value can be obtained for the temperature at D. This leads to an improved time derivative at D and hence to an improved value for the rate of change of temperature at E through equation (11.63).

Both of the iteration methods should give results of equal accuracy for equal values of corresponding increments, but the method described in detail and used in example 2 is far more efficient for the following reasons. The first method, which involves a little more algebra initially, and uses a more complicated difference equation, has much greater stability and needs far fewer iterations at each step. In the example considered, only two iterations were needed at each step which means that the volume of calculations is only double that of the ordinary step-by-step method with the same increments. The other type of iteration frequently requires four or five iterations on each step which doubles the work again without improving the accuracy.

The method described in detail and used in example 2 is therefore recommended.

11.7.3. *Liebmann's Method or Method of Squares for Boundary Value Problems*

This method is a natural extension of that used in Section 11.4.1 to solve an ordinary differential equation of boundary value type. The application of the method to partial differential equations is explained by Thom and Apelt† who have suggested many improvements on the basic idea. Essentially, the calculation can be described as alternating between points situated in the centres of black and white squares on a chequered board, instead of between odd and even points along a line.

Considering the two dimensional version of Laplace's equation in cartesian coordinates

$$\frac{\partial^2 T}{\partial x^2} + \frac{\partial^2 T}{\partial y^2} = 0 \tag{11.64}$$

and using equation (11.32) to replace both derivatives by finite difference expressions, gives

$$\frac{T_{m+1,n} - 2T_{m,n} + T_{m-1,n}}{(\Delta x)^2} + \frac{T_{m,n+1} - 2T_{m,n} + T_{m,n-1}}{(\Delta y)^2} = 0 \tag{11.65}$$

where m and n count the x and y increments respectively. Rearrangement of equation (11.65) gives

$$2(1 + R^2)T_{m,n} = T_{m+1,n} + T_{m-1,n} + R^2(T_{m,n+1} + T_{m,n-1}) \tag{11.66}$$

where

$$R = \Delta x/\Delta y \tag{11.67}$$

If a network as shown in Fig. 11.13 is superposed on the region of the problem so that Δx and Δy are constant, then the points of intersection can be designated with a circle or a cross depending upon the sum of the subscripts being odd or even. If the values are estimated at all points marked with a cross, equation (11.66) can be used to calculate values at all points marked with a circle. The rôles of the cross and circle can then be interchanged to enable new values to be calculated to replace the original estimates. Alternate calculations between the " cross points " and " circle points " will give the solution. Difficulties can arise at the boundaries if they are not rectangular but they can be overcome by the use of " fictitious points " and linear interpolation formulae. The best solution is to use the appropriate

† Thom, A. and Apelt, C. J. " Field Computations in Engineering and Physics ". Van Nostrand, London (1961).

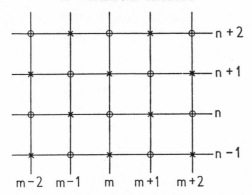

FIG. 11.13.   Classification of points in Liebmann's method

coordinate system to suit the boundary shapes so that most if not all of the boundaries correspond to lines of the lattice.

An alternative procedure for difficult boundary points is to use " irregular stars " and derive special formulae for particular boundary points. Thus, equations (11.31, 32) were derived from Taylor's theorem on the assumption of equal intervals; without this assumption the following equations are approximately true.

$$f(x_0+a) = f(x_0)+af'(x_0)+\tfrac{1}{2}a^2f''(x_0) \tag{11.68}$$

$$f(x_0-b) = f(x_0)-bf'(x_0)+\tfrac{1}{2}b^2f''(x_0) \tag{11.69}$$

Solving equations (11.68) and (11.69) for the derivatives gives

$$f'(x_0) = \frac{b^2f(x_0+a)-a^2f(x_0-b)-(b^2-a^2)f(x_0)}{ab(a+b)} \tag{11.70}$$

$$f''(x_0) = \frac{bf(x_0+a)+af(x_0-b)-(a+b)f(x_0)}{\tfrac{1}{2}ab(a+b)} \tag{11.71}$$

which can be used instead of equations (11.31, 32) where appropriate.

11.7.4. *Relaxation Methods for Boundary Value Problems*

This method which is fully described by Southwell† takes the algebra a little further than Liebmann's method and gives greater freedom to the calculator to exercise his discretion and make use of previous calculating experience. The partial derivatives are replaced as before to give a finite difference equation of the form

$$F(T_{m-1,n}, T_{m+1,n}, T_{m,n-1}, T_{m,n+1}, T_{m,n}) = 0 \tag{11.72}$$

Equation (11.72) will be satisfied at each point in the network when the solution has been obtained; but originally, values $T_{m,n}^*$ etc. can only be

---

† Southwell, R. V. " Relaxation Methods in Engineering Science ". Oxford University Press (1940). Southwell, R. V. " Relaxation Methods in Theoretical Physics ". Oxford University Press (1946).

estimated, and substitution into equation (11.72) will leave an error term $R_{m,n}$ called the " residual ". Thus

$$R_{m,n} = F(T^*_{m-1,n}, T^*_{m+1,n}, T^*_{m,n-1}, T^*_{m,n+1}, T^*_{m,n}) \qquad (11.73)$$

The object of the method is to " relax " the residuals to zero by adjusting the values $T^*_{m,n}$. If $T^*_{m,n}$ is adjusted, the alteration of $R_{m,n}$ will be given by

$$\delta R_{m,n} = \frac{\partial F}{\partial T^*_{m,n}} \delta T^*_{m,n} \qquad (11.74)$$

Equation (11.73) shows that $R_{m,n}$ is influenced by changes in five point temperatures; conversely, the adjustment of one temperature will influence the value of five residuals according to equations of the type (11.74).   These equations are therefore called the " influence equations ". Invariably there is one coefficient dominating the others in the set of five influence equations and this indicates which temperature needs to be altered by the smallest amount to relax a particular residual The mechanics of the method can best be illustrated by the following example.

Example 3. Determine the ratio of peak velocity to average velocity for the steady laminar flow of an incompressible fluid through a straight rectangular duct. The ratio of the lengths of the two sides of the rectangle is 2:1.

Solution

The Navier-Stokes equation (7.126) governs the fluid velocity, and taking cartesian coordinates x and y measured along the edges of the rectangular cross section, and z along the axis of the duct, the fluid velocity will only have a z component denoted by u. The velocity will be a function of x and y only, hence all terms arising from $\mathbf{u}.\nabla\mathbf{u}$ will be zero. Since there are no external forces acting, and the fluid flow is steady, equation (7.126) becomes

$$-\frac{1}{\rho}\nabla p + v\nabla^2\mathbf{u} = 0 \qquad \text{I}$$

Because $\mathbf{u}$ only has a z component, the x and y components of equation I become

$$\frac{\partial p}{\partial x} = 0 \qquad \frac{\partial p}{\partial y} = 0 \qquad \text{II}$$

whereas the z component of equation I gives

$$\frac{\partial^2 u}{\partial x^2} + \frac{\partial^2 u}{\partial y^2} + \alpha = 0 \qquad \text{III}$$

where α is a constant given by

$$\alpha = -\frac{1}{\mu}\frac{\partial p}{\partial z} \qquad \text{IV}$$

Equation III is " Poisson's equation ". Using equation (11.32) to replace the derivatives in equation III as in Section 11.7.3 gives

$$\frac{u_{m+1,n}-2u_{m,n}+u_{m-1,n}}{(\Delta x)^2}+\frac{u_{m,n+1}-2u_{m,n}+u_{m,n-1}}{(\Delta y)^2}+\alpha=0 \qquad \text{V}$$

Because the ratio of the lengths of the sides of the duct are in simple proportion, it is convenient to choose $\Delta y = \Delta x$. Hence equation V becomes

$$u_{m+1,n}+u_{m-1,n}+u_{m,n+1}+u_{m,n-1}-4u_{m,n}+\alpha(\Delta x)^2 = R_{m,n} \qquad \text{VI}$$

where $R_{m,n}$ is the residual which has to be relaxed to zero. If the length of the shorter side of the rectangle is L, the largest possible choice for Δx is $\frac{1}{2}L$, giving three intersections of the lattice within the rectangle as shown in Fig. 11.14.

FIG. 11.14.   Primary lattice across duct

The velocity must be zero on all boundaries; hence

$$u_{m,0} = u_{m,2} = u_{0,1} = u_{4,1} = 0 \qquad \text{VII}$$

and equation VI becomes

$$u_{m+1,1}+u_{m-1,1}-4u_{m,1}+\tfrac{1}{4}\alpha L^2 = R_{m,1} \qquad \text{VIII}$$

To avoid decimals and yet obtain accurate values for the velocities, it is convenient to choose a large value for αL^2. Dimensions have not been considered here, and putting a numerical value for αL^2 amounts to using an arbitrary set of units for velocity, length, etc. This does not cause any difficulty in the interpretation of the result as will be seen later. Therefore, put

$$\alpha L^2 = 8000 \qquad \text{IX}$$

The set of three equations from equation VIII is

$$\left. \begin{array}{r} u_{2,1}-4u_{1,1}+2000 = R_{1,1} \\ u_{3,1}+u_{1,1}-4u_{2,1}+2000 = R_{2,1} \\ u_{2,1}-4u_{1,1}+2000 = R_{3,1} \end{array} \right\} \qquad \text{X}$$

It is not worth using the full relaxation method at this stage because equations

X are quite easily solved algebraically with $R_{1,1} = R_{2,1} = R_{3,1} = 0$. The result is

$$\left.\begin{array}{c} u_{1,1} = u_{3,1} = 714 \\ u_{2,1} = 857 \end{array}\right\} \qquad \text{XI}$$

These three point values are obviously not sufficient to represent the velocity distribution adequately. Hence, Δx is put equal to $\frac{1}{4}L$ so that equation VI becomes

$$u_{m+1,n} + u_{m-1,n} + u_{m,n+1} + u_{m,n-1} - 4u_{m,n} + 500 = R_{m,n} \qquad \text{XII}$$

Because both central planes through the duct are planes of symmetry, it is only necessary to calculate the velocity distribution in a quarter of the duct. The calculation is shown in full in Table 11.9.

TABLE 11.9. *Velocity Distribution in Duct* $(\Delta x = \Delta y = \frac{1}{4}L)$

n	0	1		2		3		4	5
3		(398) 400 ~~430~~		(578) 580 ~~570~~		(655) 655 ~~645~~		(677) 675 ~~670~~ ~~660~~	
↑ n				0 5 ~~0~~ −20 −40 140	5 ~~0~~ 20 ~~0~~ 80 50 5		0 20 10 ~~0~~ −20 −60 60		
2	0 −20 40 −5	(514) 515 520		(759) 760 715		(867) 865 860 840		(897) 895 890 860	(867) 865 860 840
		XI		I		IV IX		III X	
1	−5 ~~0~~ −10 −130	(398) 400 430	−5 35 25 55 10	(578) 580 570	0 −5 −10 −20 20 10 −10	(655) 655 645	5 ~~0~~ 20 ~~0~~ 40 10	(677) 675 ~~670~~ ~~660~~	(655) 655 ~~645~~
		II		VII		VI		V VIII	
0									
	0	1		2		3		4 $m\rightarrow$ 5	

The planes of symmetry across which the velocity gradient must vanish are defined by $n = 2$ and $m = 4$. It is therefore convenient to include an extra row of points in each direction as shown. Firstly, the velocities 715 and 860 are inserted at the appropriate points as given by the earlier solution (equation XI). The velocities at the other nodes are estimated as follows.

If the axes of x and y were rotated through $45°$ and a lattice spacing $\Delta x = \Delta y = L/2$ was chosen, an equation identical to VI (with a different interpretation of m and n) would be satisfied. Using this formula with $\alpha(\Delta x)^2 = 1000$ gives the value

$$u_{1,1} = \tfrac{1}{4}(0+0+0+715+1000)$$

$$= 428\tfrac{3}{4} \qquad\qquad \text{XIII}$$

Hence the first estimate for $u_{1,1}$ is 430. This value is reflected in the plane $n = 2$ to give $u_{1,3} = 430$. Similarly,

$$u_{3,1} = \tfrac{1}{4}(0+0+715+860+1000)$$

$$= 643\tfrac{3}{4} \qquad\qquad \text{XIV}$$

Using both planes of symmetry,

$$u_{3,1} = u_{3,3} = u_{5,1} = 645 \qquad\qquad \text{XV}$$

Equation XII which is appropriate to the lattice in Table 11.9 is used to estimate the remaining velocities. These velocities are put into Table 11.9 in the positions indicated in Fig. 11.14; that is, in the lower left-hand corner of the square on the upper right-hand side of the point. The residuals $R_{m,n}$ are also calculated from equation XII and inserted as shown in Table 11.9 and Fig. 11.14. By partially differentiating equation XII the influence equations can be determined. Thus

if $\delta u_{m,n} = 1$,

$$\delta R_{m,n} = -4$$
$$\delta R_{m-1,n} = 1$$
$$\delta R_{m+1,n} = 1 \qquad\qquad \text{XVI}$$
$$\delta R_{m,n-1} = 1$$
$$\delta R_{m,n+1} = 1$$

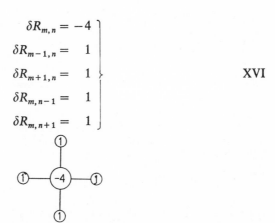

Fig. 11.15. Basic relaxation pattern

Equations XVI are usually presented as the basic relaxation pattern as shown in Fig. 11.15. This pattern was used in Table 11.9 to relax the residuals in the order shown by the roman numerals near the points. It will be noticed that the largest residual is usually relaxed at each step by altering the velocity at the same point. Unless the residuals at the neighbouring points are of opposite sign to the one being relaxed, it shortens the calculation to " over-relax " the residuals by altering the velocity so much that the sign of the residual is reversed.

$R_{2,2} = 140$ is the largest residual initially, and it is over-relaxed by making $\delta u_{2,2} = 45$. The residuals are then altered according to equations XVI or Fig. 11.15 as shown. There is no need to calculate a residual at the point (2, 3) since this is a repetition of the residual at (2, 1). The method is straightforward until point (3, 2) is relaxed at the IVth step. Here, the velocity at (5, 2) must also be adjusted by the same amount as at the point (3, 2). This results in the residual at (4, 2) being altered by a double increment since it is influenced by both velocity changes.

At the VIth step, points (3, 3) and (5, 1) must both be adjusted when the velocity at (3, 1) is altered. The results given in Table 11.9 are correct to the nearest 5 units in velocity. The calculation was continued to the nearest unit and this figure is shown in brackets. A full presentation of the calculation of residuals in the latter stages would only confuse Table 11.9.

The whole calculation can now be repeated after further subdivision of the intervals. Taking $\Delta x = \frac{1}{8}L$, the velocities given in Table 11.10 were obtained.

TABLE 11.10. *Velocity Distribution in Duct* $(\Delta x = \Delta y = \frac{1}{8}L)$

m	0	1	2	3	4	5	6	7	8
n									
0	0	0	0	0	0	0	0	0	0
1	0	155	250	310	349	374	389	398	401
2	0	246	408	516	587	633	660	677	683
3	0	294	496	634	725	785	822	843	850
4	0	309	524	671	770	835	876	898	905

After all residuals have been reduced to zero with a nominal tolerance, a technique called " residual balancing " should be used. This involves summing all residuals and relaxing still further until this residual sum is within the nominal tolerance of zero. The accuracy of the result is greatly increased by this final step.

The centre line velocity has altered by about 1% between the last two calculations, and since all velocities have moved in the same direction, the ratio of peak to average velocity will have altered by much less than 1%. The change of values can be interpreted as giving a more accurate result for the pressure drop incorporated in the value of α. Hence the figures given in Table 11.10 are sufficiently accurate.

To obtain the average velocity, Simpson's rule (Section 10.7.2) can be used since it is basically more accurate than the relaxation method and thus will not reduce the overall accuracy of the result.

The average velocity across any line at constant m is given by

$$\bar{u}_m = \tfrac{1}{12}(4u_{m,1} + 2u_{m,2} + 4u_{m3,} + u_{m,4}) \qquad \text{XVII}$$

and the average velocity across the duct is

$$\bar{u} = \tfrac{1}{24}(4\bar{u}_1 + 2\bar{u}_2 + 4\bar{u}_3 + 2\bar{u}_4 + 4\bar{u}_5 + 2\bar{u}_6 + 4\bar{u}_7 + \bar{u}_8) \qquad \text{XVIII}$$

Hence using the values given in Table 11.10 to evaluate equations XVII and XVIII,

$$\bar{u} = 453 \cdot 4 \qquad \text{XIX}$$

Therefore, to the accuracy of the calculation, the ratio of the peak velocity to the average velocity is 2.00.

In order to calculate the pressure drop along the duct, dimensions must be considered. Equation VIII shows that αL^2 must have the same dimensions as any velocity u (say $\bar{u}$). Because equation IX selects a numerical value for αL^2, the unit of velocity is implicitly determined. There is no need to derive this unit because both equations IX and XIX must be expressed in terms of this unit. Dividing these two equations by one another will give a dimensionless equation which is independent of the choice made in equation IX. Thus

$$\frac{\bar{u}}{\alpha L^2} = \frac{453 \cdot 4}{8000} \qquad \text{XX}$$

Using equation IV to eliminate α gives

$$\frac{\partial p}{\partial z} = \frac{-8000 \mu \bar{u}}{453 \cdot 4 L^2}$$

or

$$A\frac{\partial p}{\partial z} = 35 \cdot 3 \mu \bar{u} \qquad \text{XXI}$$

where A is the cross sectional area of the duct and $\bar{u}$ is the superficial velocity. The corresponding formula for laminar flow through a cylindrical pipe is

$$A\frac{\partial p}{\partial z} = 8\pi \mu \bar{u} = 25 \cdot 1 \mu \bar{u} \qquad \text{XXII}$$

Hence, the pressure drop per unit length of the rectangular duct of side ratio 2:1 is 40% greater than that along a cylindrical duct of the same cross sectional area with the same superficial velocity.

The solutions of Laplace's or Poisson's equations by relaxation methods or Liebmann's method are comparatively simple because the coefficients in the influence equations depicted in Fig. 11.15 are simple integers. In more complicated problems, such as the solution of the Navier-Stokes equation (7.126) for laminar flow around a sphere,† the influence equations are much more complicated and even vary as the calculation proceeds due to the non-linearity of the equation of motion.

† Jenson, V. G. *Proc. Roy. Soc.* **A249,** 346 (1959).

The treatment of curved boundaries is similar to Liebmann's method and either fictitious points or irregular stars can be used. The reader is referred to the specialized books already mentioned by Thom and Apelt or Southwell for further details of both methods.

The numerical work involved in solving partial differential equations by the methods described in this chapter is considerable, but the advent of the digital computer has made their use quite attractive. This development will be discussed in Chapter 14, where it will be shown that a series of similar numerical calculations favour the use of a computer, whereas an isolated calculation is best performed on a desk machine.

Chapter 12

MATRICES

12.1. Introduction

IN earlier chapters it has been shown that two variables can be combined and treated as a single complex variable, and also that three variables can be treated as components of a single vector variable. Each of these techniques has resulted in the simplification of special types of problems. A further generalization of this idea leads to the consideration of greater numbers of variables as a single quantity called a " matrix ". There is frequently a fundamental relationship between the various constituent parts of a matrix which leads to the variables being arranged as a rectangular array to draw attention to these links. Thus in Section 7.2.3, the stress tensor was written

$$\mathbf{T}_{mn} = \begin{bmatrix} p_{xx} & \tau_{xy} & \tau_{xz} \\ \tau_{yx} & p_{yy} & \tau_{yz} \\ \tau_{zx} & \tau_{zy} & p_{zz} \end{bmatrix} \tag{7.6}$$

Elements in a particular row refer to forces acting on one plane whereas elements in a particular column refer to forces acting in one direction. In general, the nine quantities are independent.

Students in engineering and science are introduced to the properties of determinants in their initial courses in mathematics, and it will be recalled that the determinant is a square array of numbers or symbols that has a specific value. Consideration of the above stress tensor should establish the fundamental difference between a matrix and the determinant which has the same elements in corresponding positions. It is that a matrix cannot be reduced to a specific value by multiplications between its constituent elements, whereas a determinant is evaluated in this manner.

The rules for addition and multiplication of matrices will be enunciated in this chapter and the subject will be developed to include matrix algebra. In addition the rules of matrix calculus will be introduced, and the types of chemical engineering problems for which matrix methods are suitable will be indicated.

12.2. THE MATRIX

The array of symbols

$$
\begin{bmatrix}
a_{11} & a_{12} & a_{13} & \cdots & a_{1n} \\
a_{21} & a_{22} & a_{23} & \cdots & a_{2n} \\
\cdot & \cdot & \cdot & & \cdot \\
\cdot & \cdot & \cdot & & \cdot \\
\cdot & \cdot & \cdot & & \cdot \\
a_{m1} & a_{m2} & a_{m3} & \cdots & a_{mn}
\end{bmatrix}
$$

is called a matrix. Each symbol such as a_{11}, a_{2n}, or a_{mn} is called an element of the matrix, and the square brackets [ ] enclosing the array signifies that it is a matrix, just as the two straight lines | | enclosing a square array signify that to be a determinant. The square brackets are thus a special part of the notation. For operations concerning the matrix rather than its elements, the above array can also be written in the short forms

$$
\mathbf{A} = [a_{ij}]
$$

where the size of the array has to be separately indicated.

The matrix represented above contains m rows and n columns. It is therefore called a " m by n matrix ", or alternatively the matrix is said to be of order " $m \times n$ ". It should be noted that the matrix is always described in terms of " rows by columns ". That is, the number of rows is always stated first and this is followed by the number of columns. For example, the array $\begin{bmatrix} 2 & 1 & 6 \\ 3 & 2 & 5 \end{bmatrix}$ is a 2 by 3 matrix implying that there are two rows and three columns. The committing to memory of the phrase " rows by columns " will be of great help later on when matrices have to be manipulated in the solution of engineering problems.

12.2.1. *The Row Matrix*

A matrix having n elements arranged in a single row is a $(1 \times n)$ matrix, called a " row matrix " or " row vector ". Thus $[a_{11}\ a_{12}\ a_{13}\ \ldots\ a_{1n}]$ is a row matrix or row vector.

The position vector of a point (Section 7.3.2) is usually described in terms of its coordinates as $[x\ y\ z]$ which is a particular (1×3) row matrix.

12.2.2. *The Column Matrix*

A matrix having m elements arranged in a single column is called a " column matrix " or " column vector ". To adhere to convention it would be written

$$\begin{bmatrix} a_{11} \\ a_{21} \\ \cdot \\ \cdot \\ \cdot \\ a_{m1} \end{bmatrix}$$

but because a vertical array of elements would occupy a larger space, such a matrix would be written $\{a_{11}\ a_{21}\ \ldots\ a_{m1}\}$. The brackets $\{\ \}$ signify that the elements are to be arranged in a vertical column.

12.2.3. *The Unit Matrix*

A matrix in which the number of rows of elements is equal to the number of columns of elements is called a " square matrix " and if all the elements except those in the diagonal from the top left-hand corner to the bottom right-hand corner are zero, the matrix is called a " diagonal matrix ". A diagonal matrix in which the diagonal elements are all unity is called the " unit matrix ". Thus

$$\mathbf{I} = \begin{bmatrix} 1 & 0 & 0 \\ 0 & 1 & 0 \\ 0 & 0 & 1 \end{bmatrix}$$

is the unit matrix of order three. Furthermore the non-zero elements are situated on the " principal diagonal ". The significance of the unit matrix will be discussed later in Section 12.3.4.

12.2.4. *The Null Matrix*

A matrix whose elements are all zero is called a " null matrix " and is denoted by **0**.

12.3. MATRIX ALGEBRA

In order to be able to use matrices in the solution of engineering problems, the manner in which the operations of addition, subtraction, multiplication, and division are performed must be defined. These mathematical processes will be considered in the following sub-sections.

12.3.1 *Matrix Addition*

This operation can only be carried out on matrices of the same order. Thus the sum of two matrices is obtained by adding together the corresponding elements of each matrix. For example, the sum of the matrices

$$\begin{bmatrix} 1 & 2 & 3 \\ 4 & 5 & 2 \\ 6 & 1 & 0 \end{bmatrix} \text{ and } \begin{bmatrix} 1 & 2 & 6 \\ 3 & 8 & 4 \\ 2 & 2 & 0 \end{bmatrix} \text{ is:}$$

$$\begin{bmatrix} 1 & 2 & 3 \\ 4 & 5 & 2 \\ 6 & 1 & 0 \end{bmatrix} + \begin{bmatrix} 1 & 2 & 6 \\ 3 & 8 & 4 \\ 2 & 2 & 0 \end{bmatrix} = \begin{bmatrix} 2 & 4 & 9 \\ 7 & 13 & 6 \\ 8 & 3 & 0 \end{bmatrix} \quad (12.1)$$

Similarly, subtraction is negative addition. Thus

$$\begin{bmatrix} 1 & 2 & 3 \\ 4 & 5 & 2 \\ 6 & 1 & 0 \end{bmatrix} - \begin{bmatrix} 1 & 2 & 6 \\ 3 & 8 & 4 \\ 2 & 2 & 0 \end{bmatrix} = \begin{bmatrix} 0 & 0 & -3 \\ 1 & -3 & -2 \\ 4 & -1 & 0 \end{bmatrix} \quad (12.2)$$

These operations can be extended to any number of matrices of the same order, irrespective of whether the elements consist of real or complex numbers or symbols. The sum or difference does not exist if the matrices are of different order.

12.3.2 Scalar Multiplication

If any matrix is multiplied by a number, the elements of the matrix so formed are the products of the number and the corresponding elements of the original matrix. Thus

$$k\begin{bmatrix} 1 & 2 \\ 4 & 6 \end{bmatrix} + m\begin{bmatrix} 3 & 7 \\ 5 & -2 \end{bmatrix} = \begin{bmatrix} k+3m & 2k+7m \\ 4k+5m & 6k-2m \end{bmatrix} \quad (12.3)$$

Both k and m are scalar quantities and each operates on a matrix. For this reason such an operation is called " scalar multiplication ". It should be noted from the above illustration that the coefficients k and m multiply each element within their respective matrix, and in this respect matrices differ from determinants.

12.3.3. Matrix Multiplication

The product of two matrices will exist only when the number of columns of the first matrix is equal to the number of rows in the second matrix. When this condition is satisfied the two matrices are said to be " conformable " and they yield a product. Thus if $\mathbf{A}$ is a matrix of order $(m \times n)$ and $\mathbf{B}$ is a matrix of order $(n \times p)$ the product $\mathbf{AB}$ will exist and will be a matrix of order $(m \times p)$. However the product $\mathbf{BA}$ will not exist since $(n \times p)$ is not conformable with $(m \times n)$. The following example will make this point clear.

Example 1. Evaluate the product

$$\begin{bmatrix} 3 & -4 & -1 & 2 \\ 1 & 2 & 0 & 3 \\ 6 & 5 & 6 & 7 \end{bmatrix} \begin{bmatrix} 1 & 2 \\ 4 & 8 \\ 0 & 4 \\ 7 & 9 \end{bmatrix}$$

I

$$\begin{bmatrix} 3 & -4 & -1 & 2 \\ 1 & 2 & 0 & 3 \\ 6 & 5 & 6 & 7 \end{bmatrix} \begin{bmatrix} 1 & 2 \\ 4 & 8 \\ 0 & 4 \\ 7 & 9 \end{bmatrix} = \begin{bmatrix} (3\times1)+(-4\times4)+(-1\times0)+(2\times7) \\ (1\times1)+(2\times4)+(0\times0)+(3\times7) \\ (6\times1)+(5\times4)+(6\times0)+(7\times7) \end{bmatrix}$$

$$\begin{bmatrix} (3\times2)+(-4\times8)+(-1\times4)+(2\times9) \\ (1\times2)+(2\times8)+(0\times4)+(3\times9) \\ (6\times2)+(5\times8)+(6\times4)+(7\times9) \end{bmatrix}$$

$$= \begin{bmatrix} 1 & -12 \\ 30 & 45 \\ 75 & 139 \end{bmatrix} \qquad \text{II}$$

In the above example it will be seen that the first element in the final matrix is obtained by multiplying corresponding elements from the first row of the first matrix and the first column of the second matrix and summing the products; thus

$$[3 \quad -4 \quad -1 \quad 2] \{1 \quad 4 \quad 0 \quad 7\} = 3-16-0+14 = 1 \quad (12.4)$$

This product of a row and a column is called an " inner product ".

It can also be seen that the first matrix in the above example is of order (3×4) whereas the second matrix is of order (4×2) and the product matrix is of order (3×2). That is

$$(3 \times 4).(4 \times 2) = (3 \times 2) \qquad (12.5)$$

No product would exist if the (4×2) matrix was multiplied by the (3×2) matrix since they are not conformable. Hence the order of terms in a matrix product is important.

In certain cases the product of two matrices will exist irrespective of the order in which the multiplication is carried out. For example, if the matrix **A** is of order $(m \times n)$ and the matrix **B** is of order $(n \times m)$ the product **C** of

$$\mathbf{AB} = \mathbf{C} \qquad (12.6)$$

is a matrix of order $(m \times n).(n \times m) = (m \times m)$. On the other hand, the product **D** of

$$\mathbf{BA} = \mathbf{D} \qquad (12.7)$$

is a matrix of order $(n \times m).(m \times n) = (n \times n)$. In particular, this condition will exist for square matrices, but even with these, the product will not be the same in general. It is thus necessary to use terminology which specifies the order of multiplication. Equation (12.6) can alternatively be described as:

(i) $\mathbf{C}$ is obtained by pre-multiplying $\mathbf{B}$ by $\mathbf{A}$.

(ii) $\mathbf{C}$ is obtained by post-multiplying $\mathbf{A}$ by $\mathbf{B}$.

In the exceptional case when the products of two square matrices are equal, i.e.

$$\mathbf{AB} = \mathbf{BA} \qquad (12.8)$$

the matrices are said to commute, or be commutable.

In Section 12.2.3 the unit matrix was shown to be a diagonal matrix in which the elements were unity. The significance of unity is that when it is multiplied by a number or function, the value of the number or function remains unchanged. Therefore the definition of the unit matrix must satisfy this condition. Thus consider the unit matrix of order three to operate on a third order column vector

$$\begin{bmatrix} 1 & 0 & 0 \\ 0 & 1 & 0 \\ 0 & 0 & 1 \end{bmatrix} \begin{bmatrix} x_1 \\ x_2 \\ x_3 \end{bmatrix} = \begin{bmatrix} (1 \times x_1) + (0 \times x_2) + (0 \times x_3) \\ (0 \times x_1) + (1 \times x_2) + (0 \times x_3) \\ (0 \times x_1) + (0 \times x_2) + (1 \times x_3) \end{bmatrix} = \begin{bmatrix} x_1 \\ x_2 \\ x_3 \end{bmatrix} \qquad (12.9)$$

Hence the unit matrix conforms to a fundamental law of mathematics.

The unit matrix is usually given the symbol $\mathbf{I}$ and can be written into an equation as such, thereby conserving space. For example equation (12.9) would be written:

$$\mathbf{Ix} = \mathbf{xI} = \mathbf{x} \qquad (12.10)$$

The reader can check that the matrices in equation (12.10) are commutable. Further evidence that the unit matrix conforms to the fundamental laws of mathematics is that

$$\mathbf{I}^p = \mathbf{I} \qquad (12.11)$$

and again the reader is asked to check equation (12.11).

It is also important to note that the product of two matrices can be the null matrix without either of the original matrices being null.

Example 2. Find the two results of multiplying $\mathbf{A}$ and $\mathbf{B}$ together where

$$\mathbf{A} = \begin{bmatrix} 1 & 3 & 5 \\ -2 & 4 & 0 \\ 0 & 2 & 2 \end{bmatrix} \quad \text{and} \quad \mathbf{B} = \begin{bmatrix} 2 & 0 & 6 \\ 1 & 0 & 3 \\ -1 & 0 & -3 \end{bmatrix}$$

$$\mathbf{AB} = \begin{bmatrix} 0 & 0 & 0 \\ 0 & 0 & 0 \\ 0 & 0 & 0 \end{bmatrix} \quad \text{but } \mathbf{BA} = \begin{bmatrix} 2 & 18 & 22 \\ 1 & 9 & 11 \\ -1 & -9 & -11 \end{bmatrix}$$

The above property gives rise to the same difficulties when defining a division process as were encountered with vectors in Chapter 7. However, division by a square matrix is possible, as will be shown in Section 12.7.

12.4. Determinants of Square Matrices and Matrix Products

The determinant of a square matrix is an array of elements which are identical with the corresponding elements of the matrix with respect to both magnitude and position. The determinant of a square matrix $\mathbf{A}$ would be written $|\mathbf{A}|$. Obviously matrices that are not square do not possess a corresponding determinant.

It has been shown in texts on determinants that the product of two determinants $|\mathbf{A}|$ and $|\mathbf{B}|$ of the same order $(n \times n)$ is also a determinant of order $(n \times n)$. Furthermore the product

$$|\mathbf{A}| \times |\mathbf{B}| = |\mathbf{B}| \times |\mathbf{A}| = |\mathbf{C}| \quad \text{say.} \tag{12.12}$$

From equation (12.12) it can be seen that the elements in $|\mathbf{C}|$ will be identical with the corresponding elements in the matrix product $\mathbf{AB}$. Hence the determinant of the product of two square matrices is equal to the product of their determinants. That is,

$$|\mathbf{A}|\,|\mathbf{B}| = |\mathbf{AB}| \quad \text{and} \quad |\mathbf{B}|\,|\mathbf{A}| = |\mathbf{BA}| \tag{12.13}$$

so that
$$|\mathbf{AB}| = |\mathbf{BA}| \tag{12.14}$$

even though in general $\mathbf{AB} \neq \mathbf{BA}$.

Finally if $\mathbf{A}$ is a square matrix and $|\mathbf{A}| = 0$, the matrix is called a " singular matrix ". On the other hand if $|\mathbf{A}| \neq 0$, the matrix is " nonsingular ".

12.5. The Transpose of a Matrix

If the rows of a $(n \times m)$ matrix are written in the form of columns, a new matrix of order $(m \times n)$ will be formed. This new matrix is called the " transpose " of the original matrix. If the original matrix is denoted by $\mathbf{A}$, the transpose will be denoted by $\mathbf{A}'$, the accent in the top right-hand corner signifying that $\mathbf{A}$ has been transposed. Thus if

$$\mathbf{A} = \begin{bmatrix} 2 & 0 \\ 3 & -1 \\ 4 & 6 \end{bmatrix} \quad \mathbf{A}' = \begin{bmatrix} 2 & 3 & 4 \\ 0 & -1 & 6 \end{bmatrix} \tag{12.15}$$

In a similar manner it can be seen that the transpose of a row vector is a column vector.

A matrix and its transpose are always conformable for multiplication and if

$$\mathbf{AA}' = \mathbf{I} \tag{12.16}$$

the matrix $\mathbf{A}$ is said to be " orthogonal ".

12.5.1 The Transpose of the Product of Matrices

Let $\mathbf{A}$ be a matrix of order $(m \times n)$ and let $\mathbf{B}$ be a matrix of order $(n \cdot p)$. The product of these two matrices will be

$$\mathbf{AB} = \mathbf{C} \tag{12.17}$$

where $\mathbf{C}$ is a matrix of order $(m \times p)$ whose typical element in the ith row and jth column will be

$$c_{ij} = \sum_{k=1}^{n} a_{ik} b_{kj} \qquad (12.18)$$

but the typical element in the transposed matrix will be c'_{ij} where

$$c'_{ij} = c_{ji} = \sum_{k=1}^{n} a_{jk} b_{ki} = \sum_{k=1}^{n} a'_{kj} b'_{ik} = \sum_{k=1}^{n} b'_{ik} a'_{kj} \qquad (12.19)$$

Therefore extending equation (12.19) to all the elements in the product $(\mathbf{AB})'$ it follows that

$$(\mathbf{AB})' = \mathbf{B}'\mathbf{A}' \qquad (12.20)$$

That is, the transpose of the product of two matrices is equal to the product of their transposes taken in the reverse order. This idea can be extended to any number of matrices that are conformable. Thus

$$(\mathbf{ABC})' = \mathbf{C}'\mathbf{B}'\mathbf{A}' \qquad (12.21)$$

12.6. ADJOINT MATRICES

If a_{ij} is any element of a square matrix of order $(n \times n)$, and the cofactor of a_{ij} in the determinant $|\mathbf{A}|$ is A_{ij}, the transpose of the matrix whose elements are made up of all the A_{ij}s is called the "adjoint of $\mathbf{A}$"; and is written

$$\text{adj } \mathbf{A} = [A_{ji}] \qquad (12.22)$$

Example. Evaluate the adjoint of the matrix

$$\begin{bmatrix} 3 & 0 & 3 \\ -2 & 1 & 1 \\ 4 & 2 & 5 \end{bmatrix}$$

$$\mathbf{A} = \begin{bmatrix} 3 & 0 & 3 \\ -2 & 1 & 1 \\ 4 & 2 & 5 \end{bmatrix} \qquad \text{adj } \mathbf{A} = \begin{bmatrix} 3 & 6 & -3 \\ 14 & 3 & -9 \\ -8 & 6 & 3 \end{bmatrix}$$

12.7. RECIPROCAL OF A SQUARE MATRIX

Consider a square matrix $\mathbf{A}$ to be non-singular and of order $(n \times n)$. The product of this matrix with its adjoint is

$$\mathbf{A} \text{ adj } \mathbf{A} = \left[\sum_{r=1}^{n} a_{ir} A_{rj} \right] \qquad (12.23)$$

Since the properties of determinants show that

$$\sum_{r=1}^{n} a_{ir} A_{rj} = 0 \qquad (i \neq j) \qquad (12.24)$$

it follows that all the elements in the matrix product **A** adj **A** except those on the principal diagonal will be zero, hence

$$
\mathbf{A} \text{ adj } \mathbf{A} =
\begin{bmatrix}
|\mathbf{A}| & 0 & 0 & 0 & \cdots & 0 \\
0 & |\mathbf{A}| & 0 & 0 & \cdots & 0 \\
0 & 0 & |\mathbf{A}| & 0 & \cdots & 0 \\
\cdot & \cdot & \cdot & \cdot & & \cdot \\
\cdot & \cdot & \cdot & \cdot & & \cdot \\
\cdot & \cdot & \cdot & \cdot & & \cdot \\
0 & 0 & 0 & 0 & \cdots & |\mathbf{A}|
\end{bmatrix}
= |\mathbf{A}|
\begin{bmatrix}
1 & 0 & 0 & \cdots & 0 \\
0 & 1 & 0 & \cdots & 0 \\
0 & 0 & 1 & \cdots & 0 \\
\cdot & \cdot & \cdot & & \cdot \\
\cdot & \cdot & \cdot & & \cdot \\
\cdot & \cdot & \cdot & & \cdot \\
0 & 0 & 0 & \cdots & 1
\end{bmatrix}
$$

or
$$\mathbf{A} \text{ adj } \mathbf{A} = |\mathbf{A}|\mathbf{I} \tag{12.25}$$

Since **A** is non-singular, equation (12.25) can be divided by $|\mathbf{A}|$; and if a new matrix $\mathbf{A}^{-1}$ is defined by

$$\mathbf{A}^{-1} = \frac{\text{adj } \mathbf{A}}{|\mathbf{A}|} \tag{12.26}$$

equation (12.25) becomes

$$\mathbf{A}\mathbf{A}^{-1} = \mathbf{I} \tag{12.27}$$

$\mathbf{A}^{-1}$ is thus seen to be the reciprocal of the non-singular square matrix **A**. Each element of this reciprocal matrix is obtained thus

$$a_{ij} = \frac{A_{ji}}{|\mathbf{A}|} \tag{12.28}$$

Hence matrix division is accomplished by multiplying the one matrix by the reciprocal of the other. As with all multiplications, the order of terms must be specified, but any matrix will commute with its own reciprocal.

$$\mathbf{A}\mathbf{A}^{-1} = \mathbf{I} = \mathbf{A}^{-1}\mathbf{A} \tag{12.29}$$

12.7.1. *The Reciprocal of the Product of Square Matrices*

Consider **A** and **B** to be two square non-singular matrices of the same order. Their reciprocals $\mathbf{A}^{-1}$ and $\mathbf{B}^{-1}$ will exist and thus the product of each is

$$(\mathbf{AB})(\mathbf{B}^{-1}\mathbf{A}^{-1}) = \mathbf{A}\mathbf{I}\mathbf{A}^{-1} = \mathbf{A}\mathbf{A}^{-1} = \mathbf{I} \tag{12.30}$$

Therefore $\mathbf{B}^{-1}\mathbf{A}^{-1}$ is the reciprocal of the product **AB**, or

$$(\mathbf{AB})^{-1} = \mathbf{B}^{-1}\mathbf{A}^{-1} \tag{12.31}$$

That is, the reciprocal of the product of two non-singular conformable square matrices is equal to the product of their reciprocals in the reverse order.

This concept can be extended to any number of conformable square matrices, and in general

$$(\mathbf{ABC}\ldots\mathbf{XYZ})^{-1} = \mathbf{Z}^{-1}\mathbf{Y}^{-1}\mathbf{X}^{-1}\ldots\mathbf{C}^{-1}\mathbf{B}^{-1}\mathbf{A}^{-1} \tag{12.32}$$

12.7.2. *The Reciprocal of a Transposed Matrix*

In a manner very similar to that given above it can be shown that the reciprocal of a transpose of a matrix is equal to the transpose of its reciprocal; or

$$(\mathbf{A}^{-1})' = (\mathbf{A}')^{-1} \tag{12.33}$$

It is left to the reader to verify this.

12.8. The Rank and Degeneracy of a Matrix

These two important terms are employed extensively in matrix calculus and algebra, and they must be understood in order to make use of matrices in the solution of simultaneous equations. However, the reader must be reminded of other definitions, which arise elsewhere in elementary mathematics, in order to appreciate the significance of " degeneracy " and " rank ". These will be considered first.

12.8.1. *Linear Dependence*

Let $x_1, x_2, x_3 \ldots x_n$ be initially a set of scalar variables that satisfy the equation

$$p_1 x_1 + p_2 x_2 + p_3 x_3 + \ldots + p_n x_n = 0 \tag{12.34}$$

where $p_1, p_2 \ldots p_n$ are constants, some but not all of which may be zero. Since these scalar variables satisfy equation (12.34) they are linearly dependent.

This idea can be extended to matrices in the following way. Thus let $\mathbf{x}_1, \mathbf{x}_2, \mathbf{x}_3$, etc. be a set of vectors of the same order, and the zero on the right of equation (12.34) be a null matrix of order corresponding to the vectors. Since p_1, p_2, p_3, etc. are not all zero the vectors are linearly dependent. However, if equation (12.34) was satisfied only when the constants were zero the vectors would be " linearly independent ".

The vectors $\mathbf{x}_1, \mathbf{x}_2$, etc. could be the n columns of a $(m \times n)$ matrix $\mathbf{X}$, and if there exists a set of n scalar constants p_1, p_2, etc. not all zero so that equation (12.34) is satisfied, the columns of the matrix are linearly dependent. In particular if the matrix $\mathbf{X}$ is square, its columns will be linearly dependent only if the determinant $|\mathbf{X}| = 0$. Furthermore, if $|\mathbf{X}| = 0$

$$|\mathbf{X}| = |\mathbf{X}'| = 0 \tag{12.35}$$

so that the rows of $\mathbf{X}$ will also be linearly dependent. To sum up, if the rows or columns of a matrix are linearly dependent the matrix is singular.

12.8.2. *The Minor of a Matrix*

Let $\mathbf{A}$ be a matrix of order $(m \times n)$ in which m is less than n. The determinants formed from the m rows and any m of the n columns are called " minors " of the matrix $\mathbf{A}$. Furthermore if r is an integer which is less than m and all the minors of order r are zero, it follows that all the minors of order greater than r will also be zero. Thus the value of the determinant of any minor of order $(r+1)$ is the sum of the products of each element in the $(r+1)$th column and its cofactor. Since these cofactors are minors of order r which are all zero, the minors of order $(r+1)$ must all be zero. By repeating this argument to the minors of order m it can be seen that all the minors of order greater than r will be zero.

Minors of a matrix are often referred to as the first minor, second minor, and so on. By this is meant that the minor of highest order is the first minor, the next highest minor is the second minor, and so on to the minor that will contain a single element only. For a square matrix of order $(n \times n)$ the first minor will be the determinant of the matrix and of order n. The second minor will be of order $(n-1)$, and so on to the minor of order 1.

12.8.3. *Degeneracy*

A matrix of order $(m \times n)$ is said to have a degeneracy of r when at least one of its $(r+1)$th minors does not vanish, whereas all of its rth minors are equal to zero.

For a square matrix of order $(n \times n)$ and degeneracy r this means that there are r linear relationships between the n columns of the matrix. Thus the columns of a singular matrix are related by a single equation of the type (12.34), where $\mathbf{x}_1$, $\mathbf{x}_2$, etc. are the columns of the matrix and such a matrix is " singly degenerate ", or has a degeneracy of one.

Example. Show that the matrix below has a degeneracy of one.

$$\begin{bmatrix} 2 & 4 & -2 \\ 3 & 0 & 4 \\ 5 & 4 & 2 \end{bmatrix}$$

The determinant of this matrix is

$$\begin{vmatrix} 2 & 4 & -2 \\ 3 & 0 & 4 \\ 5 & 4 & 2 \end{vmatrix} = 0 \qquad\qquad \text{I}$$

Hence the matrix is singular. However, all the minors of order two are non-vanishing so that the degeneracy is one, and therefore the columns of the matrix are related by the single relationship

$$8\{2 \quad 3 \quad 5\} - 7\{4 \quad 0 \quad 4\} - 6\{-2 \quad 4 \quad 2\} = \mathbf{0} \qquad\qquad \text{II}$$

Similarly the rows are related by a single relationship

$$1[2 \quad 4 \quad -2] + 1[3 \quad 0 \quad 4] - 1[5 \quad 4 \quad 2] = \mathbf{0} \qquad\qquad \text{III}$$

12.8.4. *The Rank of a Matrix*

The rank of a matrix is equal to the order of the highest order non-vanishing minor. In the above example, the rank of the matrix

$$\begin{bmatrix} 2 & 4 & -2 \\ 3 & 0 & 4 \\ 5 & 4 & 2 \end{bmatrix}$$

is two. For a square matrix of order n and degeneracy r, the rank is equal to $(n-r)$.

From the above definition it will be apparent that all matrices except the null matrix have a rank equal to or greater than one. Thus the matrix

$$\begin{bmatrix} 0 & 0 & 0 & 0 \\ 0 & 0 & 0 & 0 \\ 0 & 0 & 0 & 0 \\ 0 & 0 & 0 & 1 \end{bmatrix}$$

is of order 4, degeneracy 3, and rank 1.

12.9. THE SUB-MATRIX

It is frequently convenient in matrix calculations to divide a matrix of high order by dotted vertical or horizontal lines to form what are termed "sub-matrices". Thus the matrix of order 4 below is divided into four second order matrices.

$$\begin{bmatrix} a_{11} & a_{12} & a_{13} & a_{14} \\ a_{21} & a_{22} & a_{23} & a_{24} \\ a_{31} & a_{32} & a_{33} & a_{34} \\ a_{41} & a_{42} & a_{43} & a_{44} \end{bmatrix} = \begin{bmatrix} \mathbf{A}_1 & \mathbf{A}_2 \\ \mathbf{A}_3 & \mathbf{A}_4 \end{bmatrix}$$

where

$$\mathbf{A}_1 = \begin{bmatrix} a_{11} & a_{12} \\ a_{21} & a_{22} \end{bmatrix} \qquad \mathbf{A}_2 = \begin{bmatrix} a_{13} & a_{14} \\ a_{23} & a_{24} \end{bmatrix} \text{ etc.}$$

The dotted lines are said to "partition" the matrix.

This technique is especially useful for handling large matrices in digital computers, because it allows the matrix to be considered as a combination of smaller matrices.

12.10. SOLUTION OF LINEAR ALGEBRAIC EQUATIONS

Matrices are often used to express a system of linear algebraic equations in concise form. Thus consider the set of linear algebraic equations

$$\left. \begin{aligned} 2x_1 - 3x_2 - 2x_4 &= 8 \\ 3x_2 + 2x_3 + x_4 &= 5 \\ x_1 - 2x_2 - 4x_3 + 2x_4 &= 2 \\ 2x_1 + x_2 - 3x_3 - x_4 &= 6 \end{aligned} \right\} \tag{12.36}$$

This set can be written in matrix notation thus

$$\begin{bmatrix} 2 & -3 & 0 & -2 \\ 0 & 3 & 2 & 1 \\ 1 & -2 & -4 & 2 \\ 2 & 1 & -3 & -1 \end{bmatrix} \begin{bmatrix} x_1 \\ x_2 \\ x_3 \\ x_4 \end{bmatrix} = \begin{bmatrix} 8 \\ 5 \\ 2 \\ 6 \end{bmatrix}$$

or more concisely

$$\mathbf{Ax} = \mathbf{b} \qquad (12.37)$$

where $\mathbf{A}$ represents a square matrix of order 4 whilst $\mathbf{x}$ and $\mathbf{b}$ are each column vectors of order 4. The solution of equation (12.37) is

$$\mathbf{x} = \mathbf{A}^{-1}\mathbf{b} \qquad (12.38)$$

which is possible only if the reciprocal of the matrix $\mathbf{A}$ can be evaluated. Consequently in this text the method of solution is confined to square matrices, and in the particular case of equations (12.36)

$$\begin{bmatrix} x_1 \\ x_2 \\ x_3 \\ x_4 \end{bmatrix} = \begin{bmatrix} 0.39 & -0.10 & 0.11 & -0.15 \\ -0.11 & 0.06 & -0.10 & 0.04 \\ 0.12 & 0.22 & -0.02 & -0.24 \\ 0.50 & -0.02 & -0.02 & -0.21 \end{bmatrix} \begin{bmatrix} 8 \\ 5 \\ 2 \\ 6 \end{bmatrix} \qquad (12.39)$$

from which

$$x_1 = 1.93; \qquad x_2 = 0.56; \qquad x_3 = 0.58; \qquad x_4 = 1.0$$

It should be pointed out that a solution of equations (12.36) will be obtained only if $\mathbf{A}$ and $\mathbf{Ab}$ are of the same rank. When this is so the set of equations is said to be consistent. $\mathbf{A}$ is called the matrix of the equation, and $\mathbf{Ab}$ the " augmented matrix " of the equation.

12.11. MATRIX SERIES

Matrices can form series in much the same way as scalar variables, with each term in the series containing powers of a matrix. Hence before discussing series it is proposed to consider the properties of powers of matrices.

12.11.1. *Powers of Matrices*

If $\mathbf{A}$ is a matrix of order $(n \times m)$, the product $\mathbf{AA}$ will only exist if the components of the product are conformable. That is if $m = n$. Thus the continued product of a matrix will exist only if the matrix is square. When this is the case the continued product can be written in the form

$$\mathbf{A}_1\mathbf{A}_2\mathbf{A}_3\mathbf{A}_4 \dots \mathbf{A}_n = \mathbf{A}^n \qquad (12.40)$$

Raising a matrix to a power n signifies that the matrix is to be multiplied by itself n times and not that each element in the matrix is raised to the power n.

For example:

$$\begin{bmatrix} a_1 & a_3 \\ a_2 & a_4 \end{bmatrix}^2 = \begin{bmatrix} a_1 & a_3 \\ a_2 & a_4 \end{bmatrix} \begin{bmatrix} a_1 & a_3 \\ a_2 & a_4 \end{bmatrix} = \begin{bmatrix} a_1^2 + a_2 a_3 & a_1 a_3 + a_3 a_4 \\ a_1 a_2 + a_2 a_4 & a_2 a_3 + a_4^2 \end{bmatrix}$$

$$(12.41)$$

The usual algebraic rules for integer indices apply to matrices. Thus

$$\mathbf{A}^n \times \mathbf{A}^m = \mathbf{A}^{n+m} \tag{12.42}$$

and

$$(\mathbf{A}^n)^p = \mathbf{A}^{np} \tag{12.43}$$

If the exponent of a matrix is fractional implying that the nth root of a matrix is sought, the resulting matrix will be of the same order as, and commutable with the parent. However, it is possible that the number of roots may be infinite, but this will have to be established for each particular matrix whose roots are required.

12.11.2 *Matrix Polynomials*

Matrix series can be formed from different powers of a square matrix, and these series have similar properties to the familiar scalar series. For example

$$a_0 \mathbf{X}^n + a_1 \mathbf{X}^{n-1} + a_2 \mathbf{X}^{n-2} + \ldots a_{n-1} \mathbf{X} + a_n \mathbf{I} = \mathbf{0} \tag{12.44}$$

is typical. In this series $\mathbf{X}$ is a square matrix and the coefficients a_0, a_1, a_2, $\ldots a_n$ are scalar constants. It will be noticed that the coefficient a_n has been multiplied by the unit matrix of the same order as the matrix $\mathbf{X}$ so that all terms in equation (12.44) are conformable for addition.

Series of the type expressed by equation (12.44) can contain a finite or an infinite number of terms; and the summation and tests for convergence of such series are best made by the use of the Cayley-Hamilton theorem and Sylvester's theorem which will be treated in Sections 12.14.2 and 12.15. However certain properties will be dealt with here.

It is possible to factorize matrix polynomials in the same manner as scalar polynomials as illustrated by the following example.

Example. Evaluate the matrix polynomial

$$\mathbf{X}^3 - 9\mathbf{X}^2 + 26\mathbf{X} - 24\mathbf{I}$$

where

$$\mathbf{X} = \begin{bmatrix} 2 & 1 \\ 3 & 4 \end{bmatrix}$$

The polynomial

$$\mathbf{X}^3 - 9\mathbf{X}^2 + 26\mathbf{X} - 24\mathbf{I} \qquad\qquad\text{I}$$

can be factorized:

$$(\mathbf{X} - 2\mathbf{I})(\mathbf{X} - 3\mathbf{I})(\mathbf{X} - 4\mathbf{I}) \qquad\qquad\text{II}$$

The first factor is

$$\begin{bmatrix} 2 & 1 \\ 3 & 4 \end{bmatrix} - 2 \begin{bmatrix} 1 & 0 \\ 0 & 1 \end{bmatrix} = \begin{bmatrix} 0 & 1 \\ 3 & 2 \end{bmatrix} \qquad\qquad\text{III}$$

and the second and third factors are

$$\begin{bmatrix} 2 & 1 \\ 3 & 4 \end{bmatrix} - \begin{bmatrix} 3 & 0 \\ 0 & 3 \end{bmatrix} = \begin{bmatrix} -1 & 1 \\ 3 & 1 \end{bmatrix}$$

and

$$\begin{bmatrix} 2 & 1 \\ 3 & 4 \end{bmatrix} - \begin{bmatrix} 4 & 0 \\ 0 & 4 \end{bmatrix} = \begin{bmatrix} -2 & 1 \\ 3 & 0 \end{bmatrix} \qquad \text{IV}$$

Hence the value of the polynomial is

$$\begin{bmatrix} 0 & 1 \\ 3 & 2 \end{bmatrix} \begin{bmatrix} -1 & 1 \\ 3 & 1 \end{bmatrix} \begin{bmatrix} -2 & 1 \\ 3 & 0 \end{bmatrix} = \begin{bmatrix} -3 & 3 \\ 9 & 3 \end{bmatrix} = 3 \begin{bmatrix} -1 & 1 \\ 3 & 1 \end{bmatrix} \qquad \text{V}$$

Finally it is possible for matrices to be exponents of the scalar quantity or function, and the well known exponential function is written

$$e^X = I + \frac{X}{1!} + \frac{X^2}{2!} + \frac{X^3}{3!} + \dots \qquad (12.45)$$

where X is a square matrix.

The matrix exponent X in e^X behaves in a similar manner to a scalar exponent. Thus if Y is a second square matrix of the same order as X

$$e^X e^Y = e^Y e^X = e^{(X+Y)} \qquad (12.46)$$

Similarly

$$e^X e^{-X} = I \qquad (12.47)$$

where the unit matrix I must be of the same order as X.

12.12. DIFFERENTIATION AND INTEGRATION OF MATRICES

The elements of a matrix may be functions of an independent variable, or derivatives. In both cases the matrix can be differentiated with respect to the independent variable and integrated. Each of these operations will now be discussed.

12.12.1. Differentiation

Consider a square matrix Y whose elements are functions of an independent variable x. A small change in the value of x will bring about a corresponding change in the value of the matrix Y, and the limit of the change in Y for an infinitesimal change in x is the derivative of the matrix with respect to x. This is written in the normal way (dY/dx).

The differential coefficient of the product of two or more matrices with respect to an independent variable is obtained in a manner similar to that of the differential coefficient of the product of scalar functions, but in the case of the derivative of a matrix product the order of the matrices in the product must be maintained. Thus

$$\frac{d}{dx}(XYZ) = \frac{dX}{dx}YZ + X\frac{dY}{dx}Z + XY\frac{dZ}{dx} \qquad (12.48)$$

Finally the differentiation of the exponential function of a matrix is similar to the differentiation of a scalar exponential function. That is,

$$\frac{d}{dt}(e^{\mathbf{X}t}) = \mathbf{X} + \frac{\mathbf{X}^2 t}{1!} + \frac{\mathbf{X}^3 t^2}{2!} + \dots = \mathbf{X}\,e^{\mathbf{X}t} \tag{12.49}$$

as would be expected.

12.12.2. *Integration*

Integration of a matrix whose elements are derivatives or functions of an independent variable is accomplished by integrating each element with respect to the independent variable. Thus if the typical element $y_{ij}(x)$ of the matrix $\mathbf{Y}$ is a function of x, then the new element in the integrated matrix will be

$$\int \mathbf{Y}\,dx = \left[\int y_{ij}(x)\,dx\right] \tag{12.50}$$

An integration series that arises frequently in the solution of systems of linear differential equations is known as " the matrizant " which by definition is

$$M_0^x(\mathbf{A}) = \mathbf{I} + \int_0^x \mathbf{A}(x_1)\,dx_1 + \int_0^x \mathbf{A}(x_1) \int_0^{x_1} \mathbf{A}(x_2)\,dx_2\,dx_1$$

$$+ \int_0^x \mathbf{A}(x_1) \int_0^{x_1} \mathbf{A}(x_2) \int_0^{x_2} \mathbf{A}(x_3)\,dx_3\,dx_2\,dx_1 \dots \tag{12.51}$$

where $M_0^x(\mathbf{A})$ is the matrizant of the matrix $\mathbf{A}$. The form of the matrizant given in equation (12.51) is of little value in calculations because of its complexity. However, if the number of integration terms in equation (12.51) is large, the value of the matrizant over specified limits approximates to

$$M_0^x(\mathbf{A}) = \lim_{n \to \infty} \prod_{1}^{n} \left[\mathbf{I} + \mathbf{A}(x_{s-1})\frac{x}{n}\right] \tag{12.52}$$

where n is the number of integrals in equation (12.51). If all the elements in the matrix $\mathbf{A}$ are constants the matrizant becomes

$$M_0^x(\mathbf{A}) = \mathbf{I} + \frac{\mathbf{A}(x-x_0)}{1!} + \frac{\mathbf{A}^2(x-x_0)^2}{2!} + \dots = e^{\mathbf{A}(x-x_0)} \tag{12.53}$$

12.13. LAMBDA-MATRICES

Matrices of this type arise in many fields of applied mathematics where systems of linear differential equations are to be solved. Therefore they deserve consideration. A λ-matrix is a square matrix in which the elements are functions of a scalar parameter λ. Such a matrix is completely defined by its order, rank, and degree. Its order depends on the number of rows or columns as described above. Its rank is the order of the highest non-vanishing minor irrespective of the value assigned to λ, and finally the degree of a λ-matrix is the highest degree of λ in any of the elements of such a matrix.

Example. What is the order, rank and degree of the λ-matrix:

$$\begin{bmatrix} \lambda^2+1 & -1 & \lambda-3 \\ \lambda^2+\lambda & -\lambda^2 & \lambda+1 \\ 2\lambda^2-3\lambda+1 & 1-\lambda & \lambda^2 \end{bmatrix}$$

and expand this matrix into a matrix series.

When $\lambda = 1$ the determinant of the matrix $\Delta(\lambda)$ is zero, and hence this matrix is singular. However, its minors of order two are non-vanishing, therefore the λ-matrix is of rank 2.

The highest degree of λ in any element is 2 and therefore the λ-matrix is of degree 2.

The expansion of this matrix is

$$\begin{bmatrix} \lambda^2+1 & -1 & \lambda-3 \\ \lambda^2+\lambda & -\lambda^2 & \lambda+1 \\ 2\lambda^2-3\lambda+1 & 1-\lambda & \lambda^2 \end{bmatrix}$$

$$= \begin{bmatrix} 1 & 0 & 0 \\ 1 & -1 & 0 \\ 2 & 0 & 1 \end{bmatrix} \lambda^2 + \begin{bmatrix} 0 & 0 & 1 \\ 1 & 0 & 1 \\ -3 & -1 & 0 \end{bmatrix} \lambda + \begin{bmatrix} 1 & -1 & -3 \\ 0 & 0 & 1 \\ 1 & 1 & 0 \end{bmatrix} \quad \text{I}$$

The rank of the λ-matrix can be easily verified from equation I.

The addition, multiplication and division of λ-matrices is similar to other matrices. However, the reciprocal of a λ-matrix is normally independent of λ and is not therefore a λ-matrix.

12.13.1. *The Determinantal Equation*

A λ-matrix is usually represented by the symbol $\mathbf{f}(\lambda)$, its adjoint by $\mathbf{F}(\lambda)$ and its determinant by $\Delta(\lambda)$ or $\det(\lambda)$. These are related by the equation

$$\mathbf{f}(\lambda)\mathbf{F}(\lambda) = \mathbf{F}(\lambda)\mathbf{f}(\lambda) = \Delta(\lambda)\mathbf{I} \tag{12.54}$$

Equation (12.54) can be differentiated with respect to λ to give

$$\frac{d}{d\lambda}[\mathbf{f}(\lambda)\mathbf{F}(\lambda)] = \frac{d}{d\lambda}[\mathbf{F}(\lambda)\mathbf{f}(\lambda)] = \frac{d}{d\lambda}[\Delta(\lambda)] \tag{12.55}$$

and the differentiation can be repeated until the derivatives vanish.

The equation formed by equating (12.54) to zero, that is

$$\Delta(\lambda) = 0 \tag{12.56}$$

is called the " determinantal equation " and its roots which may be distinct or multiple, are of great importance in matrix analysis. Thus let λ_p be a root of the determinantal equation; then the matrix formed by substitution of λ_p into the original matrix is $\mathbf{f}(\lambda_p)$ and it will be singular. However, if λ_p is a multiple root, $\mathbf{f}(\lambda_p)$ need not have a degeneracy greater than one.

Thus the λ-matrix

$$\begin{bmatrix} (\lambda - a) & b & 0 \\ 0 & (\lambda - a) & 0 \\ 0 & 0 & (\lambda - b) \end{bmatrix}$$

has a root $\lambda = b$, and a double root $\lambda = a$, but is of degeneracy one. When $\mathbf{f}(\lambda_p)$ is of degeneracy one the adjoint $\mathbf{F}(\lambda_p)$ is of unit rank.

When $\mathbf{f}(\lambda_p)$ has a degeneracy of q, at least q roots of the determinantal equation are equal. Furthermore the adjoint matrix and its derivatives up to and including $\mathbf{F}^{q-2}(\lambda_p)$ are all null.

12.14. THE CHARACTERISTIC EQUATION

Let $\mathbf{A}$ be a square matrix of order n whose elements are all constants, and let $\mathbf{x}$ be a column vector whose elements are related by the equation

$$\mathbf{Ax} = \lambda \mathbf{x} \tag{12.57}$$

where λ is a scalar coefficient. Equation (12.57) may be written in the matrix form thus

$$(\mathbf{A} - \lambda \mathbf{I})\mathbf{x} = \mathbf{0} \tag{12.58}$$

where $(\mathbf{A} - \lambda \mathbf{I})$ is a square λ-matrix of order n. The solution to equation (12.58) will be non-trivial if and only if

$$|\mathbf{A} - \lambda \mathbf{I}| = 0 \tag{12.59}$$

Hence λ can only take values that will satisfy equation (12.59) and for this reason equation (12.59) is called the " characteristic equation " of the matrix $\mathbf{A}$. Its roots λ_p are called the " latent roots " or the " eigenvalues " (see Section 8.7.1) of $\mathbf{A}$.

When $|\mathbf{A} - \lambda \mathbf{I}|$ is zero, $|(\mathbf{A} - \lambda \mathbf{I})'|$ is zero, and since $(\mathbf{A} - \lambda \mathbf{I})' = \mathbf{A}' - \lambda \mathbf{I}$, both $\mathbf{A}$ and its transpose have the same latent roots.

12.14.1. *Diagonal Canonical Form*

For each root of equation (12.59) there will be a corresponding set of values for the elements in the column vector $\mathbf{x}$, and each set of values constitute a vector of the latent root. For this reason the vector corresponding to the latent root is called a " latent column vector " and there will be a latent column vector for each latent root. Furthermore, if the latent roots are distinct, the latent column vectors are linearly independent. Therefore consider a non-singular square matrix $\mathbf{A}$ of order n, and let the latent roots of $\mathbf{A}$ be distinct. In addition let $\mathbf{k}_1$, $\mathbf{k}_2$, $\mathbf{k}_3$, ... $\mathbf{k}_n$ be the latent column vectors corresponding to the latent roots of $\mathbf{A}$, and $\mathbf{K}$ the square matrix comprising all the column vectors. $\mathbf{K}$ will be of order n and non-singular. Also

$$\mathbf{Ak}_1 = \lambda_1 \mathbf{k}_1; \quad \mathbf{Ak}_2 = \lambda_2 \mathbf{k}_2; \quad \ldots; \quad \mathbf{Ak}_n = \lambda_n \mathbf{k}_n \tag{12.60}$$

and

$$\mathbf{AK} = \mathbf{K\Lambda} \tag{12.61}$$

where

$$\Lambda = \begin{bmatrix} \lambda_1 & 0 & \cdots & 0 \\ 0 & \lambda_2 & \cdots & 0 \\ \cdot & \cdot & & \cdot \\ \cdot & \cdot & & \cdot \\ \cdot & \cdot & & \cdot \\ 0 & 0 & \cdots & \lambda_n \end{bmatrix}$$ (12.62)

Therefore $\mathbf{K}^{-1}\mathbf{A}\mathbf{K} = \mathbf{K}^{-1}\mathbf{K}\Lambda = \Lambda$ (12.63)

showing that the matrix $\mathbf{A}$ can be reduced to what is known as "diagonal canonical form".

In a similar manner, latent row vectors can be determined which in turn can be used to reduce $\mathbf{A}$ to the diagonal canonical form.

Example 1. Evaluate the latent roots and reduce the following matrix to diagonal form.

$$\begin{bmatrix} 2 & -3 & 1 \\ 3 & 1 & 3 \\ -5 & 2 & -4 \end{bmatrix}$$

The characteristic equation can be expressed in the form

$$|\mathbf{I}\lambda - \mathbf{A}| = 0 \qquad\qquad \text{I}$$

in order to eliminate the negative signs from in front of the latent roots. Thus in matrix form

$$\begin{bmatrix} \lambda-2 & 3 & -1 \\ -3 & \lambda-1 & -3 \\ 5 & -2 & \lambda+4 \end{bmatrix} = \mathbf{0} \qquad\qquad \text{II}$$

expanding the determinant of equation II

$$(\lambda-1)[(\lambda-2)(\lambda+4)+8] = 0 \qquad\qquad \text{III}$$

from which $\lambda_1 = 0; \quad \lambda_2 = 1; \quad \lambda_3 = -2$

When $\lambda = \lambda_1 = 0$, the adjoint is

$$\begin{bmatrix} -10 & -10 & -10 \\ -3 & -3 & -3 \\ 11 & 11 & 11 \end{bmatrix} = \begin{bmatrix} -10 \\ -3 \\ 11 \end{bmatrix} \begin{bmatrix} 1 & 1 & 1 \end{bmatrix} \qquad\qquad \text{IV}$$

When $\lambda = \lambda_2 = 1$, the adjoint is

$$\begin{bmatrix} -6 & -13 & -9 \\ 0 & 0 & 0 \\ 6 & 13 & 9 \end{bmatrix} = \begin{bmatrix} -1 \\ 0 \\ 1 \end{bmatrix} \begin{bmatrix} 6 & 13 & 9 \end{bmatrix} \qquad\qquad \text{V}$$

and when $\lambda = \lambda_3 = -2$, the adjoint is

$$\begin{bmatrix} -12 & -4 & -12 \\ -9 & -3 & -9 \\ 21 & 7 & 21 \end{bmatrix} = \begin{bmatrix} -4 \\ -3 \\ 7 \end{bmatrix} \begin{bmatrix} 3 & 1 & 3 \end{bmatrix} \qquad \text{VI}$$

From equations IV, V, and VI the **K** matrix is

$$\mathbf{K} = \begin{bmatrix} -10 & -1 & -4 \\ -3 & 0 & -3 \\ 11 & 1 & 7 \end{bmatrix} \text{ and } \mathbf{K}^{-1} = -\frac{1}{6}\begin{bmatrix} 3 & 3 & 3 \\ -12 & -26 & -18 \\ -3 & -1 & -3 \end{bmatrix} \qquad \text{VII}$$

so that

$$\begin{bmatrix} 2 & -3 & 1 \\ 3 & 1 & 3 \\ -5 & 2 & 4 \end{bmatrix}$$

$$= -\frac{1}{6}\begin{bmatrix} -10 & -1 & -4 \\ -3 & 0 & -3 \\ 11 & 1 & 7 \end{bmatrix}\begin{bmatrix} 0 & 0 & 0 \\ 0 & 1 & 0 \\ 0 & 0 & -2 \end{bmatrix}\begin{bmatrix} 3 & 3 & 3 \\ -12 & -26 & -18 \\ -3 & -1 & -3 \end{bmatrix} \qquad \text{VIII}$$

12.14.2. *The Cayley-Hamilton Theorem*

This theorem can be stated as follows: Any square matrix satisfies its own characteristic equation.

The proof of this theorem will not be given; however, any interested reader is recommended to see " Elementary Matrices " by Fraser, Duncan, & Collar.† Here it will suffice to illustrate its application to the above third order matrix.

Example 2. Show that the square matrix

$$\begin{bmatrix} 2 & -3 & 1 \\ 3 & 1 & 3 \\ -5 & 2 & -4 \end{bmatrix}$$

satisfies its own characteristic equation.

The characteristic equation of the given matrix is

$$|\mathbf{I}\lambda - \mathbf{A}| = \lambda(\lambda - 1)(\lambda + 2) = 0 \qquad \text{I}$$

By the Cayley-Hamilton theorem

$$\mathbf{A}(\mathbf{A} - \mathbf{I})(\mathbf{A} + 2\mathbf{I}) = 0 \qquad \text{II}$$

† Fraser, R. A., Duncan, W. J. and Collar, A. R. ÷ Elementary Matrices ", Cambridge University Press (1960).

where $\mathbf{0}$ in equation II is the null matrix. That is,

$$\begin{bmatrix} 2 & -3 & 1 \\ 3 & 1 & 3 \\ -5 & 2 & -4 \end{bmatrix} \begin{bmatrix} 1 & -3 & 1 \\ 3 & 0 & 3 \\ -5 & 2 & -5 \end{bmatrix} \begin{bmatrix} 4 & -3 & 1 \\ 3 & 3 & 3 \\ -5 & 2 & -2 \end{bmatrix} = \begin{bmatrix} 0 & 0 & 0 \\ 0 & 0 & 0 \\ 0 & 0 & 0 \end{bmatrix} \qquad \text{III}$$

The Cayley-Hamilton theorem can be used to calculate powers of matrices. Thus since a square matrix satisfies its own characteristic equation, the characteristic equation containing the matrix in place of λ can be expanded and rearranged to give the desired power of the matrix as illustrated below.

Example 3. Calculate $\mathbf{A}^4$ if $\mathbf{A} = \begin{bmatrix} -1 & 3 \\ -2 & 4 \end{bmatrix}$

The characteristic equation is

$$|\mathbf{I}\lambda - \mathbf{A}| = \lambda^2 - 3\lambda + 2 = 0 \qquad \text{I}$$

Replacing λ by $\mathbf{A}$ and rearranging gives

$$\mathbf{A}^2 = 3\mathbf{A} - 2\mathbf{I} \qquad \text{II}$$

Multiplying by $\mathbf{A}$ gives

$$\mathbf{A}^3 = 3\mathbf{A}^2 - 2\mathbf{A} = 9\mathbf{A} - 6\mathbf{I} - 2\mathbf{A}$$
$$= 7\mathbf{A} - 6\mathbf{I} \qquad \text{III}$$

Repeating the process of multiplying by $\mathbf{A}$ and using equation II gives

$$\mathbf{A}^4 = 15\mathbf{A} - 14\mathbf{I} \qquad \text{IV}$$

Hence using equation I,

$$\mathbf{A}^4 = \begin{bmatrix} -29 & 45 \\ -30 & 46 \end{bmatrix} \qquad \text{V}$$

This process can be repeated to any positive or negative integer power of a square matrix.

12.15. SYLVESTER'S THEOREM

From the above section it will be seen that in general

$$\mathbf{A}^n = p_1 \mathbf{A}^{n-1} + p_2 \mathbf{A}^{n-2} + p_3 \mathbf{A}^{n-3} + \ldots + p_n \mathbf{I} \qquad (12.64)$$

where $\mathbf{A}$ is a square matrix and $p_1, p_2, \ldots p_n$ are scalar coefficients. Let the series on the right of equation (12.64) be represented by $P(\mathbf{A})$, then applying Lagrange's interpolation formula (Section 9.4.3)

$$P(\mathbf{A}) = P(\lambda_1) \frac{(\mathbf{A} - \mathbf{I}\lambda_2)(\mathbf{A} - \mathbf{I}\lambda_3)(\ldots)(\mathbf{A} - \mathbf{I}\lambda_n)}{(\lambda_1 - \lambda_2)(\lambda_1 - \lambda_3)(\ldots)(\lambda_1 - \lambda_n)} +$$
$$+ P(\lambda_2) \frac{(\mathbf{A} - \mathbf{I}\lambda_1)(\mathbf{A} - \mathbf{I}\lambda_3)(\ldots)(\mathbf{A} - \mathbf{I}\lambda_n)}{(\lambda_2 - \lambda_1)(\lambda_2 - \lambda_3)(\ldots)(\lambda_2 - \lambda_n)} +$$
$$+ \ldots\ldots\ldots$$

$$= \sum_{i=1}^{n} P(\lambda_i) \frac{\prod_{\substack{j \neq i}}^{n} (\mathbf{A} - \mathbf{I}\lambda_j)}{\prod_{\substack{j \neq i}}^{n} (\lambda_i - \lambda_j)} \tag{12.65}$$

where $\lambda_1, \lambda_2, \ldots \lambda_n$ can be chosen as the roots of the characteristic equation which are assumed to be distinct in the case under consideration. Equation (12.65) is an expression of " Sylvester's theorem " but the extended products in the numerator and denominator are sometimes inconvenient computationally. However, they can be simplified as follows.

Denoting the λ-matrix

$$\mathbf{A} - \mathbf{I}\lambda = \mathbf{f}(\lambda) \tag{12.66}$$

equation (12.54) shows that

$$(\mathbf{A} - \mathbf{I}\lambda_i)\mathbf{F}(\lambda_i) = \Delta(\lambda_i)\mathbf{I} = 0 \tag{12.67}$$

since λ_i is one of the distinct roots of the characteristic equation. Furthermore,

$$\mathbf{A} - \mathbf{I}\lambda_i \neq 0 \quad \text{and} \quad \mathbf{F}(\lambda_i) \neq 0 \tag{12.68}$$

Similarly,

$$(\mathbf{A} - \mathbf{I}\lambda_i) \prod_{\substack{j \neq i}}^{n} (\mathbf{A} - \mathbf{I}\lambda_j) = \prod_{j=1}^{n} (\mathbf{A} - \mathbf{I}\lambda_j) = 0 \tag{12.69}$$

but

$$\prod_{\substack{j \neq i}}^{n} (\mathbf{A} - \mathbf{I}\lambda_j) \neq 0 \tag{12.70}$$

Hence it can be shown that

$$\prod_{\substack{j \neq i}}^{n} (\mathbf{A} - \mathbf{I}\lambda_j) = \mathbf{C}\mathbf{F}(\lambda_i) \tag{12.71}$$

where $\mathbf{C}$ can be any diagonal matrix with constant elements. The matrices in equations (12.67) and (12.69) are commutative in each case; therefore $\mathbf{C}$ must be some constant (α) times the unit matrix. By selecting square matrices of different orders in which all elements are unity it can be shown that $\alpha = (-1)^{n-1}$. Thus

$$\prod_{\substack{j \neq i}}^{n} (\mathbf{A} - \mathbf{I}\lambda_j) = (-1)^{n-1}\mathbf{F}(\lambda_i) = \prod_{\substack{j \neq i}}^{n} \mathbf{f}(\lambda_j) \tag{12.72}$$

where n is the order of the square matrix.

The denominator of equation (12.65) can be simplified as follows.

$$\Delta(\lambda) = \prod_{j=1}^{n} (\lambda_j - \lambda) = (-1)^n \prod_{j=1}^{n} (\lambda - \lambda_j) \tag{12.73}$$

but

$$\frac{d}{d\lambda} [\Delta(\lambda)]\big|_{\lambda = \lambda_i} = (-1)^n \prod_{\substack{j \neq i}}^{n} (\lambda_i - \lambda_j) = \Delta'(\lambda_i) \tag{12.74}$$

Hence Sylvester's theorem becomes

$$P(\mathbf{A}) = - \sum_{i=1}^{n} \frac{P(\lambda_i)\mathbf{F}(\lambda_i)}{\Delta'(\lambda_i)} \tag{12.75}$$

If $\mathbf{f}(\lambda)$ is defined as $\mathbf{I}\lambda - \mathbf{A}$ instead of by equation (12.66) the only effect is to change some of the signs. The negative sign in front of equation (12.75) has to be removed, but equations (12.65) and (12.72) are not changed.

Finally, when the characteristic equation has multiple roots Sylvester's theorem takes a much more complicated form due to $\Delta'(\lambda_i)$ vanishing for the repeated roots. Equations (12.65) and (12.75) can be modified by using L'Hôpital's rule until the indeterminate fractions are resolved, but the work involved shows no significant advantage over evaluating the original polynomial (12.64) directly. However, this form is known as the " confluent form " and is derived by Fraser, Duncan, & Collar.†

12.16. TRANSFORMATION OF MATRICES

In many calculations involving matrices it is advantageous to rearrange the matrix into an " equivalent form " having the same rank, degeneracy, and latent roots as the original matrix, but being more suitable for the particular problem. This can be accomplished by

(i) Interchange of any two columns or rows.
(ii) Addition of any multiple of any column or row to any other column or row.
(iii) Multiplication of any column or row by a scalar.

12.16.1. *Interchange of Columns or Rows*

Consider the post-multiplication of a third order matrix $\mathbf{A}$ by the modified unit matrix

$$\begin{bmatrix} 1 & 0 & 0 \\ 0 & 0 & 1 \\ 0 & 1 & 0 \end{bmatrix}$$

which has its second and third columns interchanged. The result is

$$\begin{bmatrix} a_{11} & a_{12} & a_{13} \\ a_{21} & a_{22} & a_{23} \\ a_{31} & a_{32} & a_{33} \end{bmatrix} \begin{bmatrix} 1 & 0 & 0 \\ 0 & 0 & 1 \\ 0 & 1 & 0 \end{bmatrix} = \begin{bmatrix} a_{11} & a_{13} & a_{12} \\ a_{21} & a_{23} & a_{22} \\ a_{31} & a_{33} & a_{32} \end{bmatrix} \quad (12.76)$$

In equation (12.76) it can be seen that the second and third columns of the matrix $\mathbf{A}$ have been interchanged. It will also be readily seen that if the second and third rows of the unit matrix had been interchanged and the matrix $\mathbf{A}$ pre-multiplied by this modified unit matrix the result would have been the interchange of the second and third rows of $\mathbf{A}$.

† Fraser, R. A., Duncan, W. J. and Collar, A. R. " Elementary Matrices ", Cambridge University Press (1960).

It should be observed that the modified unit matrix is the same as its transpose and that

$$\begin{bmatrix} 1 & 0 & 0 \\ 0 & 0 & 1 \\ 0 & 1 & 0 \end{bmatrix} \begin{bmatrix} 1 & 0 & 0 \\ 0 & 0 & 1 \\ 0 & 1 & 0 \end{bmatrix} = \begin{bmatrix} 1 & 0 & 0 \\ 0 & 1 & 0 \\ 0 & 0 & 1 \end{bmatrix} \tag{12.77}$$

and therefore the modified unit matrix has the properties of unity. It is equivalent to the unit matrix.

These operations can be extended to matrices of any order.

12.16.2. *Addition of any Column or Row, or a Multiple of any Column or Row, to any other Column or Row*

Consider the product

$$\begin{bmatrix} a_{11} & a_{12} & a_{13} \\ a_{21} & a_{22} & a_{23} \\ a_{31} & a_{32} & a_{33} \end{bmatrix} \begin{bmatrix} 1 & \beta & 0 \\ 0 & 1 & 0 \\ 0 & 0 & 1 \end{bmatrix} = \begin{bmatrix} a_{11} & (\beta a_{11}+a_{12}) & a_{13} \\ a_{21} & (\beta a_{21}+a_{22}) & a_{23} \\ a_{31} & (\beta a_{31}+a_{32}) & a_{33} \end{bmatrix} \tag{12.78}$$

Post-multiplication of the matrix **A** by the second matrix on the left of equation (12.78) had the effect of adding β times the first column to the second column. Pre-multiplication of **A** by this matrix would have brought about the addition of β times the first row to the second row.

The matrix which operates on **A** is a unit matrix to which has been added the element β in its first row and second column. Its determinant is unity.

12.16.3. *Multiplication of any Column or Row by a Scalar*

Consider the product

$$\begin{bmatrix} a_{11} & a_{12} & a_{13} \\ a_{21} & a_{22} & a_{23} \\ a_{31} & a_{32} & a_{33} \end{bmatrix} \begin{bmatrix} 1 & 0 & 0 \\ 0 & \gamma & 0 \\ 0 & 0 & 1 \end{bmatrix} = \begin{bmatrix} a_{11} & \gamma a_{12} & a_{13} \\ a_{21} & \gamma a_{22} & a_{23} \\ a_{31} & \gamma a_{32} & a_{33} \end{bmatrix} \tag{12.79}$$

The result of this operation is that the second column of **A** has been multiplied by the scalar γ. This was accomplished by exchanging the central unit element for the scalar γ. If the matrix **A** had been pre-multiplied by this matrix the effect would have been to multiply the second row by the scalar γ.

The determinant of the converted unit matrix is γ.

12.16.4. *Equivalent Matrices*

Two matrices are said to be " equivalent " to one another if it is possible to pass from one to the other by a series of transformations of the types presented above.

The above definition of equivalent matrices includes λ-matrices. However, with this latter type of matrix the matrices that bring about the transformations must have determinants that are independent of λ but still finite. Thus if $\mathbf{f}_1(\lambda)$ and $\mathbf{f}_2(\lambda)$ are two equivalent λ-matrices, then if

$$\mathbf{f}_2(\lambda) = \mathbf{A}\mathbf{f}_1(\lambda)\mathbf{B} \tag{12.80}$$

$\mathbf{A}$ and $\mathbf{B}$ will be λ-matrices whose determinants will each be constant.

12.17. Quadratic Form

An expression of the type

$$\begin{bmatrix} x_1 & x_2 & x_3 & \cdots & x_n \end{bmatrix} \begin{bmatrix} a_{11} & a_{12} & a_{13} & \cdots & a_{1n} \\ a_{21} & a_{22} & a_{23} & \cdots & a_{2n} \\ a_{31} & a_{32} & a_{33} & \cdots & a_{3n} \\ \cdot & \cdot & \cdot & & \cdot \\ \cdot & \cdot & \cdot & & \cdot \\ \cdot & \cdot & \cdot & & \cdot \\ a_{n1} & a_{n2} & a_{n3} & \cdots & a_{nn} \end{bmatrix} \begin{bmatrix} x_1 \\ x_2 \\ x_3 \\ \cdot \\ \cdot \\ \cdot \\ x_n \end{bmatrix} \tag{12.81}$$

is called a " quadratic form ". It is a homogeneous function of the second degree. The coefficient of $x_i x_j$ in the quadratic form where $i \neq j$ is $(a_{ij}+a_{ji})$. For example, the conic

$$ax^2 + 2hxy + by^2 = \begin{bmatrix} x & y \end{bmatrix} \begin{bmatrix} a & h \\ h & b \end{bmatrix} \begin{bmatrix} x \\ y \end{bmatrix} = c \tag{12.82}$$

can be written more concisely in the quadratic form.

$$\mathbf{x}'\mathbf{A}\mathbf{x} = c \tag{12.83}$$

whilst the equation

$$a_1 x_1^2 + a_2 x_2^2 + a_3 x_3^2 + \ldots a_n x_n^2 = 0 \tag{12.84}$$

would be written

$$\begin{bmatrix} x_1 & x_2 & x_3 & \cdots & x_n \end{bmatrix} \begin{bmatrix} a_1 & 0 & 0 & \cdots & 0 \\ 0 & a_2 & 0 & \cdots & 0 \\ 0 & 0 & a_3 & \cdots & 0 \\ \cdot & \cdot & \cdot & & \cdot \\ \cdot & \cdot & \cdot & & \cdot \\ \cdot & \cdot & \cdot & & \cdot \\ 0 & 0 & 0 & \cdots & a_n \end{bmatrix} \begin{bmatrix} x_1 \\ x_2 \\ x_3 \\ \cdot \\ \cdot \\ \cdot \\ x_n \end{bmatrix} = \mathbf{x}'[A_{ii}]\mathbf{x} \tag{12.85}$$

where the symbol $[A_{ii}]$ indicates that the matrix $\mathbf{A}$ is a diagonal matrix.

Example. Determine the nature of the quadric

$$6x^2 + 3y^2 - 2z^2 + 4xy = 14$$

and evaluate the lengths of the semi axes and equations of the principal planes.

The equation

$$6x^2 + 3y^2 - 2z^2 + 4xy = 14 \qquad \text{I}$$

can be written in matrix form

$$\begin{bmatrix} x & y & z \end{bmatrix} \begin{bmatrix} 6 & 2 & 0 \\ 2 & 3 & 0 \\ 0 & 0 & -2 \end{bmatrix} \begin{bmatrix} x \\ y \\ z \end{bmatrix} = 14 = \mathbf{x'Ax} \qquad \text{II}$$

The latent roots of $\mathbf{A}$ are obtained from

$$\begin{vmatrix} 6-\lambda & 2 & 0 \\ 2 & 3-\lambda & 0 \\ 0 & 0 & -(2+\lambda) \end{vmatrix} = 0 \qquad \text{III}$$

or

$$(\lambda+2)(\lambda-2)(\lambda-7) = 0 \qquad \text{IV}$$

and the latent roots are $\lambda_1 = -2$; $\lambda_2 = 2$; $\lambda_3 = 7$. The latent column vector $\mathbf{k}_1$ corresponding to the root $\lambda_1 = -2$ is

$$\mathbf{Ak}_1 = \lambda_1 \mathbf{k}_1 = -2\mathbf{k}_1 \qquad \text{V}$$

or

$$\begin{bmatrix} 6 & 2 & 0 \\ 2 & 3 & 0 \\ 0 & 0 & -2 \end{bmatrix} \begin{bmatrix} k_{11} \\ k_{21} \\ k_{31} \end{bmatrix} = -2 \begin{bmatrix} k_{11} \\ k_{21} \\ k_{31} \end{bmatrix} \qquad \text{VI}$$

or

$$\left. \begin{aligned} 6k_{11} + 2k_{21} &= -2k_{11} \\ 2k_{11} + 3k_{21} &= -2k_{21} \\ -2k_{31} &= -2k_{31} \end{aligned} \right\} \qquad \text{VII}$$

from which $k_{11} = k_{21} = 0$, and k_{31} is arbitrary. It is normal to choose orthogonal column vectors which satisfy equation (12.16), and thus $k_{31} = 1$. Therefore, the latent column vector corresponding to the latent root $\lambda_1 = -2$ is $\{0 \quad 0 \quad 1\}$.

In a similar manner, the latent column vector corresponding to the latent root $\lambda_2 = 2$ is $\{1/\sqrt{5} \quad -2/\sqrt{5} \quad 0\}$, and corresponding to $\lambda_3 = 7$ is $\{2/\sqrt{5} \quad 1/\sqrt{5} \quad 0\}$.

Then by equation (12.63)

$$\begin{bmatrix} 0 & 0 & 1 \\ 1/\sqrt{5} & -2/\sqrt{5} & 0 \\ 2/\sqrt{5} & 1/\sqrt{5} & 0 \end{bmatrix} \begin{bmatrix} 6 & 2 & 0 \\ 2 & 3 & 0 \\ 0 & 0 & -2 \end{bmatrix} \begin{bmatrix} 0 & 1/\sqrt{5} & 2/\sqrt{5} \\ 0 & -2/\sqrt{5} & 1/\sqrt{5} \\ 1 & 0 & 0 \end{bmatrix} = \begin{bmatrix} -2 & 0 & 0 \\ 0 & 2 & 0 \\ 0 & 0 & 7 \end{bmatrix}$$

$$\text{VIII}$$

Applying the orthogonal transformation $\mathbf{x} = \mathbf{KX}$ where

$$\mathbf{X} = \{X \quad Y \quad Z\} \qquad\qquad \text{IX}$$

then
$$\mathbf{K'x} = \mathbf{K'KX} = \mathbf{X} \qquad\qquad \text{X}$$

or
$$\begin{bmatrix} 0 & 0 & 1 \\ 1/\sqrt{5} & -2/\sqrt{5} & 0 \\ 2/\sqrt{5} & 1/\sqrt{5} & 0 \end{bmatrix} \begin{bmatrix} x \\ y \\ z \end{bmatrix} = \begin{bmatrix} X \\ Y \\ Z \end{bmatrix} \qquad \text{XI}$$

or
$$z = X; \qquad \frac{x}{\sqrt{5}} - \frac{2y}{\sqrt{5}} = Y; \qquad \frac{2x}{\sqrt{5}} + \frac{y}{\sqrt{5}} = Z \qquad \text{XII}$$

Furthermore, from equation II
$$(\mathbf{KX})'\mathbf{A}(\mathbf{KX}) = 14 \qquad\qquad \text{XIII}$$

and by Section 12.5.1
$$\mathbf{X'K'AKX} = \mathbf{X'\Lambda X} = 14 \qquad\qquad \text{XIV}$$

or
$$-2X^2 + 2Y^2 + 7Z^2 = 14 \qquad\qquad \text{XV}$$

or in standard form
$$\frac{-X^2}{7} + \frac{Y^2}{7} + \frac{Z^2}{2} = 1 \qquad\qquad \text{XVI}$$

which is a hyperboloid of one sheet with semiaxes $\sqrt{7}{:}\sqrt{7}{:}\sqrt{2}$.

The principal planes are $X = 0$, $Y = 0$, and $Z = 0$ when referred to the new axes. With respect to the original axes, the principal planes are

$$x - 2y = 0; \qquad 2x + y = 0; \qquad z = 0$$

12.18. APPLICATION TO THE SOLUTION OF DIFFERENTIAL EQUATIONS

Matrices can be applied to the solution of systems of differential equations, and in this respect they are of great utility in the solution of engineering problems. Hence the essential features of the application technique will be presented in this section.

Consider a system of linear differential equations expressing relationships between a number of dependent variables $y_1, y_2, y_3, \ldots y_n$ and an independent variable x. These equations can be written in conventional form

$$\left.\begin{aligned} f_{11}(D)y_1 + f_{12}(D)y_2 + \ldots + f_{1n}(D)y_n &= \phi_1(x) \\ f_{21}(D)y_1 + f_{22}(D)y_2 + \ldots + f_{2n}(D)y_n &= \phi_2(x) \\ \cdots\cdots\cdots\cdots\cdots\cdots\cdots\cdots\cdots \\ f_{n1}(D)y_1 + f_{n2}(D)y_2 + \ldots + f_{nn}(D)y_n &= \phi_n(x) \end{aligned}\right\} \quad (12.86)$$

or written in condensed matrix form

$$\mathbf{f}(D)\{y\} = [f_{ij}(D)]\{y\} = \{\phi(x)\} \qquad (12.87)$$

In equations (12.86) and (12.87) $f_{ij}(D)$ is a polynomial of the differential operator having constant coefficients. The matrix of differential operators $\mathbf{f}(D)$ is analogous to the λ-matrix and in the determination of the complementary function the technique depends upon the substitution of λ for D. However, certain nomenclature are required and in addition to the terms for λ-matrices given in Section 12.13 the following are necessary.

$\mathbf{f}(D)$ is called the D-matrix.

$|\mathbf{f}(D)|$ is called the D-determinant and is frequently expressed $\Delta(D)$.

The highest degree of D in any of the elements of $\mathbf{f}(D)$ is said to be the order of the system.

12.18.1. *Solution by Conversion to an Equivalent System*

In some systems of differential equations it is possible to transform the D-matrix into such a form that will permit ready solution of the differential equations. This is accomplished by pre-multiplying the D-matrix by another non-singular D-matrix of the same order whose D-determinant is free from the differential operator D. The following example will clarify the method.

Example. Solve the system of equations

$$D^3 y_1 + (D^2 + 3D - 2)y_2 = x$$

$$D^2 y_1 - Dy_2 = \sin x$$

These equations can be put in matrix form thus

$$\begin{bmatrix} D^3 & (D^2 + 3D - 2) \\ D^2 & -D \end{bmatrix} \begin{bmatrix} y_1 \\ y_2 \end{bmatrix} = \begin{bmatrix} x \\ \sin x \end{bmatrix} \qquad \text{I}$$

Pre-multiplying both sides of equation I by

$$\begin{bmatrix} 1 & -D \\ -D & D^2 + 2 \end{bmatrix} \qquad \text{II}$$

gives

$$\begin{bmatrix} 1 & -D \\ -D & D^2 + 2 \end{bmatrix} \begin{bmatrix} D^3 & (D^2 + 3D - 2) \\ D^2 & -D \end{bmatrix} \begin{bmatrix} y_1 \\ y_2 \end{bmatrix} = \begin{bmatrix} 1 & -D \\ -D & D^2 + 2 \end{bmatrix} \begin{bmatrix} x \\ \sin x \end{bmatrix} \qquad \text{III}$$

$$\therefore \quad \begin{bmatrix} 0 & (2D^2 + 3D - 2) \\ 2D^2 & -(2D^3 + 3D^2) \end{bmatrix} \begin{bmatrix} y_1 \\ y_2 \end{bmatrix} = \begin{bmatrix} x - D\sin x \\ -Dx + (D^2 + 2)\sin x \end{bmatrix} \qquad \text{IV}$$

$$\therefore \quad (2D^2 + 3D - 2)y_2 = x - \cos x \qquad \text{V}$$

$$2D^2 y_1 - 2D^3 y_2 - 3D^2 y_2 = -1 + \sin x \qquad \text{VI}$$

Solving equation V by the methods of Chapter 2 gives

$$y_2 = Ae^{-2x} + Be^{\frac{1}{2}x} - \tfrac{1}{2}x - \tfrac{3}{4} + \tfrac{1}{25}(4\cos x - 3\sin x) \qquad \text{VII}$$

Integrating equation VI twice and then for y_2 from equation substituting VII gives

$$y_1 = C + Ex - \tfrac{1}{4}x^2 - \tfrac{1}{2}A e^{-2x} + 2B e^{\frac{1}{2}x} + \tfrac{1}{25}(3\cos x - 21\sin x) \qquad \text{VIII}$$

where A, B, C, and E are the four arbitrary constants required by this third order system of equations.

In the above example the matrix

$$\begin{bmatrix} 1 & -D \\ -D & D^2 + 2 \end{bmatrix}$$

was obtained by trial. but guided by the aim that all but one of the dependent variables were to be eliminated from one of the equations. This enabled that variable to be evaluated and inserted into the other equation which was subsequently solved by conventional methods. When there are a large number of dependent variables it is necessary to convert the D-matrix into triangular form by pre-multiplication by another D-matrix whose determinant is a constant. The transformed system must be of the type

$$\begin{bmatrix} f_{11}(D) & f_{12}(D) & f_{13}(D) & \cdots & f_{1n}(D) \\ 0 & f_{22}(D) & f_{23}(D) & \cdots & f_{2n}(D) \\ 0 & 0 & f_{33}(D) & \cdots & f_{3n}(D) \\ \cdot & \cdot & \cdot & & \cdot \\ \cdot & \cdot & \cdot & & \cdot \\ \cdot & \cdot & \cdot & & \cdot \\ 0 & 0 & 0 & \cdots & f_{nn}(D) \end{bmatrix} \begin{bmatrix} y_1 \\ y_2 \\ y_3 \\ \cdot \\ \cdot \\ \cdot \\ y_n \end{bmatrix} = \begin{bmatrix} \phi_1(x) \\ \phi_2(x) \\ \phi_3(x) \\ \cdot \\ \cdot \\ \cdot \\ \phi_n(x) \end{bmatrix} \qquad (12.88)$$

In equation (12.88) it can be seen that the last row is a function of y_n only, whilst the row above is a function of y_n and y_{n-1} only. Hence the equation of the last row will give an expression for y_n which will be inserted into the equation of the row above to give an expression for y_{n-1} and so on until the system has been solved.

12.19. Solutions of Systems of Linear Differential Equations

Systems of linear differential equations can be solved in a similar manner to single linear differential equations by establishing the complementary function and the particular integral. However, with systems of equations the process will be much more complicated because of the inter-relationship between the dependent variables and the effect of one solution on the particular integrals of the others. Each part of the complete solution will now be considered separately.

12.19.1. *The Complementary Function*

A system of linear differential equations has been written in matrix form in equation (12.87) and the complementary function of this equation will be obtained by solving when $\{\phi(x)\}$ is zero. That is by solving the equation

$$\mathbf{f}(D)\{y\} = \mathbf{0} \tag{12.89}$$

The solution of equation (12.89) will depend on the latent roots of the D-matrix, and each latent root is said to contribute a " constituent solution " to the complementary function. Hence the solution of equation (12.89) depends upon whether the latent roots of $\mathbf{f}(D)$ are distinct or multiple. These will be considered separately.

(i) *Distinct latent roots.* Let λ_r be any distinct root of $\Delta(\lambda) = 0$ obtained by substituting λ for D in the D-matrix. Then since

$$\mathbf{f}(D)\, e^{\lambda_r x}\, \mathbf{F}(\lambda_r) = e^{\lambda_r x}\, \mathbf{f}(\lambda_r)\mathbf{F}(\lambda_r) = \mathbf{0} \tag{12.90}$$

$e^{\lambda_r x}\, \mathbf{F}(\lambda_r)$ is a solution of equation (12.89), but as λ_r is a simple root $\mathbf{F}(\lambda_r)$ can be written in the form

$$\mathbf{F}(\lambda_r) = \{k_r\}\,[\kappa_r] \tag{12.91}$$

so that the constituent solution corresponding to the distinct root λ_r is an arbitrary multiple of $e^{\lambda_r x}\mathbf{k}_r$.

(ii) *Multiple latent roots.* Let λ_s be any one of s repeated latent roots. Then if the matrices

$$\mathbf{W}_0(x, \lambda_s) = e^{\lambda_s x}\,\mathbf{F}(\lambda_s)$$

and

$$\mathbf{W}_p(x, \lambda_s) = \left[\frac{\partial^p}{\partial \lambda_s^p} e^{\lambda_s x}\,\mathbf{F}(\lambda_s)\right] = e^{\lambda_s x}\left(\frac{\partial}{\partial \lambda_s} + x\right)^p \mathbf{F}(\lambda_s)$$

it can be shown by a similar procedure to that given for distinct roots that

$$\mathbf{f}(D)\{y\} = \mathbf{f}(D)\mathbf{W}_p(x, \lambda_s) \tag{12.92}$$

so that $\mathbf{W}_0(x, \lambda_s)$; $\mathbf{W}_1(x, \lambda_s)$; $\ldots \mathbf{W}_p(x, \lambda_s)$ all satisfy the system of differential equations. In all the above $p = (s-1)$ for obvious reasons.

It is convenient to write the matrix $\mathbf{W}_p(x, \lambda_s)$ in the form $e^{\lambda_s x}\mathbf{Z}_p(x, \lambda_s)$ where

$$\mathbf{Z}_p(x, \lambda_s) = \mathbf{F}^p(\lambda_s) + \frac{px\mathbf{F}^{p-1}(\lambda_s)}{1!} + \frac{p(p-1)x^2\mathbf{F}^{p-2}(\lambda_s)}{2!} + \ldots + x^p\mathbf{F}(\lambda_s) \tag{12.93}$$

and there will be s matrices of $\mathbf{Z}$ corresponding to the set of repeated roots. Hence since each matrix will have n columns (the order of $\mathbf{f}(D)$) there will be ns constituent solutions, but of these only s solutions will be linearly independent. Hence for a root λ_s from s repeated roots the constituent solution will be

$$\{y\} = \{k_{1s}(x) \quad k_{2s}(x) \quad \ldots \quad k_{ns}(x)\}\, e^{\lambda_s x} \tag{12.94}$$

and the s columns of the type represented by equation (12.94) corresponding to the s equal roots may be chosen to be proportional to any s linearly independent columns of the matrices

$$\mathbf{Z}_0(x, \lambda_s) = \mathbf{F}(\lambda_s)$$

$$\mathbf{Z}_1(x, \lambda_s) = \mathbf{F}'(\lambda_s) + x\mathbf{F}(\lambda_s)$$

$$\cdots \quad \cdots \quad \cdots \quad \cdots \quad \cdots \quad \cdots \quad \cdots$$

$$\mathbf{Z}_p(x, \lambda_s) = \mathbf{F}^p(\lambda_s) + \frac{px\mathbf{F}^{p-1}(\lambda_s)}{1!} + \frac{p(p-1)x^2\mathbf{F}^{p-2}(\lambda_s)}{2!} + x^p\mathbf{F}(\lambda_s)$$

Since $p = s-1$ the elements in the column vector of equation (12.94) will be polynomials in x of degree $(s-1)$. These column vectors are called " modal columns " and the matrix formed from all the n roots of $\mathbf{f}(D)$ is

$$\mathbf{K}(x) = \begin{bmatrix} k_{11}(x) & k_{12}(x) & \cdots & k_{1n}(x) \\ k_{21}(x) & k_{22}(x) & \cdots & k_{2n}(x) \\ \cdot & \cdot & & \cdot \\ \cdot & \cdot & & \cdot \\ k_{m1}(x) & k_{m2}(x) & \cdots & k_{mn}(x) \end{bmatrix} \qquad (12.95)$$

and is known as the " modal matrix ". Those columns obtained from distinct roots will have constant elements.

Finally if the exponential functions $e^{\lambda_n x}$ are collected into a diagonal matrix $\mathbf{M}(x)$ where

$$\mathbf{M}(x) = \begin{bmatrix} e^{\lambda_1 x} & 0 & 0 & \cdots & 0 \\ 0 & e^{\lambda_2 x} & 0 & \cdots & 0 \\ 0 & 0 & e^{\lambda_3 x} & \cdots & 0 \\ \cdot & \cdot & \cdot & & \cdot \\ \cdot & \cdot & \cdot & & \cdot \\ \cdot & \cdot & \cdot & & \cdot \\ 0 & 0 & 0 & \cdots & e^{\lambda_n x} \end{bmatrix} \qquad (12.96)$$

and $\{C\}$ is a column of n arbitrary constants, the complementary function of the system is

$$\{y\} = \mathbf{K}(x)\, \mathbf{M}(x)\, \{C\} \qquad (12.97)$$

Example. Solve the following system of differential equations.

$$(D^2 - 3D + 2)y_1 + (D^2 - 1)y_2 = 0$$

$$(D^2 + 4D + 3)y_2 - (D^2 + D + 2)y_1 = 0$$

The above equations can be written in matrix form thus

$$\begin{bmatrix} (D^2 - 3D + 2) & (D^2 - 1) \\ -(D^2 + D + 2) & (D^2 + 4D + 3) \end{bmatrix} \begin{bmatrix} y_1 \\ y_2 \end{bmatrix} = \mathbf{0} \qquad \text{I}$$

The λ-matrix obtained from the D-matrix is

$$\begin{bmatrix} (\lambda - 1)(\lambda - 2) & (\lambda - 1)(\lambda + 1) \\ -(\lambda^2 + \lambda + 2) & (\lambda + 1)(\lambda + 3) \end{bmatrix}$$

rom which $\qquad \Delta(\lambda) = (\lambda - 1)^2 (\lambda + 1)(\lambda + 2) \qquad$ II

The latent roots are

$$\lambda_1 = -1; \qquad \lambda_2 = -2; \qquad \lambda_3 = \lambda_4 = 1$$

The respective adjoints are for λ_1 and λ_2

$$\mathbf{F}(\lambda_1) = \begin{bmatrix} 0 & 0 \\ 2 & 6 \end{bmatrix} = \begin{bmatrix} 0 \\ 2 \end{bmatrix} \begin{bmatrix} 1 & 3 \end{bmatrix} \qquad \text{III}$$

$$\mathbf{F}(\lambda_2) = \begin{bmatrix} -1 & -3 \\ 4 & 12 \end{bmatrix} = \begin{bmatrix} -1 \\ 4 \end{bmatrix} \begin{bmatrix} 1 & 3 \end{bmatrix} \qquad \text{IV}$$

and the adjoints for λ_3 and λ_4 are

$$\mathbf{F}(\lambda_3) = \begin{bmatrix} 8 & 0 \\ 4 & 0 \end{bmatrix} = \begin{bmatrix} 2 \\ 1 \end{bmatrix} \begin{bmatrix} 4 & 0 \end{bmatrix} \qquad \text{V}$$

$$\mathbf{F}'(\lambda_3) = \begin{bmatrix} 2\lambda+4 & -2\lambda \\ 2\lambda+1 & 2\lambda-3 \end{bmatrix}_{\lambda=1} = \begin{bmatrix} 6 & -2 \\ 3 & -1 \end{bmatrix} = \begin{bmatrix} 2 \\ 1 \end{bmatrix} \begin{bmatrix} 3 & -1 \end{bmatrix} \qquad \text{VI}$$

and for the latent roots λ_3 and λ_4 the modal columns are

$$\mathbf{k}_3(x) = \{2 \quad 1\} \qquad \text{VII}$$
$$\mathbf{k}_4(x) = \{2 \quad 1\} + \{2 \quad 1\} x \qquad \text{VIII}$$

and the complementary function is

$$\begin{bmatrix} y_1 \\ y_2 \end{bmatrix} = \begin{bmatrix} 0 & -1 & 2 & 2(1+x) \\ 2 & 4 & 1 & (1+x) \end{bmatrix} \begin{bmatrix} e^{-x} & 0 & 0 & 0 \\ 0 & e^{-2x} & 0 & 0 \\ 0 & 0 & e^x & 0 \\ 0 & 0 & 0 & e^x \end{bmatrix} \begin{bmatrix} C_1 \\ C_2 \\ C_3 \\ C_4 \end{bmatrix} \qquad \text{IX}$$

or the conventional result is

$$y_1 = 2[C_3 + C_4(1+x)]e^x - C_2 e^{-2x} \qquad \text{X}$$

and

$$y_2 = 2C_1 e^{-x} + 4C_2 e^{-2x} + [C_3 + C_4(1+x)]e^x \qquad \text{XI}$$

12.19.2 *The Particular Solution*

To complete the solution of the system of linear differential equations it is necessary to obtain a particular solution of equation (12.87). Essentially this solution will be

$$\{y_p\} = \mathbf{f}(D)^{-1}\{\phi(x)\} = \frac{\mathbf{F}(D)}{\Delta(D)}\{\phi(x)\} \qquad (12.98)$$

Hence it is necessary to be able to evaluate the last term in equation (12.98). Therefore consider the case $\phi(x) = \mathbf{R}e^{\theta x}$ where $\mathbf{R}$ is a column of constants. Then

$$\{y_p\} = \frac{\mathbf{F}(D)}{\Delta(D)}\mathbf{R}e^{\theta x} = e^{\theta x}\frac{\mathbf{F}(\theta)}{\Delta(\theta)}\mathbf{R} \qquad (12.99)$$

which is the particular solution when $\phi(x)$ is exponential provided that $\Delta(\theta) \neq 0$.

When $\Delta(\theta) = 0$ the following procedure must be carried out. Let the particular solution be

$$\{y_p\} = \mathbf{b}[\mathbf{F}'(\theta) + x\mathbf{F}(\theta)]\, e^{\theta x} \tag{12.100}$$

where $\mathbf{b}$ is constant. Then

$$\mathbf{f}(D)\mathbf{b}[\mathbf{F}'(\theta) + x\mathbf{F}(\theta)]\, e^{\theta x} = \mathbf{R}e^{\theta x} \tag{12.101}$$

from which

$$\mathbf{b}\,e^{\theta x}\mathbf{f}(D+\theta)[\mathbf{F}'(\theta) + x\mathbf{F}(\theta)] = \mathbf{R}\,e^{\theta x} \tag{12.102}$$

Using Taylor's theorem to expand $\mathbf{f}(D+\theta)$, and operating with the powers of D upon x gives

$$\mathbf{b}\,e^{\theta x}[\mathbf{f}(\theta)\mathbf{F}'(\theta) + \mathbf{f}'(\theta)\mathbf{F}(\theta) + x\mathbf{f}(\theta)\mathbf{F}(\theta)] = \mathbf{R}\,e^{\theta x} \tag{12.103}$$

Since
$$\mathbf{f}(\theta)\mathbf{F}(\theta) = \Delta(\theta) = 0$$

and
$$\mathbf{f}'(\theta)\mathbf{F}(\theta) + \mathbf{f}(\theta)\mathbf{F}'(\theta) = \Delta'(\theta)$$

equation (12.103) gives the value

$$\mathbf{b} = \mathbf{R}/\Delta'(\theta) \tag{12.104}$$

Hence the particular solution is

$$\{y_p\} = \frac{\mathbf{R}}{\Delta'(\theta)}[\mathbf{F}'(\theta) + x\mathbf{F}(\theta)]\, e^{\theta x} \tag{12.105}$$

Other forms for $\phi(x)$ can be treated in a similar manner to the corresponding forms of $\phi(x)$ in the inverse operator method (Section 2.5.5).

Finally, the complete solution is the sum of the complementary function and the particular integral as for linear differential equations.

Example. A battery of N stirred tank reactors are arranged to operate isothermally in series. Each reactor has a volume of V ft^3 and is equipped with a perfect agitator so that the composition of the reactor effluent is the same as the tank contents. If initially the tanks contain pure solvent only, and at a time designated t_0, q ft^3/min of a reactant A of concentration C_0 lb moles/ft^3 are fed to the first tank, estimate the time required for the concentration of A leaving the Nth tank to be C_N lb moles/ft^3.

The stoichiometry of the reaction is represented by the equation

$$A \underset{k_1'}{\overset{k_1}{\rightleftharpoons}} B \underset{k_2'}{\overset{k_2}{\rightleftharpoons}} C$$

All the reactions are first order and the feed to the reactor does not contain any product B or C, but is assumed to contain a catalyst that initiates the reaction as soon as the feed enters the first reactor.

Solution

The concentration of A will be written C_A
The concentration of B will be written C_B
The concentration of C will be written C_C.

Q

Then a mass balance on any tank n will be

$$V\frac{dC}{dt} = qC_{n-1} - qC_n - rV \qquad\qquad \text{I}$$

where r is the rate of chemical reaction.
For component A this gives

$$V\frac{dC_{A,n}}{dt} = qC_{A,n-1} - (qC_{A,n} + Vk_1C_{A,n} - Vk_1'C_{B,n}) \qquad\qquad \text{II}$$

for component B,

$$V\frac{dC_{B,n}}{dt} = qC_{B,n-1} - (qC_{B,n} + Vk_1'C_{B,n} + Vk_2C_{B,n} - Vk_1C_{A,n} - Vk_2'C_{C,n})$$

$$\text{III}$$

and for component C,

$$V\frac{dC_{C,n}}{dt} = qC_{C,n-1} - (qC_{C,n} + Vk_2'C_{C,n} - Vk_2C_{B,n}) \qquad\qquad \text{IV}$$

Dividing equations II, III, and IV by V and calling (V/q), θ the nominal holding time, gives

$$\frac{dC_{A,n}}{dt} = \frac{C_{A,n-1}}{\theta} - \left(\frac{1}{\theta} + k_1\right)C_{A,n} + k_1'C_{B,n} \qquad\qquad \text{V}$$

$$\frac{dC_{B,n}}{dt} = \frac{C_{B,n-1}}{\theta} - \left(\frac{1}{\theta} + k_2 + k_1'\right)C_{B,n} + k_1C_{A,n} + k_2'C_{C,n} \qquad\qquad \text{VI}$$

and

$$\frac{dC_{C,n}}{dt} = \frac{C_{C,n-1}}{\theta} - \left(\frac{1}{\theta} + k_2'\right)C_{C,n} + k_2C_{B,n} \qquad\qquad \text{VII}$$

Equations V, VI, and VII can be written in matrix form as follows

$$\frac{d}{dt}\begin{bmatrix} C_{A,n} \\ C_{B,n} \\ C_{C,n} \end{bmatrix} = \frac{1}{\theta}\begin{bmatrix} C_{A,n-1} \\ C_{B,n-1} \\ C_{C,n-1} \end{bmatrix} - \begin{bmatrix} (1/\theta + k_1) & -k_1' & 0 \\ -k_1 & (1/\theta + k_2 + k_1') & -k_2' \\ 0 & -k_2 & (1/\theta + k_2') \end{bmatrix}\begin{bmatrix} C_{A,n} \\ C_{B,n} \\ C_{C,n} \end{bmatrix}$$

$$\text{VIII}$$

or more concisely

$$\frac{d\mathbf{C}_n}{dt} = \frac{\mathbf{C}_{n-1}}{\theta} - \mathbf{GC}_n \qquad\qquad \text{IX}$$

where $\mathbf{C}_n$ and $\mathbf{C}_{n-1}$ are column vectors and $\mathbf{G}$ is a third order square matrix with constant elements. Equation IX can be applied to the first reactor thus

$$\frac{d\mathbf{C}_1}{dt} = \frac{\mathbf{C}_0}{\theta} - \mathbf{GC}_1 \qquad\qquad \text{X}$$

The solution of equation X is

$$C_1 = \frac{G^{-1}C_0}{\theta} + e^{-Gt}K_1 \qquad\qquad XI$$

where K_1 is the constant of integration.

When $\qquad\qquad\qquad t = 0, \qquad C_1 = 0$

$$\therefore \quad K_1 = -G^{-1}C_0/\theta \qquad\qquad XII$$

$$\therefore \quad C_1 = \frac{1}{\theta}(I - e^{-Gt})G^{-1}C_0 \qquad\qquad XIII$$

Applying equation IX to the second tank and substituting the expression for C_1 given by equation XIII gives

$$C_2 = \frac{G^{-2}C_0}{\theta^2} - \frac{G^{-1}C_0}{\theta^2}t\,e^{-Gt} + e^{-Gt}K_2 \qquad\qquad XIV$$

When $t = 0$, $C_2 = 0$

$$\therefore \quad K_2 = -G^{-2}C_0/\theta^2$$

and

$$C_2 = \frac{1}{\theta^2}(I - e^{-Gt} - Gt\,e^{-Gt})G^{-2}C_0 \qquad\qquad XV$$

Applying equation IX to the third tank, substituting the expression for C_2 and evaluating the constant of integration gives

$$C_3 = \frac{1}{\theta^3}\left[I - e^{-Gt} - \frac{(Gt)}{1!}e^{-Gt} - \frac{(Gt)^2}{2!}e^{-Gt}\right]G^{-3}C_0 \qquad\qquad XVI$$

Extending this to tank N by comparing equations XIII, XV, and XVI the concentration of the effluent from tank N is

$$C_N = \frac{G^{-N}C_0}{\theta^N} = \frac{e^{-Gt}}{\theta^N}\left[I + \frac{Gt}{1!} + \frac{(Gt)^2}{2!} + \dots + \frac{(Gt)^{N-1}}{(N-1)!}\right]G^{-N}C_0 \qquad XVII$$

By Sylvester's theorem (Section 12.15)

$$e^{-Gt} = -\sum_{j=1}^{3}e^{-\lambda_j t}\frac{F(\lambda_j)}{\Delta'(\lambda_j)} \qquad\qquad XVIII$$

on the assumption that all the latent roots of G are distinct, and therefore equation XVII can be written in the very useful form that

$$C_N = \frac{-1}{\theta^N}\sum_{j=1}^{3}\left(\frac{1}{\lambda_j}\right)^N\left\{1 - e^{-\lambda_j t}\sum_{i=0}^{N-1}\frac{(\lambda_j t)^i}{i!}\right\}\frac{F(\lambda_j)}{\Delta'(\lambda_j)}C_0 \qquad XIX$$

Equation XIX was initially derived by Acrivos and Amundson† who also present equations for the transient behaviour of plate extractors, absorbers, and distillation equipment. The reader interested in the further application of matrix analysis to the solution of stagewise processes is recommended to read this article.

† Acrivos, A. and Amundson, N. R. *I.E.C.* **47**, 1533 (1955).

12.20. CONCLUSIONS

This chapter has attempted to present the elements of matrix algebra and calculus which has had to be concise because of the limited space available for this topic. The reader may draw the conclusion that the arithmetic involved will be exorbitant. This is true, but when one considers that these methods can be used in conjunction with high speed digital computers it will be appreciated that the arithmetic need not prevent these methods being applied. Equation XIX in the above example looks quite formidable, but when used in conjunction with a computer the value of C_N for different process conditions and a large number of tanks is quickly obtained.

Chapter 13

OPTIMIZATION

13.1. Introduction

OPTIMIZATION in the chemical process industries infers the selection of equipment and operating conditions for the production of a given material so that the profit will be a maximum. This could be interpreted as meaning the maximum output of a particular substance for a given capital outlay, or the minimum investment for a specified production rate. The former is a mathematical problem of evaluating the appropriate values of a set of variables to maximize a dependent variable, whereas the latter may be considered to be one of locating a minimum value. However, in terms of the profit, both types of problem are maximization problems, and the solution of both is generally accomplished by means of an economic balance between capital and operating costs. Such a balance can be represented as shown in Fig. 13.1 in which the capital, operating and total costs are plotted against

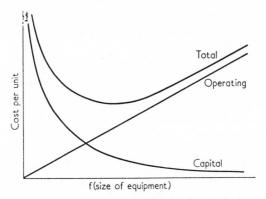

Fig. 13.1. Economic balance of process

f (size of equipment), where f (size of equipment) implies some function of the size of the equipment. It could be the actual size of the equipment; number of pieces of equipment such as number of stirred tank reactors in a reactor battery or frames in a filter press; or some parameter related to the size of the equipment such as the reflux ratio in a distillation unit, or the solvent to feed ratio in a solvent extraction process.

In certain circumstances it is unnecessary to make a complete economic balance involving all the variables of a process. Thus, in Section 9.6.3,

the number of stirred tank reactors for the maximum output of a product B
for the chemical reaction

$$A \rightarrow B \rightarrow C \tag{13.1}$$

was evaluated without cost data. This was possible because in the example
quoted the size of the reaction vessels was specified. If vessel size was
included as a parameter in the analysis, an economic balance would have been
necessary. That does not mean to say that in the example quoted a " non
problem " was solved because in the chemical industry it is possible that the
equipment will already exist, and the engineer is expected to find the optimum
operating conditions. Hence problems involving two variables are worth
considering initially, even though in the majority of problems encountered
more than two variables will be required to describe the process, or operation
adequately. However, before attempting this, it is necessary to classify
different types of optimization.

13.2. TYPES OF OPTIMIZATION

Optimization in the chemical field can be divided into two classes which
have been defined by Himsworth† as

(i) Static optimization
(ii) Dynamic optimization.

13.2.1. *Static Optimization*

Static optimization is the establishment of the most suitable steady state
operation conditions of the process. These include optimum size of equipment and production levels, in addition to temperatures, pressures and
flow rates. They would be established by setting up the best possible
mathematical model of the process which is maximized by some suitable
technique to give the most favourable operating conditions. These conditions would be nominal conditions and would not take into account
fluctuations in the process about these nominal conditions.

13.2.2. *Dynamic Optimization*

Dynamic optimization is the establishment of the best procedure for
correcting the fluctuations in the process conditions about the nominal
conditions established in the static optimization analysis. It requires a knowledge of the dynamic characteristics of the equipment and also necessitates
predicting the best way in which a change in the process conditions can be
corrected. In reality it is an extension of the automatic control analysis of
the process.

In addition to the above types of optimization there are the operational
research aspects, but these are common to many industries and will not be
discussed in this text.

† Himsworth, F. R. *Trans. Inst. Chem. Eng.* **40**, 345 (1962).

13.3. Analytical Procedures

When a process can be described by a small number of variables, it is possible to find the maxima or minima by differentiating and equating the resulting expressions to zero. These are then solved in order to find the optimum conditions. However, as the number of variables increases, the solution of the resulting equations becomes prohibitive. Therefore analytical optimization procedures have limited applicability, but they deserve brief consideration.

13.3.1. *Problems Involving Two Variables*

On rare occasions it is possible to establish the optimum conditions of a process or operation by determining the maxima of an equation containing one independent and one dependent variable. For example the optimum number of stirred tanks was evaluated by solution of such an equation in Section 9.6.3 and has been referred to above. The reader will be familiar with the technique of differentiating and equating to zero to find the maxima or minima and it need not be repeated here. However, it must be emphasized that such an optimum will in all probability be a " curtailed optimum ", and should be treated cautiously because one or two parameters have been specified arbitrarily.

13.3.2. *Problems Involving Three Variables*

Many engineering operations of a simple type can be optimized by solution of an equation containing two independent variables. Thus let an operation be represented by the equation

$$z = f(x, y) \tag{13.2}$$

where x and y are the two independent variables. Equation (13.2) can be expressed in three dimensions by a surface in which the maximum value of z will be represented by the peak of a mountain. Similarly the minimum will be the lowest point of the bowl in the surface. Mathematically this means that for z to be a maximum at a point (x, y) it is obvious that the function $f(x, y)$ must be a maximum for displacements away from the point in any direction. That is, the conditions

$$\frac{\partial z}{\partial x} = 0 \qquad \text{and } \frac{\partial z}{\partial y} = 0 \tag{13.3}$$

must be satisfied simultaneously, which means that the tangent plane to the surface expressed by equation (13.2) is horizontal. In the case of functions of one independent variable, the first derivative vanishes at a maximum, a minimum, or a point of inflexion; these being resolved by reference to the second derivative. Similarly in the case of two independent variables, there may be a true maximum in the surface where all sections exhibit a maximum, a true minimum, or the two orthogonal sections may be any combination of maximum, minimum, and point of inflexion. The special combination of a maximum with respect to x and a minimum with respect to y is termed a

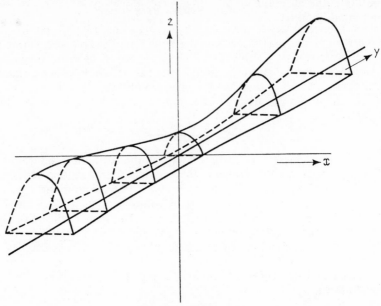

FIG. 13.2   Saddle point

" saddle point " and is illustrated in Fig. 13.2. To ensure that a particular point is actually a maximum or minimum, it is necessary to fulfil the conditions stated below.

Consider Fig. 13.3 in which z is represented as a function of position over the xy plane. Let P be any point in the plane and let the value of z change

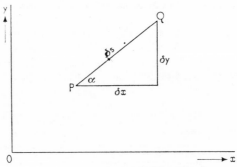

FIG. 13.3.   Directional derivatives

at different rates as the function moves away from P in different directions. If PQ is one direction, the derivative of z in that direction may be defined as

$$\lim_{Q \to P} \left[\frac{f(x, y)_Q - f(x, y)_P}{PQ} \right] \tag{13.4}$$

where PQ is the absolute length between the points P and Q. Let this be δs and in addition let

$$f(x, y)_Q - f(x, y)_P = \delta z \tag{13.5}$$

Then the derivative of z in the direction PQ is

$$\lim_{Q \to P} \frac{\delta z}{\delta s}$$

But

$$\delta z = \frac{\partial z}{\partial x} \delta x + \frac{\partial z}{\partial y} \delta y$$

$$\therefore \quad \frac{dz}{ds} = \lim_{Q \to P} \frac{\delta z}{\delta s} = \frac{\partial z}{\partial x} \frac{\delta x}{\delta s} + \frac{\partial z}{\partial y} \frac{\delta y}{\delta s} \tag{13.6}$$

but from Fig. 13.3

$$\frac{\delta x}{\delta s} = \cos \alpha \quad \text{and} \quad \frac{\delta y}{\delta s} = \sin \alpha \tag{13.7}$$

hence

$$\frac{dz}{ds} = \frac{\partial z}{\partial x} \cdot \cos \alpha + \frac{\partial z}{\partial y} \sin \alpha \tag{13.8}$$

where $\partial z/\partial x$ and $\partial z/\partial y$ are the derivatives in the x and y directions. The condition for a maximum or minimum is that equation (13.3) is satisfied irrespective of the value of α. Differentiating equation (13.8) with respect to s gives

$$\frac{d^2 z}{ds^2} = \frac{d}{ds}\left(\frac{dz}{ds}\right) = \frac{d}{ds}\left(\cos \alpha \frac{\partial z}{\partial x} + \sin \alpha \frac{\partial z}{\partial y}\right)$$

$$= \cos \alpha \frac{\partial^2 z}{\partial x^2} \frac{\partial x}{\partial s} + \cos \alpha \frac{\partial^2 z}{\partial x \partial y} \frac{\partial y}{\partial s} + \sin \alpha \frac{\partial^2 z}{\partial x \partial y} \frac{\partial x}{\partial s} + \sin \alpha \frac{\partial^2 z}{\partial y^2} \frac{\partial y}{\partial s} \tag{13.9}$$

since $\dfrac{d}{ds}\left(\dfrac{dz}{ds}\right)$ is the total differential of $\dfrac{dz}{ds}$ with respect to s. But equations (13.7) give the derivatives of x and y with respect to s in terms of α, therefore

$$\frac{d^2 z}{ds^2} = \cos^2 \alpha \frac{\partial^2 z}{\partial x^2} + 2 \sin \alpha \cos \alpha \frac{\partial^2 z}{\partial x \partial y} + \sin^2 \alpha \frac{\partial^2 z}{\partial y^2} \tag{13.10}$$

For any value of α, $d^2 z/ds^2 > 0$ for z to be a minimum and $d^2 z/ds^2 < 0$ for z to be a maximum. That is $d^2 z/ds^2$ must have the same sign for all values of α. Thus letting

$$z_{xx} = \frac{\partial^2 z}{\partial x^2}; \qquad z_{xy} = \frac{\partial^2 z}{\partial x \partial y}; \qquad z_{yy} = \frac{\partial^2 z}{\partial y^2}$$

substituting into equation (13.10) and dividing by z_{xx} gives

$$\frac{d^2 z}{ds^2} = \frac{1}{z_{xx}}\left[(\cos \alpha \, z_{xx} + \sin \alpha \, z_{xy})^2 + (z_{xx} z_{yy} - z_{xy}^2) \sin^2 \alpha\right] \tag{13.11}$$

It can be seen from equation (13.11) that if $z_{xx} z_{yy} > z_{xy}^2$ the terms inside the square bracket will be greater than zero for all values of α, and d^2z/ds^2 will have the same sign as z_{xx}.

If z_{xx} is negative, z will be a maximum.

If z_{xx} is positive, z will be minimum.

In the special case $z_{xx}z_{yy} = z_{xy}^2$, there will be some values for α which exhibit a point of inflexion whereas all other values of α give a consistent maximum or minimum. If $z_{xx}z_{yy} < z_{xy}^2$, the surface has a saddle point.

The above principles of maxima and minima have been used by Jenson and Jeffreys[†] for the evaluation of the optimum number of stages in solvent extraction processes. The analysis for counter current processes is as follows.

Consider a feed solution containing X_0 lb solute per lb of solute-free liquor to be fed to stage 1 of a countercurrent extraction process at the rate of C lb/h on a solute-free basis. Let the process contain N stages and let an extracting solvent be fed into stage N at the rate of B lb/h on a solute-free basis. The solvent passes countercurrent to the feed liquor through the plant, finally emerging as the final extract from stage 1. The spent feed will be discharged from stage N with a solute concentration X_N. The carrier liquor of the feed will be assumed to be immiscible in the extracting solvent.

Assume that the feed rate and the solute content of the feed are constant and let the unit cost of the feed in any system of currency be γ per lb of solute. Let the total hourly cost of each stage including operation, fixed charges, and the depreciation of capital be α. Finally let the cost of the solvent, including recovery from the final extract and make-up of spillage losses, be β per lb of solvent. Then on the basis of one hour's operation:

$$\text{Cost of feed is} \qquad \gamma C X_0 \qquad (13.12)$$

$$\text{Cost of solvent is} \quad \beta B \qquad (13.13)$$

Similarly if λ is the value of $1\cdot0$ lb of extract product, the total value of the product is

$$\lambda C(X_0 - X_N) \qquad (13.14)$$

and the hourly profit from the process is given by

$$P = \lambda C(X_0 - X_N) - (\alpha N + \beta B + \gamma C X_0) \qquad (13.15)$$

But X_N is related to X_0 by

$$X_N = X_0 \left[\frac{S^{N+1} - S^N}{S^{N+1} - 1} \right] \quad \text{(see Section 9.6.3)} \qquad (13.16)$$

where $S = \dfrac{C}{mB}$ and m is the distribution ratio.

Substitution of equation (13.16) into (13.15) gives

$$P = \lambda C X_0 \left[\frac{S^N - 1}{S^{N+1} - 1} \right] - \left[\gamma C X_0 + \alpha N + \beta B \right] \qquad (13.17)$$

in which the variables are N and B. The maximum value of P is obtained

† Jenson, V. G. and Jeffreys, G. V. *Brit. Chem. Eng.* **6,** 676 (1960).

by the procedure presented above. Thus

$$\frac{\partial P}{\partial N} = \lambda C X_0 S^N \left[\frac{S-1}{(S^{N+1}-1)^2}\right] \ln S - \alpha = 0 \qquad (13.18)$$

From which

$$\frac{\alpha}{\lambda C X_0} = \frac{S^N(S-1)\ln S}{(S^{N+1}-1)^2} \qquad (13.19)$$

and

$$\frac{\partial P}{\partial B} = \lambda C X_0 \left[\frac{N(S^{N+1}-1)S^{N-1}-(N+1)(S^N-1)S^N}{(S^{N+1}-1)^2}\right]\left(\frac{-mS^2}{C}\right) - \beta = 0 \qquad (13.20)$$

or

$$\frac{\beta}{\lambda m X_0} = S^{N+1}\left[\frac{(S^{N+1}+N-NS-S)}{(S^{N+1}-1)^2}\right] \qquad (13.21)$$

In equations (13.19) and (13.21) the cost terms have been separated from the process terms. They are two complex simultaneous algebraic equations that will be difficult to solve analytically, but since N is a whole number, an approximate but sufficiently accurate solution can be obtained as follows.

The right-hand sides of equations (13.19) and (13.21) can be evaluated for any pair of values of S and N to give a numerical value for each of the dimensionless cost groups $\frac{\alpha}{\lambda C X_0}$ and $\frac{\beta}{\lambda m X_0}$. Hence by taking a series of pairs of values of S and N repeating the calculations, a contour chart can be drawn for each cost group using S as ordinate and N as abscissa. Such contour charts have been prepared by the above authors for values of N ranging from 0 to 20 and values of S between 0 and 2; these are shown in Figs. 13.4 and 13.5.

In a particular example the basic cost terms would be known enabling the cost groups to be evaluated, and for these values equation (13.19) is satisfied along one curve in Fig. 13.4 and equation (13.21) satisfied along a curve in Fig. 13.5. Both equations can only be satisfied simultaneously at the point of intersection of these two chosen curves. This point is easily located by superimposing the two contour charts as shown in Fig. 13.6 and the coordinates of the point of intersection give the modified solvent to feed ratio and number of ideal stages for optimum operation.

Figure 13.6 is an accurate version of the graphical solution in which the values of S have been restricted to between 0 and 1.0 since for conventional solvent extraction this is considered to be the most applicable range.

The procedure applied to the optimization of counter flow extraction using Fig. 13.6 is perfectly general and the figure has universal application for the evaluation of the optimum solvent to feed ratio and number of ideal stages. The technique employed of using contour charts can be extended to other fields of chemical engineering.

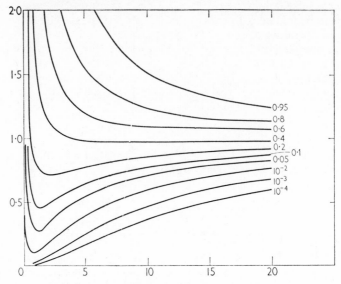

FIG. 13.4. Contour chart of equation (13.19)

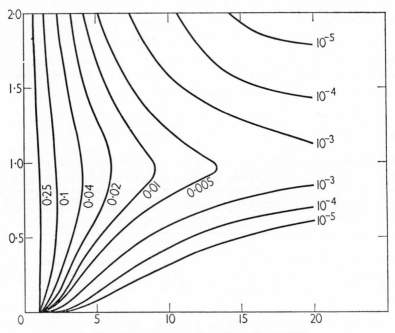

FIG. 13.5. Contour chart of equation (13.21)

Example. 8000 lb/h of a 5% by weight solution of acetaldehyde in toluene is to be treated with water to extract the acetaldehyde. If the annual capital and operating costs per stage are estimated to be £1600, the cost of supplying, pumping and regenerating the solvent from the final extract is estimated to be £4·5 per ton, and the value of the acetaldehyde is taken to be £155 per ton; what is the optimum number of stages and quantity of solvent required for the process. The distribution ratio of weight of acetaldehyde in water to acetaldehyde in toluene may be considered constant at 2·2.

Solution

5% feed solution gives $X_0 = 0·053$.

$CX_0 = 400$ lb/h.

$\alpha = 4$s. per day: $\beta = 0·0402$s. per lb: $\lambda = 1·384$s. per lb.

FIG. 13.6. Optimization chart

$$\therefore \quad \frac{\alpha}{\lambda C X_0} = 0\cdot0072 \quad \text{and} \quad \frac{\beta}{\lambda m X_0} = 0\cdot251$$

From Fig. 13.6

$$N = 10 \text{ or } 11 \text{ stages}$$
$$S = 0\cdot9 \equiv 3840 \text{ lb/h of solvent}$$

13.3.3. Problems Involving Four Variables

The analytical procedure presented above can be extended to four variables. That is, the maximum or minimum values of

$$w = f(x, y, z) \tag{13.22}$$

can be located by differentiating equation (13.22) and equating to zero. Thus

$$dw = \frac{\partial f}{\partial x} dx + \frac{\partial f}{\partial y} dy + \frac{\partial f}{\partial z} dz = 0 \tag{13.23}$$

when the conditions

$$\frac{\partial f}{\partial x} = 0; \quad \frac{\partial f}{\partial y} = 0; \quad \frac{\partial f}{\partial z} = 0 \tag{13.24}$$

are satisfied.

In problems containing four or more variables, the analytical solution becomes increasingly complex and impracticable. Therefore, other techniques of optimization must be applied, and these will be considered in later sections of this chapter.

13.3.4. Optimization with a Restrictive Condition

In some optimization problems a relationship must be satisfied by the independent variables. In vapour-liquid equilibria for example, the temperature, pressure, and compositions of liquid and vapour are related by the boiling point condition. One variable, say temperature, can always be eliminated analytically, but this may not be algebraically convenient, and an alternative method is available.

Thus consider equation (13.22) with the restrictive condition

$$g(x, y, z) = 0 \tag{13.25}$$

Differentiating equation (13.25) gives

$$\frac{\partial g}{\partial x} dx + \frac{\partial g}{\partial y} dy + \frac{\partial g}{\partial z} dz = 0 \tag{13.26}$$

At the optimum point, equations (13.23) and (13.26) must be satisfied for displacements in any direction, and in particular for $dx = 0$. Hence the equations

$$\frac{\partial f}{\partial y} dy + \frac{\partial f}{\partial z} dz = 0 \tag{13.27}$$

$$\frac{\partial g}{\partial y} dy + \frac{\partial g}{\partial z} dz = 0 \tag{13.28}$$

must be consistent. This is only possible if

$$\frac{\partial f}{\partial y} + \lambda \frac{\partial g}{\partial y} = 0 \quad \text{and} \quad \frac{\partial f}{\partial z} + \lambda \frac{\partial g}{\partial z} = 0 \qquad (13.29)$$

By relaxing the conditions that $dx = 0$, and imposing the condition $dy = 0$, it follows that

$$\frac{\partial f}{\partial x} + \lambda \frac{\partial g}{\partial x} = 0 \qquad \text{13.30)}$$

Equations (13.29) and (13.30) can be obtained by optimizing the function

$$W = f(x, y, z) + \lambda g(x, y, z) \qquad (13.31)$$

when the optimum point is given by the solution of the equations

$$\left.\begin{aligned}
\frac{\partial f}{\partial x} + \lambda \frac{\partial g}{\partial x} &= 0 \\[2mm]
\frac{\partial f}{\partial y} + \lambda \frac{\partial g}{\partial y} &= 0 \\[2mm]
\frac{\partial f}{\partial z} + \lambda \frac{\partial g}{\partial z} &= 0 \\[2mm]
g(x, y, z) &= 0
\end{aligned}\right\} \qquad (13.32)$$

which contain the four unknowns (x, y, z, λ). λ is known as a " Lagrange multiplier ". The above method can be extended to two restrictive conditions by introducing two arbitrary multipliers.

13.4. The Method of Steepest Ascent

The method of steepest ascent is one of the best known methods of optimization when the number of variables involved is large. The procedure was developed by Box and his co-workers.† Essentially the method consists of defining the criterion to be maximized as the " response " of the process. This may be the profit, the yield, or the output from a process and will depend on a number of factors such as temperature, concentration, pressure, etc. The relationship between the response and these factors can be written in the form

$$\eta = f(x_1, x_2, x_3, \ldots, x_n) \qquad (13.33)$$

which is called the "'response function "
The response function can be plotted in terms of two of the factors to give what is known as the " response surface ". Such a surface will be undulating and reaching the optimum will correspond to climbing the highest hill on the surface. Generally speaking the greatest gradient will be in the direction of the maximum, and therefore if the steepest ascent can be

† Box, G. E. P. and Wilson, K. B. *J. Statistical Soc.* **1,** B13 (1951).

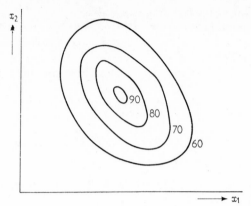

Fig. 13.7.   Response contour map

located on a response surface, it will lead in the direction of the optimum response. However it is very difficult to represent a surface on paper, consequently it is advantageous to plot the surface in the form of lines of equal response on a graph whose coordinates are two of the variables. These lines are called " response contours " and are shown in Fig. 13.7. The line of steepest ascent starting from any point is obtained by trial by drawing lines perpendicular to the contours. These lines will show the extent to which the different factors must be varied in order to give a maximum increase in the response.

This procedure will only direct the way to the optimum conditions since at the maximum the gradient is zero, and as the maximum is approached the line of steepest ascent becomes more difficult to predict. Hence this

Fig. 13.8.   Yield contours of chloramine synthesis

method alone will not locate the maximum but will rapidly show the engineer the region of optimum conditions. This technique was employed by Jeffreys, Ellis and Wharton† in establishing the optimum conditions for the preparation of chloramine from sodium hypochlorite and ammonia. Some of their results are shown in Fig. 13.8 where it can be seen that yield contours have been drawn in between the experimental results denoted by points. It can be seen that the maximum yield is obtained at low hypochlorite concentration irrespective of the ammonia concentration.

13.5. The Sequential Simplex Method

This method is an extension of the steepest ascent method and was proposed by Himsworth.‡ It differs from the above method in that no attempt is made to find the lines of steepest ascent, but rather that a rapid determination is made of a direction which is steep although not necessarily the steepest, so that moves are made frequently in a favourable direction.

For a process involving two variables the procedure is as follows. In Fig. 13.9, three points are selected fairly close together in such a manner

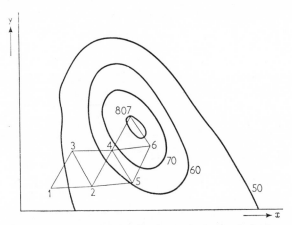

Fig. 13.9. The sequential simplex method of optimization

that they form the vertices of an equilateral triangle. Let these be points 1, 2, and 3. Following this, three further points are selected such that each one forms an equilateral triangle with any two of the first three points. If the response surface is locally a plane or nearly so, one of the possible new points will give a higher result than the other two, and furthermore the point 4 will be a " mirror image " to the lowest point in the first triangle. Hence after the first three trials the point giving the lowest results is rejected and

† Jeffreys, G. V., Ellis, S. R. M. and Wharton, T. H. " Rashig Synthesis of Hydrazine ". *I.E.C.* (Process Design Section) to be published.
‡ Himsworth, F. R. *Trans. Inst. Chem. Eng.* **40,** 345 (1952).

replaced by the mirror image point forming the second triangle. This construction process is repeated until the summit is reached. Thus as long as the surface is sloping and reasonably plane over the area of a particular triangle, each step in the construction leads to a more favourable region and the path taken from the starting point will zig-zag about the line of steepest ascent.

For a system containing more than two variables, the procedure will be similar except that $(k+1)$ trial points will be made, where k is the number of variables. The most favourable of these points is retained to replace the appropriate member of the original set, thus completing a move towards the optimum. The $(k+1)$ points correspond to the vertices of a regular simplex in k dimensions. Hence the name of the optimizing technique.

It is claimed that this method has the following advantages:

   (i) The calculations are elementary requiring no mathematical or statistical knowledge.
  (ii) Each move is determined by the previous result and therefore human judgement is eliminated.
 (iii) It is possible to add a variable at any time.
 (iv) A numerical measure of the response is not required. It is only necessary to rank the result and discard the lowest.

13.6. Dynamic Programming

This method is probably the most powerful method of optimization and has been developed by Bellman.[†] It finds considerable application in the optimization of multi-stage processes with no feedback such as stirred tank reactor batteries, crossflow extractors and whole chemical processes. Thus dynamic programming formulation reduces a classical problem containing N variables to N problems containing one variable, and when this technique is used in conjunction with high speed computers it offers a powerful method of solving "multi-dimensional" constrained optimization problems encountered in chemical engineering.

In this section it is only possible to introduce the elements of dynamic programming, and therefore any reader wishing to acquire a greater knowledge of this optimization technique should consult Bellman's text book referred to above, and also "The Optimal Design of Chemical Reactors" by Aris.[‡] However, for an understanding of the basis of this technique certain terms and definitions must be understood and these will be considered initially. Thus consider a multi-stage chemical engineering process, as for example a cross flow extraction plant into which a feed of known composition is fed continuously at a constant rate. This feed enters stage 1 and mass transfer occurs to produce an extract and raffinate. The raffinate will pass to the next stage for further treatment and will subsequently emerge from

---

† Bellman, R., " Dynamic Programming ". Princetown University Press (1957).
‡ Aris, R., " The Optimal Design of Chemical Reactors ". Academic Press (1960).

stage N with considerably reduced concentration of solute, it is hoped. Extraction will occur in each stage and the extent of extraction will depend on the interfacial area (a function of agitation), on the solubility and the temperature, etc., which are variables selected by the chemical engineer. That is the selection of the process variables calls for decisions to be taken at each stage, and these decisions affect the change in composition of the raffinate produced by any one stage. Since the raffinate passes through each stage in turn these decisions affect the state of the final raffinate from the process. The set of all decisions taken is called the " operating policy " or simply the policy and the set of decisions that optimizes the extraction process is called " the optimal policy ".

Bellman[†] stated that the essential condition of an optimal policy was that whatever the transformation that took place in the first stage of an N stage process, the remaining stages must make use of an optimal $(N-1)$-stage policy with respect to the state of the product from the first stage, if the whole process is to operate at optimum conditions. Furthermore, by varying the operating conditions of the first stage systematically and employing the optimal $(N-1)$-stage policy for the remaining stages it will be possible to find the optimum policy for all N stages of the process. By applying these concepts to a one-stage process, then a two-stage process and so on until all the N stages have been considered, it is possible to establish the optimal policy for any number of stages in a process provided that there is no feedback.

The advantage of analyzing an optimization problem in this way is that it is only necessary to vary the operating parameters of one stage at a time. For example, if there are p operating variables to each stage of a process, and the difficulty of evaluating the state of the product from a stage for one set of conditions of the p operating variables is measured by a constant A; the determination of the optimum operating conditions for the whole process for a given feed state will involve NA^p mathematical operations by dynamic programming, whereas the classical solution of the same problem would require A^{Np} mathematical operations. This constitutes considerable saving of mathematical effort and computing time.

Aris, Bellman and Kalaba[‡] illustrated the principles of dynamic programming in a simple manner by evaluating the minimum energy required for the compression of a gas from P_0 to P_N in an N stage compressor with perfect interstage cooling. Thus consider the operation of a gas compressor containing N stages with perfect intercooling so that the temperature of the gas is the same at the entrance to each stage. Let the fixed charges on the compressor depend on the number of stages, but be independent of the interstage pressures employed. Furthermore let the cost of cooling be a fixed charge included as part of the stage cost. Then the problem becomes the

† Bellman, R., *op. cit.*
‡ Aris, R., Bellman, R. and Kalaba, R., " C.E.P. Symposium Series ". **56, No. 31,** 95 (1960).

determination of the interstage pressure ratio for which the energy consumption is a minimum. Thus the total energy consumed by an N stage compressor is

$$E_N = \frac{nRT\gamma}{\gamma-1}\left[\left(\frac{p_1}{p_0}\right)^{(\gamma-1)/\gamma} + \left(\frac{p_2}{p_1}\right)^{(\gamma-1)/\gamma} + \dots + \left(\frac{p_N}{p_{N-1}}\right)^{(\gamma-1)/\gamma} - N\right] \quad (13.34)$$

Let

$$K = \frac{nRT\gamma}{\gamma-1}: \quad \alpha = \frac{\gamma-1}{\gamma}: \quad r_i = \frac{p_i}{p_{i-1}}$$

which on substitution into equation (13.34) gives

$$E_N = K\left(\sum_{i=1}^{N} r_i^\alpha - N\right) \quad (13.35)$$

Also

$$r_1\, r_2\, r_3 \dots r_N = \prod_{i=1}^{N} r_i = \frac{p_N}{p_0} = r \quad \text{(say)} \quad (13.36)$$

For one stage

$$r_{1,1} = p_N/p_0$$

and

$$E_1 = K(r_1^\alpha - 1) \quad (13.37)$$

which is the only solution.

For two stages

$$r_{2,1} = \frac{p_1}{p_0} \qquad r_{2,2} = \frac{p_N}{p_1}$$

and

$$E_2 = K\left[\left(\frac{p_1}{p_0}\right)^\alpha + \left(\frac{p_N}{p_1}\right)^\alpha - 2\right] \quad (13.38)$$

The only variable is p_1, hence

$$\frac{dE_2}{dp_1} = K\left[\frac{\alpha}{p_1}\left(\frac{p_1}{p_0}\right)^\alpha - \frac{\alpha}{p_1}\left(\frac{p_N}{p_1}\right)^\alpha\right] = 0 \quad (13.39)$$

$$\therefore \quad \frac{p_1}{p_0} = \frac{p_N}{p_1} \quad (13.40)$$

The optimal policy is to choose $r_{2,1} = r_{2,2}$ and this gives an optimum energy consumption denoted by $f_2(r)$ where r from equation (13.36) is the pressure ratio across the two stages.

For three stages

$$r_{3,1} = \frac{p_1}{p_0}, \qquad r_{3,2} = \frac{p_2}{p_1}, \qquad r_{3,3} = \frac{p_N}{p_2}$$

The energy consumption in the first stage will be

$$E_{3,1} = K(r_{3,1}^\alpha - 1) \quad (13.41)$$

but the optimal policy for the other two stages has already been determined, and the optimal energy consumption is

$$_2\left(\frac{p_N}{p_1}\right) = f_2\left(\frac{r}{r_{3,1}}\right)$$

The optimal three-stage policy will be obtained from

$$f_3(r) = \underset{r_{3,1}}{\text{Min}} \left[K(r_{3,1}^\alpha - 1) + f_2(r/r_{3,1}) \right] \tag{13.42}$$

where $r_{3,1}$ is the only variable.

For k stages.

The optimal policy for $(k-1)$ stages will have been determined, and the optimal energy consumption for the latter $(k-1)$ stages will be $f_{k-1}(r/r_{k,1})$. The energy consumed in the first stage will be

$$E_{k,1} = K(r_{k,1}^\alpha - 1) \tag{13.43}$$

hence the optimal k stage policy will be determined by

$$f_k(r) = \underset{r_{k,1}}{\text{Min}} \left[K(r_{k,1}^\alpha - 1) + f_{k-1}(r/r_{k,1}) \right] \tag{13.44}$$

By repeated application of equation (13.44), the N dimensional problem with no feedback has been converted into a sequence of N one dimensional problems. Generally at this point, solution of the equations would be made by means of a digital computer, but in this particular problem an analytical solution is possible which can be found in most texts on chemical engineering thermodynamics.† The solution will show that the pressure will be the same for each stage.

To conclude this introduction to dynamic programming, consider the optimization of a cross flow extraction process.

Example. In a cross flow extraction process, a solute B is to be extracted form its solution in a parent liquid C by means of a solvent A which is completely immiscible with C. The feed rate to the process is to be q lb/h and W lb/h of solvent are to be distributed between the N stages of the process in order to obtain the maximum amount of extract product. The cost of pumping, regenerating and providing make-up solvent may be taken to be a fraction (λ) of the value of the extract.

The equilibrium relation of the solute B between the phases is

$$y_n = m x_n$$

Solution

A mass balance over stage n in the process is

$$q(x_{n-1} - x_n) = w_n y_n \qquad\qquad \text{I}$$

Since the phases are immiscible q is constant; therefore for any stage n let

$$\frac{w_n}{q} = v_n \qquad\qquad \text{II}$$

so that $\qquad\qquad x_{n-1} - x_n = v_n y_n \qquad\qquad \text{III}$

Since the cost of pumping, etc. of the solvent is to be a fraction λ of the value

† Dodge, B., " Chemical Engineering Thermodynamics ". McGraw Hill, New York (1944).

of the extract, the problem can be treated as one in which the quantity of solvent fed to each stage is such that the profit is a maximum. That is the profit is $P_N(x_0)$

$$P_N(x_0) = q(x_0 - x_N) - \lambda \sum_1^N w_n \qquad \text{IV}$$

$$= q \sum_1^N [(x_{n-1} - x_n) - \lambda v_n] \qquad \text{V}$$

$$= q \sum_1^N v_n(y_n - \lambda) \qquad \text{VI}$$

Now let
$$P_N(x_0) = \operatorname*{Max}_{v_n} \sum_1^N v_n(y_n - \lambda) \qquad \text{VII}$$

Then the functional equation corresponding to the formalism of dynamic programming is that

$$P_N(x_0) = \operatorname*{Max}_{v_1} [P_{N-1}(x_1) + v_1(y_1 - \lambda)] \qquad \text{VIII}$$

where
$$x_1 = x_0 - v_1 y_1 = \frac{y_1}{m} \qquad \text{IX}$$

and
$$P_0(x_0) = 0 \qquad \text{X}$$

From equation IX,

$$x_1 = \frac{x_0}{mv_1 + 1} \quad \text{and} \quad y_1 = \frac{mx_0}{mv_1 + 1} \qquad \text{XI}$$

Substituting into equation VII gives for stage 1,

$$P_1(x_0) = \operatorname*{Max}_{v_1} \left[v_1 \left(\frac{mx_0}{mv_1 + 1} - \lambda \right) \right] \qquad \text{XII}$$

Differentiating with respect to v_1 gives

$$\frac{dP_1}{dv_1} = \left(\frac{mx_0}{mv_1 + 1} - \lambda \right) - v_1 \frac{m^2 x_0}{(mv_1 + 1)^2} = 0 \qquad \text{XIII}$$

or
$$mx_0 - \lambda(mv_1 + 1)^2 = 0 \qquad \text{XIV}$$

from which, with the aid of equation XI

$$v_1 = \sqrt{\frac{x_0}{m\lambda}} - \frac{1}{m}; \qquad x_1 = \sqrt{\frac{x_0 \lambda}{m}}; \qquad y_1 = \sqrt{\lambda m x_0} \qquad \text{XV}$$

Substituting the terms in equations XV into equation VII with $N = 1$ gives

$$P_1(x_0) = x_0 - 2\sqrt{x_0 \lambda / m} + \lambda / m \qquad \text{XVI}$$

Using the functional equation VIII on stage 2 gives

$$P_2(x_0) = \operatorname*{Max}_{v_1} \left[v_1 \left(\frac{mx_0}{mv_1 + 1} - \lambda \right) + P_1(x_1) \right] \qquad \text{XVII}$$

whence by differentiating equation XVII in a manner similar to that already presented,

$$v_1 = \sqrt[3]{\frac{x_0}{m^2\lambda}} - \frac{1}{m}; \qquad x_1 = \sqrt[3]{\frac{x_0^2\lambda}{m}}; \qquad y_1 = \sqrt[3]{m^2 x_0^2 \lambda} \qquad \text{XVIII}$$

and

$$P_2(x_0) = x_0 - 3\sqrt[3]{\frac{x_0\lambda^2}{m^2}} + \frac{2\lambda}{m} \qquad \text{XIX}$$

The flow ratio v_2 is obtained from the functional equation VIII by considering the second stage to be using an optimal one-stage policy with a feed of composition x_1. Then by repeating the procedure given above, it can be shown that

$$v_2 = v_1 = \sqrt[3]{\frac{x_0}{m^2\lambda}} - \frac{1}{m} \qquad \text{XX}$$

That is, for the two-stage policy the ratio of solvent to raffinate rate to each stage must be the same, or extending this concept to N stages, the optimal policy is obtained by dividing the total quantity of solvent available equally between the N stages.

The above problem was presented by Aris *et al.*† and extended to more complex crossflow extractions in which the solvent and the parent liquid in the feed to the process are partially miscible, and the equilibrium is not represented by a straight line. Solution of such problems can only be solved by computer and these authors did in fact use a Univac Scientific Computer Model 1103.

† Aris, R., Rudd, D. F. and Amundson, N. R. *Chem. Eng. Sci.* **12**, 88 (1960).

Chapter 14

COMPUTERS

14.1. INTRODUCTION

IN engineering mathematics, the need for numerical calculation constantly arises. For instance in the method of Frobenius and separation of variables, terms of an infinite series have to be evaluated for many values of the variables. In addition, the solution of difference equations by graphical methods (Section 9.7.1) is a less accurate but more convenient way than the corresponding numerical method of successive substitution. Much numerical work is involved in inverting and multiplying matrices, but the most arduous computation occurs in the numerical methods of Chapter 11. Because arithmetical operations are basically simple, and desk calculating machines and slide rules are in everyday use, the complete mechanization of arithmetic has been a natural consequence. The development has taken place along two channels leading to analogue computers and digital computers. Whereas the analogue computer is a development of the slide rule principle, the digital computer is a development of the desk calculating machine. The slide rule operates by representing each number by a geometrical length, a particular length on one scale always representing the same series of digits. The basic scales are logarithmic, but most slide rules have double logarithmic scales, and scales with varying lengths representing the logarithmic unit (i.e. squares, cubes). The principle is to replace a number by an equivalent length, and to calculate in terms of these lengths. In the general purpose analogue computer, each number is replaced by an equivalent electrical potential, and the calculation is then performed electrically in terms of these potentials.

The digital computer is a development of the desk calculating machine which is capable of storing its own calculating instructions in the form of a program. Speeds have been increased enormously by using electronic valves and electrical signals instead of revolution counters and mechanical linkages, and improved electronic techniques are constantly increasing the speed of calculation still further.

The essential difference between the two computers can be illustrated by comparing the slide rule with the desk machine. The fraction $\frac{1}{3}$ can in principle be located exactly on a slide rule; only human error limits the accuracy. However, the fraction must be approximated by 0·33333333 on an eight-figure desk machine and there is thus a physical limit to the accuracy. Although the fraction exists on a slide rule but not on a calculating machine, no-one would suggest that the slide rule was more accurate. This same argument applies to a comparison of analogue and digital computers; the analogue computer uses a continuous number scale, whereas the digital computer uses a discrete number scale.

Analogue and digital computers also use different modes of calculation; the analogue calculates in parallel whereas the digital operates in series. In the analogue method, all dependent variables are continuously available and can be displayed graphically on a multibeam oscilloscope, but the digital computer can only perform a set sequence of commands as stored in its program and can only offer discrete values for one variable at a time. Attempts are being made to develop parallel digital computers with multiple arithmetic units, and series analogue computers with memory facilities. This is leading naturally to the production of hybrid computers.

The great advantage of automatic calculation is that once an analogue has been constructed or a program has been written, a whole set of problems with a range of values for many parameters can be solved very quickly, enabling the optimum choice of parameters to be made. Also, particular characteristics of the behaviour of the system can be associated with various controlling parameters thus helping in the instrumentation and choice of control system for a plant.

14.2. Passive Analogue Computers

This is by far the simplest type of computer to understand, and its mots common form is an inter-connected arrangement of electrical impedances. The differential equation relating the potential at any point in the network to time is chosen to be of the same form as the differential equation it is desired to solve. Provided that the boundary conditions are also analogous, the behaviour of the voltage at a point will be identical to the behaviour of the dependent variable at the analogous point.

FIG. 14.1.   Typical section of passive analogue circuit

Consider, for example, the section of an electrical circuit depicted in Fig. 14.1.   Denoting the electric potential at point n by e_n, and using Kirchoff's law

$$\frac{e_{n+1} - e_n}{R} + \frac{e_{n-1} - e_n}{R} = C\frac{de_n}{dt} \tag{14.1}$$

or

$$\frac{de_n}{dt} = \frac{1}{RC}(e_{n+1} - 2e_n + e_{n-1}) \tag{14.2}$$

which expresses the rate of change of potential at n as a function of the potentials at neighbouring points. Comparing equations (14.2) and (11.52), it can be seen that e_n will have the same behaviour as T_n if

$$RC = (\Delta x)^2/\alpha \qquad (14.3)$$

Equation (14.3) is thus the equation linking the one dimensional heat conduction equation to its electrical analogue (Fig. 14.1), and both sides of the equation have the dimensions of time. It is not essential that equation (14.3) should be satisfied for the use of the analogue, but if

$$RC = 2(\Delta x)^2/\alpha \qquad (14.4)$$

the electrical potentials will alter at half the rate of the corresponding temperatures. In moving from equation (14.3) to (14.4), the time scale of the analogue has been modified. This technique enables slow processes to be accelerated for investigation purposes, and fast processes to be retarded.

Whilst the circuit of Fig. 14.1 is suitable within the range of the problem, special circuits must be constructed to terminate the repeated circuit in conformity with the boundary conditions. The terminal circuits for two boundary conditions are illustrated in Fig. 14.2. The closing of the switch

Fig. 14.2. Analogue circuit for boundary conditions

in (a) causes a step change in the electric potential at the end of the circuit which corresponds to a sudden change in temperature at one face of a large slab. The reason for the resistor of value $R/2$ is as follows. In the analogue, electrical resistance represents reciprocal thermal conductivity, whereas electrical condensers represent thermal capacity. R and C thus represent the thermal resistance and capacity of a space increment. Considering a symmetrical system in which both faces of the slab are subject to the same step change; circuit (a) would terminate both ends of the system. To maintain the correct total resistance and capacity within the system and maintain symmetry, the first resistor in the chain must have half of the resistance of any other member.

Figure 14.2(b) shows the termination of the circuit corresponding to an insulated face. A similar argument to the above explains the condenser of half value.

The analogue is used by alternately closing the switch and discharging the system. Using a potentiometer circuit, the potential at any point can be determined as a function of time, or an oscilloscope can be used to display the behaviour. The benefits from using the analogue are the ease and rapidity of making measurements, and the repeatability of the results.

It will be seen that this type of analogue involves the finite difference representation of the prototype system, and hence it intrinsically contains the errors associated with curtailing a Taylor series.

14.2.1. *Electrolytic Tanks*

The flow of electric current in an extended conductor obeys Laplace's equation, hence by studying the potential distribution in such a conductor, any solution of Laplace's equation can be inferred. The most common example of this technique is the electrolytic trough which consists of a shallow flat bottom tank containing an electrolyte with submerged electrodes and insulators to represent the boundaries. By the nature of the system, the tank has a uniformly distributed resistance, but its electrical capacity is negligible. It is thus suitable for boundary value problems associated with Laplace's equation, but not for initial value problems associated with Poisson's equation,

$$\nabla^2 T = \alpha \frac{\partial T}{\partial t} \tag{14.5}$$

The analogy is obviously restricted to one or two dimensions, although axi-symmetrical systems can be studied in a tilted tank which is analogous to a typical wedge section from a cylinder. Boundary conditions of type 1 (dependent variable fixed) are represented by electrodes of the same shape as the boundary maintained at the analogous constant potential. Lines of symmetry or other type 2 boundary conditions are represented by insulated boundaries, or electrodes with fixed current supplies. Type 3 boundary conditions have to be imposed by trial and error, matching the potential on the electrode with the current drawn from or supplied by it. The analogue is used by exploring the tank with a fine probe and plotting the equipotentials.

The mechanical and electrical systems need careful design. A double pantograph is frequently used so that a recording pen will follow an identical path to the probe, but the system must be accurately constructed because both the curvature and spacing of the equipotentials are physically important. Unless the electrolyte has the same depth at all parts of the tank, the equipotentials will be distorted; hence a well supported glass plate is usually used for the bottom of the tank.

The electrical system has to be chosen to avoid gas formation on the electrodes, polarization potentials, and yet be at a safe voltage for operation. The probe must be submerged sufficiently to mask the effect of the meniscus, and not draw sufficient current to distort the equipotentials it is trying to locate. It is normal to use about 20 volts at 1000 c/s to eliminate electrolysis and polarization effects without introducing serious phase lags due to the natural capacitance of the system. The probe is often connected to the grid of a triode valve with cathode bias to avoid drawing current from the tank.

If the tank is being used to simulate a two dimensional flow field, a double probe is needed to differentiate the potential field and obtain a velocity component. It is of vital importance in this connection that neither probe influences the potential distribution in the neighbourhood of the other probe. Carefully designed electronic circuits are also needed to detect the small difference between two larger alternating voltages.

For studying solutions of Laplace's equation with awkward shaped boundaries, the electrolytic tank is ideal; the alternative solution using numerical methods (Section 11.7.4) is frequently too large for the rapid store of a digital computer (see Section 14.4.3) and too laborious for manual calculation.

14.3. ACTIVE ANALOGUE COMPUTERS

An analogue computer for general calculations, as opposed to the above special purpose analogues, will be described in this section. The basic unit of such a computer is the " operational amplifier ", which is capable of amplifying D.C. voltages with an amplification factor of 10^6–10^8. The size of an analogue computer is usually expressed in terms of the number of operational amplifiers it contains. Although the high gain amplifier is the basic unit of the computer, its accuracy really depends upon the tolerance of the resistors and condensers in the associated calculating circuits. Three figure accuracy is all that can be expected even from good quality components, and hence this is the limit to which this type of computer can work.

14.3.1. *Basic Amplifier for Addition*

Figure 14.3 illustrates the arrangement of computing elements around the operational amplifier during the addition process. The standard symbol

FIG. 14.3. Addition circuit

for the operational amplifier is a triangle, and the diagram illustrates the amplifier with a feed-back resistor (R_F) connecting its output potential (e_0) to its input at the " summing junction " (S.J.). Three input resistors of equal value (R) connect the summing junction to three input potentials (e_1, e_2, e_3).

Denoting the summing junction potential by e_s and the amplification factor by μ, the following current balance can be obtained at the summing junction.

$$\frac{e_1-e_s}{R}+\frac{e_2-e_s}{R}+\frac{e_3-e_s}{R}+\frac{e_0-e_s}{R_F}=0 \qquad (14.6)$$

because the amplifier draws no current, and the amplifying factor equation

$$e_0 = -\mu e_s \qquad (14.7)$$

Eliminating e_s between equations (14.6) and (14.7) and rearranging,

$$e_0 = -\frac{R_F}{R}(e_1+e_2+e_3)\left(1+\frac{R+3R_F}{\mu R}\right) \qquad (14.8)$$

If R_F and R are chosen to have the same value, and μ is sufficiently large, equation (14.8) simplifies to

$$e_0 = -(e_1+e_2+e_3) \qquad (14.9)$$

which shows that the output potential is equal to the sum of the input potentials but of opposite polarity. Provided $\mu > 10^5$, the error caused by assuming that μ is infinite is less than one part in 10^4.

A typical computer arrangement has a 1 megohm resistor in the feedback circuit, two 1 megohm resistors and two 100 kilohm resistors in the input circuit. Thus the ratio $R_F/R = 10$ in the latter case, resulting in the insertion of a scale factor into the addition. Incidentally, this reduces the accuracy of the addition by a factor of ten and hence μ is usually chosen to exceed 10^6.

The standard range of potentials for computing purposes is usually $\pm$ 100 volts, hence equation (14.7) shows that

$$e_s < 10^{-4} \text{ volts} \qquad (14.10)$$

i.e. the summing junction is virtually at earth potential during a calculation.

It is fortunate that equation (14.9) gives addition of the inputs with a sign change, since this facilitates subtraction. Putting a single input into the addition circuit with $R = R_F$, results in a sign change only. Hence to subtract one potential from another, its sign is changed by an amplifier, and then it is added in a second amplifier.

14.3.2. *Basic Amplifier for Integration*

To obtain an integrating circuit, it is only necessary to replace the feedback resistor (R_F) in Fig. 14.3 with a condenser. This is shown in Fig. 14.4

FIG. 14.4.   Integration circuit

where only one input is shown for simplicity. Assuming that the summing junction is still at earth potential due to the high amplification factor, a

similar current balance gives

$$\frac{e_1}{R} = -C\frac{de_0}{dt} \tag{14.11}$$

Integrating equation (14.11) gives

$$e_0 = \frac{-1}{RC}\int_0^t e_1\,dt \tag{14.12}$$

Choosing a megohm resistor and a microfarad condenser gives

$$e_0 = -\int_0^t e_1\,dt \tag{14.13}$$

where t is measured in seconds. The physical interpretation of equation (14.13) is that if e_1 is a constant potential, the output potential (e_0) increases in value by an amount e_1 during each second of operation.

By connecting other inputs through resistors (R) to the summing junction many variables can be simultaneously added together and integrated. With input resistors of different values, the addition can be in different proportions. It should again be noted that equation (14.13) involves a change of polarity indicated by the negative sign in front of the integral.

14.3.3. *Multiplication by a Constant*

A simple earthed potentiometer has the effect of multiplying a potential by any fractional constant. Thus in Fig. 14.5,

$$e_0 = ke_1 \tag{14.14}$$

provided no current is drawn from e_0. The elements in a computer installation are usually chosen so that a much larger current passes down the

FIG. 14.5.   Multiplication by a constant

resistor than is likely to be drawn from e_0. In addition, facilities are usually provided for setting the potential at e_0 at the desired fraction of the reference voltage temporarily applied at e_1 with e_0 under loaded conditions. Thus errors due to loading the potentiometer arm can be eliminated.

4.3.4. *Multiplication by a Variable*

There are four kinds of multiplier in general use; the servo-multiplier, the mark-space multiplier, the quarter-square multiplier, and the Hall effect multiplier. The first is electro-mechanical, but the other three are purely electronic.

The servo-multiplier consists of a small D.C. motor coupled to all of the wiper arms of a gang of about six potentiometers. One variable is fed to the end of any potentiometer, as e_1 in Fig. 14.5, and the other variable is used to position the armature of the D.C. motor; thus giving an output potential, which is representative of the product, from the wiper arm of the potentiometer. The key to the design of this item of equipment is the positioning of the armature to represent the variable. The standard reference voltage (100 V) is applied to one of the potentiometer gang and the output from its wiper will be uniquely determined by the position of the D.C. motor armature. This potential is compared electronically with the value of the variable, and a signal is generated in proportion to the discrepancy. The signal is fed to the motor so that its armature rotates in such a direction as to reduce the difference. Hence it can be seen that a strongly coupled feedback of this nature will cause the armature to follow the changing value of the variable. There is inevitably a time lag due to the inertia of the armature and coupled wiper arms, but a safe frequency limit is always quoted by the supplier of the instrument.

The mark-space multiplier operates by generating a square wave of fixed frequency and wavelength (λ) as illustrated in Fig. 14.6. The height (h) is

FIG. 14.6.   Square wave in mark-space multiplier

determined by one variable, and the ratio (a/λ) is fixed by the other variable. Thus the average height of this curve is a measure of the product of the two variables. Integration of the curve to determine the average height is also performed electronically, and provided λ is small, the output will be smooth and faithful.

An algebraic identity

$$xy = \tfrac{1}{4}[(x+y)^2 - (x-y)^2]$$

is exploited in the quarter-square multiplier. The addition and two subtractions on the right hand side present little difficulty, and two standard units for generating the square of a variable are the only new equipment required. It will be shown in Section 14.3.5 that such a function can be represented as a succession of straight line segments using biased diodes. The circuits for the above operations are usually combined into a single unit, so that the details of the above circuitry need not be understood.

If an electrical potential difference is applied across one pair of faces of a cubic block of semi-conductor, and a magnetic field is imposed across a second pair of faces, then an electrical potential difference appears across the remaining pair of faces. This is known as the " Hall effect " and the potential difference generated is proportional to both the input potential difference and the magnetic field strength. The device can be used for multiplication by generating a current which is proportional to the one variable and passing it through an electromagnet to produce the magnetic field. The other variable potential is applied to the appropriate pair of faces, and the resultant potential difference will represent the product.

All of the above multipliers have their uses, but the servo-multiplier is restricted in frequency range, and the Hall effect multiplier must be shielded from stray magnetic fields.

14.3.5. *Function Generation*

With the exception of the simple trigonometrical and exponential functions which can be obtained by solving linear differential equations with constant coefficients, a device is needed for generating arbitrary functions of a variable. This need arises particularly when experimental data in the form of a graph is to be presented to the computer. Such a device makes use of the rectifying characteristic of a diode. Compared with the input resistors of the operational amplifier, the diode resistance is negligible to potential differences of one polarity but infinite to the other. Thus if a diode is inserted in any line connecting computing components, only signals of one polarity will be conducted. If the diode is suitably biased using a resistance network, the cut-off point can be varied from zero to either positive or negative potentials.

FIG. 14.7.   Basic diode circuit

Consider Fig. 14.7 which shows a diode interupting the passage of an input signal e_1 to a summing amplifier. The diode will not conduct until the armature of the potentiometer picks up a positive potential, and hence the output potential e_0 will be zero until e_1 reaches a certain positive potential determined by both the position of the armature and the fixed negative potential $(-K)$. The rate of change of e_0 with respect to e_1 is independent of K, therefore the slope of the output versus input line can be chosen by positioning the armature of the potentiometer, and the starting point is then fixed by the value of K. A combination of circuits similar to Fig. 14.7 all feeding the summing junction of the same amplifier from the same source e_1 results in e_0 representing the sum of many straight line segments which together will represent a functional relationship between e_0 and e_1. A unit which utilizes these ideas in a more efficient circuit is called a " diode function generator ", and to generate a given function it is only necessary to represent the curve by a series of straight line segments and then to set two potentiometers for each segment.

14.3.6. *Application to Differential Equations*

It was shown in Section 14.3.2 that an amplifier can be used to integrate a function with respect to time. Since there is only one time variable (as opposed to three coordinates) it is only possible to integrate with respect to a single variable in an analogue computer. Hence analogue computers are restricted to solving ordinary differential equations. The numerical methods of Section 11.7 can be used to transform many partial differential equations into difference-differential equations and in this form they are amenable to solution by analogue methods; although much computing equipment is required.

The application of analogue computers to ordinary differential equations is further restricted because the independent variable is represented by time which is of necessity an open range variable. Hence initial value problems can be solved directly, but boundary value problems have to be solved by trial and error using the method presented in Section 11.4. The method will be illustrated by the following example of an initial value problem involving linear differential equations.

Example. Solve the differential equations

$$\frac{d^2y}{dx^2} + 2\frac{dy}{dx} + \frac{dz}{dx} + 3y - 7z = 0$$

$$\frac{dz}{dx} - y + 5z = 2$$

subject to the initial conditions:

at $\qquad\qquad x = 0, \qquad z = 4, \qquad y = 1, \qquad dy/dx = 0$

Solution

A signal representing y or z can always be obtained by integrating a signal representing its derivative. In order to solve the given equations, signals representing y, z, dy/dx, dz/dx, and d^2y/dx^2 must be generated, and the first three can be obtained by integration from the last two. Hence the differential

R

equations must be rearranged to generate dz/dx and d^2y/dx^2 algebraically. Thus

$$\frac{d^2y}{dx^2} = -2\frac{dy}{dx} - \frac{dz}{dx} - 3y + 7z \qquad \text{I}$$

$$\frac{dz}{dx} = y - 5z + 2 \qquad \text{II}$$

A simple potentiometer can be used as in Fig. 14.5 to multiply by a fractional constant, thus it is convenient to represent the independent variable (x) by the computer time variable (t) using a scale factor (a) to prevent the coefficients in equations I and II exceeding unity. Thus putting

$$x = at \qquad \text{III}$$

$$\frac{d^2y}{dt^2} = -2a\frac{dy}{dt} - a\frac{dz}{dt} - 3a^2y + 7a^2z \qquad \text{IV}$$

$$\frac{dz}{dt} = ay - 5az + 2a \qquad \text{V}$$

Choosing the maximum suitable value of a, equations III, IV, and V become

$$x = 0\cdot 2t \qquad \text{VI}$$

$$\frac{d^2y}{dt^2} = -0\cdot 4\frac{dy}{dt} - 0\cdot 2\frac{dz}{dt} - 0\cdot 12y + 0\cdot 28z \qquad \text{VII}$$

$$\frac{dz}{dt} = 0\cdot 2y - z + 0\cdot 4 \qquad \text{VIII}$$

Equation VII can be simplified by eliminating dz/dt using equation VIII. Thus

$$\frac{d^2y}{dt^2} = -0\cdot 4\frac{dy}{dt} - 0\cdot 16y + 0\cdot 48z - 0\cdot 08 \qquad \text{IX}$$

In most analogue systems, there is a limit to the electrical potential allowed within the computing circuits and 100 volts will be assumed for this limit. The initial values of y and z are 1 and 4 respectively, and assuming a stable system in which all derivatives vanish as $x \to \infty$, $y = 1\frac{3}{4}$, $z = \frac{3}{4}$. The unit of y and z is therefore chosen as 25 volts.

The circuit shown in Fig. 14.8 can thus be constructed. It is self-explanatory except for the four feeds from the $\pm$ 100 V supplies. In order to set the initial conditions, the condenser in the feedback line of the integrating amplifier must be charged to an appropriate potential. The electronic means of doing this usually involves a sign change, and the polarities of the supplies for the initial conditions have been chosen to allow for this. The initial condition part of the circuit is automatically disconnected as the computation starts. Two further connections are made to the supply points to represent the constant terms in equations VIII and IX.

Fig. 14.8. Active analogue computing circuit

A double beam oscilloscope connected to the outputs of the amplifiers producing y and z is the best means of exhibiting the solution, but calculations repeatedly suspended at fixed time intervals and measured by a bridge circuit give the most accurate solution.

Assuming an integrating time constant of one second, as in Section 14.3.2, equation VI shows that 5 seconds of computing time correspond to a unit increase in the value of x. The accuracy of the potentiometer settings can be checked by allowing the calculation to proceed for a long time and comparing the potentials with the known values of y and z at steady state.

14.3.7. *Application to Process Control Systems*

In the above sections, the operational amplifier has been shunted with a feedback resistance (R_F) to give an addition operator, or with a condenser (C) to give an integrating operator; but these two circuits can be combined as shown in Fig. 14.9 to represent a further useful operation. Taking the usual current balance at the summing junction gives

$$\frac{e_1}{R} + \frac{e_0}{R_F} + C\frac{de_0}{dt} = 0 \tag{14.15}$$

Introducing the differential operator (D) and rearranging,

$$(D+a)e_0 = -be_1 \qquad (14.16)$$

where $$a = 1/R_F C \quad \text{and} \quad b = 1/RC \qquad (14.17)$$

At this stage, it is necessary to establish the equivalence between the differential operator (D) and the Laplace transform parameter (s) when the

FIG. 14.9. Simple transfer function

initial conditions of the problem are irrelevant. Putting

$$f(0) = f'(0) = \ldots\ldots = f^{(n-1)}(0) = 0$$

in equation (6.13) gives

$$\mathscr{L}[D^n f(t)] = s^n \bar{f}(s) \qquad (14.18)$$

which can be generalized to give

$$\mathscr{L}[F(D)f(t)] = F(s)\bar{f}(s) \qquad (14.19)$$

showing that the operator $F(D)$ transforms to $F(s)$. Also, the shifting theorem of Section 6.2.2 is identical to:

$$f(D)(ye^{px}) = e^{px} f(D+p)y \qquad (2.79)$$

with s replaced by D. Hence, in control theory where it can be assumed that the system is initially running at steady state, the differential operator (D) can be replaced by the Laplace transform parameter (s). Thus equation (14.16) can be written

$$e_0 = \frac{-b}{s+a} e_1 \qquad (14.20)$$

and the circuit of Fig. 14.9 represents the transfer function $-b/(s+a)$ with an input signal (e_1) and an output signal (e_0). The response of the control system characterized by the above transfer function can therefore be studied by altering e_1 in any desired manner.

Any control system can be simulated by combining circuits of the type shown in Fig. 14.9, and the stability can be studied quickly on the analogue computer. If the various resistors have adjustable values, the best settings for the real control system can be determined by trial and error on the computer without introducing any hazard into the real process.

14.3.8. *Application to Simulation*

It has been shown above that the analogue computer can simulate the behaviour of a control system. This idea can be extended to any process which can be represented in the form of ordinary differential equations. A useful application of this nature is to the study of reaction mechanisms and the evaluation of rate constants. If experimental curves are available to exhibit the concentrations of the initial reactants, the intermediate products, and the final products; any proposed mechanism can be studied on the computer by displaying the various concentrations on an oscilloscope. By adjusting potentiometer ratios, the rate constants can be varied until the computer gives results of similar appearance to the experimental results. The final settings of the potentiometers will thus determine the reaction rate constants in the proposed mechanism. Having determined the rate constants, the yield of any product can be maximized by trial and error, by feeding different reaction mixtures to the system and allowing the reaction to proceed for different lengths of time. Thus the computer can save time and expense in the way of chemicals and analysis of samples after the initial investigation has been performed experimentally.

14.4. DIGITAL COMPUTERS

In digital computation, every calculation is reduced to basic fundamentals. All calculations are performed in the " arithmetic unit " which can only perform the four operations of addition, subtraction, multiplication, and division. Even these operations are not fundamental, since the other three operations are performed by repeated subtractions. Nevertheless any one of the above four operations can be performed on a pair of numbers entering the unit. Other operations, such as extracting a square root, must be expressed in terms of the four basic operations, but only two numbers and a result can simultaneously exist in the arithmetic unit. Hence there must be an orderly flow of numbers through the arithmetic unit. The control of this flow is governed by the " program " which refers to each quantity in the calculation by a label called its " address ". The numbers can be considered to be stored in a set of pigeon-holes, each hole having a unique address. The calculation proceeds by extracting numbers from the pigeon-holes, processing them in the arithmetic unit, and re-allocating the results to the pigeon-holes. One point which must be appreciated at this stage is that the program itself must also be stored in a section of the pigeon-holes. A piece of stored program information consists of an instruction accompanied by a reference to the address of the next piece of program. The calculation thus proceeds by the logic of the program controlling the passage of numbers through the arithmetic unit, and at the same time maintaining its own relentless progress. The operation of the various parts of the digital computer will be discussed in the following sub-sections.

14.4.1. *The Binary System*

The decimal system of calculation has little to recommend it except familiarity. The structure of a number in decimal notation is exposed in the equation:

$$723 = 7 \times 10^2 + 2 \times 10^1 + 3 \times 10^0 \tag{14.21}$$

This notation removes the necessity of having a different symbol for each number by repeating the ten basic symbols in various orders, the position of a digit implying the power of ten by which it is to be multiplied. To store a decimal digit in a computer requires a device having ten distinct states which is inconvenient. There are many devices having two distinct states such as off/on, or charged/discharged, and it is simpler to use these devices for storing numbers. Each digit can only have two values in this system, and the powers of two have to be used instead of the powers of ten. Thus the quantity given in equation (14.21) is written

$$1011010011 = 2^9 + 2^7 + 2^6 + 2^4 + 2 + 1 \tag{14.22}$$

in the binary system. Strictly, 2 and its powers should also be written in binary notation, but there is no ambiguity in equation (14.22) as written. All computers will automatically translate decimal numbers into equivalent binary numbers, so the translation details need not be considered.

14.4.2. *Floating Point Arithmetic*

Equation (14.22) shows that a large number of digits are required to express a number in normal form. There is a more economical way of establishing an extensive number scale with a restricted number of digits and this will be illustrated in the decimal system.

In the normal way, four digits can express any number in the range $0 \to 9999$; but using three digits for a number and one digit for an exponent, the range covered can be increased to $0 \cdot 1 \to 10^9$. Thus

$$723 = 0 \cdot 723 \times 10^3 \tag{14.23}$$

With the convention that the number written lies between $0 \cdot 1$ and $0 \cdot 999$, and the fourth digit is the exponent, the number in equation (14.23) can be stored as 7233. A number written in this form is known as its " floating point " form. Both the number and the exponent are written in the binary notation, and a standard number consisting of 40 binary digits is interpreted as follows. The first digit gives the sign of the number, the next 30 digits express the number, the next digit gives the sign of the exponent, and the last 8 digits give the magnitude of the exponent of two. Thus any number in the range

$$10^{-76} < |x| < 10^{76}$$

can be stored to nine significant figures in the form

$$a \times 2^b$$

where $\qquad\qquad \frac{1}{2} \leqslant a < 1, \qquad |b| < 256 (= 2^8)$

In floating point arithmetic, the quantity " zero " cannot exist! Whenever the number zero arises, the computer represents it as 10^{-76}. This eliminates the necessity for special treatment of the division process to reject zero as a divisor because the case can never arise.

14.4.3. *Storage Echelons*

If all information in the storage space of the computer is to be equally accessible, the complete store must be scanned for each item. As the size of problems and hence stores increases, much valuable time is lost in such searches. All calculations are therefore broken down into convenient sections so that one part can be dealt with at a time. Thus, during a section of the calculation, only a small part of the storage space need be scanned for the next piece of information. The storage is therefore divided into at least two sections: an inner " rapid access " store which always contains the current section of calculation, and the " main " store which may have 16 or 32 times the capacity of the rapid access store. The complete program is initially read into the main store (drum), and one complete section is transferred to the inner store (core). On completion of this section of calculation, the contents of the core are transferred to the drum and the next section is brought into the core. It is not necessary to transfer the complete core contents on each occasion, but it is more economical to transfer large portions than small portions.

If the main store is not large enough to hold the complete problem, part of the program or data can be put on to magnetic tape to be read into the main store as required by the program. Such a facility is called a " backing store ".

14.4.4. *Input and Output Devices*

As mentioned above, information can be inserted and extracted by using magnetic tape but this is an unusual method for normal programs. The most convenient methods of transmitting data are by means of holes punched in paper tape, or holes punched in cards. Since a hole is either present or absent, this representation is of a binary nature. The information on the paper tape can be translated into electrical signals in the computer by a pair of contacts closing in every hole as it passes. The output tape can similarly be used to operate a line printer or teleprinter. A printed output can also be obtained directly by coupling the line printer to the output channel of the computer.

14.4.5. *Sub-routines*

In many manual calculations, reference must be made to various tables of functions such as trigonometric, exponential, or Bessel functions. It is not economical to occupy large sections of the main store with detailed tables and interpolation formulae; it is much simpler to program a calculation of each function. With the trigonometric functions for example, the series expansions can be used to calculate the function of any angle between 0 and $\frac{1}{4}\pi$, and the result extended to any other angle by recurrence relations.

Programs for such frequently used functions are usually permanently stored within the computer as " sub-routines ". Whenever such a function has to be evaluated, the appropriate sub-routine is called into the core, used to evaluate the result, and then sent back to its own storage location. Other special sub-routines can be written by the programmer to insert tables of physical properties, or vapour-liquid equilibria, etc.

14.4.6. *The Program*

The series of instructions which the computer obeys are stored in the particular " machine code " which the logical and arithmetic units of the computer understand. Only an expert can write a program in such a language and each manufacturer designs into his machine a translator which enables the operator to converse with the computer in a simpler language called an " autocode " or " user language ". An example of such a language is " Fortran ". The idea behind an autocode is to enable the user to write the instructions in a reasonably intelligible form which can be punched into paper tape for example. The computer then accepts this tape as a sequence of punched holes which the translating program is designed to sort out. There must be no ambiguity either in the step from a written program to a punched tape, or from a punched tape to a stored or " compiled " program. Unfortunately, different manufacturers use different program languages, and different installations of computers of the same type use different dialects of the basic language. It is difficult therefore to describe programming in any detail, since the most efficient program can only be written by someone who is familiar with the particular computer being used.

All but the simplest programs must be sub-divided into sections, each of which can be stored in the core of the computer, and this should be arranged so that there is a minimum number of changes from one section to another. A computer mentality must also be acquired which distinguishes between a good manual calculation system and a good computer system. An example of this is the solution of partial differential equations of boundary value type. In Sections 11.7.3 and 11.7.4, Liebmann's method and the relaxation method were both described. The most efficient relaxation technique is usually to relax the largest residual at each stage and to call upon experience to under- or over-relax. To the computer, the above description presents two difficulties; firstly, all residuals must be compared in pairs to locate the largest at each stage, and secondly, it is not easy to write a simple instruction regarding the policy of under- or over-relaxing. Liebmann's method on the other hand systematically recalculates half of the values at each stage and is admirably suited to computer calculations. A further illustration has already been given in that a computer can calculate a function by means of a sub-routine more conveniently than consulting a table.

Considerable time can be spent in writing a program and running it a few times to remove the faults, and for isolated calculations the computer may not save time. For example, the reactor design in Section 11.7 would require a fairly lengthy program and the sum of programming time and computing time would be comparable with the manual calculation time. The decision is likely to rest upon the availability of a suitable computer and the urgency of the problem; but if the diameter of the reactor tubes is to be selected by repeat calculations for a range of tube diameters, a computer program must be written. The programming time is a fixed charge which can be likened to obtaining a photographic negative, and each calculation of a similar set can be performed very economically, just as any number of prints of any size can easily be obtained from a negative.

14.5. COMPARISON OF THE USES OF ANALOGUE AND DIGITAL COMPUTERS

Before comparing the capabilities of the two types of general purpose computer, it is necessary to investigate the circumstances in which the use of any computer is economically or otherwise justified. In the design of chemical engineering equipment, laborious trial and error calculations are frequently encountered, and alternative equipment can be considered. For example, a reaction can be carried out batchwise, in a stirred tank reactor system, or a tubular reactor. In each type of equipment there are many parameters which can be varied, and therefore it is desirable to design the most efficient reactor of each type in order to compare the optimum designs. A great deal of repetitive calculation is thus required, and a computer investigation can be profitable in terms of cost and time. Long manual calculations are very boring, and barren in intellectual content, whereas time spent designing a computer layout or program stimulates fundamental logical thought. Once the computer is set up, the location of the optimum design is relatively simple in most cases, and the end product of the investigation will be a reliable optimum. In simulation studies, the effect of control system failures, and operation under foreign conditions can be studied without risk to any equipment.

The digital computer is most useful for dealing with numerical data and should be used to apply statistical methods (such as least mean squares) to experimental results. There is no reasonable limit to the accuracy or complexity of a calculation, and non-linear problems can be solved just as easily as linear problems. However, digital computers are usually expensive, and are made in large complex units of moderate overall reliability. Calculating by an ordered sequence of single instructions, the time taken is governed by the length of the sequence and the speed of the machine. Thus the digital computer cannot work in real time.

An analogue computer imitates the real system and it is a simple matter to study the development of the solution. Each potentiometer adjustment can often be associated with variations of a particular physical parameter, and the operator thus retains the " feel " of the system. Since the calculation is of a parallel nature, the computer can work in real time and act as a control system for relatively simple pieces of equipment subject to rapid disturbances. The mechanism is simple, relatively cheap, and reliable, and small units can be purchased and built into a computer of any size. Unfortunately, the individual accuracy of a unit is rarely better than $0 \cdot 1 \%$ and cumulative errors limit the size of useful equipment. Because special purpose units are used separately for addition, multiplication, integration, etc., many of the units will be idle in a particular calculation, which is not efficient. Problems containing many non-linearities require a large number of multiplying units which are expensive, and division can only be performed on a specially connected multiplier. Another important restriction on the analogue computer is its inability to deal with more than one independent variable, without borrowing the digital technique of changing a partial differential equation into a difference-differential equation. Overall, the digital computer is much more flexible, but the ability of the analogue computer to work in real time gives it many useful chemical engineering applications.

In many establishments a choice has to be made between purchasing an analogue or a digital computer. Depending primarily upon the interests of the department requiring the computer, either type may be obtained. This computer is then pressed into service for as many applications as possible because it is available, rather than because it is suitable. There is little harm in this situation since any computer is usually better than none, but due to its greater flexibility, the digital computer is usually selected.

Currently the analogue computer is being equipped with a memory unit so that large problems can be solved in sections with a reduced amount of hardware. This is leading to a reduction of cost and can maintain the speed advantage over digital computers by retaining parallel operation. Meanwhile digital computers are being developed with multiple arithmetic units to give a degree of parallel operation. Success in this field will revolutionize computer programming which at present is of a serial nature.

Computers are growing in size, and digital machines are becoming ever faster, but as the machines grow, so do the fields of application. The demands made upon computers are also increasing and this will ensure that computer developments will not be wasted. Computers are now solving problems which are completely insoluble by other methods, and this creates a new difficulty; it is impossible to check independently whether the answer is correct or not.

Although some of the advances in computer technique are astonishing, it must be realized that the computer is just an instrument which can only be fully exploited by an expert, or a team, knowing both the capabilities of the machine and the fundamentals of the problem. The best computer in the world is of no value to the chemical engineer unless he can understand his own problem, formulate it, and devise a method of solution.

PROBLEMS

1. It is desired to produce a substance B from a raw material A in a continuous stirred tank reactor of effective volume V ft^3. If Q ft^3/min of a solution of A of concentration C_0 is fed to the empty reactor, and the chemical reaction of A is represented by

$$A \overset{k_1}{\underset{k_2}{\rightleftharpoons}} B \overset{k_3}{\rightarrow} C$$

in which all the reactions are first order, show that the number of moles of B in the initial discharge from the reactor is given by the solution of the differential equation

$$\frac{d^2 N_B}{dt^2} + P \frac{dN_B}{dt} + RN_B = C$$

where

$$P = k_1 + k_2 + k_3$$

$$R = k_1 k_3$$

$$C = QC_0 k_1$$

2. Find the general solution of the differential equation

$$\frac{dy}{dx} + 2y \tan x = 4 \sin x$$

If $y = 0$ when $x = \pi/3$, show that y has a maximum value of $\frac{1}{2}$.

3. Solve the differential equation

$$x^3 \frac{d^2 y}{dx^2} + x^2 \left(\frac{dy}{dx}\right)^2 - y^2 = 0$$

with the help of the boundary conditions:

At $\qquad\qquad x = 1, \qquad y = 2, \qquad \dfrac{dy}{dx} = -1$

4. Solve the equation

$$\frac{d^2 y}{dx^2} + 2 \frac{dy}{dx} + 2y = e^{-x} \cos x$$

Birmingham 1962.

5. Solve the equation

$$x^2\frac{d^2y}{dx^2} + 2x\frac{dy}{dx} + 2y = x + \ln x$$

Birmingham 1960.

6. It is proposed to produce X, Y, and Z from A and B by chemical reaction on a semi-batch basis. That is, 20 moles of pure A is charged into the reactor and B is added at the rate of $0\cdot75$ moles/min. If all the reactions are second order and are represented stoichiometrically by the equations

$$A + B \rightarrow X \qquad\qquad 1$$
$$X + B \rightarrow Y \qquad\qquad 2$$
$$Y + B \rightarrow Z \qquad\qquad 3$$

prepare a plot of the composition of the reaction mixture as a function of the number of moles of B reacted.

The specific reaction rate constants are:

for reaction 1, $k_1 = 1\cdot8 \times 10^{-4}$ 1/mole.min
for reaction 2, $k_2 = 0\cdot3 \times 10^{-4}$ 1/mole.min
for reaction 3, $k_3 = 0\cdot1 \times 10^{-3}$ 1/mole.min

7. Product from a plant flows at a rate of 2 tons/hr into a storage vessel holding 20 tons of material and is then pumped to another process. Owing to a mishap in the plant, the material flowing to storage contains 1% of a contaminant.

(a) If the flow from storage is 2 tons/hr and the contamination of supply lasts for 1 hour, what is the peak contamination in the discharge?

(b) What is the peak contamination in (a) if the discharge is reduced to 1 ton/hr?

(c) For how long would the 1% contamination of supply have to continue before the discharge contamination became $0\cdot8$% with flows as in (a)?

(d) In (a), if the supply contamination ceased completely after 1 hour, what further time would elapse before the discharge contamination fell to $0\cdot01$%?

(e) In (a), what supply contamination could be tolerated for 1 hour if discharge contamination could be allowed up to 1%?

Assume complete mixing in the storage vessel.

8. A component A is absorbed from a gas phase by a liquid containing a constituent B with which it reacts chemically by a pseudo first order reaction. The rate of absorption can be assumed to depend on both the rate of chemical reaction and the rate of molecular diffusion through the laminar film of liquid of thickness δ. Show that when the concentration

of A at a liquid depth δ is zero, the concentration profile of A through the film is

$$C_A = \frac{C_{A,i}\sinh[\alpha(\delta-x)]}{\sinh(\alpha\delta)}$$

where C_A is the concentration at depth x, and $\alpha = \surd(k/D)$.

Show also that the rate of mass transfer through the surface is

$$N_A = \frac{DC_{A,i}}{\delta}\left[\frac{\alpha\delta}{\tanh(\alpha\delta)}\right]$$

where $\left[\dfrac{\alpha\delta}{\tanh(\alpha\delta)}\right]$ is a dimensionless quantity known as the Hatta number.

9. (a) Two thin wall pipes of 1 in external diameter have flanges $\frac{1}{2}$ in thick and 4 in diameter on the ends joining them together. If the conductivity of the flange metal is k Btu/h ft^2 °F ft^{-1}, and the exposed surfaces of the flange lose heat to the surroundings which are at T_1°F by means of a heat transfer coefficient h Btu/h ft^2 °F, show that the equation giving the temperature distribution in the flange is

$$6k\left(r\frac{d^2T}{dr^2} + \frac{dT}{dr}\right) = h\,r(T-T_1)$$

where r is the radial distance coordinate in inches.

(b) If, in addition, the circular faces of the flanges are thermally insulated (i.e. $h = 0$) and the flanges only lose heat through the rim where $h = 20$, solve the simplified equation and determine the rim temperature if the pipe temperature is 200°F, $T_1 = 60$°F, and $k = 200$.

M.Sc., Birmingham 1961.

10. A second order irreversible chemical reaction between two materials A and B takes place in a single stirred tank reactor according to

$$A+B \rightarrow C+D$$

Two feed streams enter the tank each at a rate of R lb mole/h, the one stream contains $4C_0$ mole fraction of A, and the other contains $2C_0$ mole fraction of B. Material leaves the tank continuously at a rate $2R$ lb mole/h so that the tank always contains M lb moles and V ft^3 of material. The specific reaction rate constant is k ft^3/lb mole/h.

When the reactor is closed down, both feeds are stopped, the vessel remains full, and the reaction goes to completion leaving C_0 mole fraction of A unreacted. If the reactor is started from this condition, by turning on both feed streams simultaneously, perform the following calculations:

(a) Show that the difference in concentration between the two reactants A and B in the tank remains constant during start-up.

(b) Determine how the concentration of B in the tank varies with time during start-up.

(Note. In part (b) a quadratic equation should arise which will not factorize; denote the roots by α and β and continue the calculation in terms of α and β.)

M.Sc., Birmingham 1962.

11. As liquid flows across any plate of a distillation column its composition (x) changes from the entry concentraction (x_0) to the exit concentration (x_1). The composition at any point on the plate is influenced by the passage of the stripping gas at a rate G, the bulk flow of the liquid at a rate L, and mixing on the plate which can be expressed in terms of an eddy diffusivity (D_E). Assuming a constant Murphree point efficiency given by

$$E_{MV}^* = \frac{y - y_1}{y^* - y_1}$$

and a straight line equilibrium curve given by $y^* = mx + b$ show that the liquid composition satisfies the equation

$$D_E \frac{d^2 x}{dz^2} - V \frac{dx}{dz} - \frac{mGV}{Lz_1} E_{MV}^*(x - x^*) = 0$$

where z is the distance measured along the plate from the inlet weir,
$\quad\quad\quad z_1$ is the distance between the weirs,
$\quad\quad\quad V$ is the linear velocity of the liquid,
$\quad\quad\quad x^*$ is the liquid composition in equilibrium with the entering gas which is constant across the plate.

Allowing for diffusion in the entry section where no gas flows, find the liquid composition at all points on the plate.

Andrew, S. P. S., Hutchinson, R. C., and Mackay, R. W.,
Chem. Eng. Sci. **17**, 541 (1962).

12. A surge tank of 20 ft^3 capacity initially contains 10 ft^3 of liquid. There are two inlet streams to the tank and one outlet stream. The first inlet stream is steady at 2 ft^3/min with a temperature of 100°F, whereas the second inlet stream at a temperature of 200°F is subject to surging on a 2 minute cycle. During the first minute, the flow rate is steady at 2 ft^3/min; and during the second minute the flow stops completely; it then continues to start and stop at 1 minute intervals. The outlet stream is always steady at 3 ft^3/min.

If the tank is well stirred and the temperature in the outlet stream is always the same as that in the tank, over what range does this outlet temperature vary when the system has settled to its equilibrium cycle?

M.Sc., Birmingham 1960.

13. Two vertical cylindrical tanks of 6 ft diameter and 4 ft diameter are joined at the base by a horizontal pipe 2 ft 6 in long and $\frac{1}{2}$ in diameter. The 6 ft diameter tank also has an outlet at the base consisting of a horizontal tube 2 ft long and $\frac{1}{2}$ in in diameter.

If the larger tank is filled with oil to a depth of 12 ft whilst the smaller tank is empty, and both tubes are open simultaneously, prove that the maximum depth of oil occurring in the smaller tank will be 4·81 ft.

Assume that the flow in both tubes is laminar and neglect kinetic losses.

14. Derive an expression giving the true average temperature difference, in terms of the terminal temperatures and fluid properties, which is applicable to a split flow heat exchanger.

(*This problem has been solved by D. Q. Kern and C. LeRoy Carpenter,*
Chem. Eng. Prog. **47**, 211, 1951.)

15. Is the series

$$\frac{1}{2} + \frac{1.3}{2.4} + \frac{1.3.5}{2.4.6} + \dots$$

convergent or divergent?

16. Although the series $\sum \frac{1}{n}$ is divergent, show that the series obtained from it by removing all terms in which the digit "0" occurs is convergent, i.e.

$$1 + \tfrac{1}{2} + \tfrac{1}{3} + \dots + \tfrac{1}{9} + \tfrac{1}{11} + \tfrac{1}{12} + \dots + \tfrac{1}{19} + \tfrac{1}{21} + \dots$$

17. " Log-mean " temperature differences are frequently used and defined by

$$T_m = \frac{T_2 - T_1}{\ln(T_2/T_1)}$$

What is T_m when $T_2 = T_1$?

Show further that the log-mean value tends to the arithmetic mean value as $T_2/T_1 \to 1$.

18. Given the differential equation

$$x\frac{d^2 y}{dx^2} + k\frac{dy}{dx} + y = 0$$

(a) Use the method of Frobenius to find the roots of the indicial equation and determine the recurrence relation.

(b) State without further calculation what form the complete solution takes for all real values of k.

(c) Complete the solution for the case when $k = \frac{1}{2}$.

Birmingham 1960.

19. Use the method of Frobenius to solve the equations:

(a)
$$x\frac{d^2y}{dx^2} + (1-2x)\frac{dy}{dx} - 2y = 0$$

(b)
$$x(1-x)\frac{d^2y}{dx^2} + (3-7x)\frac{dy}{dx} - 9y = 0$$

20. A constant temperature vessel is supported on a truncated cone which is in turn resting on another surface which is at constant temperature. The small end of the support is of radius 1·5 in and is at 130°F, the temperature of the vessel; whilst the wide end of the support is of radius 2·0 in and is at 50°F, the temperature of the surface. The vertical height of the support is 4·0 in and its thermal conductivity is 40 Btu/h ft² °F ft⁻¹.

The curved surface of the support loses heat to the surroundings at a temperature 50°F according to a heat transfer coefficient of 2 Btu/h ft² °F.

By assuming that the temperature is constant across any circular cross-section of the support and by measuring all temperatures relative to the temperature of the base, calculate the first five terms in the series giving the temperature distribution within the support.

M.Sc., Birmingham 1960.

21. (a) Use the substitution $x = ae^{it}$ to solve
$$\frac{d^2y}{dt^2} - a^2e^{2it}y = 0$$

(b) Use the substitution $y = wx^{-\frac{1}{2}}$ to solve
$$\frac{d^2y}{dx^2} + \frac{2}{x}\frac{dy}{dx} + k^2y = \frac{p^2}{x^2}y$$

22. Show that the nth roots of unity can be expressed as $1, z, z^2, ..., z^{n-1}$, where $z = \cos(2\pi/n) + i\sin(2\pi/n)$.

Hence, or otherwise, prove that

$$z^a + z^{2a} + ... + z^{na} = \begin{cases} 0 \text{ if } n \text{ is not a factor of } a \\ n \text{ if } n \text{ is a factor of } a \end{cases}$$

where a is any integer.

23. By using the known trigonometrical identities, and equation (4.59, 60, 61);
    (a) express $\tanh(a+b)$ in terms of $\tanh a$ and $\tanh b$,
    (b) express $\sinh a$ in terms of $\cosh 2a$,
    (c) prove that
$$\sinh^{-1}a + \sinh^{-1}b = \sinh^{-1}(a\sqrt{1+b^2} + b\sqrt{1+a^2})$$

24. By putting $z = e^{i\theta}$, show that

$$\int \frac{dz}{\sqrt{z}} = -4e^{i\phi/2}$$

where the integral is taken around a unit circle centred at the origin, starting from the point $e^{i\phi}$.

If two circuits of the origin are permitted by allowing θ to vary from ϕ to $\phi + 4\pi$, show that the integral is zero for all values of ϕ.

(This example illustrates the importance of making $z^{-\frac{1}{2}}$ single valued by taking a branch cut at $\theta = \phi$.)

25. Integrate the following functions around any finite curve enclosing the origin.

(a) $\dfrac{\sin z}{z^2}$ (b) $\dfrac{\cos z}{z^2}$

26. By integrating $e^{imz}/(1+z^2)$ around a suitable contour, show that

$$\int_0^\infty \frac{\cos mx}{1+x^2} dx = \frac{\pi}{2} e^{-m}$$

for all positive real values of m.

27. Evaluate the residue of $\dfrac{e^z}{z \sin z}$ at the origin.

28. Integrate the function $e^{iz}z^{a-1}$ around a contour consisting of the parts of two circles centred at the origin which lie in the first quadrant, and the parts of the positive real and imaginary axes joining the two arcs. By allowing the one circle to increase in radius indefinitely, and the other to shrink to the origin, show that

$$\int_0^\infty x^{a-1} \cos x \, dx = \Gamma(a) \cos \tfrac{1}{2}\pi a$$

provided $0 < a < 1$.

29. By raising the trigonometrical identity, $\sin 2\theta = 2 \sin \theta \cos \theta$, to the $(2n-1)$th power and integrating with respect to θ over the range 0 to $\frac{1}{2}\pi$, prove the duplication formula for the gamma function.

$$\Gamma(2n) = 2^{2n-1}\pi^{-\frac{1}{2}}\Gamma(n)\Gamma(n+\tfrac{1}{2})$$

30. Prove by substitution that the function

$$I(x) = \int_0^\pi \cos(n\phi - x\sin\phi)\,d\phi$$

satisfies Bessel's equation of order n provided that n is an integer or zero. Hence prove that

$$I(x) = \pi J_n(x)$$

31. Show that

$$\int_0^\infty \frac{\cos ax - \cos bx}{x}\,dx = \ln\left(\frac{a}{b}\right)$$

(Introduce the function $e^{-\alpha x}$ and use the method of Section 5.5.3.)

32. Show that the Laplace Transform of:

(i) $$J_0(t) = \frac{s}{(s^2+1)^{\frac{1}{2}}}$$

(ii) $$\cos \omega t = \frac{s}{s^2+\omega^2}$$

(iii) $$e^{-at}\sin \omega t = \frac{\omega}{(s+a)^2+\omega^2}$$

33. Invert the following Laplace Transforms.

(i) $\dfrac{s-1}{s(s+2)}$ (ii) $\dfrac{sA+B}{(s+i\omega)(s-i\omega)}$ (iii) $\dfrac{1}{(s^2+4)(s^2+1)}$

34. Prove by integration that $\dfrac{a^n}{s(s+a)^n}$ is the Laplace Transform of

$$1-e^{-at}\left[1+at+\frac{a^2t^2}{2!}+\dots+\frac{a^{n-1}t^{n-1}}{(n-1)!}\right]$$

35. The diagram illustrates a hydraulic device used in automatic control mechanisms. It operates as follows. The movable cylinder A is completely filled with oil, and when a sudden change in pressure occurs at

the piston B, oil is forced via the line C through the valve D which has a very narrow aperture so that the flow of oil is restricted. Consequently the cylinder A moves against the spring S, but as the oil passes through the valve the compressed spring forces the cylinder to return to its original position.

For a pressure change ΔP and corresponding displacement x show that if the cross-sectional area of the piston is a, the spring constant is k and the flow of oil through the valve is laminar, the differential equation describing the system is

$$\frac{d^2x}{dt^2} + \left(\frac{a}{mK}\right)\frac{dx}{dt} + \frac{k}{m}x = 0$$

where K is the pressure change-flow proportionality constant,
$\quad m$ is the effective mass of the system.

Solve this equation using the initial conditions that the displacement of the cylinder is initially x_0.

36. A stirred tank reactor of effective volume V ft^3 containing a solution of a reactant A, of concentration $C_{A,0}$ is heated to such a temperature that the pseudo first order reaction

$$A \rightarrow B$$

takes place. When the chemical reaction is initiated a solution of A of concentration $C_{A,I}$ is fed continuously to the reactor at the rate of q ft^3/min. If the specific reaction rate is k min^{-1} and the vessel is assumed to contain a perfect stirrer, develop an expression giving the concentration of A in the effluent as a function of time.

37. A liquid feed stream of heat capacity C_p is passed through a small bore cylindrical pipe of radius a ft at the rate of R lb/h. The pipe wall is maintained at a temperature of $T_1°$F and the entering liquid at $T_0°$F. Determine the temperature of the liquid as a function of time and distance from the inlet if the pipe is initially full of hot liquid at $T_1°$F when the flow is suddenly started.

The heat transfer coefficient is a function of distance x ft along the pipe from the inlet and is expressed as

$$U = kx^{-\frac{1}{2}}$$

where k is constant.

Conduction within the liquid can be neglected and radial variation of temperature can be assumed to be zero.

38. The temperature of a liquid flowing at a rate q through an agitated electrically heated vessel of volume V is to be controlled by placing a temperature detecting element in the liquid leaving the vessel. The detector is connected to a controller which regulates the supply of energy

to an immersion heater in such a way that the heat supplied is proportional to the temperature difference $(T_m - T)$; where T_m is the constant safe maximum temperature of the heating element, and T is the temperature of the liquid. The immersion heater supplies heat to the liquid at a rate $Q_c = U_c A(T_c - T)$; where A is the heat transfer area, U_c is the overall heat transfer coefficient and T_c is the surface temperature of the coil.

If the temperature of the entering liquid suddenly falls from T_0 to a new steady state temperature T_1, develop an equation to show the variation of liquid temperature as a function of time, during the period of transient behaviour.

The effective mass of the immersion heater can be taken to be m and the specific heat of the heater material s, the heat capacity of the liquid C_p and its density ρ. Agitation in the vessel can be assumed to be perfect.

39 The denominator of the complete transfer function of a control system can be represented by

$$6s^4 + 5(\alpha - 1)s^3 + 5\alpha s^2 + (\alpha^2 - 2\alpha + 1)s - (\alpha - 6) = 0$$

For what range of values of α is the system stable?

40. Plot the Nyquist diagram and discuss the stability of the system

$$\bar{G}_1(s)\bar{G}_2(s) = \frac{-2}{(s-1)(4s+1)}$$

41. Prove the following by vector methods:

(a) In any skew quadrilateral, the mid-points of the sides are at the corners of a parallelogram.

(b) A cube has twelve edges, six of which form the corners at the ends of one diagonal. Prove that the mid-points of the other six edges form the corners of a regular hexagon.

42. (a) Find the unit vector perpendicular to the vectors $2i + 3j + 4k$, $i + 2j - 2k$. Also determine the angle between these two vectors.

(b) Prove that the vectors $i + 3j - 2k$, $i - 5j + 3k$, and $2i - 2j + k$ are coplanar.

43. (a) Show that

$$(A \wedge B).(A \wedge C) = A^2(B.C) - (A.B)(A.C)$$

(b)   If $(A \wedge B) \wedge (A \wedge D) = A$,   what is $(A \wedge B) \wedge (B \wedge D)$?

44. If A, B, and C are three independent vectors, find the values of x, y, and z which make

$$M \wedge N = xA + yB + zC$$

Hence show that

$$M \wedge N = \begin{vmatrix} A & A.M & A.N \\ B & B.M & B.N \\ C & C.M & C.N \end{vmatrix} \quad [A, B, C]$$

45. If r is the position vector, show that:

   (a) div $r = 3$ (c) div $r^n r = (n+3)r^n$

   (b) curl $r = 0$ (d) curl $r^n r = 0$

46. Use the theorems connecting line, surface, and volume integrals to establish the results

   (i) $\int_C (A \wedge \phi).dr = \int_S (\nabla.\phi)A.dS - \int_S (A.\nabla)\phi.dS$

   (ii) $\int_S U\phi.dS = \int_\sigma U\nabla.\phi \, d\sigma + \int_\sigma \phi.\nabla U \, d\sigma$

   (iii) $\int_\sigma \psi.\nabla \wedge \phi \, d\sigma = \int_S (\phi \wedge \psi).dS + \int_\sigma \phi.\nabla \wedge \psi \, d\sigma$

   where A is a constant vector, ϕ and ψ are variable vectors and U is a variable scalar.

                                                    Birmingham (Maths) 1953.

47. In a porous medium, the continuity equation can be written

$$\varepsilon \frac{\partial \rho}{\partial t} = -\nabla.\rho u$$

   where ε is the porosity; and the equation of motion (Darcy's law) can be written

$$u = -\frac{\kappa}{\mu}\nabla p$$

   where gravity is neglected, κ is the permeability and μ the viscosity.

   (a) Show that for an incompressible fluid, $\nabla^2 p = 0$.

   (b) Show that for isothermal flow of a compressible gas.

$$\frac{2\varepsilon\mu\rho_0}{\kappa} \frac{\partial \rho}{\partial t} = \nabla^2\rho^2$$

48. Show that the equation of fluid motion (7.126) can be expressed in the alternative forms:

   (a) $$\frac{\partial u}{\partial t} - u \wedge \zeta = -\nabla\chi + \nu\nabla^2 u$$

(b)
$$\frac{\partial \boldsymbol{u}}{\partial t} - \boldsymbol{u}\wedge\zeta = -\nabla\chi - v\nabla\wedge\zeta$$

where
$$\chi = p/\rho + \tfrac{1}{2}u^2 + \Omega$$

and
$$F = -\nabla\Omega$$

49. Two concentric spherical metallic shells of radii a and b cm ($a < b$) are separated by a solid of thermal diffusivity α cm^2/sec. The outer surface of the inner shell is maintained at $T_0°$C and the inner surface of the outer shell at $T_1°$C. Derive the differential equation governing the unsteady state temperature distribution in the solid as a function of time and radial coordinate.

Show that the solution takes the form

$$T = \frac{T_1 b - T_0 a}{b-a} + \frac{ab}{r}\frac{T_0 - T_1}{b-a} + \sum_{n=1}^{\infty}\frac{B_n}{r}\sin\{\beta(r-a)\}\,e^{-\beta^2\alpha t}$$

where $\beta = n\pi/(b-a)$. Show how B_n can be determined from any initial temperature distribution.

50. A cylindrical block of metal at a uniform temperature $T_0°$F has its circular faces thermally insulated. The temperature of the curved surface is suddenly raised to and maintained at $T_1°$F. Prove that the temperature T of any point in the block at any time t is given by:

$$\frac{T_1 - T}{T_1 - T_0} = \frac{2}{a}\sum_{n=1}^{\infty}\frac{J_0(\alpha_n r)}{\alpha_n J_1(\alpha_n a)}e^{-\alpha_n^2 K t}$$

where r is the radial coordinate, a is the radius of the cylinder, K is the thermal diffusivity, and α_n are the positive roots of

$$J_0(\alpha_n a) = 0$$

M.Sc., Birmingham 1962.

51. If a liquid is flowing through a fixed bed at a rate v cm/sec when a pulse of a tracer is added, show that the later distribution of the tracer is given by the solution of

$$E\frac{\partial^2 C}{\partial x^2} - v\frac{\partial C}{\partial x} = \frac{\partial C}{\partial t}$$

where E is the mixing coefficient which operates in the axial direction (x) only. Removing x by the substitution $z = x - vt$, and assuming an infinite bed length, solve the above equation.

Show that the maximum concentration of tracer passing a downstream observation station arrives earlier than the residence time by an amount E/v^2.

(*See J. J. Carberry and R. H. Bretton, A.I.Ch.E.J. 4, 367, 1958.*)

52. Considering two dimensionless flow and neglecting the inertia terms in the Navier-Stokes equation, show that the change of variables given by

$$u = -\frac{\partial \phi}{\partial x} - \frac{\partial \psi}{\partial y}$$

$$v = -\frac{\partial \phi}{\partial y} + \frac{\partial \psi}{\partial x}$$

$$p = p_0 - g\rho y + \rho\frac{\partial \phi}{\partial t} - F_y \rho y$$

yields the equations

$$\frac{\partial^2 \phi}{\partial x^2} + \frac{\partial^2 \phi}{\partial y^2} = 0$$

$$\frac{\mu}{\rho}\left(\frac{\partial^2 \psi}{\partial x^2} + \frac{\partial^2 \psi}{\partial y^2}\right) = \frac{\partial \psi}{\partial t}$$

Show that a solution of these equations takes the form

$$\phi = A e^{-Ky+nt}\cos Kx + My$$

$$\psi = B e^{-my+nt}\sin Kx$$

if

$$m = \sqrt{K^2 + (\rho n/\mu)}$$

(This method has been used to describe flow in fluidized beds by W. J. Rice and R. H. Wilhelm, A.I.Ch.E.J. 4, 423, 1958.)

53. The steady laminar flow of a liquid through a heated cylindrical pipe has a parabolic velocity distribution if natural convection effects and variation of physical properties with temperature are neglected. If the fluid entering the heated section is at a uniform temperature (t_1), and the wall is maintained at a constant temperature (t_w), develop Graetz's solution by neglecting the thermal conductivity in the axial direction.

(The solution is reported by T. B. Drew, Trans. Am. Inst. Chem. Engrs. 26, 26, 1931.)

54. Assuming that Stokes' approximation is valid and that the interfacial tension (γ) varies according to

$$\gamma = \alpha\cos\theta + \beta$$

determine the fall velocity of a spherical droplet of a material of viscosity μ_1 through a medium of viscosity μ_2; where θ is the polar angle measured from the front of the droplet.

Show that there is only motion inside the droplet if

$$a^2 g\Delta\rho > 3\alpha$$

where a is the radius of the drop and $\Delta\rho$ is the density difference.

55. The sudden closure of a valve generates a pressure wave within the liquid flowing in the pipe leading to the valve. The passage of this wave causes compression of the liquid and expansion of the pipe. Show that the velocity of the liquid and the pressure are related by the equations

$$-\frac{\partial p}{\partial x} = \frac{\rho}{g}\frac{\partial v}{\partial t}$$

and

$$\frac{\partial^2 p}{\partial t^2} = c^2\frac{\partial^2 p}{\partial x^2}$$

where c is the velocity of propagation of the pressure wave.

If it can be assumed that a uniform pipe of length L connects a reservoir at $x = 0$ to the valve at $x = L$, show that

$$p(x, t) = p_0 + \frac{4c\rho v_0}{\pi g}\sum_{n=0}^{\infty}\frac{(-1)^n}{(2n+1)}\sin(2n+1)\frac{\pi x}{2L}\sin(2n+1)\frac{\pi ct}{2L}$$

(*G. R. Rich*, Trans. A.S.M.E. **67**, 361, 1945.)

56. A liquid at a uniform temperature falls as a thin film down a flat vertical surface. Determine the velocity distribution and the steady state thickness of the film.

If a short section of the wall is maintained at a higher temperature than the liquid, determine the average heat transfer coefficient in the heated section. The velocity distribution can be simplified in the thin layer where temperature gradients are important.

57. Given that the values of sinh x for $x = 0{\cdot}1, 0{\cdot}15, 0{\cdot}2, 0{\cdot}25, 0{\cdot}30$ and $0{\cdot}35$ are $0{\cdot}100, 0{\cdot}150, 0{\cdot}201, 0{\cdot}253, 0{\cdot}305$ and $0{\cdot}357$; estimate the value of sinh x when $x = 0{\cdot}328$.

58. The thermal conductivity of methyl chloride at the temperatures 50°F, 100°F, 150°F, 200°F. 250°F, 300°F, 350°F and 400°F is $0{\cdot}0057, 0{\cdot}0069, 0{\cdot}0081, 0{\cdot}0092, 0{\cdot}0104, 0{\cdot}0116, 0{\cdot}0127$ and $0{\cdot}0139$; estimate the thermal conductivity at 413°F.

59. Solve the difference equations

(i) $$y_{n+3} - 6y_{n+2} + 11y_{n+1} - 6y_n = 0$$

(ii) $$y_n y_{n+2} = y_{n+1}^2$$

(iii) $$y_{n+4} - 9y_{n+3} + 30y_{n+2} - 44y_{n+1} + 24y_n = 4^n a$$

60. Solve the difference equation

$$y_{n+2} + 2Ay_{n+1} + By_n = 0$$

given that $y_0 = 0;$ $y_1 = 3;$ $y_2 = 6;$ $y_3 = 36$

61. G lb/h of a carrier gas containing Y_0 lb solute A per lb of carrier gas is fed into the base of a plate column containing N ideal plates and contacted with L lb/h of solute-free liquid containing X_{N+1} lb solute A per lb of solute-free liquor. If the concentration of A in the exit gas and liquid streams are Y_N and X_1 respectively, show that the concentration of A in the gas phase leaving any plate n in the column is given by

$$Y_n = \left(\frac{Y_0 - HX_1}{1 - HG/L}\right)\left(\frac{HG}{L}\right)^n + \left(HX_0 - \frac{HG}{L}Y_N\right)\Big/\left(1 - \frac{HG}{L}\right)$$

where H is Henry's law constant expressed by $Y_N = HX_N$.

62. Calculate the number of plates required to absorb 99% mole ketene from 135 lb moles/h of gas containing 4·36% ketene by volume using 138 lb moles/h of glacial acetic acid. The plate efficiency, of a 3·5 ft diameter tower containing 0·7D weirs and therefore a plate hold-up of 2·09 lb moles liquid, is 40%. The pseudo first order reaction rate constant for the chemical absorption process may be taken to be 0·075 sec^{-1} and the equilibrium relationship

$$Y^* = 2X$$

where Y^* is the lb moles ketene/lb mole carrier gas in equilibrium with X lb moles ketene/lb mole of acetic acid in the liquid.

(*Problem taken from* A Problem of Chemical Engineering Design, *by G. V. Jeffreys; published by Institution of Chemical Engineers,* London, 1962.)

63. Butyl acetate is to be produced in a battery of continuous stirred tank reactors operating in series by reacting 2000 lb/h of butanol with 326 lb/h of glacial acetic acid containing sufficient sulphuric acid to catalyze the reaction at 100°C. Under these conditions the rate of reaction can be expressed by the equation

$$r = kC_A^2$$

where k is 0·28 ft^3/lb mole.min
and C_A is the concentration of acetic acid in lb moles/ft^3.
    If the effective volume of each tank is 10 ft^3 and the density of the reaction mixture is assumed to be constant at 48 lb/ft^3, estimate the number of reaction vessels required if the concentration of the acetic acid in the final discharge is not to exceed 3 lb/ft^3.

64. A reactant A is to be converted into a product B in a battery of N continuous stirred tank reactors of total volume V ft^3. If the feed rate is q ft^3/min and the concentration of A is $C_{A,0}$ show that the production of B is a maximum when all the tanks are the same size. The rate of reaction can be taken to be first order and the battery is to operate isothermally.

S

526   MATHEMATICAL METHODS IN CHEMICAL ENGINEERING

65. 8000 lb/h of a 5% by weight solution of acetaldehyde in toluene is to be treated with 5000 lb/h of water in a 6 theoretical stage extraction column operating under counterflow conditions. If the concentration of the feed conditions is suddenly changed to a 3% by weight solution, how long will it take for the extractor to settle down to steady state operation under the new conditions?

The equilibrium relation is $Y = 2 \cdot 2X$

where Y = lb acetaldehyde per lb of water
X = lb acetaldehyde per lb of toluene.

The hold up per stage can be assumed to be constant at
$$750 \text{ lb toluene}; \quad 300 \text{ lb water}.$$

66. A block of metal 12 in × 12 in × 2 in has its rectangular faces thermally insulated and its vertical square faces losing heat to the surroundings at 60°F by means of a heat transfer coefficient. It can be assumed that the temperature in the block is uniform and that the properties of the metal are:

specific heat $c = 0 \cdot 10$,   density $\rho = 420 \text{ lb/ft}^3$

The following table gives the metal temperature as a function of time:

Time (min)	0	5	10	15	20	25	30	35	40
Temperature (°F)	200	186	173	161	151	141	133	125	119

Determine the heat transfer coefficient.

In addition to the experimental readings, the given values are subject to the following errors:

$c, \pm 1\%; \quad \rho, \pm 0 \cdot 1\%; \quad$ all dimensions, $\pm \frac{1}{20}''$

Assuming that the thermocouples are accurate, how accurately is the heat transfer coefficient determined?

Birmingham 1961.

67. Use the method of averages to find the best curve of the type:
$$y = A \sin(x+B)$$
which fits the following values. A and B are constant.

x	0°	30°	60°	90°	120°	150°
y	0·944	1·242	1·208	0·850	0·264	−0·392

68. Use the method of least squares to fit the best equation of the type
$$Nu = aPr^n$$
to the following data.

Pr	Nu	Pr	Nu	Pr	Nu
0·46	24·8	10·0	84·5	32	140
0·53	26·5	17·7	115	31·6	127
0·63	28·5	18·6	115	70·3	189
0·74	30·0	25·3	150	93	245
4·2	60·3	41·0	170	185	315
5·6	69·0	37·0	165	340	380
3·0	58·4	58·5	193	590	480
5·0	70·7	95·0	245	55	195

(The information above was collected from various sources by W. L. Friend and A. B. Metzner, A.I.Ch.E.J. **4**, 393, 1958.)

69. The top product leaving a batch distillation column is being continuously reprocessed so that it is difficult to measure directly the amount produced. However, the flow rate can be continuously measured and samples are taken at hourly intervals giving the following results.

Time (hours)	0	1	2	3	4	5	6	7	8
More volatile component (%)	90	92	91	91	89	87	84	80	75
Flow rate (lb/min)	60	62	63	62	62	60	59	57	57

(a) What is the total amount produced during the period of 8 hours?
(b) What proportion of this total is the more volatile component?

70. The reaction rate constant for the decomposition of a substituted dibasic acid has been determined at various temperatures as follows.

T (°C)	50·0	70·1	89·4	101·0
$k \times 10^4$ (hr^{-1})	1·08	7·34	45·4	138

Use the method of least squares to determine the activation energy (E) in the equation

$$k = A e^{-E/RT}$$

where T is measured in degrees Kelvin.

71. Calculate the first four positive roots of

$$x \tan x = 2$$

to four decimal places.

Show graphically why the method of successive approximation (Section 11.5.3) oscillates about the root and converges slowly, whereas Newton's method yields the answer far more efficiently.

72. Calculate the number of plates required to absorb 95% mole of a component A from 500 lb moles/h of a gas containing 5% of A by volume using 600 lb moles/h of a 5% mole solution of the absorbent B. A reacts with B according to a second order irreversible reaction

$$r = kC_A C_B$$

If the liquid hold up on each tray is 4 lb moles and gaseous hold up is negligible, show that the difference equation takes the form (9.71). The plate efficiency is 15%, $k = 2 \times 10^8$ ft^3/lb mole.h, the absorbent solution has the physical properties of water, and Henry's law constant is $1 \cdot 2 \times 10^3$ moles/mole.

73. A mathematical model for the washing of a filter cake has been proposed by M. T. Kuo (*A.I.Ch.E.J.* **6**, 566, 1960). It is assumed that the wash liquor is in plug flow through the pores of the cake, and that a stagnant film of filtrate remains on the pore walls. A mass transfer coefficient governs the passage of solute across the boundary between the two liquid layers. Show that the process is described by the equations:

$$A_2 \frac{\partial c_2}{\partial t} = hS(c_1 - c_2)$$

$$A_1 \frac{\partial c_1}{\partial t} = hS(c_2 - c_1) - A_1 U \frac{\partial c_1}{\partial x}$$

for $0 < x < L$; $t > x/U$.

  U velocity of the wash liquor.
  L length of the pore channel.
  h mass transfer coefficient.
  S transfer area per unit length of pore.
  A_1 cross sectional area occupied by wash liquor.
  A_2 cross sectional area occupied by filtrate.
  C_1 concentration of solute in wash liquor.
  C_2 concentration of solute in filtrate.

Calculate the concentration of the exit wash liquor as a function of time for the following numerical values.

$$U = 0 \cdot 0030 \text{ in/sec} \qquad\qquad L = 1 \cdot 1 \text{ in}$$
$$hS/A_1 = 0 \cdot 00682 \text{ sec}^{-1} \qquad hS/A_2 = 0 \cdot 00475 \text{ sec}^{-1}$$

Initial concentration of filtrate is $0 \cdot 015$ moles/ft^3.

74. An oil bearing formation is assumed to be of uniform depth, and circular in shape. A single well penetrates the formation at a point midway between the centre of the formation and its perimeter. If oil is withdrawn at constant pressure, determine how the pressure distribution in the formation changes, and the rate of production of oil as a function of time. (The governing equation can be checked with Example 4, Section 8.8.)

75. Two immiscible liquids are in laminar flow through a cylindrical pipe, and the flow rates are adjusted so that each liquid occupies a semi-circular section of the pipe. If the viscosity ratio between the two liquids is 10 : 1, find the flow rate ratio.

(*Relaxation methods have been used to solve this problem by A. R. Gemmel and N. Epstein; Canad. J. Chem. Eng.* **40**, 215, 1962.)

76. If a matrix $\mathbf{A} = \begin{bmatrix} 1 & 2 & 3 \\ -1 & 1 & 3 \\ 3 & 0 & 2 \end{bmatrix}$ and a matrix $\mathbf{B} = \begin{bmatrix} 1 & -3 & 0 \\ 2 & 0 & 1 \\ 4 & 1 & 3 \end{bmatrix}$

write down

    (i) $\mathbf{A+B}$;   (ii) $\mathbf{AB}$;   (iii) $\mathbf{BA}$;   (iv) $\mathbf{AB^{-1}}$

77. Determine the latent roots of each of the following matrices.

  (i) $\begin{bmatrix} 2 & -3 & 1 \\ 3 & 1 & 3 \\ -5 & 2 & -4 \end{bmatrix}$ and (ii) $\begin{bmatrix} 7 & 4 & -1 \\ 4 & 7 & -1 \\ -4 & -4 & 4 \end{bmatrix}$

What is the rank and degeneracy of each of these matrices?

78. 10,000 lb/h of sulphuric acid (sp. heat 0·36) is to be cooled in a three-stage countercurrent cooler of the following type. Hot acid at 174°C is fed to tank No. 1 where it is thoroughly agitated in contact with cooling coils. The continuous discharge from this tank at 88°C flows to a second stirred tank and leaves at 45°C. Thereafter it flows to the third stirred tank and leaves at 28°C. Cooling water at 18°C flows into the coil of tank No. 3 and thence to the coils of tank No. 2 and finally to the coils of the first tank. The temperature of the water leaving the coils of the hot acid tank is 88°C. To what temperatures would the contents of each tank rise if due to trouble in the supply, the cooling water suddenly stopped for one hour?

On restoration of the water supply, water is put on the system at the rate of 12,000 lb/h. Calculate the acid discharge temperature after one hour. The capacity of each tank is 8,000 lb of acid and the overall co-efficient of heat transfer in tank 1 is 230 C.H.U/h.ft² °C, in tank 2 is 180 C.H.U/h.ft² °C and in tank 3 is 120 C.H.U/h.ft² °C which may be assumed constant.

79. A battery of N stirred tank reactors are arranged to operate isothermally in series. Each reactor has a volume of V ft³ and is equipped with a perfect agitator so that the composition of the reactor effluent is the same as the tank contents. If initially the tanks contain pure solvent

only, and at a time designated t_0, q ft^3/min of a reactant A of concentration C_0 lb moles/ft^3 are fed to the first tank, estimate the time required for the concentration of A leaving the Nth tank to be C_N lb moles/ft^3.

The reaction can be represented stoichiometrically by the equation

$$A \underset{k_2}{\overset{k_1}{\rightleftharpoons}} B \overset{k_3}{\to} C$$

and all the reactions are first order. There is no B or C in the feed but it may be assumed that the feed contains a catalyst that initiates the reaction as soon as the feed enters the first reactor.

80. 4,000 lb/h of dry coal gas containing 0·2 lb light oil/lb dry gas is to be treated with 2,500 lb/h of wash oil in a 6 plate absorption column to remove the light oil. If the concentration of light oil in the feed suddenly changes to 0·3 lb light oil/lb dry gas show that the disturbance in the absorption column can be described by the equation

$$\frac{a\mathbf{X}}{dt} = \mathbf{RX} + \mathbf{PQ}$$

where

$$\mathbf{X} = \{X_1 \quad X_2 \quad \dots \quad X_6\}$$

$$\mathbf{P} = \left\{ \begin{matrix} A & 0 & \dots & 0_6 \\ 0 & \cdot & \dots & C \end{matrix} \right\}$$

$$\mathbf{Q} = \left\{ X_0 \quad \frac{Y_{N+1}-b}{m} \right\}$$

$$\mathbf{R} = \begin{bmatrix} B & C & 0 & \cdot & \cdot & 0_6 \\ A & B & C & \cdot & \cdot & \cdot \\ 0 & A & B & \cdot & \cdot & \cdot \\ \cdot & 0 & \cdot & \cdot & \cdot & \cdot \\ \cdot & \cdot & \cdot & A & B & C \\ 0_6 & \cdot & \cdot & 0 & A & B_6 \end{bmatrix}$$

and

$$A = \frac{L}{mH+h}; \quad B = \frac{L+mG}{mH+h}; \quad C = \frac{mG}{mH+h}$$

The symbols:

h = liquid hold-up on each plate and may be taken to be 75 lb.
H = vapour hold-up on each plate and may be taken to be 1·0 lb.
L and G are the wash oil and dry gas flow rates and the equilibrium

relationship of the light oil between gas and liquid may be written $Y = mX$
where m is 0·7.

Solve the transient equation and plot the composition of light oil on each plate as a function of time.

81. X_0 lb of a solute/lb solute-free liquor is fed to the first stage of a N stage crossflow extraction process at the rate of C lb/h on a solute-free basis. If B lb of extracting solvent free from solute is fed to each stage and the solute distribution ratio is m, calculate the optimum number of stages and solvent to feed ratio using the data given below.

> Total cost of operating one stage is α including operation, fixed charges and depreciation of capital.
> Cost of solvent is β per lb of solvent.
> Cost of feed liquor is γ per lb of solute.
> Cost of extract product is λ per lb of solute.

> (*Problem taken from: V. G. Jenson and G. V. Jeffreys;*
> Brit. Chem. Eng. **6**, 676, 1961.)

82. 1,000 ft³/h of an aqueous liquor containing 5 lb of diethylamine per ft³ of solution is to be treated with toluene in a countercurrent liquid extraction process. Estimate the optimum number of stages and the quantity of solvent required if the capital and operating cost of each stage including vessels, pumps and labour is estimated to be $7000 per annum. The cost of regenerating, recycling and adding make-up solvent is estimated to be $0·015 per ft³ of solvent and the value of the diethylamine is estimated to be $0·53 per lb. The plant is to be operated 8000 hours per annum and the distribution ratio of diethylamine between toluene and water is 0·86.

In question 81 above it will be found that the optimum number of stages for a crossflow extraction is related to the other cost and process variables by the equation

$$1 - \frac{\alpha m}{C\beta} = \left(\frac{\beta}{\lambda m X_0}\right)^{N+1}\left[1 + \frac{1}{N+1}\ln\left(\frac{\beta}{\lambda m X_0}\right)\right]$$

Therefore, compare the two methods of operation in carrying out the extraction of diethylamine.

APPENDIX

TABLE OF LAPLACE TRANSFORMS

	$\bar{f}(s)$	$f(t)$
1	$\dfrac{1}{s}$	1
2	$\dfrac{1}{s^2}$	t
3	$\dfrac{1}{s^n}\,(n = 1, 2, \ldots)$	$\dfrac{t^{n-1}}{(n-1)!}$
4	$\dfrac{1}{\sqrt{s}}$	$\dfrac{1}{\sqrt{\pi t}}$
5	$s^{-\frac{3}{2}}$	$2\sqrt{\dfrac{t}{\pi}}$
6	$s^{-(n+\frac{1}{2})}\,(n = 1, 2, \ldots$	$\dfrac{2^n t^{n-\frac{1}{2}}}{1 \times 3 \times 5 \ldots (2n-1)\sqrt{\pi}}$
7	$\dfrac{\Gamma(k)}{s^k}\,(k > 0)$	t^{k-1}
8	$\dfrac{1}{s-a}$	e^{at}
9	$\dfrac{1}{(s-a)^2}$	$t\,e^{at}$
10	$\dfrac{1}{(s-a)^n}\,(n = 1, 2, \ldots$	$\dfrac{1}{(n-1)!}t^{n-1}\,e^{at}$
11	$\dfrac{\Gamma(k)}{(s-a)^k}\,(k > 0)$	$t^{k-1}\,e^{at}$
12*	$\dfrac{1}{(s-a)(s-b)}$	$\dfrac{1}{a-b}(e^{at} - e^{bt})$

* Here a and b represent distinct constants.

(From *Operational Mathematics* (Ed. 2) by R. V. Churchill. Copyright 1958, McGraw-Hill Book Company Inc. Used by permission.)

TABLE OF LAPLACE TRANSFORMS (*continued*)

	$\bar{f}(s)$	$f(t)$
13*	$\dfrac{s}{(s-a)(s-b)}$	$\dfrac{1}{a-b}(a\,e^{at}-b\,e^{bt})$
14*	$\dfrac{1}{(s-a)(s-b)(s-c)}$	$-\dfrac{(b-c)\,e^{at}+(c-a)\,e^{bt}+(a-b)\,e^{ct}}{(a-b)(b-c)(c-a)}$
15	$\dfrac{1}{s^2+a^2}$	$\dfrac{1}{a}\sin at$
16	$\dfrac{s}{s^2+a^2}$	$\cos at$
17	$\dfrac{1}{s^2-a^2}$	$\dfrac{1}{a}\sinh at$
18	$\dfrac{s}{s^2-a^2}$	$\cosh at$
19	$\dfrac{1}{s(s^2+a^2)}$	$\dfrac{1}{a^2}(1-\cos at)$
20	$\dfrac{1}{s^2(s^2+a^2)}$	$\dfrac{1}{a^3}(at-\sin at)$
21	$\dfrac{1}{(s^2+a^2)^2}$	$\dfrac{1}{2a^3}(\sin at - at\cos at)$
22	$\dfrac{s}{(s^2+a^2)^2}$	$\dfrac{t}{2a}\sin at$
23	$\dfrac{s^2}{(s^2+a^2)^2}$	$\dfrac{1}{2a}(\sin at + at\cos at)$
24	$\dfrac{s^2-a^2}{(s^2+a^2)^2}$	$t\cos at$
25	$\dfrac{s}{(s^2+a^2)(s^2+b^2)}\,(a^2\neq b^2)$	$\dfrac{\cos at-\cos bt}{b^2-a^2}$
26	$\dfrac{1}{(s-a)^2+b^2}$	$\dfrac{1}{b}e^{at}\sin bt$
27	$\dfrac{s-a}{(s-a)^2+b^2}$	$e^{at}\cos bt$

* Here a, b, and (in 14) c represent distinct constants.

TABLE OF LAPLACE TRANSFORMS (continued)

	$\bar{f}(s)$	$f(t)$
28	$\dfrac{3a^2}{s^3+a^3}$	$e^{-at}-e^{at/2}\times$ $\times\left(\cos\dfrac{at\sqrt{3}}{2}-\sqrt{3}\sin\dfrac{at\sqrt{3}}{2}\right)$
29	$\dfrac{4a^3}{s^4+4a^4}$	$\sin at\cosh at-\cos at\sinh at$
30	$\dfrac{s}{s^4+4a^4}$	$\dfrac{1}{2a^2}\sin at\sinh at$
31	$\dfrac{1}{s^4-a^4}$	$\dfrac{1}{2a^3}(\sinh at-\sin at)$
32	$\dfrac{s}{s^4-a^4}$	$\dfrac{1}{2a^2}(\cosh at-\cos at)$
33	$\dfrac{8a^3s^2}{(s^2+a^2)^3}$	$(1+a^2t^2)\sin at-at\cos a$
34*	$\dfrac{1}{s}\left(\dfrac{s-1}{s}\right)^n$	$L_n(t)=\dfrac{e^t}{n!}\dfrac{d^n}{dt^n}(t^n e^{-t})$
35	$\dfrac{s}{(s-a)^{\frac{3}{2}}}$	$\dfrac{1}{\sqrt{\pi t}}e^{at}(1+2at)$
36	$\sqrt{s-a}-\sqrt{s-b}$	$\dfrac{1}{2\sqrt{\pi t^3}}(e^{bt}-e^{at})$
37	$\dfrac{1}{\sqrt{s}+a}$	$\dfrac{1}{\sqrt{\pi t}}-ae^{a^2t}\operatorname{erfc}(a\sqrt{t})$
38	$\dfrac{\sqrt{s}}{s-a^2}$	$\dfrac{1}{\sqrt{\pi t}}+ae^{a^2t}\operatorname{erf}(a\sqrt{t})$
39	$\dfrac{\sqrt{s}}{s+a^2}$	$\dfrac{1}{\sqrt{\pi t}}-\dfrac{2a}{\sqrt{\pi}}e^{-a^2t}\displaystyle\int_0^{a\sqrt{t}}e^{\lambda^2}\,d\lambda$
40	$\dfrac{1}{\sqrt{s}(s-a^2)}$	$\dfrac{1}{a}e^{a^2t}\operatorname{erf}(a\sqrt{t})$
41	$\dfrac{1}{\sqrt{s}(s+a^2)}$	$\dfrac{2}{a\sqrt{\pi}}e^{-a^2t}\displaystyle\int_0^{a\sqrt{t}}e^{\lambda^2}\,d\lambda$

* $L_n(t)$ is the Laguerre polynomial of degree n.

TABLE OF LAPLACE TRANSFORMS (*continued*)

	$\bar{f}(s)$	$f(t)$
42	$\dfrac{b^2-a^2}{(s-a^2)(b+\sqrt{s})}$	$e^{a^2t}[b-a\,\mathrm{erf}(a\sqrt{t})]$ $\qquad -b\,e^{b^2t}\,\mathrm{erfc}(b\sqrt{t})$
43	$\dfrac{1}{\sqrt{s}(\sqrt{s}+a)}$	$e^{a^2t}\,\mathrm{erfc}(a\sqrt{t})$
44	$\dfrac{1}{(s+a)\sqrt{s+b}}$	$\dfrac{1}{\sqrt{b-a}}\,e^{-at}\,\mathrm{erf}(\sqrt{b-a}\,\sqrt{t})$
45	$\dfrac{b^2-a^2}{\sqrt{s}(s-a^2)(\sqrt{s}+b)}$	$e^{a^2t}\left[\dfrac{b}{a}\,\mathrm{erf}(a\sqrt{t})-1\right]$ $\qquad\qquad +e^{b^2t}\,\mathrm{erfc}(b\sqrt{t})$
46*	$\dfrac{(1-s)^n}{s^{n+\frac{1}{2}}}$	$\dfrac{n!}{(2n)!\sqrt{\pi t}}\,H_{2n}(\sqrt{t})$
47	$\dfrac{(1-s)^n}{s^{n+\frac{3}{2}}}$	$-\dfrac{n!}{\sqrt{\pi}(2n+1)!}\,H_{2n+1}(\sqrt{t})$
48†	$\dfrac{\sqrt{s+2a}}{\sqrt{s}}-1$	$a\,e^{-at}[I_1(at)+I_0(at)]$
49	$\dfrac{1}{\sqrt{s+a}\sqrt{s+b}}$	$e^{-\frac{1}{2}(a+b)t}I_0\left(\dfrac{a-b}{2}t\right)$
50	$\dfrac{\Gamma(k)}{(s+a)^k(s+b)^k}\;(k>0)$	$\sqrt{\pi}\left(\dfrac{t}{a-b}\right)^{k-\frac{1}{2}}e^{-\frac{1}{2}(a+b)t}$ $\qquad\qquad \times I_{k-\frac{1}{2}}\left(\dfrac{a-b}{2}t\right)$
51	$\dfrac{1}{(s+a)^{\frac{1}{2}}(s+b)^{\frac{3}{2}}}$	$te^{-\frac{1}{2}(a+b)t}\left[I_0\left(\dfrac{a-b}{2}t\right)\right.$ $\qquad\qquad \left.+I_1\left(\dfrac{a-b}{2}t\right)\right]$
52	$\dfrac{\sqrt{s+2a}-\sqrt{s}}{\sqrt{s+2a}+\sqrt{s}}$	$\dfrac{1}{t}e^{-at}I_1(at)$
53	$\dfrac{(a-b)^k}{(\sqrt{s+a}+\sqrt{s+b})^{2k}}\;(k>0)$	$\dfrac{k}{t}e^{-\frac{1}{2}(a+b)t}I_k\left(\dfrac{a-b}{2}t\right)$

* $H_n(x)$ is the Hermite polynomial, $H_n(x)=e^{z^2}\dfrac{d^n}{dx^n}(e^{-z^2})$.

† $I_n(x)=i^{-n}J_n(ix)$, where J_n is Bessel's function of the first kind.

TABLE OF LAPLACE TRANSFORMS (*continued*)

	$\bar{f}(s)$	$f(t)$
54	$\dfrac{(\sqrt{s+a}+\sqrt{s})^{-2v}}{\sqrt{s}\sqrt{s+a}}\ (v>-1)$	$\dfrac{1}{a^v}e^{-\frac{1}{2}at}I_v(\tfrac{1}{2}at)$
55	$\dfrac{1}{\sqrt{s^2+a^2}}$	$J_0(at)$
56	$\dfrac{(\sqrt{s^2+a^2}-s)^v}{\sqrt{s^2+a^2}}\ (v>-1)$	$a^v J_v(at)$
57	$\dfrac{1}{(s^2+a^2)^k}(k>0)$	$\dfrac{\sqrt{\pi}}{\Gamma(k)}\left(\dfrac{t}{2a}\right)^{k-\frac{1}{2}}J_{k-\frac{1}{2}}(at)$
58	$(\sqrt{s^2+a^2}-s)^k\ (k>0)$	$\dfrac{ka^k}{t}J_k(at)$
59	$\dfrac{(s-\sqrt{s^2-a^2})^v}{\sqrt{s^2-a^2}}\ (v>-1)$	$a^v I_v(at)$
60	$\dfrac{1}{(s^2-a^2)^k}(k>0)$	$\dfrac{\sqrt{\pi}}{\Gamma(k)}\left(\dfrac{t}{2a}\right)^{k-\frac{1}{2}}I_{k-\frac{1}{2}}(at)$
61	$\dfrac{e^{-ks}}{s}$	$S_k(t)=\begin{cases}0 & \text{when } 0<t<k \\ 1 & \text{when } t>k\end{cases}$
62	$\dfrac{e^{-ks}}{s^2}$	$\begin{cases}0 & \text{when } 0<t<k \\ t-k & \text{when } t>k\end{cases}$
63	$\dfrac{e^{-ks}}{s^\mu}\ (\mu>0)$	$\begin{cases}0 & \text{when } 0<t<k \\ \dfrac{(t-k)^{\mu-1}}{\Gamma(\mu)} & \text{when } t>k\end{cases}$
64	$\dfrac{1-e^{-ks}}{s}$	$\begin{cases}1 & \text{when } 0<t<k \\ 0 & \text{when } t>k\end{cases}$
65	$\dfrac{1}{s(1-e^{-ks})}=\dfrac{1+\coth\frac{1}{2}ks}{2s}$	$S(k,t)=n$ when $(n-1)k<t<nk$ (Fig. 6.4)
66	$\dfrac{1}{s(e^{ks}-a)}$	$\begin{cases}0 \text{ when } 0<t<k \\ 1+a+a^2+\ldots+a^{n-1} \\ \quad\text{when } nk<t<(n+1)k \\ \quad (n=1,2,\ldots)\end{cases}$
67	$\dfrac{1}{s}\tanh ks$	$M(2k,t)=(-1)^{n-1}$ when $2k(n-1)<t<2kn$ $(n=1,2,\ldots)$

TABLE OF LAPLACE TRANSFORMS (*continued*)

	$\bar{f}(s)$	$f(t)$
68	$\dfrac{1}{s(1+e^{-ks})}$	$\frac{1}{2}M(k,t)+\frac{1}{2}=\dfrac{1-(-1)^n}{2}$ when $(n-1)k<t<nk$
69	$\dfrac{1}{s^2}\tanh\frac{1}{2}ks$	$H(k,t)=\begin{cases} t & \text{when } 2nk<t \\ & <(2n+1)k \\ 2k-t & \text{when } (2n+1)k \\ & <t<(2n+2)k \end{cases}$
70	$\dfrac{1}{s\sinh ks}$	$F(t)=2(n-1)$ when $(2n-3)k<t<(2n-1)k$ $(t>0)$
71	$\dfrac{1}{s\cosh ks}$	$M(2k,t+3k)+1=1+(-1)^n$ when $(2n-3)k<t<(2n-1)k$ $(t>0)$
72	$\dfrac{1}{s}\coth ks$	$F(t)=2n-1$ when $2k(n-1)<t<2kn$
73	$\dfrac{k}{s^2+k^2}\coth\dfrac{\pi s}{2k}$	$\lvert\sin kt\rvert$
74	$\dfrac{1}{(s^2+1)(1-e^{-\pi s})}$	$\begin{cases} \sin t & \text{when } (2n-2)\pi \\ & <t<(2n-1)\pi \\ 0 & \text{when } (2n-1)\pi<t<2n\pi \end{cases}$
75	$\dfrac{1}{s}e^{-(k/s)}$	$J_0(2\sqrt{kt})$
76	$\dfrac{1}{\sqrt{s}}e^{-(k/s)}$	$\dfrac{1}{\sqrt{\pi t}}\cos 2\sqrt{kt}$
77	$\dfrac{1}{\sqrt{s}}e^{k/s}$	$\dfrac{1}{\sqrt{\pi t}}\cosh 2\sqrt{kt}$
78	$\dfrac{1}{s^{\frac{3}{2}}}e^{-(k/s)}$	$\dfrac{1}{\sqrt{\pi k}}\sin 2\sqrt{kt}$
79	$\dfrac{1}{s^{\frac{3}{2}}}e^{k/s}$	$\dfrac{1}{\sqrt{\pi k}}\sinh 2\sqrt{kt}$
80	$\dfrac{1}{s^\mu}e^{-(k/s)}\ (\mu>0)$	$\left(\dfrac{t}{k}\right)^{(\mu-1)/2}J_{\mu-1}(2\sqrt{kt})$
81	$\dfrac{1}{s^\mu}e^{k/s}\ (\mu>0)$	$\left(\dfrac{t}{k}\right)^{(\mu-1)/2}I_{\mu-1}(2\sqrt{kt})$

TABLE OF LAPLACE TRANSFORMS (*continued*)

	$\bar{f}(s)$	$f(t)$
82	$e^{-k\sqrt{s}}(k>0)$	$\dfrac{k}{2\sqrt{\pi t^3}}\exp\left(-\dfrac{k^2}{4t}\right)$
83	$\dfrac{1}{s}e^{-k\sqrt{s}}(k\geqq 0)$	$\text{erfc}\left(\dfrac{k}{2\sqrt{t}}\right)$
84	$\dfrac{1}{\sqrt{s}}e^{-k\sqrt{s}}(k\geqq 0)$	$\dfrac{1}{\sqrt{\pi t}}\exp\left(-\dfrac{k^2}{4t}\right)$
85	$s^{-\frac{3}{2}}e^{-k\sqrt{s}}(k\geqq 0)$	$2\sqrt{\dfrac{t}{\pi}}\exp\left(-\dfrac{k^2}{4t}\right)-k\,\text{erfc}\left(\dfrac{k}{2\sqrt{t}}\right)$
86	$\dfrac{ae^{-k\sqrt{s}}}{s(a+\sqrt{s})}(k\geqq 0)$	$-e^{ak}e^{a^2t}\,\text{erfc}\left(a\sqrt{t}+\dfrac{k}{2\sqrt{t}}\right)$ $+\text{erfc}\left(\dfrac{k}{2\sqrt{t}}\right)$
87	$\dfrac{e^{-k\sqrt{s}}}{\sqrt{s}(a+\sqrt{s})}(k\geqq 0)$	$e^{ak}e^{a^2t}\,\text{erfc}\left(a\sqrt{t}+\dfrac{k}{2\sqrt{t}}\right)$
88	$\dfrac{e^{-k\sqrt{s(s+a)}}}{\sqrt{s(s+a)}}$	$\begin{cases}0 & \text{when } 0<t<k \\ e^{-\frac{1}{2}at}I_0(\frac{1}{2}a\sqrt{t^2-k^2}) & \text{when } t>k\end{cases}$
89	$\dfrac{e^{-k\sqrt{s^2+a^2}}}{\sqrt{s^2+a^2}}$	$\begin{cases}0 & \text{when } 0<t<k \\ J_0(a\sqrt{t^2-k^2}) & \text{when } t>k\end{cases}$
90	$\dfrac{e^{-k\sqrt{s^2-a^2}}}{\sqrt{s^2-a^2}}$	$\begin{cases}0 & \text{when } 0<t<k \\ I_0(a\sqrt{t^2-k^2}) & \text{when } t>k\end{cases}$
91	$\dfrac{e^{-k(\sqrt{s^2+a^2}-s)}}{\sqrt{s^2+a^2}}(k\geqq 0)$	$J_0(a\sqrt{t^2+2kt})$
92	$e^{-ks}-e^{-k\sqrt{s^2+a^2}}$	$\begin{cases}0 & \text{when } 0<t<k \\ \dfrac{ak}{\sqrt{t^2-k^2}}J_1(a\sqrt{t^2-k^2}) & \\ & \text{when } t>k\end{cases}$
93	$e^{-k\sqrt{s^2-a^2}}-e^{-ks}$	$\begin{cases}0 & \text{when } 0<t<k \\ \dfrac{ak}{\sqrt{t^2-k^2}}I_1(a\sqrt{t^2-k^2}) & \\ & \text{when } t>k\end{cases}$

TABLE OF LAPLACE TRANSFORMS (*continued*)

	$\bar{f}(s)$	$f(t)$
94	$\dfrac{a^v e^{-k\sqrt{s^2+a^2}}}{\sqrt{s^2+a^2}\,(\sqrt{s^2+a^2}+s)^v}\ (v>-1)$	$\begin{cases} 0 \quad \text{when } 0<t<k \\ \left(\dfrac{t-k}{t+k}\right)^{\frac{1}{2}v} J_v(a\sqrt{t^2-k^2}) \\ \qquad\qquad\qquad \text{when } t>k \end{cases}$
95	$\dfrac{1}{s}\log s$	$\Gamma'(1) - \log t \quad [\Gamma'(1) = -0{\cdot}5772]$
96	$\dfrac{1}{s^k}\log s\,(k>0)$	$t^{k-1}\left[\dfrac{\Gamma'(k)}{[\Gamma(k)]^2} - \dfrac{\log t}{\Gamma(k)}\right]$
97*	$\dfrac{\log s}{s-a}\,(a>0)$	$e^{at}[\log a - \mathrm{Ei}(-at)]$
98*	$\dfrac{\log s}{s^2+1}$	$\cos t\,\mathrm{Si}(t) - \sin t\,\mathrm{Ci}(t)$
99*	$\dfrac{s\log s}{s^2+1}$	$-\sin t\,\mathrm{Si}(t) - \cos t\,\mathrm{Ci}(t)$
100*	$\dfrac{1}{s}\log(1+ks)\,(k>0)$	$-\mathrm{Ei}\left(-\dfrac{t}{k}\right)$
101	$\log\dfrac{s-a}{s-b}$	$\dfrac{1}{t}(e^{bt} - e^{at})$
102*	$\dfrac{1}{s}\log(1+k^2 s^2)$	$-2\,\mathrm{Ci}\left(\dfrac{t}{k}\right)$
103*	$\dfrac{1}{s}\log(s^2+a^2)\,(a>0)$	$2\log a - 2\,\mathrm{Ci}(at)$
104*	$\dfrac{1}{s^2}\log(s^2+a^2)\,(a>0)$	$\dfrac{2}{a}[at\log a + \sin at - at\,\mathrm{Ci}(at)]$
105	$\log\dfrac{s^2+a^2}{s^2}$	$\dfrac{2}{t}(1 - \cos at)$
106	$\log\dfrac{s^2-a^2}{s^2}$	$\dfrac{2}{t}(1 - \cosh at)$
107	$\arctan\dfrac{k}{s}$	$\dfrac{1}{t}\sin kt$

* The exponential-integral, cosine-integral, and sine-integral functions $\mathrm{Ei}(-t)$, $\mathrm{Ci}(t)$, and $\mathrm{Si}(t)$ are defined in Section 5.5.3.

TABLE OF LAPLACE TRANSFORMS (*continued*)

	$\bar{f}(s)$	$f(t)$
108	$\dfrac{1}{s}\arctan\dfrac{k}{s}$	$\text{Si}\,(kt)$
109	$e^{k^2 s^2}\,\text{erfc}\,(ks)\,(k>0)$	$\dfrac{1}{k\sqrt{\pi}}\exp\left(-\dfrac{t^2}{4k^2}\right)$
110	$\dfrac{1}{s}e^{k^2 s^2}\,\text{erfc}\,(ks)\,(k>0)$	$\text{erf}\left(\dfrac{t}{2k}\right)$
111	$e^{ks}\,\text{erfc}\,\sqrt{ks}\,(k>0)$	$\dfrac{\sqrt{k}}{\pi\sqrt{t(t+k)}}$
112	$\dfrac{1}{\sqrt{s}}\,\text{erfc}\,(\sqrt{ks})$	$\begin{cases}0 & \text{when } 0<t<k \\ (\pi t)^{-\frac{1}{2}} & \text{when } t>k\end{cases}$
113	$\dfrac{1}{\sqrt{s}}e^{ks}\,\text{erfc}\,(\sqrt{ks})\,(k>0)$	$\dfrac{1}{\sqrt{\pi(t+k)}}$
114	$\text{erf}\left(\dfrac{k}{\sqrt{s}}\right)$	$\dfrac{1}{\pi t}\sin\,(2k\sqrt{t})$
115	$\dfrac{1}{\sqrt{s}}e^{k^2/s}\,\text{erfc}\left(\dfrac{k}{\sqrt{s}}\right)$	$\dfrac{1}{\sqrt{\pi t}}e^{-2k\sqrt{t}}$
116	$K_0(ks)$	$\begin{cases}0 & \text{when } 0<t<k \\ (t^2-k^2)^{-\frac{1}{2}} & \text{when } t>k\end{cases}$
117	$K_0(k\sqrt{s})$	$\dfrac{1}{2t}\exp\left(-\dfrac{k^2}{4t}\right)$
118	$\dfrac{1}{s}e^{ks}K_1(ks)$	$\dfrac{1}{k}\sqrt{t(t+2k)}$
119	$\dfrac{1}{\sqrt{s}}K_1(k\sqrt{s})$	$\dfrac{1}{k}\exp\left(-\dfrac{k^2}{4t}\right)$
120	$\dfrac{1}{\sqrt{s}}e^{k/s}K_0\left(\dfrac{k}{s}\right)$	$\dfrac{2}{\sqrt{\pi t}}K_0(2\sqrt{2kt})$
121	$\pi e^{-ks}I_0(ks)$	$\begin{cases}[t(2k-t)]^{-\frac{1}{2}} & \text{when } 0<t<2k \\ 0 & \text{when } t>2k\end{cases}$
122	$e^{-ks}I_1(ks)$	$\begin{cases}\dfrac{k-t}{\pi k\sqrt{t(2k-t)}} & \text{when } 0<t<2k \\ 0 & \text{when } t>2k\end{cases}$

TABLE OF LAPLACE TRANSFORMS (*continued*)

	$\bar{f}(s)$	$f(t)$
123	$-e^{as}\text{Ei}(-as)$	$\dfrac{1}{t+a}\,(a>0)$
124	$\dfrac{1}{a}+se^{as}\text{Ei}(-as)$	$\dfrac{1}{(t+a)^2}\,(a>0)$
125	$\left(\dfrac{\pi}{2}-\text{Si}\,s\right)\cos s+\text{Ci}\,s\sin s$	$\dfrac{1}{t^2+1}$

SUBJECT INDEX

A

Absolute convergence, 76
Absolute value of complex numbers, 75, 119
Absorption factor, 325, 326
Acetaldehyde, extraction of, 481–482
Acetic anhydride, hydrolysis of, 341–343
Acrivos and Amundson equation, 471
Addition of matrices, 439–440
Addition of vectors, 203–210
" Address " of numbers, 505
Adsorption coefficients, 365–369
Algebra, complex, 117–148; see also under *complex*
  matrix, 439–442
  three basic laws, 51, 52, 206, 213
Algebraic equations
  linear, solution by matrices, 448–449
  numerical methods of solving, 397–406
Alternating series, 79
Ammonia vapour, pressure and density of, 317–318
Amplifier
  basic for addition, 496–497
  basic for integration, 497–498
  operational, 496
Amplitude of complex number, 119
Amplitude of elliptic integrals, 157, 158
Analysis of a continuous fat hydrolysing plant, 62–66, 328–331
Analytic functions of complex variable, 131–148
Arbitrary constant, 18, 42, 45, 290, 323
Argand diagram, 118–119, 120, 199, 200, 399
  algebraic operations on, 120–123
Argument of
  beta function, 154
  complex number, 119, 122, 136
  gamma function, 152
Ascent, steepest—method of optimization, 483–485

Associative law of Algebra, 51, 52, 206, 213
Autocode, 508
Average point, 362
Averages, method in curve fitting, 361–364
Axial symmetry, 234–236, 248–250, 276, 354–355

B

Benzene, batchwise chlorination of, 26–28
Benzene—toluene, feed in distillation column, 336–338
Benzoic acid
  extraction from toluene, 1, 2, 3, 5, 9
Bernoulli's theorem, 235
Bessel equation, 106–116, 173, 282, 283, 287, 296, 306
  integral properties of, 115
Bessel functions
  first kind, 107
  modified, 110
  second kind, 107–109
  tables of (Chistova), 317
Bessel's interpolation formula, 319
Beta function, 154–155
  argument of, 154
  relation with gamma function, 156–157
Binary system of digital computers, 506
Binomial power series, 80
Binomial theorem, 80, 143, 181, 182, 340
Block diagram, 189, 191
Boundary conditions, 18
  analogue circuit for, 494, 502
  at fixed temperature, 19
  constant heat flow rate, 19
  initial condition, 19
  in Laplace transformation, 166
  in partial differential equations, 252–259